MELBOURNE & VICTORIA

Brighton

MELBOURNE & VICTORIA

AUSTRALIA'S SOUTHERN JEWEL

NEW HOLLAND

Many thanks to Joel Fulton and Gary Angliss for their invaluable assistance.

Published in 2013 by New Holland Publishers
London •Sydney •Auckland
www.newhollandpublishers.com

The Chandlery, 50 Westminster Bridge Road, London SE1 7QY, United Kingdom
1/66 Gibbes Street, Chatswood, NSW 2067, Australia
5/39 Woodside Ave, Northcote, Auckland 0627, New Zealand

newhollandpublishers.com

A record of this book is held at the British Library or the National Library of Australia.

ISBN: 9781742574783

Managing Director: Fiona Schultz
Publisher: Fiona Schultz
Project Editor: Kate Sherington
Designer: Keisha Galbraith
Production Director: Olga Dementiev
Printer: Hang Tai Printing Company Limited

10 9 8 7 6 5 4 3

Keep up with New Holland Publishers on Facebook
facebook.com/NewHollandPublishers

Introduction

Tucked below the Murray River in south-eastern Australia, Victoria may be the second-smallest state in the nation, but it has the second-largest population, with two-thirds of Victorians living in Melbourne—the state's sophisticated and cosmopolitan coastal capital and Australia's second-largest city. Outside Melbourne, within easy driving distance, Victoria is dotted with towns large and small, from the isolated villages of the rugged eastern highlands to the agricultural centres of the Murray basin in the north-west, and the fishing ports found along the length of the state's spectacular and varied coastline.

First settled by the British in response to fears of rival occupation by the French—and in spite of Aboriginal resistance—the area now known as Victoria became a separate colony from New South Wales in 1851, just as the Australian gold rushes began. As people flocked to the goldfields around Ballarat and Bendigo, the colony's population soared.

Much of the wealth engendered by the gold rush was poured into the many fine buildings, public and private, still in evidence throughout Victoria today—magnificent edifices such as Ballarat's imposing Town Hall, completed in the 1870s, Bendigo's splendidly decorated Italianate Shamrock Hotel, and the many well-preserved historic buildings that contribute to the unique architectural fabric of modern Melbourne. St Patrick's Cathedral is a spectacular example of Gothic Revival architecture, with a spire soaring 100 metres above the street, and the vast bluestone and freestone bulk of Parliament House, with its sweeping steps and grand colonnade, presides over the city centre from the top of Bourke Street.

But Melbourne today is more than magnificent buildings—Australia's vibrant cultural capital of over 3.1 million people, wrapped around the Yarra River, offers a smorgasbord of diverse experiences. City life reflects the well-known Melburnian loves of culture, coffee and sport, not necessarily in that order. While the city (in fact, the whole state!) takes a public holiday for the Melbourne Cup, held at Flemington Racecourse each November, the Victorian Arts Centre, in the arts precinct near the Princes Bridge, is home to the Australian Ballet. And the multitude of theatres and festivals, including the world-class International Comedy Festival and the Melbourne International Frestival of the Arts, combine to cement Melbourne's reputation as Australia's centre for the performing arts.

If you prefer retail therapy to the National Gallery, and the amazing sculptures along the promenade at the Southgate complex are the closest you get to art, why not shop 'til you drop at Melbourne Central, Australia's largest shopping complex. Or take a tram to the bustling Queen Victoria Market, where hundreds of stalls offer everything from seafood to handicrafts, before you head for cafe hotspots across the city like seaside St Kilda, Brunswick Street, Fitzroy and Chapel Street, Prahran.

Melbourne is not all hustle. The Royal Botanic, Alexandra and Queen Victoria Gardens stretch invitingly along the Yarra, providing tranquil relief from the buzz, and for those who yearn for more wide open spaces, much of the rest of the state is within easy reach of the city. The rolling Dandenong Ranges rise just to the east, Little Penguins march nightly along the beach at Phillip Island to the south, and the spectacular rock formations visible from the Great Ocean Road, west of the city, are only a short drive away. A bit further afield, rugged Wilsons Promontory— the southernmost point of the Australian mainland—juts out into Bass Strait, and the snowfields in the high country lie only a few hours to the north-east. With so much to see and so much to explore, this book presents you with just the tip of the iceberg of Melbourne and Victoria's splendours.

Melbourne

Twice named the world's most liveable city in *The Economist's* annual report, Melbourne was settled by Europeans in 1835. Opportunistic John Batman, who had travelled from Tasmania in hopes of finding good farmland, made a dubious agreement with the local Indigenous people, claiming they had signed 250,000 hectares of land over to him. Within the space of a few years, the illegal settlement was home to 350 new settlers and 55,000 sheep, and NSW Governor Richard Bourke was forced to acknowledge the area. He helped to mark out the city boundaries himself, circling the area on horseback with a surveyor, Robert Hoddle, and named the township 'Melbourne' after the British prime minister of the day.

Through the chaos of the gold rush, the Land Boom and its attendant crash, the hardships of the Great Depression, and the effects of two World Wars, Melbourne has emerged as a city of diversity, openness and sophistication. Locals are passionate about the arts, sport, food, fashion and coffee, and the city prides itself on being a 'European-style', uniquely Australian capital, embracing a melting pot of people, cultures and cuisines.

Whether you are wandering through city laneways or exploring the bustling Queen Victoria Market, checking out stylish Chapel Street or standing on windswept St Kilda beach, in Melbourne there is always a feeling of possibility, the palpable sense that anything might happen—a lingering reminder, perhaps, of the city's pioneering beginnings.

The city

Melbourne's city centre is based on a grid design by Robert Hoddle, who drew up the plans in 1837 after visiting the fledgling colony with NSW Governor Richard Bourke. The grid was extended and today covers the whole area from Flinders Street to Queen Victoria Market, and from Spencer Street to Spring Street. The design features both wide streets and narrow lanes, the latter having produced the colourful laneway culture for which the city centre is known today. The grand names given to these inner-city streets—La Trobe and Flinders, for example, after two much-admired explorers—spoke to the city's ideals of exploration and adventure.

When gold was found in Victoria, it opened the floodgates, bringing many people who sought their fortunes and a new life. In 1852, emigrants from Britain bought more tickets to Melbourne than to any other city in the world, and thousands of people flowed into the area each week. Infectious diseases like diphtheria and typhoid were rampant. Rain easily caused flooding in well-trodden city streets—some, like Elizabeth St, being poorly situated along the path of the natural waterway—which saw people and animals drown in attempted crossings. Even much later, in 1891, one resident recounted that while he waited for his mail at the Post Office he was 'startled by seeing a great tidal wave rolling along Elizabeth Street [...] I got up the ornamental base of one of the pillars and clung there, with the water dashing over my waist, while some less fortunate ones were swept away.'

Gas lighting was introduced on city streets in 1857, in the hopes of dissuading unsavoury characters from lingering in laneways. By 1860, theatres and music halls had been established on Bourke St, while the western end of Little Collins Street was home to various law firms. A large fountain once stood at the intersection of Collins and Swanston Streets, but was removed to lay tram tracks in the mid-1860s and placed in the Carlton Gardens, where it can be found today.

The 1880s were a boom time of construction and growth, with buildings up to 12 storeys high being erected, and by 1910 the CBD was wired for electricity. Systems changed accordingly—letter carriers and errand boys were out of a job as high-flying business types telephoned their clients, and clerks went up to their offices in state-of-the-art lifts.

Flinders Street Station as we know it today was raised between 1905 and 1910, and was the gateway to the city, its clock dictating city time for many thousands of commuters. Trams also came to the fore, ferrying people in from the inner suburbs and giving access to the major shopping strips of Sydney Road, Puckle Street, Glenferrie Road and Chapel Street, while Bourke St was the department store hub, with Myer, Buckley & Nunn, Foy & Gibson, Payners Bon Marche, and Hicks, Atkinson and Sons all in close proximity to one another.

The 1930s were spent in the grip of the Great Depression, as rickety, unsafe buildings were demolished to establish a more uniform look in the city. The Manchester Unity Building on the corner of Swanston and Collins Streets is still one of the most impressive structures in town, completed in 1932 using a rotation of constant eight-hour shifts. Widespread construction continued after the Second World War, as a number of older buildings were demolished to make way for skyscrapers, but the city centre was still the domain of office workers, and a veritable ghost town after 5pm.

In the 1950s, many people left a devastated Europe to search for a better life, and landed in Australia. A European-influenced café culture emerged in Melbourne. The Legend café at 280 Bourke St, run by the Greek Nicolades family, attracted a diverse and curious clientele with its continental vibe. It was demolished in 1970, but by then Melbourne was well and truly hooked on coffee, and countless other cafes have sprung up in the decades since.

The 'demon drink' had been a problem since the city's beginnings (William Howitt wrote, 'I have scarcely seen a tree under which do not lie the remains of bottles which have been dashed against it'), and drew the attention of the temperance movement back in the late 19th century. So-called coffee palaces sprang up throughout the city centre, including the Grand in Spring Street (now the Hotel Windsor) and the Federal on the corner of Collins and King Streets, now demolished. These luxuriously appointed buildings offered accommodation and entertainment, as well as the service of nonalcoholic beverages. Temperance advocates were doomed to lose the battle with alcohol, though—ironically, many coffee palaces later applied for liquor licenses. As Melbourne grew into a more sophisticated state capital, its pub and bar culture also evolved, and remains an important part of the city's identity today.

Trams

In 1877, businessman Francis Boardman Clapp bought the Victorian patents to a revolutionary cable tram system, already operating in San Francisco, and in 1883 the colony's government proposed to begin construction of the city's tram network. The first tram cars, imported from the US, were small and light, with room for 22 passengers seated and 34 standing. They would later be built at Clapp's workshop in North Fitzroy.

The first cable tram line opened in 1885. By 1891, there were 71km of cable tramway in Melbourne, and tram 'ropes' ran along most streets in the city. Electric trams were introduced in 1889, with a 3.6km track from Box Hill to Doncaster, but were not in serious use until 1906, when an electric tram line opened from St Kilda Station (now Stop 132 on Route 96) to Brighton. By 1916, trams were carrying more than 100 million people per year, and by 1920 almost 100 electric trams were running over 56km of track. Cable tramways were gradually removed to make way for electric, with the last cable tram running on 26 October 1940, to Northcote.

Many Australian cities did away with their trams in the 1950s, but Melbourne continued to refurbish and update them, much to the city's benefit. With varying classes of electric tram in operation, the city eventually settled on the W class, which became a Melbourne icon. These were in use until the 1970s, when the orange Z class was brought in. In the 1980s, A class and B class trams (the latter air-conditioned) were introduced.

Today, the whole tram system is run by Yarra Trams. In 2011–12, there were 191.6 million tram boardings in Melbourne.

Media Unit. Courtesy Tourism Victoria.

Above: The iconic W-class tram
Left: The City Circle Tram

Above and left: Flinders Street Station

Photographer: Enzo Amato

Federation Square

Affectionately known as 'Fed Square', this landmark public space in Melbourne's city centre is a fairly recent addition. The Kulin Aboriginal peoples occupied the land for thousands of years before European settlement, after which the site became home to the city morgue, a fish market, the Gas and Fuel Buildings, and rail yards. The push to develop the area came when the number of rail lines running parallel to the Yarra was reduced. It was decided that the old lines ought to be built over in order to connect the city to the river and put the space to good public use.

In the late 1990s, in anticipation of centenary celebrations for Federation in 2001, the state government launched a design competition to redevelop the site as a civic square. The chosen design, by London-based architecture studio Lab, who later partnered with Melbourne's Bates Smart firm, was an exciting conception for a modern city, aiming to bring Melbourne's diverse characteristics into a unified design and reflecting the principles of Federation unique individual buildings comprising a greater whole. The design included lots of spaces for art and performance, and though not without controversy, began construction in 1998. The square was completed and opened to the public in 2002.

As the city's best-known meeting place, Fed Square is situated on the corner of Swanston and Flinders Streets, across the road from Flinders Street Station, and is easily accessible by public transport, car or foot. It is home to venues including Deakin Edge theatre, The Atrium restaurant, and a 300-seater open-air amphitheatre. There is always a constant buzz of activity to be found in the square, with large screens broadcasting cultural events, art projects, news and sports. The area can accommodate up to 15,000 people.

Peter Dunphy. Courtesy Tourism Victoria.

Above and right: Federation Square

Above: Docklands
Right: Melbourne Exhibition Centre, Southbank

Webb Bridge, Docklands

Above and right: Seafarers Bridge

Left and above: Rowers on the Yarra River

Crown Casino Fountain
Left: The flames of Melbourne's Crown Casino

Melbourne Aquarium

There has been an aquarium in Melbourne since 1885. At that time, it was housed in the Royal Exhibition Building, which had been built for the International Melbourne Exhibition in 1880. When the aquarium was installed in the building a few years later, it became a major tourist draw, but was destroyed by fire in 1953.

The current building was constructed from 1998 to 1999 and opened to the public in 2000. Visitors can marvel at the thousands of ocean creatures who call the 2.2 million litre Oceanarium home, including sharks, eels, coral and colourful fish, as well as the other water-dwelling creatures in the aquarium, such as penguins and frogs. Situated on the corner of Flinders and King Streets, on the banks of the Yarra River, the aquarium runs several conservation projects, including a turtle rescue program, sub-antarctic penguin and weedy seadragon breeding efforts, and education programs for school students.

Courtesy Melbourne Aquarium

This page and left: Melbourne Aquarium

Webb Bridge at Docklands

Sculptures at Docklands
Right: Limonetto at Docklands

David Hannah. Courtesy Tourism Victoria.

Below and right: Lygon Street

Tim Webster. Courtesy Tourism Victoria.

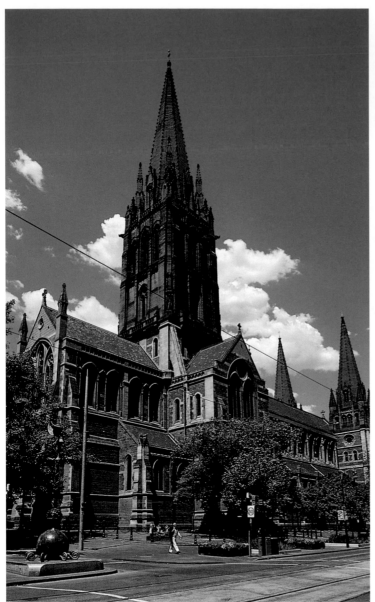

Above left: St Paul's Anglican Cathedral

Above right: St Patrick's Cathedral

Opposite: Parliament House

Old Melbourne Gaol

The original Melbourne Gaol was built in Collins Street West in 1839. A second gaol, at the current site, was built over the course of 1841–44 to adjoin the Supreme Court, then situated at the corner of Russell and La Trobe Streets. Chronically overcrowded, the gaol continued to expand through ensuing decades, with extensions and revisions being made to boundary walls, homes for gaolers built on site, and the establishment of a new block for female prisoners.

After a review of the penal system, which recommended prisoners be moved to somewhere more 'suitable', the gaol was slowly shut down and finally closed in 1929, though it did reopen briefly for the incarceration of AWOL soldiers during World War II. Today, it's managed by the National Trust of Australia, and is a popular tourist attraction.

The most famous person to have been held in Old Melbourne Gaol is bushranger Ned Kelly, an iconic figure in Australian history whose exploits have been romanticised in literature, film and folklore. The son of an Irish convict, Kelly often clashed with authorities, and went on the run with his gang in 1878. Eventually cornered by police, he made a last stand at Glenrowan on 28 June 1880, dressed in homemade armour. He was captured and taken into custody. Convicted on three counts of murder, he was hanged at Old Melbourne Goal on 11 November 1880.

Melbourne Zoo

Located just north of the city centre in Royal Park, Melbourne Zoo has been an attraction for visitors for more than 150 years, making it Australia's oldest zoo—and one of the oldest in the world.

Established by the Zoological Society of Victoria, ostensibly for scientific purposes, the 'zoological gardens' were situated adjacent to the botanic gardens and featured a mix of private menagerie and native animals. Soon in need of government funding, it became a place where livestock, birds and other domestic animals could be safely kept as they acclimatised to life in Australia. The current site at Royal Park was established in 1862.

The zoo's management, renamed The Acclimitisation Society, made many (largely unsuccessful) attempts to introduce new animals to Australia. These included livestock such as camels and ostriches, and unusual breeds of sheep and goats, none of which became major industries. The introduction of brown trout was a success, but carp became a pest when numbers swelled in the 1960s. Songbirds, too, like sparrows and starlings, posed problems as their numbers grew. Sparrows in particular were blamed for the destruction of fruit crops.

When Albert Le Souëf was put in charge of the Society in 1870, he brought much-needed change to the struggling zoo. To make it more attractive, he added amenities such as bathrooms and benches, and improved the look of the area with decorative architecture and landscaping. He broadened the range of native animals held at the zoo, as well as bringing in exotic creatures like lions, tigers, bears and monkeys, which were a great draw for the public.

When Le Souëf died, his son Dudley continued the work, importing more exotic animals (including an elephant, Queenie, who children could ride, and an orangutan called Mollie, who was taught to wear gloves and smoke cigarettes). He also made some advancements in the design of the animal enclosures by using naturalistic settings, though these did not last long after his premature death, with brick-and-bar enclosures then being the norm.

Facing another decline in financial health through the Depression years, the government stepped in to provide funds, and the zoo had to be saved again in the 1960s, this time by scientist Alfred Dunbavin Butcher. Butcher completely overhauled the zoo, aiming to educate the public about the animals, their habitats and their welfare.

THE ROYAL MELBOURNE ZOOLOGICAL GARDENS

Melbourne Botanical Gardens

Established in 1846, early in the city's history, the Royal Botanic Gardens have gradually been transformed from a veritable swamp into the two beautiful areas in South Yarra (38ha) and Cranbourne (363ha) that we know today. The Gardens are home to more than 10,000 plant species from all over the world, and are dedicated to botanical conservation, display and appreciation.

One of the Gardens' most influential directors was Ferdinand von Mueller, who introduced a plantation of conifers, as well as a decorative fountain and a formal garden to show the relationships between different plants. During his time in charge, the Gardens hosted various profile-raising shows, including a famous exhibition of the Giant Waterlily in 1867. Mueller also established the National Herbarium of Victoria, today the country's most important collection of preserved plant life. After Mueller's retirement, his successor William Guilfoyle had an important influence in terms of the Gardens' landscaping. He was responsible for the careful arrangements of beds and trees and the sweeping lawns for which the site is so admired now, as well as the Fern Gully, the Temple of the Winds and the Ornamental Lake.

In 1970, the state government acquired 363ha of land south-east of Melbourne to showcase native Australian flora and environments. This area became the Royal Botanic Gardens Cranbourne, where visitors can enjoy walking tracks, cycling, picnics and barbecues in a natural bush setting. Both sites have strong support from the local community and state government, as an important part of Melbourne's cultural life and history, as well as an attraction for tourists and locals alike.

Opposite and above left: Royal Botanic Gardens Melbourne
Above right: A statue at the Fitzroy Gardens

Royal Botanic Gardens Melbourne

The Princess Theatre

Melbourne is known as the cultural heart of Australia, and has been home to a theatrical tradition since early colonial days, when pantomimes and musical theatre were all the rage and authorities struggled to control bawdy audiences. The Princess Theatre is among the oldest venues in the city and one of its most impressive landmarks.

Established in 1854 for live performance by actor George Coppin, who also owned the Olympic and would take over the Theatre Royal in Bourke Street, the site of today's Princess Theatre was originally home to Astley's Amphitheatre, which was gradually extended. The Victorian building we see on Spring Street now was built on the site in 1886 and was a world-class venue, featuring the first ever retractable ceiling. The building was renovated in 1922, then sympathetically restored in the 1980s, reopening in 1989 with productions of *Les Miserables* and *The Phantom of the Opera*. The latter set records as the longest-running production in Australia.

It is said that the ghost of singer Frederick 'Federici' Baker, who died of a heart attack in 1888 after performing in the opera *Faust*, still lingers in the theatre today. For many years, on opening night, a seat was left vacant for him in the dress circle.

The Princess Theatre seats an audience of more than 1,400 and continues to put on major, award-winning shows. Other well-known theatres in Melbourne include venues housed in the modern Arts Centre, such as the State Theatre and the Playhouse, the Malthouse Theatre (based in a former brewery building) in Southbank, and the Regent Theatre, a former cinema.

Regent Theatre on Collins Street
Right: Forum Theatre on Collins Street

Entrance to the Regent Theatre

Above. Deborah Halpern's 'Angel' sculpture, outside the National Gallery of Victoria
Left: Inside the National Gallery of Victoria

63

Above: Moomba Festival
Left: Sidney Myer Music Bowl

Shopping

Whether you're looking for food, fashion, furniture or something completely different, Melbourne is the ideal shopping destination, with a vast offering of stores for every taste and budget. The Queen Victoria Market is the largest open-air market in the Southern Hemisphere, selling everything from secondhand clothing to fresh fruit, while independent boutiques flourish in the CBD's quirky laneways. Flagship stores gleam temptingly down Chapel Street, especially at the South Yarra end, and events such as Melbourne Spring Fashion Week lure designers and style icons from all over the world.

This page and opposite: Queen Victoria Markets

Above: Queen Victoria Market

Left: A mural at Queen Victoria Market

Queen Victoria Market
Right: Royal Arcade

Above: Coop's Shot Tower in Melbourne Central
Right: Southgate Shopping Complex

Above and right: Chapel Street, South Yarra

Above: Chapel Street, South Yarra

Right: Jam Factory on Chapel Street, South Yarra

Above: Footbridge at Southgate Complex
Right: Bolte Bridge

Above: Melbourne Cricket Ground

Right: Hawthorn vs Geelong at Melbourne Cricket Ground

Melbourne Cup at Flemington Racecourse

Australian Formula One Grand Prix

Above: Rod Laver Arena

Left: Football fans outside Etihad Stadium

Rod Laver Arena

Above and right: The inner-city suburb of Carlton

Above and right: Brunswick Street in Fitzroy

Brunswick Street at night

Above: St Kilda Pier
Right: Luna Park in St Kilda

Luna Park

Above and right: Acland Street in St Kilda

Above: Point Lonsdale Lighthouse
Left: St Kilda Foreshore Promenade and Beach

NHIL (Shaen Adey)

Above: The Heads, Port Phillip Bay
Right: Seaford

Rippon Lea Estate, Elsternwick

The Ozone Hotel, Queenscliff

Boats moored of Williamstown

Above: Brighton Beach

Left: The Marina at the Brighton Yacht Club

Brighton Beach

Whale watching on the Great Ocean Road

The south-west coast

Victoria's south-west coastline is among the most beautiful in the world. From natural wonders like the Apostles and London Arch to the relaxed seaside pleasures of Port Fairy and Apollo Bay, the state's pristine beaches and coastal landscapes truly must be seen to be believed.

The best way to enjoy the south-west coast is by driving along the heritage-listed Great Ocean Road. Built by returned World War I serviceman, this major route winds its way between Torquay, just outside of Melbourne, and Warrnambool in the west. Passing through a range of landscapes and environments, it offers incredible ocean views, sometimes over near-vertical cliffs, and provides access to major landmarks. Different parts of the coastline are variously known as the Surf Coast and the Shipwreck Coast.

In terms of geological highlights, visitors are spoiled for choice. The Port Campbell National Park features some incredible sights, including a group of stacked limestone formations known as the Twelve Apostles, a must-see attraction, particularly as they are unlikely to stand forever. Formed by erosion, these nine (rather than twelve) pillars were once part of the cliffs, but eroded to form caves, and then arches, which collapsed into the stacks we see today. Since a further collapse in 2005, only eight stacks remain. Just around the corner is London Arch, formerly London Bridge, a natural rock arch that formed a complete bridge until a collapse in 1990, which briefly left two tourists stranded.

Loch Ard Gorge is another feature of the national park that demonstrates the effects of erosion. The two pillars (previously an archway) are named Tom and Eva after the sole survivors of the wrecked *Loch Ard*, a clipper bringing immigrants from England to Melbourne in 1878. Tom was a fifteen-year-old ship's apprentice who rescued seventeen-year-old Irishwoman Eva from the water.

Picturesque towns dot the south-west shore. West of Warrnambool, Port Fairy is home to 3,000 residents and a popular spot for pleasure-seeking tourists. First named in the 19th century by whalers who worked the local waters, the town has many historic buildings and is famed today for the Port Fairy Folk Festival, held in March of each year. The little seaside township of Apollo Bay, nearly 200 kilometres away, is also known for its festivals, and is situated in the foothills of the Otway Ranges, acting as a gateway to the Otways' incredible rainforests and waterfalls.

Coastlines of the Great Ocean Road

Above: The Great Ocean Road

Right: Sunrise at Lorne

116

Lorne

Torquay

Above and right: Torquay

Above and right: Apollo Bay

124

Above: Warrnambool

Left: Cannon Hill Lookout, Warrnambool

Above: Warrnambool

Right: Flagstaff Hill Lighthouse Lodge, Warrnambool

Above: The Apostles
Left: Loch Ard Gorge, Port Campbell National Park

The Apostles

London Arch

Port Fairy on the Moyne River

This page and right: Port Fairy

This page and right: Cape Nelson Light Station

Phillip Island

Located about 140km south of Melbourne, Phillip Island is a fascinating place. The traditional owners of the island were the Boonwurrung people, comprising six clans. They would likely have visited the island during the mutton bird season, looking for eggs and young birds to eat, rather than dwelling there permanently. The first European to visit the island was George Bass in 1798. Sealers followed soon after, hunting on the Bass Strait islands and surrounding waters.

In 1842, the McHaffie brothers leased the whole island to graze sheep, and lost all but 640 acres when the island opened up for wider settlement in the late 1860s. Conditions were very difficult for farming, but chicory proved suitable for the climate, and was grown there for more than a century. The chicory kilns still stand today, a local landmark.

The island also became a tourist attraction in the 1870s, with a ferry service bringing regular visitors from 1878, and guesthouses being raised in the 1880s. Tourists could hire a horse-drawn buggy to visit the beautiful beaches and watch the mutton birds dig their burrows in the cliffs. The mutton birds, also known as Short-tailed Shearwaters, migrate from Alaska to Phillip Island for breeding, leaving their eggs in burrows to go out and find food. At sunset, they return en masse, in a sight that has always awed visitors. Little Penguins, the world's smallest species, were also a major draw from the 1920s. People still love to watch them waddle ashore after a day of fishing in the Bass Strait.

The Australian Grand Prix was held on the island from 1928, but dust from the unsealed roads posed a problem, and the event was moved after 1938. A new circuit opened in 1952, but went into decline in the next decade, until it was revived and refurbished for the 1989 Motorbike GP. It has operated ever since.

Today, viewings of mutton birds and penguins on Phillip Island are as popular as ever. Visitors can explore the rugged coastline by foot, kayak, bicycle, or nearly any other form of transport. Nature parks and trails are great for hiking, while museums, markets, restaurants, spas and boutique local shops cater to every visitor's need in these stunning surrounds. The Nobbies, a gorgeous headland, can be traversed by purpose-built boardwalk and offer majestic views across the Bass Strait. Seal Rocks, home to Australia's largest colony of fur seals, stand just a kilometre off-shore.

Left: Nobbies, Phillip Island

Above: The Penguin Parade Visitor Centre

Left: Boardwalk looking out over the Nobbies rock formation

Penguins on Phillip Island

Red Rocks on Phillip Island

Above: The Nobbies at dusk

Right: Penguin Parade at Phillip Island Nature Park

148

Yarra Valley and Dandenongs

For pure indulgence, not much can beat the culinary delights of the Yarra Valley, the wine-growing area surrounding the upper Yarra River an hour northeast of Melbourne. This cool climate region was the first in Victoria to establish a grape-growing industry, back in 1838. Visitors can take leisurely tours from winery to winery, knocking on the cellar doors of small, boutique establishments like Maddens Rise and Soumah, as well as established heavyweights like DeBortoli. Many wineries run their own restaurants, where house wines are matched with fresh and delicious produce. It is possible to stop at orchards, farm gates and roadside stalls throughout the area, buying direct from the farmer, or picking fruit straight from the tree or bush.

Just south of the Yarra Valley, the Dandenong Ranges are a group of low mountains, mainly consisting of rolling hills and sheltered gullies, where rainforest and fern glades flourish. Mount Dandenong, the highest point in the range at 633 metres, was traditionally the summer hunting ground for the Bunurong and Woiworung peoples. Large areas of vegetation were cleared after European settlement, but today the Dandenong Ranges National Park protects some of the region's most important tall forests, which can be accessed via a network of excellent walking tracks in the park. Less than an hour east of Melbourne, the ranges are an easy day trip from the capital and well worth the scenic drive, with villages throughout the mountains known for local art, boutique dining and romantic accommodation.

For a trip back through time, as well as through the Dandenongs' stunning mountain scenery, take a ride on a Puffing Billy steam train. The railway was one of several constructed to open up rural areas in the early 1900s, but struggled financially. The services were due to be shut down in the 1950s, but special 'final' Puffing Billy trips were very successful, and encouraged enthusiasts to campaign for the preservation of the service. Today, trains still run every day thanks to the dedication of 900 volunteers. Just as it did in the early 20th century, the Puffing Billy railway takes travellers on a 24km journey from Belgrave to Lakeside and Gembrook. Along the way, there are natural and historic highlights, such as Sherbrooke Forest, a famous timber trestle bridge, and views of Port Phillip Bay.

Hot air balloon flight over the Yarra

Courtesy Tourism Victoria

Above: Yarra Valley and Dandenong Ranges

Left: Lake Mountain

Above: Sunrise over the Yarra Valley

Opposite: The Puffing Billy steam train in the Blue Dandenongs

CLEARANCE
45m

Above: Tesselaar's annual Tulip Festival at Silvan in the Dandenongs

Right: The Black Spur Forest near Healesville

Above: Tarraford Estate near Yarra Glen
Left: Selovers Lookout near Healesville

Yarra Glen

Maroondah Highway in the Black Spur forest

The goldfields

When Edward Hargraves, recently returned from California, made a tiny discovery of gold near Bathurst, New South Wales, in 1851, he could not have imagined the lasting social and economic change his find would herald. Not four months later, the site was home to 1,000 diggers, and the *Bathurst Free Press* was compelled to write, 'A complete mental madness appears to have seized almost every member of the community. There has been a universal rush to the diggings.'

In Victoria, state authorities had to act fast if they wanted to prevent a mass exodus of their population to New South Wales. They offered a reward to anyone discovering gold within 200 miles of Melbourne and, sure enough, a find was made at Ballarat. The Victorian rush soon revealed the full extent of the Mount Alexander goldfield, an area yielding several million ounces of gold, most in the first two years of the rush and within five metres of the surface. It was easy pickings for a digger, at least at first. As gold was subsequently found in Bendigo, Castlemaine, Daylesford and surrounds, people from all over the world descended on these provincial towns, which quickly grew to accommodate their fortune-seeking residents.

In 1854, the state government established a policy of issuing gold licences, which would allow miners to search only on a specific plot of land, and had to be bought whether gold was found or not. Those who didn't pay up would be chained to a log until they could produce the money. Corruption in the checking of licences by police brewed resentment among the diggers, which eventually led to the famous Eureka Stockade in Ballarat; a digger was murdered, and when his killer went unpunished, miners burned the Eureka Hotel to the ground, along with their licences. They demanded fairer conditions and set up a stockade against government troops. Dozens of men were killed in the confrontation, but the miners did win a better deal on the goldfields.

By the time the last mine closed in Ballarat in 1918, the city had developed enough other forms of industry to support itself, and was firmly established. It now offers fascinating historical attractions, including a replica gold-rush town at Sovereign Hill and a sound and light show, 'Blood on the Southern Cross', that tells the story of the Eureka uprising. Bendigo also celebrates its fascinating goldfields past, with a deep-shaft mine experience preserved for tourists, and many impressive buildings of the period still standing.

Hanging Rock is another draw of this area. The site of the disappearance of a group of schoolgirls in 1900, a mysterious incident made famous by the 1975 film *Picnic at Hanging Rock*, this unique 718m high rock formation, known as a 'mamelon', is the result of magma emerging from a vent and congealing in place around six million years ago. Over time, the formation broke up into columns, which weathered to form the pillars we see now. Distinctive geological features of Hanging Rock include the Colonnade, the Eagle and the 'Hanging Rock' itself, a boulder caught between two others and suspended over the main entrance to the site.

NHIL (Shaen Adey)

Above: Ballarat

Right: The Arch of Victory, Ballarat

Above: The Eureka flag

Left: The Bentley Hotel 'burns' in the nightly 'Blood on the Southern Cross' performance

Above: Begonia Festival at Ballarat's botanical gardens
Right: Sovereign Hill's 'living museum'

Above: The Alexandra Fountain in Bendigo
Left: The Shamrock Hotel, Bendigo

This page: Chinese Temple, Bendigo
Left: The Conservatory, Bendigo

Above: Daylesford

Left: Castlemaine

View from Hanging Rock

Gippsland

Gippsland is a large region of the state of Victoria, stretching east of the suburbs of Melbourne all the way to the New South Wales border. It is divided into five smaller regions—East, West, South and Central Gippsland, and the Latrobe Valley—each with its special charms. East Gippsland in particular is admired for its natural wonders, specifically its remarkable old growth forests and the Gippsland Lakes, which comprise the major river basins of the Mitchell, Tambo and Nicholson Rivers.

A huge proportion of East Gippsland is made up of national parks, with two of the largest being the Snowy River National Park and the Errinundra National Park. The former is known for breathtaking gorges and the wild waters of the Snowy River; the latter has a wetter climate—often totally inaccessible from June to October—and is home to some of the most ancient forests in Australia. Though both parks can be tricky to explore, the remote splendours of each are worth any difficulties encountered along the way.

The major town of the East Gippsland area is Bairnsdale. First surveyed in 1859, the town thrived on the banks of the Mitchell River, and was declared a city in 1990. From Bairnsdale, the Great Alpine Road leads thrill-seekers north into the Australian Alps, to major ski resorts like Mount Hotham. Bairnsdale also serves as a tourist gateway to nearby Lakes Entrance, where a manmade channel links the Bass Strait with the Gippsland Lakes. Excellent views can be found at Jemmy's Point, off the Princes Highway. Lakes Entrance itself is a seaside village with a surf beach, marina and attractive waterfront esplanade. And along the East Gippsland coast, Ninety Mile Beach is exactly what it says on the tin—more than 150 kilometres of golden sand. There, visitors may take in an endless vista of beach, stretching all the way to the horizon.

Whatever the magic of East Gippsland, the other diverse subregions of this area should not be neglected. Wilson's Promontory in South Gippsland, for example, a peninsula that forms the southernmost tip of mainland Australia, gives stunning outlooks. The area has been protected in some form or another since 1898 and its national park represents the largest section of coastal wilderness in the country.

Above: Bairnsdale's Grand Terminus Hotel

The Bairnsdale courthouse, finished in 1893

Lakes Entrance

Above and right: Lakes Entrance

Bridge across the Latrobe River near Sale

Mallacoota Inlet, Croajingolong National Park

Above: Dunes between Ninety Mile Beach and the town of Seaspray

Left: Ninety Mile Beach

Giant boulders at Skeaky Beach on Wilsons Promontory

North-east Victoria

The north-east is one of the fastest growing regions in the state. With a climate of four distinct seasons, it is perhaps best known for its snowfields. Nearly 92 percent of the area's alpine shire is public land, encompassing Mount Buffalo National Park, sections of the Alpine National Park, and many state forests, as well as the two major ski resorts, Mouth Hotham and Falls Creek. Bright, Myrtleford and Mount Beauty are the main towns in this mountain zone.

At less lofty heights, Wodonga is a fast-growing regional hub, located on the banks of the Murray and the Victoria–NSW border. It was originally a customs post, paired with the town of Albury on the other side of the Murray, and expanded after the opening of the first bridge across the river in 1860. The sleepy Rural City of Wangaratta, meanwhile, is a wine and food connoisseur's dream, surrounded by rich agricultural lands, and lays claim to a major historic landmark—the township of Glenrowan, where bushranger Ned Kelly made his last stand against police in a suit of homemade armour.

Autumn colours in Bright

Above: Mount Buller, Victoria's largest ski resort

Left: A climber on 'Peroxide Blonde', a climb on the face of The Horn, the highest peak in Mount Buffalo National Park

Mount Feathertop and Razorback Ridge

Above and left: Ned Kelly sights in Glenrowan

Mildura and north-central Victoria

In north-west Victoria, the Mildura region's first inhabitants were the Latje Latje and Paakantyi people—Mildura means 'red earth' in Latje Latje. The area was settled by Europeans after Charles Sturt discovered the confluence of the Murray and Darling Rivers in 1830, with squatters moving in to work the fertile riverside land. Once paddleboats were introduced, the little town of Wentworth became a major centre for river-based transportation. After a drought, though, more advanced measures for irrigation were put in place and a rundown sheep station at Mildura became the first irrigation settlement.

Since then, the area has transformed into a major agricultural zone, with Mildura soon becoming the main town. It produces most of Australia's dried fruit, seventy percent of its table grapes and twenty percent of its citrus—many will recognise 'Mildura' as a famous fruit juice brand. The Murray cod and Mallee lamb of the region are renowned for their quality.

In the north-central area, we find uniquely Victorian townships such as Swan Hill. When Francis Cadell travelled up the Murray in his paddle steamer in 1853, Swan Hill was the furthest point he reached. There, he greeted the whole town, a total of 12 people. On the banks of the majestic Murray, Swan Hill grew up around the only punt crossing for 100km, where Burke and Wills crossed in 1860. The punt was in action until 1896, when a bridge was constructed.

Nowadays, 16,000 residents make Swan Hill and its surrounds their home. The town features an historic attraction, the Pioneer Settlement, which uses restored or recreated shops and buildings to give tourists a flavour of 19th century life by the river. Many wineries are within easy reach, as are nature parks and reserves, while houseboat and paddle steamer trips are a popular pursuit. The local produce is fresh and delicious, including yabbies, avocado and stone fruits.

The twin towns of Echuca and Moama, only a two-and-a-half hour drive from Melbourne, provide the closest access to the Murray from the capital. Known as the country's 'paddlesteamer capital', Echuca operates the largest fleet of these historic riverboats in the world, running cruises day and night, as well as regional eco-tours and adventure sports.

Vineyards, Mildura

Above: Grapes drying on racks near Mildura
Left: Grapes protected from the weather

Gums on the bank of the Murray River near Robinvale

Bridge over the Murray River at Swan Hill

Swan Hill's National Trust 1840s homestead 'Tyntynder'

NHIL IShaen Adey.'

Pioneer settlement, Swan Hill

Gunbower Island, near Cohuna

Houseboat on the Murray River, Echuca

Above: The Barmah State Forest at Echuca
Right: Echuca

Above: Chinese graves at Beechworth Cemetery

Left: Sunset on the Murray River

The Grampians

In western Victoria, 235 kilometres west of Melbourne, Grampians National Park is home to spectacular mountain ranges, gorgeous wildflowers in spring, and rare sites of ancient rock art. The Grampians themselves comprise five sandstone ridges, with steep slopes on the eastern side and gentle slopes to the west. The result is an impressive landscape of high peaks and deep valleys, complete with waterfalls. Aboriginal rock paintings have been protected by shelters and can still be viewed today, tens of thousands of years after they were made.

The park facilitates fishing and canoeing in Lakes Bellfield and Wartook, and, of course, bushwalking and rock climbing. The track to Mount Abrupt is a serious hike, but gives astounding views from the summit, where it is possible to spot wedge-tailed eagles and peregrine falcons. The Mackenzie River Track is one of the most popular walks in the park, winding its way between a riverside picnic area and the Mackenzie Falls. Recently refurbished, it reopened in 2013 with new footbridges and river crossings.

The town of Halls Gap is an excellent base from which to explore the many wonders of the Grampians.

Mount Abrupt

Halls Gap

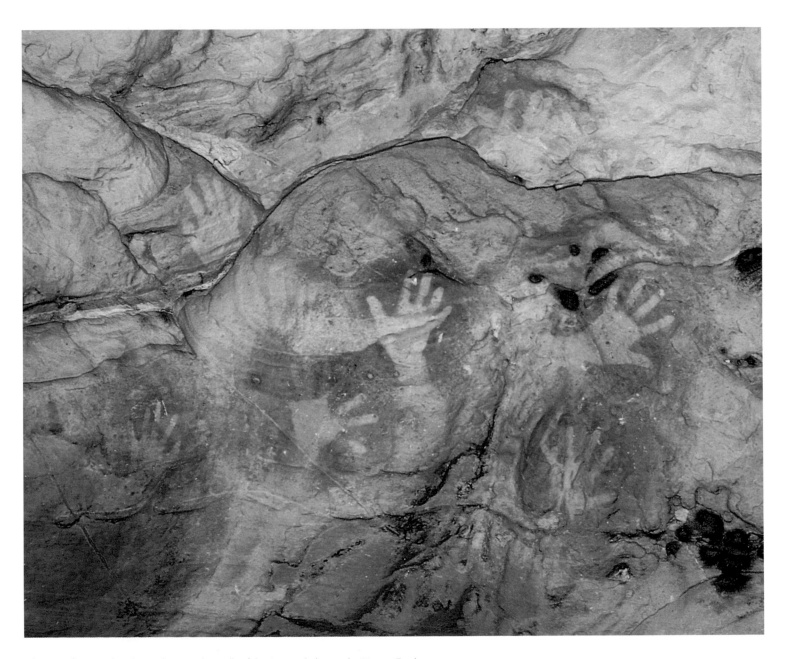

Above: Indigenous hand stencils cover the walls of the Manja shelter on the Harrop Track

Left: Falls on the Mackenzie River

The Bulconies rock formation in the Grampians National Park

GATEWAY TO THE GREAT BOOKS

GATEWAY
TO THE
GREAT BOOKS

Gateway
to the
Great Books

ROBERT M. HUTCHINS, MORTIMER J. ADLER
Editors in Chief

CLIFTON FADIMAN
Associate Editor

3

IMAGINATIVE

LITERATURE

Encyclopædia Britannica, Inc.

WILLIAM BENTON
Publisher

Chicago, London, Toronto, Geneva, Sydney, Tokyo, Manila

The following works in this volume
are reprinted under the arrangements listed below:

"Billy Budd" reprinted from *Billy Budd, Sailor,* by Herman Melville, edited by Harrison Hayford and Merton M. Sealts, Jr., by permission of The University of Chicago Press. © 1962 by The University of Chicago. All rights reserved.

"The Gentleman from San Francisco" reprinted from *The Gentleman from San Francisco* by Ivan Bunin, translated by Bernard Guilbert Guerney, by permission of Alfred A. Knopf, Inc., and Agence Hoffman. Copyright 1923, 1950 by Alfred A. Knopf, Inc.

"First Love" from *Selected Tales of Turgenev,* translated by David Magarshack. Copyright © 1960 by David Magarshack. Reprinted by permission of Doubleday & Company, Inc.

"White Nights" from *Notes from the Underground and Selected Stories* by Fyodor Dostoevsky, translated by Andrew R. MacAndrew, copyright © 1961 by Andrew R. MacAndrew, published by arrangement with The New American Library of World Literature, Inc., New York.

"The Apple-Tree"
(Copyright 1916, 1917 International Magazines Company, Inc.; renewal copyright 1944, 1945 Hearst Magazines) is reprinted with the permission of Charles Scribner's Sons and William Heinemann Ltd. from *Five Tales* and *Caravan* by John Galsworthy.

"The Legend of Saint Julian the Hospitaller" reprinted from *Three Tales* by Gustave Flaubert, translated by Arthur McDowall, by permission of Alfred A. Knopf, Inc. Copyright 1924 by Alfred A. Knopf, Inc.

"The Diamond as Big as the Ritz"
(Copyright 1922 Smart Set Company, Inc.; renewal copyright 1950 Frances Scott Fitzgerald Lanahan) is reprinted with the permission of Charles Scribner's Sons and The Bodley Head Ltd. from *Tales of the Jazz Age* by F. Scott Fitzgerald.

"The Darling" from *The Portable Chekhov* by Avrahm Yarmolinsky. Copyright 1947 by The Viking Press and reprinted by their permission.

"The Spinoza of Market Street" reprinted from *The Spinoza of Market Street* by Isaac Singer, translated by Martha Glicklich and Cecil Hemley, by permission of Farrar, Straus & Cudahy, Inc., and Martin Secker & Warburg Ltd. Copyright © 1958, 1960, 1961 by Isaac Bashevis Singer.

"The Queen of Spades" from *The Poems, Prose & Plays of Alexander Pushkin,* edited by Avrahm Yarmolinsky. Copyright 1936 by Random House, Inc. Reprinted by permission.

"The Rocking-Horse Winner" from *The Lovely Lady* in *The Complete Short Stories* of D. H. Lawrence. Copyright 1933 by The Estate of D. H. Lawrence, 1960 by Angelo Ravagli and Montague C. Weekly, Executors of the Estate of Frieda Lawrence Ravagli. Reprinted by permission of The Viking Press, Inc. Acknowledgements are made to The Estate of the late Mrs. Frieda Lawrence, Messrs. Laurence Pollinger, Limited, and Messrs. William Heinemann, Limited.

Portrait illustrations are by Fred Steffen

Contents
of Volume 3

Stephen Crane

1871–1900

Stephen Crane, the fourteenth child of a Methodist Episcopal clergyman in Newark, New Jersey, was born on November 1, 1871. He spent one term at Lafayette College and another at Syracuse University, where he played varsity baseball. At that time he began a first novel, later called *Maggie*. Crane paid for its printing in 1893. Scarcely a copy was sold.

He was a thin, blond young man of less than medium height. His gray-blue eyes saw everything. From late 1892 until 1896 he was in and out of New York City. He made an occasional living from newspaper assignments along Park Row. In 1895 a newspaper syndicate sent him on a trip to the West and into Mexico. There he was chased by a "fashionable bandit." Crane, a good rider, got away.

The same year he published *The Black Riders*, a book of poems, and *The Red Badge of Courage*, his brilliant novel about the Civil War. (He had never seen a battle.) *The Red Badge*, hardly noticed at first, reacted to praise from England and went through fourteen American printings in 1896. In that one year *The Red Badge*, *Maggie*, and the poems came out in England. Another novel, *George's Mother*, appeared in London and New York. Crane became the most talked about young writer of his period.

Early in 1897 he was aboard the tugboat *Commodore*, outbound with arms for the Cuban insurgents. She sank off the Florida coast. *The Open Boat* derived from this misadventure. In Jacksonville he met Cora Stewart, daughter of a Boston artist. She was with him, as perhaps the first woman war correspondent, when he covered the Greco-Turkish War in 1897. Later she became his common-law wife. They settled in England, welcomed by such friends as Harold Frederic, Henry James, and Joseph Conrad.

The Spanish-American War began in April, 1898. Crane, back in New York, was rejected by the Navy. As a correspondent, he got into much of the land fighting around Santiago de Cuba. He was cited for bravery. In January, 1899, he returned to England, where Cora had found an old manor house in Sussex. His last year of work was the final battle in a war against debt, illness, and time. He was taken to a sanitarium in Germany. There he died of tuberculosis, aged twenty-eight, on June 5, 1900.

In the delirium of his last illness in the Black Forest, Crane talked about "changing places" in the boat. "By the very star of truth," he had written, "it is easier to steal eggs from under a hen than it was to change seats in the dinghy." His wife knew what boat he meant. It was a ten-foot dinghy, built for pulling in to the wharf in quiet harbors. It rode the sea, among swells "most wrongfully and barbarously abrupt and tall." This was the boat that brought Crane and three other men to the beach at Daytona after the sinking of the *Commodore*. He wrote the story quickly, after the event, in Jacksonville. Conrad, a veteran seaman, thought it a great story; and H. G. Wells said it was "beyond all question, the crown of all his work."

It needs no interpretation. Everything is there, in the story. What could be plainer than this day and night and morning in the indifferent universe of the sea, with life or death at the end of it? It is every man's life in miniature. Crane caught it when it first took fire in his imagination, while the recollection was still fresh. His all but instinctive sense of form told him where to begin and where to stop. He gives us the tugboat's sinking in one remembered image: ". . . a stump of a topmast with a white ball on it, that slashed to and fro at the waves, went low and lower, and down." After that everything is contained in the Greek unities of a boat, four men, the sea, the sky, and the land.

Like the poet Rimbaud, Crane deliberately made himself "a testing ground for all the sensations of living." He was a man who had to

---

Notes from the artist: ". . . a sparse, severe treatment of Stephen Crane as the seeker of human values in a grim, chaotic world. . . . Above his head, standing between the Union and Confederate flags, is Henry Fleming, the coward-hero of The Red Badge of Courage.*"*

STEPHEN CRANE

find out how things worked and how they felt. The discovery of this truth of feeling was his business, in baseball (he said it had taught him about war), in rowing a dinghy in the open sea, or in war itself. The things that other people dismissed as mere sensation—"sport" or "adventure" or "war"—were simply life to him. He lived them with the same faithful intensity he gave to the observation of a dog's behavior or a boy's gang fight.

This is what made it possible for Crane to create that sense of the raw world we get in *The Open Boat* and in the best of his other stories. He was called an "impressionist." The label was false. He was no passive receiver of impressions. His point of vision, in life as in his stories, was that of a participant in the given action. The "psychology" of the men in *The Open Boat* is almost purely a matter of dealing with their situation, plus the sense of community that comes out of that. Even the correspondent's reflections are only an extension of these feelings. Such treatment might have produced a melodrama. It is lifted into art by the detachment of Crane's style: by the surprises of the poet, the precision of the man of action, the oblique angle of the ironist.

The Open Boat

A Tale Intended to Be after the Fact:
Being the Experience of Four Men
from the Sunk Steamer Commodore

None of them knew the color of the sky. Their eyes glanced level, and were fastened upon the waves that swept toward them. These waves were of the hue of slate, save for the tops, which were of foaming white, and all of the men knew the colors of the sea. The horizon narrowed and widened, and dipped and rose, and at all times its edge was jagged with waves that seemed thrust up in points like rocks.

Many a man ought to have a bathtub larger than the boat which here rode upon the sea. These waves were most wrongfully and barbarously abrupt and tall, and each froth-top was a problem in small-boat navigation.

The cook squatted in the bottom, and looked with both eyes at the six inches of gunwale which separated him from the ocean. His sleeves were rolled over his fat forearms, and the two flaps of his unbuttoned vest dangled as he bent to bail out the boat. Often he said, "Gawd! that was a narrow clip." As he remarked it he invariably gazed eastward over the broken sea.

The oiler, steering with one of the two oars in the boat, sometimes raised himself suddenly to keep clear of water that swirled in over the stern. It was a thin little oar, and it seemed often ready to snap.

The correspondent, pulling at the other oar, watched the waves and wondered why he was there.

The injured captain, lying in the bow, was at this time buried in that profound dejection and indifference which comes, temporarily at least, to even the bravest and most enduring when, willy-nilly, the firm fails, the army loses, the ship goes down. The mind of the master of a vessel is rooted deep in the timbers of her, though he command for a day or a decade; and this captain had on him the stern impression of a scene in the grays of dawn of seven turned faces, and later a stump of a topmast with a white ball on it, that slashed to and fro at the waves, went low and lower, and down. Thereafter there was something strange in his voice. Although steady, it was deep with mourning, and of a quality beyond oration or tears.

"Keep 'er a little more south, Billie," said he.

"A little more south, sir," said the oiler in the stern.

A seat in his boat was not unlike a seat upon a bucking broncho, and by the same token a broncho is not much smaller. The craft pranced and reared and plunged like an animal. As each wave came, and she rose for it, she seemed like a horse making at a fence outrageously high. The manner of her scramble over these walls of water is a mystic thing, and, moreover, at the top of them were ordinarily these problems in white water, the foam racing down from the summit of each wave requiring a new leap, and a leap from the air. Then, after scornfully bumping a crest, she would slide and race and splash down a long incline, and arrive bobbing and nodding in front of the next menace.

A singular disadvantage of the sea lies in the fact that after successfully surmounting one wave you discover that there is another behind it just as important and just as nervously anxious to do something effective in the way of swamping boats. In a ten-foot dinghy one can get an idea of the resources of the sea in the line of waves that is not probable to the average experience which is never at sea in a dinghy. As each slaty wall of water approached, it shut all else from the view of the men in the boat, and it was not difficult to imagine that this particular wave was the final outburst of the ocean, the last effort of the grim water. There was a terrible grace in the move of the waves, and they came in silence, save for the snarling of the crests.

In the wan light the faces of the men must have been gray. Their eyes must have glinted in strange ways as they gazed steadily astern. Viewed from a balcony, the whole thing would doubtless have been weirdly picturesque. But the men in the boat had no time to see it, and if they had had leisure, there were other things to occupy their minds. The sun swung steadily up the sky, and they knew it was broad day because the color of the sea changed from slate to emerald green streaked with amber lights, and the foam was like tumbling snow. The process of the breaking day was unknown to them. They were aware only of this effect upon the color of the waves that rolled toward them.

In disjointed sentences the cook and the correspondent argued as to the difference between a life-saving station and a house of refuge. The cook had said: "There's a house of refuge just north of the Mosquito Inlet Light, and as soon as they see us they'll come off in their boat and pick us up."

"As soon as who see us?" said the correspondent.

"The crew," said the cook.

"Houses of refuge don't have crews," said the correspondent. "As I understand them, they are only places where clothes and grub are stored for the benefit of shipwrecked people. They don't carry crews."

"Oh, yes, they do," said the cook.

"No, they don't," said the correspondent.

"Well, we're not there yet, anyhow," said the oiler, in the stern.

"Well," said the cook, "perhaps it's not a house of refuge that I'm thinking of as being near Mosquito Inlet Light; perhaps it's a life-saving station."

"We're not there yet," said the oiler in the stern.

As the boat bounced from the top of each wave the wind tore through the hair of the hatless men, and as the craft plopped her stern down again the spray slashed past them. The crest of each of these waves was a hill, from the top of which the men surveyed for a moment a broad tumultuous expanse, shining and wind-riven. It was probably splendid, it was probably glorious, this play of the free sea, wild with lights of emerald and white and amber.

"Bully good thing it's an on-shore wind," said the cook. "If not, where would we be? Wouldn't have a show."

"That's right," said the correspondent.

The busy oiler nodded his assent.

Then the captain, in the bow, chuckled in a way that expressed humor, contempt, tragedy, all in one. "Do you think we've got much of a show now, boys?" said he.

Whereupon the three were silent, save for a trifle of hemming and hawing. To express any particular optimism at this time they felt to be childish and stupid, but they all doubtless possessed this sense of the situation in their minds. A young man thinks doggedly at such times. On the other hand, the ethics of their condition was decidedly against any open suggestion of hopelessness. So they were silent.

"Oh, well," said the captain, soothing his children, "we'll get ashore all right."

But there was that in his tone which made them think; so the oiler quoth, "Yes! if this wind holds."

The cook was bailing. "Yes! if we don't catch hell in the surf."

Canton-flannel gulls flew near and far. Sometimes they sat down on the sea, near patches of brown seaweed that rolled over the waves with a movement like carpets on a line in a gale. The birds sat comfortably in groups, and they were envied by some in the dinghy, for the wrath of the sea was no more to them than it was to a covey of prairie chickens a thousand miles inland. Often they came very close and stared at the men with black beadlike eyes. At these times they were uncanny and sinister in their unblinking scrutiny, and the men hooted angrily at them, telling them to be gone. One came, and evidently decided to alight on the top of the captain's head. The bird flew parallel to the boat and did not circle, but made short sidelong jumps in the air in chicken fashion. His black eyes were wistfully fixed upon the captain's head. "Ugly brute," said the oiler to the bird. "You look as if you were made with a jackknife." The cook and the correspondent swore darkly at the creature. The captain naturally wished to knock it away with the end of the heavy painter, but he did not dare do it, because anything resembling an emphatic gesture would have capsized this freighted boat; and so, with his open hand, the captain gently and carefully waved the gull away. After it had been discouraged from the pursuit the captain breathed easier on account of his hair, and others breathed easier because the bird struck their minds at this time as being somehow gruesome and ominous.

In the meantime the oiler and the correspondent rowed. And also they rowed. They sat together in the same seat, and each rowed an oar. Then the oiler took both oars; then the correspondent took both oars; then the oiler; then the correspondent. They rowed and they rowed. The very ticklish part of the business was when the time came for the reclining one in the stern to take his turn at the oars. By the very last star of truth, it is easier to steal eggs from under a hen than it was to change seats in the dinghy. First the man in the stern slid his hand along the thwart and moved with care, as if he were of Sèvres. Then the man in the rowing seat slid his hand along the other thwart. It was all done with the most extraordinary care. As the two sidled past each other, the whole party kept watchful eyes on the coming wave, and the captain cried: "Look out, now! Steady, there!"

The brown mats of seaweed that appeared from time to time were like islands, bits of earth. They were traveling, apparently, neither one way nor the other. They were, to all intents, stationary. They informed the man in the boat that it was making progress slowly toward the land.

The captain, rearing cautiously in the bow after the dinghy soared on a great swell, said that he had seen the lighthouse at Mosquito Inlet. Presently the cook remarked that he had seen it. The correspondent was at the oars then, and for some reason he too wished to look at the lighthouse; but his back was toward the far shore, and the waves were important, and for some time he could not seize an opportunity to turn his head. But at last there came a wave more gentle than the others, and when at the crest of it he swiftly scoured the western horizon.

"See it?" said the captain.

"No," said the correspondent, slowly; "I didn't see anything."

"Look again," said the captain. He pointed. "It's exactly in that direction."

At the top of another wave the correspondent did as he was bid, and this time his eyes chanced on a small, still thing on the edge of the swaying horizon. It was precisely like the point of a pin. It took an anxious eye to find a lighthouse so tiny.

"Think we'll make it, Captain?"

"If this wind holds and the boat don't swamp, we can't do much else," said the captain.

The little boat, lifted by each towering sea and splashed viciously by the crests, made progress that in the absence of seaweed was not apparent to those in her. She seemed just a wee thing wallowing, miraculously top up, at the mercy of five oceans. Occasionally a great spread of water, like white flames, swarmed into her.

"Bail her, cook," said the captain, serenely.

"All right, Captain," said the cheerful cook.

It would be difficult to describe the subtle brotherhood of men that was here established on the seas. No one said that it was so. No one mentioned it. But it dwelt in the boat, and each man felt it warm him. They were a captain, an oiler, a cook, and a correspondent, and they were friends —friends in a more curiously iron-bound degree than may be common. The hurt captain, lying against the water jar in the bow, spoke always in a low voice and calmly; but he could never command a more ready and swiftly obedient crew than the motley three of the dinghy. It was more than a mere recognition of what was best for the common safety. There was surely in it a quality that was personal and heart-felt. And after this devotion to the commander of the boat, there was this comradeship, that the correspondent, for instance, who had been taught to be cynical of men, knew even at the time was the best experience of his life. But no one said that it was so. No one mentioned it

"I wish we had a sail," remarked the captain. "We might try my overcoat on the end of an oar, and give you two boys a chance to rest." So the cook and the correspondent held the mast and spread wide the overcoat; the oiler steered; and the little boat made good way with her new rig. Sometimes the oiler had to scull sharply to keep a sea from breaking into the boat, but otherwise sailing was a success.

Meanwhile the lighthouse had been growing slowly larger. It had now almost assumed color, and appeared like a little gray shadow on the sky. The man at the oars could not be prevented from turning his head rather often to try for a glimpse of this little gray shadow.

At last, from the top of each wave, the men in the tossing boat could see land. Even as the lighthouse was an upright shadow on the sky, this land seemed but a long black shadow on the sea. It certainly was thinner than paper. "We must be about opposite New Smyrna," said the cook, who had coasted this shore often in schooners. "Captain, by the way, I believe they abandoned that life-saving station there about a year ago."

"Did they?" said the captain.

The wind slowly died away. The cook and the correspondent were not now obliged to slave in order to hold high the oar. But the waves continued their old impetuous swooping at the dinghy, and the little craft, no longer under way, struggled woundily over them. The oiler or the correspondent took the oars again.

Shipwrecks are apropos of nothing. If men could only train for them and have them occur when the men had reached pink condition, there would be less drowning at sea. Of the four in the dinghy none had slept any time worth mentioning for two days and two nights previous to embarking in the dinghy, and in the excitement of clambering about the deck of a foundering ship they had also forgotten to eat heartily.

For these reasons, and for others, neither the oiler nor the correspondent was fond of rowing at this time. The correspondent wondered ingenuously how in the name of all that was sane could there be people who thought it amusing to row a boat. It was not an amusement; it was a diabolical punishment, and even a genius of mental aberrations could never conclude that it was anything but a horror to the muscles and a crime against the back. He mentioned to the boat in general how the amusement of rowing struck him, and the weary-faced oiler smiled in full sympathy. Previously to the foundering, by the way, the oiler had worked a double watch in the engine room of the ship.

"Take her easy now, boys," said the captain. "Don't spend yourselves. If we have to run a surf you'll need all your strength, because we'll sure have to swim for it. Take your time."

Slowly the land arose from the sea. From a black line it became a line of black and a line of white—trees and sand. Finally the captain said that he could make out a house on the shore. "That's the house of refuge, sure," said the cook. "They'll see us before long, and come out after us."

The distant lighthouse reared high. "The keeper ought to be able to make us out now, if he's looking through a glass," said the captain. "He'll notify the life-saving people."

"None of those other boats could have got ashore to give word of this wreck," said the oiler, in a low voice, "else the lifeboat would be out hunting us."

Slowly and beautifully the land loomed out of the sea. The wind came again. It had veered from the northeast to the southeast. Finally a new sound struck the ears of the men in the boat. It was the low thunder of the surf on the shore. "We'll never be able to make the lighthouse now," said the captain. "Swing her head a little more north, Billie."

"A little more north, sir," said the oiler.

Whereupon the little boat turned her nose once more down the wind, and all but the oarsman watched the shore grow. Under the influence of this expansion doubt and direful apprehension were leaving the minds of the men. The management of the boat was still most absorbing, but it could not prevent a quiet cheerfulness. In an hour, perhaps, they would be ashore.

Their backbones had become thoroughly used to balancing in the boat, and they now rode this wild colt of a dinghy like circus men. The correspondent thought that he had been drenched to the skin, but happening to feel in the top pocket of his coat, he found therein eight cigars. Four of them were soaked with sea water; four were perfectly scatheless. After a search, somebody produced three dry matches; and thereupon the four waifs rode impudently in their little boat and, with an assurance of an impending rescue shining in their eyes, puffed at the big cigars, and judged well and ill of all men. Everybody took a drink of water.

"Cook," remarked the captain, "there don't seem to be any signs of life about your house of refuge."

"No," replied the cook. "Funny they don't see us!"

A broad stretch of lowly coast lay before the eyes of the men. It was of low dunes topped with dark vegetation. The roar of the surf was plain, and sometimes they could see the white lip of a wave as it spun up the beach. A tiny house was blocked out black upon the sky. Southward, the slim lighthouse lifted its little gray length.

Tide, wind, and waves were swinging the dinghy northward. "Funny they don't see us," said the men.

The surf's roar was here dulled, but its tone was nevertheless thunderous and mighty. As the boat swam over the great rollers the men sat listening to this roar. "We'll swamp sure," said everybody.

It is fair to say here that there was not a life-saving station within twenty miles in either direction; but the men did not know this fact, and in consequence they made dark and opprobious remarks concerning the eyesight of the nation's life-savers. Four scowling men sat in the dinghy and surpassed records in the invention of epithets.

"Funny they don't see us."

The light-heartedness of a former time had completely faded. To their sharpened minds it was easy to conjure pictures of all kinds of incompetency and blindness and, indeed, cowardice. There was the shore of the populous land, and it was bitter and bitter to them that from it came no sign.

"Well," said the captain, ultimately, "I suppose we'll have to make a try for ourselves. If we stay out here too long, we'll none of us have strength left to swim after the boat swamps."

And so the oiler, who was at the oars, turned the boat straight for the shore. There was a sudden tightening of muscles. There was some thinking.

"If we don't all get ashore," said the captain—"if we don't all get ashore, I suppose you fellows know where to send news of my finish?"

They then briefly exchanged some addresses and admonitions. As for the reflections of the men, there was a great deal of rage in them. Perchance they might be formulated thus: "If I am going to be drowned— if I am going to be drowned—if I am going to be drowned, why, in the name of the seven mad gods who rule the sea, was I allowed to come thus far and contemplate sand and trees? Was I brought here merely to have my nose dragged away as I was about to nibble the sacred cheese of life? It is preposterous. If this old ninny-woman, Fate, cannot do better than this, she should be deprived of the management of men's fortunes. She is an old hen who knows not her intention. If she has decided to drown me, why did she not do it in the beginning and save me all this trouble? The whole affair is absurd.—But no; she cannot mean to drown me. She dare not drown me. She cannot drown me. Not after all this work." Afterward the man might have had an impulse to shake his fist at the clouds. "Just you drown me, now, and then hear what I call you!"

The billows that came at this time were more formidable. They seemed always just about to break and roll over the little boat in a turmoil of foam. There was a preparatory and long growl in the speech of them. No mind unused to the sea would have concluded that the dinghy could ascend these sheer heights in time. The shore was still afar. The oiler was a wily surfman. "Boys," he said swiftly, "she won't live three minutes more, and we're too far out to swim. Shall I take her to sea again, Captain?"

"Yes; go ahead!" said the captain.

This oiler, by a series of quick miracles and fast and steady oarsmanship, turned the boat in the middle of the surf and took her safely to sea again.

There was a considerable silence as the boat bumped over the furrowed sea to deeper water. Then somebody in gloom spoke: "Well, anyhow, they must have seen us from the shore by now."

The gulls went in slanting flight up the wind toward the gray, desolate east. A squall, marked by dingy clouds and clouds brick-red like smoke from a burning building, appeared from the southeast.

"What do you think of those life-saving people? Ain't they peaches?"

"Funny they haven't seen us."

"Maybe they think we're out here for sport! Maybe they think we're fishin'. Maybe they think we're damned fools."

It was a long afternoon. A changed tide tried to force them southward, but wind and wave said northward. Far ahead, where coast line, sea, and sky formed their mighty angle, there were little dots which seemed to indicate a city on the shore.

"St. Augustine?"

The captain shook his head. "Too near Mosquito Inlet."

And the oiler rowed, and then the correspondent rowed; then the oiler rowed. It was a weary business. The human back can become the seat of more aches and pains than are registered in books for the composite anatomy of a regiment. It is a limited area, but it can become the theatre of innumerable muscular conflicts, tangles, wrenches, knots, and other comforts.

"Did you ever like to row, Billie?" asked the correspondent.

"No," said the oiler; "hang it!"

When one exchanged the rowing seat for a place in the bottom of the boat, he suffered a bodily depression that caused him to be careless of everything save an obligation to wiggle one finger. There was cold sea water swashing to and fro in the boat, and he lay in it. His head, pillowed on a thwart, was within an inch of the swirl of a wave crest, and some-times a particularly obstreperous sea came inboard and drenched him once more. But these matters did not annoy him. It is almost certain that if the boat had capsized he would have tumbled comfortably out upon the ocean as if he felt sure that it was a great soft mattress.

"Look! There's a man on the shore!"

"Where?"

"There! See 'im? See 'im?"

"Yes, sure! He's walking along."

"Now he's stopped. Look! He's facing us!"

"He's waving at us!"

"So he is! By thunder!"

"Ah, now we're all right! Now we're all right! There'll be a boat out here for us in half an hour."

"He's going on. He's running. He's going up to that house there."

The remote beach seemed lower than the sea, and it required a search-ing glance to discern the little black figure. The captain saw a floating stick, and they rowed to it. A bath towel was by some weird chance in the boat, and, tying this on the stick, the captain waved it. The oarsman did not dare turn his head, so he was obliged to ask questions.

"What's he doing now?"

"He's standing still again. He's looking, I think.—There he goes again— toward the house.—Now he's stopped again."

"Is he waving at us?"

"No, not now; he was, though."

"Look! There comes another man!"

"He's running."

"Look at him go, would you!"

"Why, he's on a bicycle. Now he's met the other man. They're both waving at us. Look!"

"There comes something up the beach."

"What the devil is that thing?"

"Why, it looks like a boat."

"Why, certainly, it's a boat."

"No; it's on wheels."

"Yes, so it is. Well, that must be the lifeboat. They drag them along shore on a wagon."

"That's the lifeboat, sure."

"No, by God, it's—it's an omnibus."

"I tell you it's a lifeboat."

"It is not! It's an omnibus. I can see it plain. See? One of these big hotel omnibuses."

"By thunder, you're right. It's an omnibus, sure as fate. What do you suppose they are doing with an omnibus? Maybe they are going around collecting the life-crew, hey?"

"That's it, likely. Look! There's a fellow waving a little black flag. He's standing on the steps of the omnibus. There come those other two fellows. Now they're all talking together. Look at the fellow with the flag. Maybe he ain't waving it!"

"That ain't a flag, is it? That's his coat. Why, certainly, that's his coat."

"So it is; it's his coat. He's taken it off and is waving it around his head. But would you look at him swing it!"

"Oh, say, there isn't any life-saving station there. That's just a winter-resort hotel omnibus that has brought over some of the boarders to see us drown."

"What's that idiot with the coat mean? What's he signaling, anyhow?"

"It looks as if he were trying to tell us to go north. There must be a life-saving station up there."

"No; he thinks we're fishing. Just giving us a merry hand. See? Ah, there, Willie!"

"Well, I wish I could make something out of those signals. What do you suppose he means?"

"He don't mean anything; he's just playing."

"Well, if he'd just signal us to try the surf again, or to go to sea and wait, or go north, or go south, or go to hell, there would be some reason in it. But look at him! He just stands there and keeps his coat revolving like a wheel. The ass!"

"There come more people."

"Now there's quite a mob. Look! Isn't that a boat?"

"Where? Oh, I see where you mean. No, that's no boat."

"That fellow is still waving his coat."

"He must think we like to see him do that. Why don't he quit it? It don't mean anything."

"I don't know. I think he is trying to make us go north. It must be that there's a life-saving station there somewhere."

"Say, he ain't tired yet. Look at 'im wave!"

"Wonder how long he can keep that up. He's been revolving his coat ever since he caught sight of us. He's an idiot. Why aren't they getting men to bring a boat out? A fishing boat—one of those big yawls—could come out here all right. Why don't he do something?"

"Oh, it's all right now."

"They'll have a boat out here for us in less than no time, now that they've seen us."

A faint yellow tone came into the sky over the low land. The shadows on the sea slowly deepened. The wind bore coldness with it, and the men began to shiver.

"Holy smoke!" said one, allowing his voice to express his impious mood, "if we keep on monkeying out here! If we've got to flounder out here all night!"

"Oh, we'll never have to stay here all night! Don't you worry. They've seen us now, and it won't be long before they'll come chasing out after us."

The shore grew dusky. The man waving a coat blended gradually into this gloom, and it swallowed in the same manner the omnibus and the group of people. The spray, when it dashed uproariously over the side, made the voyagers shrink and swear like men who were being branded.

"I'd like to catch the chump who waved the coat. I feel like socking him one, just for luck."

"Why? What did he do?"

"Oh, nothing, but then he seemed so damned cheerful."

In the meantime the oiler rowed, and then the correspondent rowed, and then the oiler rowed. Gray-faced and bowed forward, they mechanically, turn by turn, plied the leaden oars. The form of the lighthouse had vanished from the southern horizon, but finally a pale star appeared, just lifting from the sea. The streaked saffron in the west passed before the all-merging darkness, and the sea to the east was black. The land had vanished, and was expressed only by the low and drear thunder of the surf.

"If I am going to be drowned—if I am going to be drowned—if I am going to be drowned, why, in the name of the seven mad gods who rule the sea, was I allowed to come thus far and contemplate sand and trees? Was I brought here merely to have my nose dragged away as I was about to nibble the sacred cheese of life?"

The patient captain, drooped over the water jar, was sometimes obliged to speak to the oarsman.

"Keep her head up! Keep her head up!"

"Keep her head up, sir." The voices were weary and low.

This was surely a quiet evening. All save the oarsman lay heavily and listlessly in the boat's bottom. As for him, his eyes were just capable of noting the tall black waves that swept forward in a most sinister silence, save for an occasional subdued growl of a crest.

The cook's head was on a thwart, and he looked without interest at the water under his nose. He was deep in other scenes. Finally he spoke. "Billie," he murmured, dreamfully, "what kind of pie do you like best?"

"Pie!" said the oiler and the correspondent, agitatedly. "Don't talk about those things, blast you!"

"Well," said the cook, "I was just thinking about ham sandwiches and—"

A night on the sea in an open boat is a long night. As darkness settled finally, the shine of the light, lifting from the sea in the south, changed to full gold. On the northern horizon a new light appeared, a small bluish gleam on the edge of the waters. These two lights were the furniture of the world. Otherwise there was nothing but waves.

Two men huddled in the stern, and distances were so magnificent in the dinghy that the rower was enabled to keep his feet partly warm by thrusting them under his companions. Their legs indeed extended far under the rowing seat until they touched the feet of the captain forward. Sometimes, despite the efforts of the tired oarsman, a wave came piling into the boat, an icy wave of the night, and the chilling water soaked them anew. They would twist their bodies for a moment and groan, and sleep the dead sleep once more, while the water in the boat gurgled about them as the craft rocked.

The plan of the oiler and the correspondent was for one to row until he lost the ability, and then arouse the other from his sea-water couch in the bottom of the boat.

The oiler plied the oars until his head drooped forward and the overpowering sleep blinded him; and he rowed yet afterward. Then he touched a man in the bottom of the boat, and called his name. "Will you spell me for a little while?" he said, meekly.

"Sure, Billie," said the correspondent, awaking and dragging himself to a sitting position. They exchanged places carefully, and the oiler, cuddling down in the sea water at the cook's side, seemed to go to sleep instantly.

The particular violence of the sea had ceased. The waves came without snarling. The obligation of the man at the oars was to keep the boat

headed so that the tilt of the rollers would not capsize her, and to preserve her from filling when the crests rushed past. The black waves were
silent and hard to be seen in the darkness. Often one was almost upon the
boat before the oarsman was aware.

In a low voice the correspondent addressed the captain. He was not
sure that the captain was awake, although this iron man seemed to be
always awake. "Captain, shall I keep her making for that light north, sir?"

The same steady voice answered him. "Yes. Keep it about two points
off the port bow."

The cook had tied a life belt around himself in order to get even the
warmth which this clumsy cork contrivance could donate, and he seemed
almost stovelike when a rower, whose teeth invariably chattered wildly
as soon as he ceased his labor, dropped down to sleep.

The correspondent, as he rowed, looked down at the two men sleeping
underfoot. The cook's arm was around the oiler's shoulders, and, with
their fragmentary clothing and haggard faces, they were the babes of the
sea—a grotesque rendering of the old babes in the wood.

Later he must have grown stupid at his work, for suddenly there was a
growling of water, and a crest came with a roar and a swash into the boat,
and it was a wonder that it did not set the cook afloat in his life belt. The
cook continued to sleep, but the oiler sat up, blinking his eyes and shaking
with the new cold.

"Oh, I'm awful sorry, Billie," said the correspondent, contritely.

"That's all right, old boy," said the oiler, and lay down again and was
asleep.

Presently it seemed that even the captain dozed, and the correspondent thought that he was the one man afloat on all the oceans. The wind
had a voice as it came over the waves, and it was sadder than the end.

There was a long, loud swishing astern of the boat, and a gleaming
trail of phosphorescence, like blue flame, was furrowed on the black waters. It might have been made by a monstrous knife.

Then there came a stillness, while the correspondent breathed with
open mouth and looked at the sea.

Suddenly there was another swish and another long flash of bluish
light, and this time it was alongside the boat, and might almost been
reached with an oar. The correspondent saw an enormous fin speed like a
shadow through the water, hurling the crystalline spray and leaving the
long glowing trail.

The correspondent looked over his shoulder at the captain. His face was hidden, and he seemed to be asleep. He looked at the babes of the sea. They certainly were asleep. So, being bereft of sympathy, he leaned a little way to one side and swore softly into the sea.

But the thing did not then leave the vicinity of the boat. Ahead or astern, on one side or the other, at intervals long or short, fled the long sparkling streak, and there was to be heard the *whirroo* of the dark fin. The speed and power of the thing was greatly to be admired. It cut the water like a gigantic and keen projectile.

The presence of this biding thing did not affect the man with the same horror that it would if he had been a picnicker. He simply looked at the sea dully and swore in an undertone.

Nevertheless, it is true that he did not wish to be alone with the thing. He wished one of his companions to awake by chance and keep him company with it. But the captain hung motionless over the water jar, and the oiler and the cook in the bottom of the boat were plunged in slumber.

"If I am going to be drowned—if I am going to be drowned—if I am going to be drowned, why, in the name of the seven mad gods who rule the sea, was I allowed to come thus far and contemplate sand and trees?"

During this dismal night, it may be remarked that a man would conclude that it was really the intention of the seven mad gods to drown him, despite the abominable injustice of it. For it was certainly an abominable injustice to drown a man who had worked so hard, so hard. The man felt it would be a crime most unnatural. Other people had drowned at sea since galleys swarmed with painted sails, but still—

When it occurs to a man that nature does not regard him as important, and that she feels she would not maim the universe by disposing of him, he at first wishes to throw bricks at the temple, and he hates deeply the fact that there are no bricks and no temples. Any visible expression of nature would surely be pelleted with his jeers.

Then, if there be no tangible thing to hoot, he feels, perhaps, the desire to confront a personification and indulge in pleas, bowed to one knee, and with hands supplicant, saying, "Yes, but I love myself."

A high cold star on a winter's night is the word he feels that she says to him. Thereafter he knows the pathos of his situation.

The men in the dinghy had not discussed these matters, but each had, no doubt, reflected upon them in silence and according to his mind. There was seldom any expression upon their faces save the general one of complete weariness. Speech was devoted to the business of the boat.

To chime the notes of his emotion, a verse mysteriously entered the correspondent's head. He had even forgotten that he had forgotten this verse, but it suddenly was in his mind.

> A soldier of the Legion lay dying in Algiers;
> There was lack of woman's nursing, there was dearth of woman's tears;
> But a comrade stood beside him, and he took that comrade's hand,
> And he said, "I never more shall see my own, my native land."

In his childhood the correspondent had been made acquainted with the fact that a soldier of the Legion lay dying in Algiers, but he had never regarded the fact as important. Myriads of his school fellows had informed him of the soldier's plight, but the dinning had naturally ended by making him perfectly indifferent. He had never considered it his affair that a soldier of the Legion lay dying in Algiers, nor had it appeared to him as a matter for sorrow. It was less to him than the breaking of a pencil's point.

Now, however, it quaintly came to him as a human, living thing. It was no longer merely a picture of a few throes in the breast of a poet, meanwhile drinking tea and warming his feet at the grate; it was an actuality—stern, mournful, and fine.

The correspondent plainly saw the soldier. He lay on the sand with his feet out straight and still. While his pale left hand was upon his chest in an attempt to thwart the going of his life, the blood came between his fingers. In the far Algerian distance, a city of low square forms was set against a sky that was faint with the last sunset hues. The correspondent, plying the oars and dreaming of the slow and slower movements of the lips of the soldier, was moved by a profound and perfectly impersonal comprehension. He was sorry for the soldier of the Legion who lay dying in Algiers.

The thing which had followed the boat and waited had evidently grown bored at the delay. There was no longer to be heard the slash of the cutwater, and there was no longer the flame of the long trail. The light in the north still glimmered, but it was apparently no nearer to the boat. Sometimes the boom of the surf rang in the correspondent's ears, and he turned the craft seaward then and rowed harder. Southward, some one had evidently built a watch-fire on the beach. It was too low and too far to be seen, but it made a shimmering, roseate reflection upon the bluff in back of it, and this could be discerned from the boat. The wind came stronger, and sometimes a wave suddenly raged out like a mountain cat, and there was to be seen the sheen and sparkle of a broken crest.

The captain, in the bow, moved on his water jar and sat erect. "Pretty long night," he observed to the correspondent. He looked at the shore. "Those life-saving people take their time."

"Did you see that shark playing around?"

"Yes, I saw him. He was a big fellow, all right."

"Wish I had known you were awake."

Later the correspondent spoke into the bottom of the boat. "Billie!" There was a slow and gradual disentanglement. "Billie, will you spell me?"

"Sure," said the oiler.

As soon as the correspondent touched the cold, comfortable sea water in the bottom of the boat and had huddled close to the cook's life belt he was deep in sleep, despite the fact that his teeth played all the popular airs. This sleep was so good to him that it was but a moment before he heard a voice call his name in a tone that demonstrated the last stages of exhaustion. "Will you spell me?"

"Sure, Billie."

The light in the north had mysteriously vanished, but the correspondent took his course from the wide-awake captain.

Later in the night they took the boat farther out to sea, and the captain directed the cook to take one oar at the stern and keep the boat facing the seas. He was to call out if he should hear the thunder of the surf. This plan enabled the oiler and the correspondent to get respite together. "We'll give those boys a chance to get into shape again," said the captain. They curled down and, after a few preliminary chatterings and trembles, slept once more the dead sleep. Neither knew they had bequeathed to the cook the company of another shark, or perhaps the same shark.

As the boat caroused on the waves, spray occasionally bumped over the side and gave them a fresh soaking, but this had no power to break their repose. The ominous slash of the wind and the water affected them as it would have affected mummies.

"Boys," said the cook, with the notes of every reluctance in his voice, "she's drifted in pretty close. I guess one of you had better take her to sea again." The correspondent, aroused, heard the crash of the toppled crests.

As he was rowing, the captain gave him some whisky and water, and this steadied the chills out of him. "If I ever get ashore and anybody shows me even a photograph of an oar—"

At last there was a short conversation.

"Billie!—Billie, will you spell me?"

"Sure," said the oiler.

When the correspondent again opened his eyes, the sea and the sky wore each of the gray hue of the dawning. Later, carmine and gold was painted upon the waters. The morning appeared finally, in its splendor, with a sky of pure blue, and the sunlight flamed on the tips of the waves.

On the distant dunes were set many little black cottages, and a tall white windmill reared above them. No man, nor dog, nor bicycle appeared on the beach. The cottages might have formed a deserted village.

The voyagers scanned the shore. A conference was held in the boat. "Well," said the captain, "if no help is coming, we might better try a run through the surf right away. If we stay out here much longer we will be too weak to do anything for ourselves at all." The others silently acquiesced in this reasoning. The boat was headed for the beach. The correspondent wondered if none ever ascended the tall wind tower, and if then they never looked seaward. This tower was a giant, standing with its back to the plight of the ants. It represented in a degree, to the correspondent, the serenity of nature amid the struggles of the individual—nature in the wind, and nature in the vision of men. She did not seem cruel to him then, nor beneficent, nor treacherous, nor wise. But she was indifferent, flatly indifferent. It is, perhaps, plausible that a man in this situation, impressed with the unconcern of the universe, should see the innumerable flaws of his life, and have them taste wickedly in his mind, and wish for another chance. A distinction between right and wrong seems absurdly clear to him, then, in this new ignorance of the grave edge, and he understands that if he were given another opportunity he would mend his conduct and his words, and be better and brighter during an introduction or at a tea.

"Now, boys," said the captain, "she is going to swamp sure. All we can do is to work her in as far as possible, and then when she swamps, pile out and scramble for the beach. Keep cool now, and don't jump until she swamps sure."

The oiler took the oars. Over his shoulders he scanned the surf.

"Captain," he said, "I think I'd better bring her about and keep her head-on to the seas and back her in."

"All right, Billie," said the captain. "Back her in." The oiler swung the boat then, and, seated in the stern, the cook and the correspondent were obliged to look over their shoulders to contemplate the lonely and indifferent shore.

The monstrous inshore rollers heaved the boat high until the men were again enabled to see the white sheets of water scudding up the slanted beach. "We won't get in very close," said the captain. Each time a man could wrest his attention from the rollers, he turned his glance toward the shore, and in the expression of the eyes during this contemplation there was a singular quality. The correspondent, observing the others, knew that they were not afraid, but the full meaning of their glances was shrouded.

As for himself, he was too tired to grapple fundamentally with the fact. He tried to coerce his mind into thinking of it, but the mind was dominated at this time by the muscles, and the muscles said they did not care. It merely occurred to him that if he should drown it would be a shame.

There were no hurried words, no pallor, no plain agitation. The men simply looked at the shore. "Now, remember to get well clear of the boat when you jump," said the captain.

Seaward the crest of a roller suddenly fell with a thunderous crash, and the long white comber came roaring down upon the boat.

"Steady now," said the captain. The men were silent. They turned their eyes from the shore to the comber and waited. The boat slid up the incline, leaped at the furious top, bounced over it, and swung down the long back of the wave. Some water had been shipped, and the cook bailed it out.

But the next crest crashed also. The tumbling, boiling flood of white water caught the boat and whirled it almost perpendicular. Water swarmed in from all sides. The correspondent had his hands on the gunwale at this time, and when the water entered at that place he swiftly withdrew his fingers, as if he objected to wetting them.

The little boat, drunken with this weight of water, reeled and snuggled deeper into the sea.

"Bail her out, cook! Bail her out!" said the captain.

"All right, Captain," said the cook.

"Now, boys, the next one will do for us sure," said the oiler. "Mind to jump clear of the boat."

The third wave moved forward, huge, furious, implacable. It fairly swallowed the dinghy, and almost simultaneously the men tumbled into the sea. A piece of life belt had lain in the bottom of the boat, and as the correspondent went overboard he held this to his chest with his left hand.

The January water was icy, and he reflected immediately that it was colder than he had expected to find it off the coast of Florida. This appeared to his dazed mind as a fact important enough to be noted at the time. The coldness of the water was sad; it was tragic. This fact was somehow mixed and confused with his opinion of his own situation, so that it seemed almost a proper reason for tears. The water was cold.

When he came to the surface he was conscious of little but the noisy water. Afterward he saw his companions in the sea. The oiler was ahead in the race. He was swimming strongly and rapidly. Off to the correspondent's left, the cook's great white and corked back bulged out of the water; and in the rear the captain was hanging with his one good hand to the keel of the overturned dinghy.

There is a certain immovable quality to a shore, and the correspondent wondered at it amid the confusion of the sea.

It seemed also very attractive; but the correspondent knew that it was a long journey, and he paddled leisurely. The piece of life preserver lay under him, and sometimes he whirled down the incline of a wave as if he were on a hand sled.

But finally he arrived at a place in the sea where travel was beset with difficulty. He did not pause swimming to inquire what manner of current had caught him, but there his progress ceased. The shore was set before him like a bit of scenery on a stage, and he looked at it and understood with his eyes each detail of it.

As the cook passed, much farther to the left, the captain was calling to him, "Turn over on your back, cook! Turn over on your back and use the oar."

"All right, sir." The cook turned on his back, and, paddling with an oar, went ahead as if he were a canoe.

Presently the boat also passed to the left of the correspondent, with the captain clinging with one hand to the keel. He would have appeared like a man raising himself to look over a board fence if it were not for the extraordinary gymnastics of the boat. The correspondent marveled that the captain could still hold to it.

They passed on nearer to shore—the oiler, the cook, the captain— and following them went the water jar, bouncing gaily over the seas.

The correspondent remained in the grip of this strange new enemy—

a current. The shore, with its white slope of sand and its green bluff topped with little silent cottages, was spread like a picture before him. It was very near to him then, but he was impressed as one who, in a gallery, looks at a scene from Brittany or Algiers.

He thought: "I am going to drown? Can it be possible? Can it be possible? Can it be possible?" Perhaps an individual must consider his own death to be the final phenomenon of nature.

But later a wave perhaps whirled him out of this small deadly current, for he found suddenly that he could again make progress toward the shore. Later still he was aware that the captain, clinging with one hand to the keel of the dinghy, had his face turned away from the shore and toward him, and was calling his name. "Come to the boat! Come to the boat!"

In his struggle to reach the captain and the boat, he reflected that when one gets properly wearied drowning must really be a comfortable arrangement—a cessation of hostilities accompanied by a large degree of relief; and he was glad of it, for the main thing in his mind for some moments had been horror of the temporary agony. He did not wish to be hurt.

Presently he saw a man running along the shore. He was undressing with most remarkable speed. Coat, trousers, shirt. everything flew magically off him.

"Come to the boat!" called the captain.

"All right, Captain." As the correspondent paddled, he saw the captain let himself down to bottom and leave the boat. Then the correspondent performed his one little marvel of the voyage. A large wave caught him and flung him with ease and supreme speed completely over the boat and far beyond it. It struck him even then as an event in gymnastics and a true miracle of the sea. An overturned boat in the surf is not a plaything to a swimming man.

The correspondent arrived in water that reached only to his waist, but his condition did not enable him to stand for more than a moment. Each wave knocked him into a heap, and the undertow pulled at him.

Then he saw the man who had been running and undressing, and undressing and running, come bounding into the water. He dragged ashore the cook, and then waded toward the captain; but the captain waved him away and sent him to the correspondent. He was naked— naked as a tree in winter; but a halo was about his head, and he shone like a saint. He gave a strong pull, and a long drag, and a bully heave at the correspondent's hand. The correspondent, schooled in the minor formulae, said, "Thanks, old man." But suddenly the man cried, "What's that?" He pointed a swift finger. The correspondent said, "Go."

In the shallows, face downward, lay the oiler. His forehead touched sand that was periodically, between each wave, clear of the sea.

The correspondent did not know all that transpired afterward. When he achieved safe ground he fell, striking the sand with each particular part of his body. It was as if he had dropped from a roof, but the thud was grateful to him.

It seemed that instantly the beach was populated with men with blankets, clothes, and flasks, and women with coffee pots and all the remedies sacred to their minds. The welcome of the land to the men from the sea was warm and generous; but a still and dripping shape was carried slowly up the beach, and the land's welcome for it could only be the different and sinister hospitality of the grave.

When it came night, the white waves paced to and fro in the moonlight, and the wind brought the sound of the great sea's voice to the men on the shore, and they felt that they could then be interpreters.

Herman Melville

1819–1891

Herman Melville, of Scottish, Dutch, and Irish stock, was born in New York City on August 1, 1819. His father's business failure and death left Herman's mother with eight children to bring up. He tried schoolteaching. At nineteen he signed on a Liverpool trader. In January, 1841, he shipped aboard the whaler *Acushnet* outbound for the South Seas. The following year he and a companion jumped ship at Nukuhiva, in the Marquesas Islands, and lived for a while as compulsory guests of the Taipi tribe. He reached Tahiti aboard the Australian whaler *Lucy Ann*. After a short imprisonment there, another whaler, *Charles and Henry*, brought him to Maui in the Hawaiian (then Sandwich) Islands.

In Honolulu, on August 17, 1843, he signed on the frigate *United States* as an ordinary seaman. He saw fourteen months of sea duty and was discharged in Boston. That winter of 1844–45 he began to write *Typee*. It was published the next year in England and the United States. He was famous at once as "the man who had lived among cannibals." *Omoo* appeared in 1847, and was equally popular. He married Elizabeth Shaw, daughter of the Chief Justice of Massachusetts, and joined the New York literary coterie.

In 1849 he published *Mardi* and *Redburn*. That year he made a brief voyage to England and the Continent. In 1850 *White-Jacket* appeared. Melville settled near Pittsfield, Massachusetts, where he met Nathaniel Hawthorne and began *Moby Dick*, his masterpiece. The publication of that work in 1851, and of *Pierre* a year later, quenched his reputation as a popular writer. *Israel Potter, The Piazza Tales*, and *The Confidence-Man* appeared between 1855 and 1857.

In 1856 to 1857 Melville traveled in Europe and the Holy Land. He tried lecturing and in 1860 accompanied his brother, master of the clipper ship *Meteor,* on a voyage to San Francisco. In 1866 he was made a District Inspector of Customs in New York and remained at that post until 1885. During this period he published two volumes of poetry, *Battle-Pieces* and *Clarel*. Two others appeared later. Even if he had written nothing else, *Moby Dick* would have earned him a place among the highest in American and world literature. He died in New York City on September 28. 1891.

In the early winter of 1888. Melville set out to write *Billy Budd,* his last great work. He began a first revision and enlargement in March, 1889. The book, left in an all but final state at his death, remained unpublished until Raymond M. Weaver brought it out in 1924 as a part of his Melville revival. It was later turned into a play, a motion picture, and an opera composed by Benjamin Britten. Many critics have come to regard it as second only to *Moby Dick* in the Melville canon.

It is, like so much of Melville's work, a story of the sea—and what a story it is! We discover at once, as in Hugo's account of the cannon adrift or Scott's *The Two Drovers*, that the story is inseparable from its meaning. We have hardly got well into it before we begin to ask ourselves questions. We notice that these questions are chiefly ethical and philosophical. What is the nature of good and evil in human beings? Are these qualities inborn or taught? Must we make a distinction between law and justice? If so, which must we observe? Is there a justice according to law and a justice of the heart? Moreover, we observe that these questions originate, not as ideas, but in our feelings about the characters.

Claggart, the master-at-arms, falsely denounces Billy Budd to Captain Vere as a plotter of mutiny. Captain Vere summons Budd to face the charge. He, tongue-tied with horror, strikes out at Claggart and kills him. At once Captain Vere convenes a court-martial to try Budd. Is this proper? The other officers and the surgeon feel that

Notes from the artist: ". . . the sea—and some of its imaginary creatures and monsters—flows from the hair and beard of Melville, forming a living part of the author whose works often suggest the strange, fantastic effects of the sea on men's souls."

Herman
Melville

the matter should be referred to the admiral. This is evidently in accord with the laws and regulations then in force in the British navy.

Harrison Hayford and Merton M. Sealts, Jr., who have made a full study of *Billy Budd,* and whose text follows, show that the Mutiny Act cited by Melville clearly applied to British land forces, not to the navy. Moreover, naval regulations provided that a death sentence for any act other than mutiny must not be carried out until it had been reviewed and affirmed by the Admiralty or the squadron or fleet commander. Budd is not being tried for any mutinous act—no one, not even Claggart, believed him guilty of that—but for killing an officer.

Thus Captain Vere, far from being a letter-of-the-law man, is clearly exceeding his authority in convening a court-martial and executing sentence. More than that, he has made up his mind beforehand that Budd must die. The sentence of the court is in effect a directed verdict. Why? Even if Captain Vere believed that his actions were legal, his great sympathy for Budd—so great, in fact, that the French critic Mayoux has suggested that he might be Budd's natural father—darkens the mystery. Did he believe that, against the background of recent mutiny, Budd must be made a swift example? How did he know that this would not rouse the crew?

We speculate, as Melville intended we should. Is Billy Budd meant to be a Christ figure? Are he and Claggart the respective symbols of good and evil? Is the novel first of all a social criticism of a barbarous time? Or is it Melville's final "testament of acceptance"? "Acceptance" of injustice in the name of social order? Or is it all meant to be taken as dark irony? We go on questioning. But we notice that, in all our questions, we hold to our feeling of common humanity in the face of every circumstance that threatens it.

Billy Budd

DEDICATED

TO

JACK CHASE

ENGLISHMAN

Wherever that great heart may now be
Here on Earth or harbored in Paradise

Captain of the Maintop
in the year 1843
in the U.S. Frigate
United States

In the time before steamships, or then more frequently than now, a stroller along the docks of any considerable seaport would occasionally have his attention arrested by a group of bronzed mariners, man-of-war's men or merchant sailors in holiday attire, ashore on liberty. In certain instances they would flank, or like a bodyguard quite surround, some superior figure of their own class, moving along with them like Aldebaran among the lesser lights of his constellation. That signal object was the "Handsome Sailor" of the less prosaic time alike of the military and merchant navies. With no perceptible trace of the vainglorious about him, rather with the offhand unaffectedness of natural regality, he seemed to accept the spontaneous homage of his shipmates.

A somewhat remarkable instance recurs to me. In Liverpool, now half a century ago, I saw under the shadow of the great dingy street-wall of Prince's Dock (an obstruction long since removed) a common sailor so intensely black that he must needs have been a native African of the unadulterate blood of Ham—a symmetric figure much above the average height. The two ends of a gay silk handkerchief thrown loose about the neck danced upon the displayed ebony of his chest, in his ears were big hoops of gold, and a Highland bonnet with a tartan band set off his shapely head. It was a hot noon in July; and his face, lustrous with perspiration, beamed with barbaric good humor. In jovial sallies right and left, his white teeth flashing into view, he rollicked along, the center of a company of his shipmates. These were made up of such an assortment of tribes and complexions as would have well fitted them to be marched up by Anacharsis Cloots before the bar of the first French Assembly as Representatives of the Human Race. At each spontaneous tribute rendered by the wayfarers to this black pagod of a fellow—the tribute of a pause and stare, and less frequently an exclamation—the motley retinue showed that they took that sort of pride in the evoker of it which the Assyrian priests doubtless showed for their grand sculptured Bull when the faithful prostrated themselves.

To return. If in some cases a bit of a nautical Murat in setting forth his person ashore, the Handsome Sailor of the period in question evinced nothing of the dandified Billy-be-Dam, an amusing character all but extinct now, but occasionally to be encountered, and in a form yet more amusing than the original, at the tiller of the boats on the tempestuous Erie Canal or, more likely, vaporing in the groggeries along the towpath. Invariably a proficient in his perilous calling, he was also more or less of a mighty boxer or wrestler. It was strength and beauty. Tales of his prowess were recited. Ashore he was the champion; afloat the spokesman; on every suitable occasion always foremost. Close-reefing topsails in a gale, there he was, astride the weather yardarm-end, foot in the Flemish horse as stirrup, both hands tugging at the earing as at a bridle, in very much the attitude of young Alexander curbing the fiery Bucephalus. A superb figure, tossed up as by the horns of Taurus against the thunderous sky, cheerily hallooing to the strenuous file along the spar.

The moral nature was seldom out of keeping with the physical make. Indeed, except as toned by the former, the comeliness and power, always attractive in masculine conjunction, hardly could have drawn the sort of honest homage the Handsome Sailor in some examples received from his less gifted associates.

Such a cynosure, at least in aspect, and something such too in nature, though with important variations made apparent as the story proceeds, was welkin-eyed Billy Budd—or Baby Budd, as more familiarly, under circumstances hereafter to be given, he at last came to be called—aged twenty-one, a foretopman of the British fleet toward the close of the last decade of the eighteenth century. It was not very long prior to the time of the narration that follows that he had entered the King's service, having been impressed on the Narrow Seas from a homeward-bound English merchantman into a seventy-four outward-bound, H.M.S. *Bellipotent;* which ship, as was not unusual in those hurried days, having been obliged to put to sea short of her proper complement of men. Plump upon Billy at first sight in the gangway the boarding officer, Lieutenant Ratcliffe, pounced, even before the merchantman's crew was formally mustered on the quarter-deck for his deliberate inspection. And him only he elected. For whether it was because the other men when ranged before him showed to ill advantage after Billy, or whether he had some scruples in view of the merchantman's being rather short-handed, however it might be, the officer contented himself with his first spontaneous choice. To the surprise of the ship's company, though much to the lieutenant's satisfaction, Billy made no demur. But, indeed, any demur would have been as idle as the protest of a goldfinch popped into a cage.

Noting this uncomplaining acquiescence, all but cheerful, one might say, the shipmaster turned a surprised glance of silent reproach at the sailor. The shipmaster was one of those worthy mortals found in every vocation, even the humbler ones—the sort of person whom everybody agrees in calling "a respectable man." And—nor so strange to report as it may appear to be—though a plowman of the troubled waters, lifelong contending with the intractable elements, there was nothing this honest soul at heart loved better than simple peace and quiet. For the rest, he was fifty or thereabouts, a little inclined to corpulence, a prepossessing face, unwhiskered, and of an agreeable color—a rather full face, humanely intelligent in expression. On a fair day with a fair wind and all going well, a certain musical chime in his voice seemed to be the veritable unobstructed outcome of the innermost man. He had much prudence, much conscientiousness, and there were occasions when these virtues were the cause of overmuch disquietude in him. On a passage, so long as his craft was in any proximity to land, no sleep for Captain Graveling. He took to heart those serious responsibilities not so heavily borne by some shipmasters.

Now while Billy Budd was down in the forecastle getting his kit together, the *Bellipotent's* lieutenant, burly and bluff, nowise disconcerted by Captain Graveling's omitting to proffer the customary hospitalities on an occasion so unwelcome to him, an omission simply caused by preoccupation of thought, unceremoniously invited himself into the cabin, and also to a flask from the spirit locker, a receptacle which his experienced eye instantly discovered. In fact he was one of those sea dogs in whom all the hardship and peril of naval life in the great prolonged wars of his time never impaired the natural instinct for sensuous enjoyment. His duty he always faithfully did; but duty is sometimes a dry obligation, and he was for irrigating its aridity, whensoever possible, with a fertilizing decoction of strong waters. For the cabin's proprietor there was nothing left but to play the part of the enforced host with whatever grace and alacrity were practicable. As necessary adjuncts to the flask, he silently placed tumbler and water jug before the irrepressible guest. But excusing himself from partaking just then, he dismally watched the unembarrassed officer deliberately diluting his grog a little, then tossing it off in three swallows, pushing the empty tumbler away, yet not so far as to be beyond easy reach, at the same time settling himself in his seat and smacking his lips with high satisfaction, looking straight at the host.

These proceedings over, the master broke the silence; and there lurked a rueful reproach in the tone of his voice: "Lieutenant, you are going to take my best man from me, the jewel of 'em."

"Yes, I know," rejoined the other, immediately drawing back the tumbler preliminary to a replenishing. "Yes, I know. Sorry."

"Beg pardon, but you don't understand, Lieutenant. See here, now. Before I shipped that young fellow, my forecastle was a rat-pit of quarrels. It was black times, I tell you, aboard the *Rights* here. I was worried to that degree my pipe had no comfort for me. But Billy came; and it was like a Catholic priest striking peace in an Irish shindy. Not that he preached to them or said or did anything in particular; but a virtue went out of him, sugaring the sour ones. They took to him like hornets to treacle; all but the buffer of the gang, the big shaggy chap with the fire-red whiskers. He indeed, out of envy, perhaps, of the newcomer, and thinking such a "sweet and pleasant fellow," as he mockingly designated him to the others, could hardly have the spirit of a gamecock, must needs bestir himself in trying to get up an ugly row with him. Billy forebore with him and reasoned with him in a pleasant way—he is something like myself, Lieutenant, to whom aught like a quarrel is hateful—but nothing served. So, in the second dogwatch one day, the Red Whiskers in presence of the others, under pretense of showing Billy just whence a sirloin steak was cut—for the fellow had once been a butcher—insultingly gave him a dig under the ribs. Quick as lightning Billy let fly his arm. I dare say he never meant to do quite as much as he did, but anyhow he gave the burly fool a terrible drubbing. It took about half a minute, I should think. And, Lord bless you, the lubber was astonished at the celerity. And will you believe it, Lieutenant, the Red Whiskers now really loves Billy—loves him, or is the biggest hypocrite that ever I heard of. But they all love him. Some of 'em do his washing, darn his old trousers for him; the carpenter is at odd times making a pretty little chest of drawers for him. Anybody will do anything for Billy Budd; and it's the happy family here. But now, Lieutenant, if that young fellow goes—I know how it will be aboard the *Rights*. Not again very soon shall I, coming up from dinner, lean over the capstan smoking a quiet pipe—no, not very soon again, I think. Ay, Lieutenant, you are going to take away the jewel of 'em; you are going to take away my peacemaker!" And with that the good soul had really some ado in checking a rising sob.

"Well," said the lieutenant, who had listened with amused interest to all this and now was waxing merry with his tipple; "well, blessed are the peacemakers, especially the fighting peacemakers. And such are the seventy-four beauties some of which you see poking their noses out of the portholes of yonder warship lying to for me," pointing through the cabin window at the *Bellipotent*. "But courage! Don't look so down-hearted, man. Why, I pledge you in advance the royal approbation. Rest assured that His Majesty will be delighted to know that in a time when his hardtack is not sought for by sailors with such avidity as should be, a time also when some shipmasters privily resent the borrowing from them a tar or two for the service, His Majesty, I say, will be delighted to learn that *one* shipmaster at least cheerfully surrenders to the King the flower of his flock, a sailor who with equal loyalty makes no dissent. But where's my beauty? Ah," looking through the cabin's open door, "here he comes; and, by Jove, lugging along his chest—Apollo with his portmanteau! My man," stepping out to him, "you can't take that big box aboard a warship. The boxes there are mostly shot boxes. Put your duds in a bag, lad. Boot and saddle for the cavalryman, bag and hammock for the man-of-war's man."

The transfer from chest to bag was made. And, after seeing his man into the cutter and then following him down, the lieutenant pushed off from the *Rights-of-Man*. That was the merchant-ship's name, though by her master and crew abbreviated in sailor fashion into the *Rights*. The hardheaded Dundee owner was a staunch admirer of Thomas Paine, whose book in rejoinder to Burke's arraignment of the French Revolution had then been published for some time and had gone everywhere. In christening his vessel after the title of Paine's volume the man of Dundee was something like his contemporary shipowner, Stephen Girard of Philadelphia, whose sympathies, alike with his native land and its liberal philosophers, he evinced by naming his ships after Voltaire, Diderot, and so forth.

But now, when the boat swept under the merchantman's stern, and officer and oarsmen were noting—some bitterly and others with a grin—the name emblazoned there, just then it was that the new recruit jumped up from the bow where the coxswain had directed him to sit, and waving hat to his silent shipmates sorrowfully looking over at him from the taffrail, bade the lads a genial good-by. Then, making a salutation as to the ship herself, "And good-by to you too, old *Rights-of-Man*."

"Down, Sir!" roared the lieutenant, instantly assuming all the rigor of his rank, though with difficulty repressing a smile.

To be sure, Billy's action was a terrible breach of naval decorum. But in that decorum he had never been instructed; in consideration of which the lieutenant would hardly have been so energetic in reproof but for the concluding farewell to the ship. This he rather took as meant to convey a covert sally on the new recruit's part, a sly slur at impressment in general, and that of himself in especial. And yet, more likely, if satire it was in effect, it was hardly so by intention, for Billy, though happily endowed with the gaiety of high health, youth, and a free heart, was yet by no means of a satirical turn. The will to it and the sinister dexterity were alike wanting. To deal in double meanings and insinuations of any sort was quite foreign to his nature.

As to his enforced enlistment, that he seemed to take pretty much as he was wont to take any vicissitude of weather. Like the animals, though no philosopher, he was, without knowing it, practically a fatalist. And it may be that he rather liked this adventurous turn in his affairs, which promised an opening into novel scenes and martial excitements.

Aboard the *Bellipotent* our merchant sailor was forthwith rated as an able seaman and assigned to the starboard watch of the foretop. He was soon at home in the service, not at all disliked for his unpretentious good looks and a sort of genial happy-go-lucky air. No merrier man in his mess: in marked contrast to certain other individuals included like himself among the impressed portion of the ship's company; for these when not actively employed were sometimes, and more particularly in the last dog-watch when the drawing near of twilight induced reverie, apt to fall into a saddish mood which in some partook of sullenness. But they were not so young as our foretopman, and no few of them must have known a hearth of some sort, others may have had wives and children left, too

probably, in uncertain circumstances, and hardly any but must have had
acknowledged kith and kin, while for Billy, as will shortly be seen, his
entire family was practically invested in himself.

Though our new-made foretopman was well received in the top and
on the gun decks, hardly here was he that cynosure he had previously
been among those minor ship's companies of the merchant marine, with
which companies only had he hitherto consorted.

He was young; and despite his all but fully developed frame, in aspect
looked even younger than he really was, owing to a lingering adolescent
expression in the as yet smooth face all but feminine in purity of natural
complexion but where, thanks to his seagoing, the lily was quite suppressed and the rose had some ado visibly to flush through the tan.

To one essentially such a novice in the complexities of factitious life,
the abrupt transition from his former and simpler sphere to the ampler
and more knowing world of a great warship, this might well have abashed
him had there been any conceit or vanity in his composition. Among her
miscellaneous multitude, the *Bellipotent* mustered several individuals
who however inferior in grade were of no common natural stamp, sailors
more signally susceptive of that air which continuous martial discipline
and repeated presence in battle can in some degree impart even to the
average man. As the Handsome Sailor, Billy Budd's position aboard the
seventy-four was something analogous to that of a rustic beauty trans-
planted from the provinces and brought into competition with the high-
born dames of the court. But this change of circumstances he scarce
noted. As little did he observe that something about him provoked an
ambiguous smile in one or two harder faces among the bluejackets. Nor
less unaware was he of the peculiar favorable effect his person and demeanor had upon the more intelligent gentlemen of the quarter-deck.
Nor could this well have been otherwise. Cast in a mold peculiar to the
finest physical examples of those Englishmen in whom the Saxon strain
would seem not at all to partake of any Norman or other admixture, he
showed in face that humane look of reposeful good nature which the
Greek sculptor in some instances gave to his heroic strong man, Hercules.
But this again was subtly modified by another and pervasive quality. The
ear, small and shapely, the arch of the foot, the curve in mouth and
nostril, even the indurated hand dyed to the orange-tawny of the tou-
can's bill, a hand telling alike of the halyards and tar bucket; but, above
all, something in the mobile expression, and every chance attitude and
movement, something suggestive of a mother eminently favored by Love

and the Graces; all this strangely indicated a lineage in direct contradiction to his lot. The mysteriousness here became less mysterious through a matter of fact elicited when Billy at the capstan was being formally mustered into the service. Asked by the officer, a small, brisk little gentleman as it chanced, among other questions, his place of birth, he replied, "Please, Sir, I don't know."

"Don't know where you were born? Who was your father?"

"God knows, Sir."

Struck by the straightforward simplicity of these replies, the officer next asked, "Do you know anything about your beginning?"

"No, Sir. But I have heard that I was found in a pretty silk-lined basket hanging one morning from the knocker of a good man's door in Bristol."

"*Found*, say you? Well," throwing back his head and looking up and down the new recruit; "well, it turns out to have been a pretty good find. Hope they'll find some more like you, my man; the fleet sadly needs them."

Yes, Billy Budd was a foundling, a presumable by-blow, and, evidently, no ignoble one. Noble descent was as evident in him as in a blood horse.

For the rest, with little or no sharpness of faculty or any trace of the wisdom of the serpent, nor yet quite a dove, he possessed that kind and degree of intelligence going along with the unconventional rectitude of a sound human creature, one to whom not yet has been proffered the questionable apple of knowledge. He was illiterate; he could not read, but he could sing, and like the illiterate nightingale was sometimes the composer of his own song.

Of self-consciousness he seemed to have little or none, or about as much as we may reasonably impute to a dog of Saint Bernard's breed.

Habitually living with the elements and knowing little more of the land than as a beach, or, rather, that portion of the terraqueous globe providentially set apart for dance houses, doxies, and tapsters, in short what sailors call a "fiddler's green," his simple nature remained unsophisticated by those moral obliquities which are not in every case incompatible with that manufacturable thing known as respectability. But are sailors, frequenters of fiddlers' greens, without vices? No; but less often than with landsmen do their vices, so called, partake of crookedness of heart, seeming less to proceed from viciousness than exuberance of vitality after long constraint: frank manifestations in accordance with natural law. By his original constitution aided by the co-operating influences of his lot, Billy in many respects was little more than a sort of upright barbarian, much such perhaps as Adam presumably might have been ere the urbane Serpent wriggled himself into his company.

And here be it submitted that apparently going to corroborate the doctrine of man's Fall, a doctrine now popularly ignored, it is observable that where certain virtues pristine and unadulterate peculiarly characterize anybody in the external uniform of civilization, they will upon scrutiny seem not to be derived from custom or convention, but rather to be out of keeping with these, as if indeed exceptionally transmitted from a period prior to Cain's city and citified man. The character marked by such qualities has to an unvitiated taste an untampered-with flavor like that of berries, while the man thoroughly civilized, even in a fair specimen of the breed, has to the same moral palate a questionable smack as of a compounded wine. To any stray inheritor of these primitive qualities found, like Caspar Hauser, wandering dazed in any Christian capital of our time, the good-natured poet's famous invocation, near two thousand years ago, of the good rustic out of his latitude in the Rome of the Caesars, still appropriately holds:

> Honest and poor, faithful in word and thought,
> What hath thee, Fabian, to the city brought?

Though our Handsome Sailor had as much of masculine beauty as one can expect anywhere to see; nevertheless, like the beautiful woman in one of Hawthorne's minor tales, there was just one thing amiss in him. No visible blemish indeed, as with the lady; no, but an occasional liability to a vocal defect. Though in the hour of elemental uproar or peril he was everything that a sailor should be, yet under sudden provocation of strong heart-feeling his voice, otherwise singularly musical, as if expressive of the harmony within, was apt to develop an organic hesitancy, in fact more or less of a stutter or even worse. In this particular Billy was a striking instance that the arch interferer, the envious marplot of Eden, still has more or less to do with every human consignment to this planet of Earth. In every case, one way or another he is sure to slip in his little card, as much as to remind us—I too have a hand here.

The avowal of such an imperfection in the Handsome Sailor should be evidence not alone that he is not presented as a conventional hero, but also that the story in which he is the main figure is no romance.

At the time of Billy Budd's arbitrary enlistment into the *Bellipotent* that ship was on her way to join the Mediterranean fleet. No long time elapsed before the junction was effected. As one of that fleet the seventy-four participated in its movements, though at times on account of her superior sailing qualities, in the absence of frigates, dispatched on separate duty as a scout and at times on less temporary service. But with all this the story has little concernment, restricted as it is to the inner life of one particular ship and the career of an individual sailor.

It was the summer of 1797. In the April of that year had occurred the commotion at Spithead followed in May by a second and yet more serious outbreak in the fleet at the Nore. The latter is known, and without exaggeration in the epithet, as "the Great Mutiny." It was indeed a demonstration more menacing to England than the contemporary manifestoes and conquering and proselyting armies of the French Directory. To the British Empire the Nore Mutiny was what a strike in the fire brigade would be to London threatened by general arson. In a crisis when the kingdom might well have anticipated the famous signal that some years later published along the naval line of battle what it was that upon occasion England expected of Englishmen; *that* was the time when at the mastheads of the three-deckers and seventy-fours moored in her own roadstead—a fleet the right arm of a Power then all but the sole free conservative one of the Old World—the bluejackets, to be numbered by thousands, ran up with huzzas the British colors with the union and cross wiped out; by that cancellation transmuting the flag of founded law and freedom defined into the enemy's red meteor of unbridled and unbounded revolt. Reasonable discontent growing out of practical grievances in the fleet had been ignited into irrational combustion as by live cinders blown across the Channel from France in flames.

The event converted into irony for a time those spirited strains of Dibdin—as a song writer no mean auxiliary to the English government at that European conjuncture—strains celebrating, among other things, the patriotic devotion of the British tar: "And as for my life, 'tis the King's!"

Such an episode in the Island's grand naval story her naval historians naturally abridge, one of them (William James) candidly acknowledging that fain would he pass it over did not "impartiality forbid fastidiousness." And yet his mention is less a narration than a reference, having to do hardly at all with details. Nor are these readily to be found in the libraries. Like some other events in every age befalling states everywhere, including America, the Great Mutiny was of such character that national pride along with views of policy would fain shade it off into the historical background. Such events cannot be ignored, but there is a considerate way of historically treating them. If a well-constituted individual refrains from blazoning aught amiss or calamitous in his family, a nation in the like circumstance may without reproach be equally discreet.

Though after parleyings between government and the ringleaders, and concessions by the former as to some glaring abuses, the first uprising—

that at Spithead—with difficulty was put down, or matters for the time pacified; yet at the Nore the unforeseen renewal of insurrection on a yet larger scale, and emphasized in the conferences that ensued by demands deemed by the authorities not only inadmissible but aggressively insolent, indicated—if the Red Flag did not sufficiently do so—what was the spirit animating the men. Final suppression, however, there was; but only made possible perhaps by the unswerving loyalty of the marine corps and a voluntary resumption of loyalty among influential sections of the crews.

To some extent the Nore Mutiny may be regarded as analogous to the distempering irruption of contagious fever in a frame constitutionally sound, and which anon throws it off.

At all events, of these thousands of mutineers were some of the tars who not so very long afterwards—whether wholly prompted thereto by patriotism, or pugnacious instinct, or by both—helped to win a coronet for Nelson at the Nile, and the naval crown of crowns for him at Trafalgar. To the mutineers, those battles and especially Trafalgar were a plenary absolution and a grand one. For all that goes to make up scenic naval display and heroic magnificence in arms, those battles, especially Trafalgar, stand unmatched in human annals.

In this matter of writing, resolve as one may to keep to the main road, some bypaths have an enticement not readily to be withstood. I am going to err into such a bypath. If the reader will keep me company I shall be glad. At the least, we can promise ourselves that pleasure which is wickedly said to be in sinning, for a literary sin the divergence will be.

Very likely it is no new remark that the inventions of our time have at last brought about a change in sea warfare in degree corresponding to the revolution in all warfare effected by the original introduction from China into Europe of gunpowder. The first European firearm, a clumsy contrivance, was, as is well known, scouted by no few of the knights as a base implement, good enough peradventure for weavers too craven to stand up crossing steel with steel in frank fight. But as ashore knightly valor, though shorn of its blazonry, did not cease with the knights, neither on the seas—though nowadays in encounters there a certain kind of displayed gallantry be fallen out of date as hardly applicable under changed circumstances—did the nobler qualities of such naval magnates as Don John of Austria, Doria, Van Tromp, Jean Bart, the long line of British admirals, and the American Decaturs of 1812 become obsolete with their wooden walls.

Nevertheless, to anybody who can hold the Present at its worth without being inappreciative of the Past, it may be forgiven, if to such a one the solitary old hulk at Portsmouth, Nelson's *Victory*, seems to float there, not alone as the decaying monument of a fame incorruptible, but also as a poetic reproach, softened by its picturesqueness, to the *Monitors* and yet mightier hulls of the European ironclads. And this not altogether because such craft are unsightly, unavoidably lacking the symmetry and grand lines of the old battleships, but equally for other reasons.

There are some, perhaps, who while not altogether inaccessible to that poetic reproach just alluded to, may yet on behalf of the new order be disposed to parry it; and this to the extent of iconoclasm, if need be. For example, prompted by the sight of the star inserted in the *Victory's* quarter-deck designating the spot where the Great Sailor fell, these martial utilitarians may suggest considerations implying that Nelson's ornate publication of his person in battle was not only unnecessary, but not military, nay, savored of foolhardiness and vanity. They may add, too, that at Trafalgar it was in effect nothing less than a challenge to death; and death came; and that but for his bravado the victorious admiral might possibly have survived the battle, and so, instead of having his sagacious dying injunctions overruled by his immediate successor in command, he himself when the contest was decided might have brought his shattered fleet to anchor, a proceeding which might have averted the deplorable loss of life by shipwreck in the elemental tempest that followed the martial one.

Well, should we set aside the more than disputable point whether for various reasons it was possible to anchor the fleet, then plausibly enough the Benthamites of war may urge the above. But the *might-have-been* is but boggy ground to build on. And, certainly, in foresight as to the larger issue of an encounter, and anxious preparations for it—buoying the deadly way and mapping it out, as at Copenhagen—few commanders have been so painstakingly circumspect as this same reckless declarer of his person in fight.

Personal prudence, even when dictated by quite other than selfish considerations, surely is no special virtue in a military man; while an excessive love of glory, impassioning a less burning impulse, the honest sense of duty, is the first. If the name *Wellington* is not so much of a trumpet to the blood as the simpler name *Nelson*, the reason for this may perhaps be inferred from the above. Alfred [Lord Tennyson] in his funeral ode on the victor of Waterloo ventures not to call him the greatest soldier of all time, though in the same ode he invokes Nelson as "the greatest sailor since our world began."

At Trafalgar Nelson on the brink of opening the fight sat down and wrote his last brief will and testament. If under the presentiment of the most magnificent of all victories to be crowned by his own glorious death, a sort of priestly motive led him to dress his person in the jeweled vouchers of his own shining deeds; if thus to have adorned himself for the altar and the sacrifice were indeed vainglory, then affectation and fustian is each more heroic line in the great epics and dramas, since in such lines the poet but embodies in verse those exaltations of sentiment that a nature like Nelson, the opportunity being given, vitalizes into acts.

Yes, the outbreak at the Nore was put down. But not every grievance was redressed. If the contractors, for example, were no longer permitted to ply some practices peculiar to their tribe everywhere, such as providing shoddy cloth, rations not sound, or false in the measure, not the less impressment, for one thing, went on. By custom sanctioned for centuries, and judicially maintained by a Lord Chancellor as late as Mansfield, that mode of manning the fleet, a mode now fallen into a sort of abeyance but never formally renounced, it was not practicable to give up in those years. Its abrogation would have crippled the indispensable fleet, one wholly under canvas, no steam power, its innumerable sails and thousands of cannon, everything in short, worked by muscle alone; a fleet the more insatiate in demand for men, because then multiplying its ships of all grades against contingencies present and to come of the convulsed Continent.

Discontent foreran the Two Mutinies, and more or less it lurkingly survived them. Hence it was not unreasonable to apprehend some return of trouble sporadic or general. One instance of such apprehensions: In the same year with this story, Nelson, then Rear Admiral Sir Horatio, being with the fleet off the Spanish coast, was directed by the admiral in command to shift his pennant from the *Captain* to the *Theseus;* and for this reason: that the latter ship having newly arrived on the station from home, where it had taken part in the Great Mutiny, danger was apprehended from the temper of the men; and it was thought that an officer like Nelson was the one, not indeed to terrorize the crew into base subjection, but to win them, by force of his mere presence and heroic personality, back to an allegiance if not as enthusiastic as his own yet as true.

So it was that for a time, on more than one quarter-deck, anxiety did exist. At sea, precautionary vigilance was strained against relapse. At short notice an engagement might come on. When it did, the lieutenants assigned to batteries felt it incumbent on them, in some instances, to stand with drawn swords behind the men working the guns.

But on board the seventy-four in which Billy now swung his hammock, very little in the manner of the men and nothing obvious in the demeanor of the officers would have suggested to an ordinary observer that the Great Mutiny was a recent event. In their general bearing and conduct the commissioned officers of a warship naturally take their tone from the commander, that is if he have that ascendancy of character that ought to be his.

Captain the Honorable Edward Fairfax Vere, to give his full title, was a bachelor of forty or thereabouts, a sailor of distinction even in a time prolific of renowned seamen. Though allied to the higher nobility, his advancement had not been altogether owing to influences connected with that circumstance. He had seen much service, been in various engagements, always acquitting himself as an officer mindful of the welfare of his men, but never tolerating an infraction of discipline; thoroughly versed in the science of his profession, and intrepid to the verge of temerity, though never injudiciously so. For his gallantry in the West Indian waters as flag lieutenant under Rodney in that admiral's crowning victory over De Grasse, he was made a post captain.

Ashore, in the garb of a civilian, scarce anyone would have taken him for a sailor, more especially that he never garnished unprofessional talk with nautical terms, and grave in his bearing, evinced little appreciation of mere humor. It was not out of keeping with these traits that on a passage when nothing demanded his paramount action, he was the most undemonstrative of men. Any landsman observing this gentleman, not conspicuous by his stature and wearing no pronounced insignia, emerging from his cabin to the open deck, and noting the silent deference of the officers retiring to leeward, might have taken him for the King's guest, a civilian aboard the King's ship, some highly honorable discreet envoy on his way to an important post. But in fact this unobtrusiveness of demeanor may have proceeded from a certain unaffected modesty of manhood sometimes accompanying a resolute nature, a modesty evinced at all times not calling for pronounced action, which shown in any rank of life suggests a virtue aristocratic in kind. As with some others engaged in various departments of the world's more heroic activities, Captain Vere though practical enough upon occasion would at times betray a certain dreaminess of mood. Standing alone on the weather side of the quarter-deck, one hand holding by the rigging, he would absently gaze off at the blank sea. At the presentation to him then of some minor matter interrupting the current of his thoughts, he would show more or less irascibility; but instantly he would control it.

In the navy he was popularly known by the appellation "Starry Vere." How such a designation happened to fall upon one who whatever his sterling qualities was without any brilliant ones was in this wise: A favorite kinsman, Lord Denton, a freehearted fellow, had been the first to meet and congratulate him upon his return to England from his West Indian cruise; and but the day previous turning over a copy of Andrew Marvell's poems had lighted, not for the first time, however, upon the lines entitled "Appleton House," the name of one of the seats of their common ancestor, a hero in the German wars of the seventeenth century, in which poem occur the lines:

> This 'tis to have been from the first
> In a domestic heaven nursed,
> Under the discipline severe
> Of Fairfax and the starry Vere.

And so, upon embracing his cousin fresh from Rodney's great victory wherein he had played so gallant a part, brimming over with just family pride in the sailor of their house, he exuberantly exclaimed, "Give ye joy, Ed; give ye joy, my starry Vere!" This got currency, and the novel prefix serving in familiar parlance readily to distinguish the *Bellipotent*'s captain from another Vere his senior, a distant relative, an officer of like rank in the navy, it remained permanently attached to the surname.

In view of the part that the commander of the *Bellipotent* plays in scenes shortly to follow, it may be well to fill out that sketch of him outlined in the previous chapter.

Aside from his qualities as a sea officer Captain Vere was an exceptional character. Unlike no few of England's renowned sailors, long and arduous service with signal devotion to it had not resulted in absorbing and *salting* the entire man. He had a marked leaning toward everything intellectual. He loved books, never going to sea without a newly replenished library, compact but of the best. The isolated leisure, in some cases so wearisome, falling at intervals to commanders even during a war cruise, never was tedious to Captain Vere. With nothing of that literary taste which less heeds the thing conveyed than the vehicle, his bias was toward those books to which every serious mind of superior order occupying any active post of authority in the world naturally inclines: books treating of actual men and events no matter of what era—history, biography, and unconventional writers like Montaigne, who, free from cant and convention, honestly and in the spirit of common sense philosophize upon realities. In this line of reading he found confirmation of his own more reserved thoughts—confirmation which he had vainly sought in social converse, so that as touching most fundamental topics, there had got to be established in him some positive convictions which he forefelt would abide in him essentially unmodified so long as his intelligent part remained unimpaired. In view of the troubled period in which his lot was cast, this was well for him. His settled convictions were as a dike against those invading waters of novel opinion, social, political, and otherwise, which carried away as in a torrent no few minds in those days, minds by nature not inferior to his own. While other members of that aristocracy to which by birth he belonged were incensed at the innovators mainly because their theories were inimical to the privileged classes, Captain Vere disinterestedly opposed them not alone because they seemed to him insusceptible of embodiment in lasting institutions, but at war with the peace of the world and the true welfare of mankind.

With minds less stored than his and less earnest, some officers of his rank, with whom at times he would necessarily consort, found him lacking in the companionable quality, a dry and bookish gentleman, as they deemed. Upon any chance withdrawal from their company one would be apt to say to another something like this: "Vere is a noble fellow, Starry Vere. 'Spite the gazettes, Sir Horatio" (meaning him who became Lord Nelson) "is at bottom scarce a better seaman or fighter. But between you and me now, don't you think there is a queer streak of the pedantic running through him? Yes, like the King's yarn in a coil of navy rope?"

Some apparent ground there was for this sort of confidential criticism; since not only did the captain's discourse never fall into the jocosely familiar, but in illustrating of any point touching the stirring personages and events of the time he would be as apt to cite some historic character or incident of antiquity as he would be to cite from the moderns. He seemed unmindful of the circumstance that to his bluff company such remote allusions, however pertinent they might really be, were altogether alien to men whose reading was mainly confined to the journals. But considerateness in such matters is not easy to natures constituted like Captain Vere's. Their honesty prescribes to them directness, sometimes far-reaching like that of a migratory fowl that in its flight never heeds when it crosses a frontier.

The lieutenants and other commissioned gentlemen forming Captain Vere's staff it is not necessary here to particularize, nor needs it to make any mention of any of the warrant officers. But among the petty officers was one who, having much to do with the story, may as well be forthwith introduced. His portrait I essay, but shall never hit it. This was John Claggart, the master-at-arms. But that sea title may to landsmen seem somewhat equivocal. Originally, doubtless, that petty officer's function was the instruction of the men in the use of arms, sword or cutlass. But very long ago, owing to the advance in gunnery making hand-to-hand encounters less frequent and giving to niter and sulphur the pre-eminence over steel, that function ceased; the master-at-arms of a great warship becoming a sort of chief of police charged among other matters with the duty of preserving order on the populous lower gun decks.

Claggart was a man about five-and-thirty, somewhat spare and tall, yet of no ill figure upon the whole. His hand was too small and shapely to have been accustomed to hard toil. The face was a notable one, the features all except the chin cleanly cut as those on a Greek medallion; yet the chin, beardless as Tecumseh's, had something of strange protuberant broadness in its make that recalled the prints of the Reverend Dr. Titus Oates, the historic deponent with the clerical drawl in the time of Charles II and the fraud of the alleged Popish Plot. It served Claggart in his office that his eye could cast a tutoring glance. His brow was of the sort phrenologically associated with more than average intellect; silken jet curls partly clustering over it, making a foil to the pallor below, a pallor tinged with a faint shade of amber akin to the hue of time-tinted marbles of old. This complexion, singularly contrasting with the red or deeply bronzed visages of the sailors, and in part the result of his official seclusion from the sunlight, though it was not exactly displeasing, nevertheless seemed to hint of something defective or abnormal in the constitution and blood. But his general aspect and manner were so suggestive of an education and career incongruous with his naval function that when not actively engaged in it he looked like a man of high quality, social and moral, who for reasons of his own was keeping incog. Nothing was known of his former life. It might be that he was an Englishman; and yet there lurked a bit of accent in his speech suggesting that possibly he was not such by birth, but through naturalization in early childhood. Among certain grizzled sea gossips of the gun decks and forecastle went a rumor perdue that the master-at-arms was a chevalier who had volunteered into the King's Navy by way of compounding for some mysterious swindle whereof he had been arraigned at the King's Bench. The fact that nobody could substantiate this report was, of course, nothing against its secret currency. Such a rumor once started on the gun decks in reference to almost anyone below the rank of a commissioned officer would, during the period assigned to this narrative, have seemed not altogether wanting in credibility to the tarry old wiseacres of a man-of-war crew. And indeed a man of Claggart's accomplishments, without prior nautical experience entering the navy at mature life, as he did, and necessarily allotted at the start to the lowest grade in it; a man too who never made allusion of his previous life ashore; these were circumstances which in the dearth of exact knowledge as to his true antecedents opened to the invidious a vague field for unfavorable surmise.

But the sailors' dogwatch gossip concerning him derived a vague plausibility from the fact that now for some period the British Navy could so little afford to be squeamish in the matter of keeping up the muster rolls that not only were press gangs notoriously abroad both afloat and ashore but there was little or no secret about another matter, namely, that the London police were at liberty to capture any able-bodied suspect, any questionable fellow at large, and summarily ship him to the dockyard or fleet. Furthermore, even among voluntary enlistments there were instances where the motive thereto partook neither of patriotic impulse nor yet of a random desire to experience a bit of sea life and martial adventure. Insolvent debtors of minor grade, together with the promiscuous lame ducks of morality, found in the navy a convenient and secure refuge, secure because, once enlisted aboard a King's ship, they were as much in sanctuary as the transgressor of the Middle Ages harboring himself under the shadow of the altar. Such sanctioned irregularities, which for obvious reasons the government would hardly think to parade at the time and which consequently, and as affecting the least influential class of mankind, have all but dropped into oblivion, lend color to something for the truth whereof I do not vouch, and hence have some scruple in stating; something I remember having seen in print though the book I cannot recall; but the same thing was personally communicated to me now more than forty years ago by an old pensioner in a cocked hat with whom I had a most interesting talk on the terrace at Greenwich, a Baltimore Negro, a Trafalgar man. It was to this effect: In the case of a warship short of hands whose speedy sailing was imperative, the deficient quota, in lack of any other way of making it good, would be eked out by drafts culled direct from the jails. For reasons previously suggested it would not perhaps be easy at the present day directly to prove or disprove the allegation. But allowed as a verity, how significant would it be of England's straits at the time confronted by those wars which like a flight of harpies rose shrieking from the din and dust of the fallen Bastille. That era appears measurably clear to us who look back at it, and but read of it. But to the grandfathers of us graybeards, the more thoughtful of them, the genius of it presented an aspect like that of Camoëns' Spirit of the Cape, an eclipsing menace mysterious and prodigious. Not America was exempt from apprehension. At the height of Napoleon's unexampled conquests, there were Americans who had fought at Bunker Hill who looked forward to the possibility that the Atlantic might prove no barrier against the ultimate schemes of this French portentous upstart from the revolutionary chaos who seemed in act of fulfilling judgment prefigured in the Apocalypse.

But the less credence was to be given to the gun-deck talk touching Claggart, seeing that no man holding his office in a man-of-war can ever hope to be popular with the crew. Besides, in derogatory comments upon anyone against whom they have a grudge, or for any reason or no reason mislike, sailors are much like landsmen: they are apt to exaggerate or romance it.

About as much was really known to the *Bellipotent*'s tars of the master-at-arms' career before entering the service as an astronomer knows about a comet's travels prior to its first observable appearance in the sky. The verdict of the sea quidnuncs has been cited only by way of showing what sort of moral impression the man made upon rude uncultivated natures whose conceptions of human wickedness were necessarily of the narrowest, limited to ideas of vulgar rascality—a thief among the swinging hammocks during a night watch, or the man brokers and land sharks of the seaports.

It was no gossip, however, but fact that though, as before hinted, Claggart upon his entrance into the navy was, as a novice, assigned to the least honorable section of a man-of-war's crew, embracing the drudgery, he did not long remain there. The superior capacity he immediately evinced, his constitutional sobriety, an ingratiating deference to superiors, together with a peculiar ferreting genius manifested on a singular occasion; all this, capped by a certain austere patriotism, abruptly advanced him to the position of master-at-arms.

Of this maritime chief of police the ship's corporals, so called, were the immediate subordinates, and compliant ones; and this, as is to be

noted in some business departments ashore, almost to a degree inconsistent with entire moral volition. His place put various converging
wires of underground influence under the chief's control, capable when
astutely worked through his understrappers of operating to the mysterious discomfort, if nothing worse, of any of the sea commonalty.

Life in the foretop well agreed with Billy Budd. There, when not
actually engaged on the yards yet higher aloft, the topmen, who as such
had been picked out for youth and activity, constituted an aerial club
lounging at ease against the smaller stunsails rolled up into cushions,
spinning yarns like the lazy gods, and frequently amused with what was
going on in the busy world of the decks below. No wonder then that a
young fellow of Billy's disposition was well content in such society. Giving no cause of offense to anybody, he was always alert at a call. So in
the merchant service it had been with him. But now such a punctilious-
ness in duty was shown that his topmates would sometimes good-
naturedly laugh at him for it. This heightened alacrity had its cause,
namely, the impression made upon him by the first formal gangway-
punishment he had ever witnessed, which befell the day following his impressment. It had been incurred by a little fellow, young, a novice afterguardsman absent from his assigned post when the ship was being put
about; a dereliction resulting in a rather serious hitch to that maneuver,
one demanding instantaneous promptitude in letting go and making fast.
When Billy saw the culprit's naked back under the scourge, gridironed
with red welts and worse, when he marked the dire expression in the
liberated man's face as with his woolen shirt flung over him by the
executioner he rushed forward from the spot to bury himself in the
crowd, Billy was horrified. He resolved that never through remissness
would he make himself liable to such a visitation or do or omit aught that
might merit even verbal reproof. What then was his surprise and concern when ultimately he found himself getting into petty trouble occasionally about such matters as the stowage of his bag or something amiss
in his hammock, matters under the police oversight of the ship's corporals of the lower decks, and which brought down on him a vague threat
from one of them.

So heedful in all things as he was, how could this be? He could not understand it, and it more than vexed him. When he spoke to his young
topmates about it they were either lightly incredulous or found something comical in his unconcealed anxiety. "Is it your bag, Billy?" said
one. "Well, sew yourself up in it, bully boy, and then you'll be sure to
know if anybody meddles with it."

Now there was a veteran aboard who because his years began to disqualify him for more active work had been recently assigned duty as mainmastman in his watch, looking to the gear belayed at the rail roundabout that great spar near the deck. At off-times the foretopman had picked up some acquaintance with him, and now in his trouble it occurred to him that he might be the sort of person to go to for wise counsel. He was an old Dansker [Dane] long anglicized in the service, of few words, many wrinkles, and some honorable scars. His wizened face, time-tinted and weather-stained to the complexion of an antique parchment, was here and there peppered blue by the chance explosion of a gun cartridge in action.

He was an *Agamemnon* man, some two years prior to the time of this story having served under Nelson when still captain in that ship immortal in naval memory, which dismantled and in part broken up to her bare ribs is seen a grand skeleton in Haden's etching. As one of a boarding party from the *Agamemnon* he had received a cut slantwise along one temple and cheek, leaving a long pale scar like a streak of dawn's light falling athwart the dark visage. It was on account of that scar and the affair in which it was known that he had received it, as well as from his blue-peppered complexion, that the Dansker went among the *Belli-potent*'s crew by the name of Board-Her-in-the-Smoke.

Now the first time that his small weasel eyes happened to light on Billy Budd, a certain grim internal merriment set all his ancient wrinkles into antic play. Was it that his eccentric unsentimental old sapience, primitive in its kind, saw or thought it saw something which in contrast with the warship's environment looked oddly incongruous in the Handsome Sailor? But after slyly studying him at intervals, the old Merlin's equivocal merriment was modified; for now when the twain would meet, it would start in his face a quizzing sort of look, but it would be but momentary and sometimes replaced by an expression of speculative query as to what might eventually befall a nature like that, dropped into a world not without some mantraps and against whose subtleties simple courage lacking experience and address, and without any touch of defensive ugliness, is of little avail; and where such innocence as man is capable of does yet in a moral emergency not always sharpen the faculties or enlighten the will.

However it was, the Dansker in his ascetic way rather took to Billy. Nor was this only because of a certain philosophic interest in such a character. There was another cause. While the old man's eccentricities, sometimes bordering on the ursine, repelled the juniors, Billy, undeterred thereby, revering him as a salt hero, would make advances, never passing the old *Agamemnon* man without a salutation marked by that respect which is seldom lost on the aged, however crabbed at times or whatever their station in life.

There was a vein of dry humor, or what not, in the mastman; and, whether in freak of patriarchal irony touching Billy's youth and athletic frame, or for some other and more recondite reason, from the first in addressing him he always substituted *Baby* for Billy, the Dansker in fact being the originator of the name by which the foretopman eventually became known aboard ship.

Well then, in his mysterious little difficulty going in quest of the wrinkled one, Billy found him off duty in a dogwatch ruminating by himself, seated on a shot box of the upper gun deck, now and then surveying with a somewhat cynical regard certain of the more swaggering promenaders there. Billy recounted his trouble, again wondering how it all happened. The salt seer attentively listened, accompanying the foretopman's recital with queer twitchings of his wrinkles and problematical little sparkles of his small ferret eyes. Making an end of his story the foretopman asked, "And now, Dansker, do tell me what you think of it."

The old man, shoving up the front of his tarpaulin and deliberately rubbing the long slant scar at the point where it entered the thin hair, laconically said, "Baby Budd, *Jemmy Legs*" (meaning the master-at-arms) "is down on you."

"*Jemmy Legs!*" ejaculated Billy, his welkin eyes expanding. "What for? Why, he calls me 'the sweet and pleasant young fellow,' they tell me."

"Does he so?" grinned the grizzled one; then said, "Ay, Baby lad, a sweet voice has Jemmy Legs."

"No, not always. But to me he has. I seldom pass him but there comes a pleasant word."

"And that's because he's down upon you. Baby Budd."

Such reiteration along with the manner of it, incomprehensible to a novice, disturbed Billy almost as much as the mystery for which he had sought explanation. Something less unpleasingly oracular he tried to extract; but the old sea Chiron, thinking perhaps that for the nonce he had sufficiently instructed his young Achilles, pursed his lips, gathered all his wrinkles together, and would commit himself to nothing further.

Years, and those experiences which befall certain shrewder men subordinated lifelong to the will of superiors, all this had developed in the Dansker the pithy guarded cynicism that was his leading characteristic.

The next day an incident served to confirm Billy Budd in his incredulity as to the Dansker's strange summing up of the case submitted.
The ship at noon, going large before the wind, was rolling on her
course, and he below at dinner and engaged in some sportful talk with
the members of his mess chanced in a sudden lurch to spill the entire
contents of his soup pan upon the new-scrubbed deck. Claggart, the
master-at-arms, official rattan in hand, happened to be passing along the
battery in a bay of which the mess was lodged, and the greasy liquid
streamed just across his path. Stepping over it, he was proceeding on his
way without comment. since the matter was nothing to take notice of
under the circumstances, when he happened to observe who it was that
had done the spilling. His countenance changed. Pausing, he was about
to ejaculate something hasty at the sailor, but checked himself, and
pointing down to the streaming soup, playfully tapped him from behind with his rattan, saying in a low musical voice peculiar to him at
times, "Handsomely done, my lad! And handsome is as handsome did it,
too!" And with that passed on. Not noted by Billy as not coming within
his view was the involuntary smile, or rather grimace, that accompanied
Claggart's equivocal words. Aridly it drew down the thin corners of his
shapely mouth. But everybody taking his remark as meant for humorous,
and at which therefore as coming from a superior they were bound to
laugh "with counterfeited glee," acted accordingly; and Billy, tickled, it
may be, by the allusion to his being the Handsome Sailor, merrily joined
in; then addressing his messmates exclaimed, "There now, who says
that Jemmy Legs is down on me!"

"And who said he was, Beauty?" demanded one Donald with some
surprise. Whereat the foretopman looked a little foolish, recalling that it
was only one person, Board-Her-in-the-Smoke, who had suggested what
to him was the smoky idea that this master-at-arms was in any peculiar
way hostile to him. Meantime that functionary, resuming his path, must
have momentarily worn some expression less guarded than that of the
bitter smile, usurping the face from the heart—some distorting expression
perhaps, for a drummer boy heedlessly frolicking along from the opposite direction and chancing to come into light collision with his person was strangely disconcerted by his aspect. Nor was the impression
lessened when the official, impetuously giving him a sharp cut with the
rattan, vehemently exclaimed, "Look where you go!"

What was the matter with the master-at-arms? And, be the matter
what it might, how could it have direct relation to Billy Budd, with

whom prior to the affair of the spilled soup he had never come into any special contact official or otherwise? What indeed could the trouble have to do with one so little inclined to give offense as the merchant-ship's "peacemaker," even him who in Claggart's own phrase was "the sweet and pleasant young fellow"? Yes, why should Jemmy Legs, to borrow the Dansker's expression, be "down" on the Handsome Sailor? But, at heart and not for nothing, as the late chance encounter may indicate to the discerning, down on him, secretly down on him, he assuredly was.

Now to invent something touching the more private career of Claggart, something involving Billy Budd, of which something the latter should be wholly ignorant, some romantic incident implying that Claggart's knowledge of the young bluejacket began at some period anterior to catching sight of him on board the seventy-four—all this, not so difficult to do, might avail in a way more or less interesting to account for whatever of enigma may appear to lurk in the case. But in fact there was nothing of the sort. And yet the cause necessarily to be assumed as the sole one assignable is in its very realism as much charged with that prime element of Radcliffian romance, the mysterious, as any that the ingenuity of the author of *The Mysteries of Udolpho* could devise. For what can more partake of the mysterious than an antipathy spontaneous and profound such as is evoked in certain exceptional mortals by the mere aspect of some other mortal, however harmless he may be, if not called forth by this very harmlessness itself?

Now there can exist no irritating juxtaposition of dissimilar personalities comparable to that which is possible aboard a great warship fully manned and at sea. There, every day among all ranks, almost every man comes into more or less of contact with almost every other man. Wholly there to avoid even the sight of an aggravating object one must needs give it Jonah's toss or jump overboard himself. Imagine how all this might eventually operate on some peculiar human creature the direct reverse of a saint!

But for the adequate comprehending of Claggart by a normal nature these hints are insufficient. To pass from a normal nature to him one must cross "the deadly space between." And this is best done by indirection.

Long ago an honest scholar, my senior, said to me in reference to one who like himself is now no more, a man so unimpeachably respectable that against him nothing was ever openly said though among the few something was whispered, "Yes, X—— is a nut not to be cracked by the tap of a lady's fan. You are aware that I am the adherent of no organized religion, much less of any philosophy built into a system. Well, for all that, I think that to try and get into X——, enter his labyrinth and get out again, without a clue derived from some source other than what is known as 'knowledge of the world'—that were hardly possible, at least for me."

"Why," said I, "X——, however singular a study to some, is yet human, and knowledge of the world assuredly implies the knowledge of human nature, and in most of its varieties."

"Yes, but a superficial knowledge of it, serving ordinary purposes. But for anything deeper, I am not certain whether to know the world and to know human nature be not two distinct branches of knowledge, which while they may coexist in the same heart, yet either may exist with little or nothing of the other. Nay, in an average man of the world, his constant rubbing with it blunts that finer spiritual insight indispensable to the understanding of the essential in certain exceptional characters, whether evil ones or good. In a matter of some importance I have seen a girl wind an old lawyer about her little finger. Nor was it the dotage of senile love. Nothing of the sort. But he knew law better than he knew the girl's heart. Coke and Blackstone hardly shed so much light into obscure spiritual places as the Hebrew prophets. And who were they? Mostly recluses."

At the time, my inexperience was such that I did not quite see the drift of all this. It may be that I see it now. And, indeed, if that lexicon which is based on Holy Writ were any longer popular, one might with less difficulty define and denominate certain phenomenal men. As it is, one must turn to some authority not liable to the charge of being tinctured with the biblical element.

In a list of definitions included in the authentic translation of Plato, a list attributed to him, occurs this: "Natural Depravity: a depravity according to nature," a definition which, though savoring of Calvinism, by no means involves Calvin's dogma as to total mankind. Evidently its intent makes it applicable but to individuals. Not many are the examples of this depravity which the gallows and jail supply. At any rate, for notable instances, since these have no vulgar alloy of the brute in them, but invariably are dominated by intellectuality, one must go elsewhere. Civilization, especially if of the austerer sort, is auspicious to it. It folds itself in the mantle of respectability. It has its certain negative virtues serving as silent auxiliaries. It never allows wine to get within its guard. It is not going too far to say that it is without vices or small sins.

There is a phenomenal pride in it that excludes them. It is never mercenary or avaricious. In short, the depravity here meant partakes nothing of the sordid or sensual. It is serious, but free from acerbity. Though no flatterer of mankind it never speaks ill of it.

But the thing which in eminent instances signalizes so exceptional a nature is this: Though the man's even temper and discreet bearing would seem to intimate a mind peculiarly subject to the law of reason, not the less in heart he would seem to riot in complete exemption from that law, having apparently little to do with reason further than to employ it as an ambidexter implement for effecting the irrational. That is to say: Toward the accomplishment of an aim which in wantonness of atrocity would seem to partake of the insane, he will direct a cool judgment sagacious and sound. These men are madmen, and of the most dangerous sort, for their lunacy is not continuous, but occasional, evoked by some special object; it is protectively secretive, which is as much as to say it is self-contained, so that when. moreover, most active it is to the average mind not distinguishable from sanity, and for the reason above suggested: that whatever its aims may be—and the aim is never declared—the method and the outward proceeding are always perfectly rational.

Now something such a one was Claggart. in whom was the mania of an evil nature, not engendered by vicious training or corrupting books or licentious living, but born with him and innate, in short "a depravity according to nature."

Dark sayings are these, some will say. But why? Is it because they somewhat savor of Holy Writ in its phrase "mystery of iniquity"? If they do, such savor was far enough from being intended, for little will it commend these pages to many a reader of today.

The point of the present story turning on the hidden nature of the master-at-arms has necessitated this chapter. With an added hint or two in connection with the incident at the mess, the resumed narrative must be left to vindicate, as it may, its own credibility.

That Claggart's figure was not amiss, and his face, save the chin, well molded. has already been said. Of these favorable points he seemed not insensible, for he was not only neat but careful in his dress. But the form of Billy Budd was heroic; and if his face was without the intellectual look of the pallid Claggart's. not the less was it lit, like his, from within, though from a different source. The bonfire in his heart made luminous the rosetan in his cheek.

In view of the marked contrast between the persons of the twain, it is more than probable that when the master-at-arms in the scene last given applied to the sailor the proverb "Handsome is as handsome does," he there let escape an ironic inkling, not caught by the young sailors who heard it, as to what it was that had first moved him against Billy, namely, his significant personal beauty.

Now envy and antipathy, passions irreconcilable in reason, nevertheless in fact may spring conjoined like Chang and Eng in one birth. Is Envy then such a monster? Well, though many an arraigned mortal has in hopes of mitigated penalty pleaded guilty to horrible actions, did ever anybody seriously confess to envy? Something there is in it universally felt to be more shameful than even felonious crime. And not only does everybody disown it, but the better sort are inclined to incredulity when it is in earnest imputed to an intelligent man. But since its lodgment is in the heart not the brain, no degree of intellect supplies a guarantee against it. But Claggart's was no vulgar form of the passion. Nor, as directed toward Billy Budd, did it partake of that streak of apprehensive jealousy that marred Saul's visage perturbedly brooding on the comely young David. Claggart's envy struck deeper. If askance he eyed the good looks, cheery health, and frank enjoyment of young life in Billy Budd, it was because these went along with a nature that, as Claggart magnetically felt, had in its simplicity never willed malice or experienced the reactionary bite of that serpent. To him, the spirit lodged within Billy, and looking out from his welkin eyes as from windows, that ineffability it was which made the dimple in his dyed cheek, suppled his joints, and dancing in his yellow curls made him pre-eminently the Handsome Sailor. One person excepted, the master-at-arms was perhaps the only man in the ship intellectually capable of adequately appreciating the moral phenomenon presented in Billy Budd. And the insight but intensified his passion, which, assuming various secret forms within him, at times assumed that of cynic disdain, disdain of innocence—to be nothing more than innocent! Yet in an aesthetic way he saw the charm of it, the courageous free and easy temper of it, and fain would have shared it, but he despaired of it.

With no power to annul the elemental evil in him, though readily enough he could hide it; apprehending the good, but powerless to be it; a nature like Claggart's, surcharged with energy as such natures almost invariably are, what recourse is left to it but to recoil upon itself and, like the scorpion for which the Creator alone is responsible, act out to the end the part allotted it.

Passion, and passion in its profoundest, is not a thing demanding a palatial stage whereon to play its part. Down among the groundlings, among
the beggars and rakers of the garbage, profound passion is enacted. And
the circumstances that provoke it, however trivial or mean, are no measure of its power. In the present instance the stage is a scrubbed gun deck,
and one of the external provocations a man-of-war's man's spilled
soup.

Now when the master-at-arms noticed whence came that greasy fluid
streaming before his feet, he must have taken it—to some extent willfully, perhaps—not for the mere accident it assuredly was, but for the
sly escape of a spontaneous feeling on Billy's part more or less answering
to the antipathy on his own. In effect a foolish demonstration, he must
have thought, and very harmless, like the futile kick of a heifer, which
yet were the heifer a shod stallion would not be so harmless. Even so was
it that into the gall of Claggart's envy he infused the vitriol of his
contempt. But the incident confirmed to him certain telltale reports
purveyed to his ear by "Squeak," one of his more cunning corporals, a
grizzled little man, so nicknamed by the sailors on account of his squeaky
voice and sharp visage ferreting about the dark corners of the lower
decks after interlopers, satirically suggesting to them the idea of a rat
in a cellar.

From his chief's employing him as an implicit tool in laying little traps
for the worriment of the foretopman—for it was from the master-at-arms
that the petty persecutions heretofore adverted to had proceeded—
the corporal, having naturally enough concluded that his master could
have no love for the sailor, made it his business, faithful understrapper
that he was, to foment the ill blood by perverting to his chief certain
innocent frolics of the good-natured foretopman, besides inventing for
his mouth sundry contumelious epithets he claimed to have overheard
him let fall. The master-at-arms never suspected the veracity of these
reports, more especially as to the epithets, for he well knew how secretly
unpopular may become a master-at-arms, at least a master-at-arms of
those days, zealous in his function, and how the bluejackets shoot at him
in private their raillery and wit; the nickname by which he goes among
them (Jemmy Legs) implying under the form of merriment their
cherished disrespect and dislike. But in view of the greediness of hate for
pabulum it hardly needed a purveyor to feed Claggart's passion.

An uncommon prudence is habitual with the subtler depravity,
for it has everything to hide. And in case of an injury but suspected, its
secretiveness voluntarily cuts it off from enlightenment or disillusion;
and, not unreluctantly, action is taken upon surmise as upon certainty.

And the retaliation is apt to be in monstrous disproportion to the supposed offense; for when in anybody was revenge in its exactions aught else but an inordinate usurer? But how with Claggart's conscience? For though consciences are unlike as foreheads, every intelligence, not excluding the scriptural devils who "believe and tremble," has one. But Claggart's conscience, being but the lawyer to his will, made ogres of trifles, probably arguing that the motive imputed to Billy in spilling the soup just when he did, together with the epithets alleged, these, if nothing more, made a strong case against him; nay, justified animosity into a sort of retributive righteousness. The Pharisee is the Guy Fawkes prowling in the hid chambers underlying some natures like Claggart's. And they can really form no conception of an unreciprocated malice. Probably the master-at-arms' clandestine persecution of Billy was started to try the temper of the man; but it had not developed any quality in him that enmity could make official use of or even pervert into plausible self-justification; so that the occurrence at the mess, petty if it were, was a welcome one to that peculiar conscience assigned to be the private mentor of Claggart; and, for the rest, not improbably it put him upon new experiments.

Not many days after the last incident narrated, something befell Billy Budd that more graveled him than aught that had previously occurred.

It was a warm night for the latitude; and the foretopman, whose watch at the time was properly below, was dozing on the uppermost deck whither he had ascended from his hot hammock, one of hundreds suspended so closely wedged together over a lower gun deck that there was little or no swing to them. He lay as in the shadow of a hillside, stretched under the lee of the booms, a piled ridge of spare spars amidships between foremast and mainmast among which the ship's largest boat, the launch, was stowed. Alongside of three other slumberers from below, he lay near that end of the booms which approaches the foremast; his station aloft on duty as a foretopman being just over the deck station of the forecastlemen, entitling him according to usage to make himself more or less at home in that neighborhood.

Presently he was stirred into semiconsciousness by somebody, who must have previously sounded the sleep of the others, touching his shoulder, and then, as the foretopman raised his head, breathing into his ear in a quick whisper, "Slip into the lee fore-chains, Billy; there is something in the wind. Don't speak. Quick, I will meet you there," and disappearing.

Now Billy, like sundry other essentially good-natured ones, had some of the weaknesses inseparable from essential good nature; and among

these was a reluctance, almost an incapacity, of plumply saying *no* to an
abrupt proposition not obviously absurd on the face of it, nor obviously
unfriendly, nor iniquitous. And being of warm blood, he had not the
phlegm tacitly to negative any proposition by unresponsive inaction. Like
his sense of fear, his apprehension as to aught outside of the honest and
natural was seldom very quick. Besides, upon the present occasion,
the drowse from his sleep still hung upon him.

However it was, he mechanically rose and, sleepily wondering
what could be in the wind, betook himself to the designated place, a
narrow platform, one of six, outside of the high bulwarks and screened
by the great deadeyes and multiple columned lanyards of the shrouds
and backstays; and, in a great warship of that time, of dimensions com-
mensurate to the hull's magnitude; a tarry balcony in short, overhanging
the sea, and so secluded that one mariner of the *Bellipotent,* a Noncon-
formist old tar of a serious turn, made it even in daytime his private
oratory.

In this retired nook the stranger soon joined Billy Budd. There was no
moon as yet; a haze obscured the starlight. He could not distinctly see
the stranger's face. Yet from something in the outline and carriage, Billy
took him, and correctly, for one of the afterguard.

"Hist! Billy," said the man, in the same quick cautionary whisper as before. "You were impressed, weren't you? Well, so was I"; and he paused,
as to mark the effect. But Billy, not knowing exactly what to make of
this, said nothing. Then the other: "We are not the only impressed ones,
Billy. There's a gang of us. Couldn't you—help—at a pinch?"

"What do you mean?" demanded Billy, here thoroughly shaking off his
drowse.

"Hist, hist!" the hurried whisper now growing husky. "See here," and
the man held up two small objects faintly twinkling in the night light;
"see, they are yours, Billy, if you'll only——"

But Billy broke in, and in his resentful eagerness to deliver himself
his vocal infirmity somewhat intruded. "D—d—damme, I don't know
what you are d—d—driving at, or what you mean, but you had better
g—g—go where you belong!" For the moment the fellow, as confounded, did not stir; and Billy, springing to his feet, said, "If you
d—don't start, I'll t—t—toss you back over the r—rail!" There was no
mistaking this, and the mysterious emissary decamped, disappearing in
the direction of the mainmast in the shadow of the booms.

"Hallo, what's the matter?" here came growling from a forecastleman
awakened from his deck doze by Billy's raised voice. And as the foretop-

man reappeared and was recognized by him: "Ah, Beauty, is it you? Well, something must have been the matter, for you st—st—stuttered."

"Oh," rejoined Billy, now mastering the impediment, "I found an afterguardsman in our part of the ship here, and I bid him be off where he belongs."

"And is that all you did about it, Foretopman?" gruffly demanded another, an irascible old fellow of brick-colored visage and hair who was known to his associate forecastlemen as "Red Pepper." "Such sneaks I should like to marry to the gunner's daughter!"—by that expression meaning that he would like to subject them to disciplinary castigation over a gun.

However, Billy's rendering of the matter satisfactorily accounted to these inquirers for the brief commotion, since of all the sections of a ship's company the forecastlemen, veterans for the most part and bigoted in their sea prejudices, are the most jealous in resenting territorial encroachments, especially on the part of any of the afterguard, of whom they have but a sorry opinion—chiefly landsmen, never going aloft except to reef or furl the mainsail, and in no wise competent to handle a marlinespike or turn in a deadeye, say.

This incident sorely puzzled Billy Budd. It was an entirely new experience, the first time in his life that he had ever been personally approached in underhand intriguing fashion. Prior to this encounter he had known nothing of the afterguardsman, the two men being stationed wide apart, one forward and aloft during his watch, the other on deck and aft.

What could it mean? And could they really be guineas, those two glittering objects the interloper had held up to his (Billy's) eyes? Where could the fellow get guineas? Why, even spare buttons are not so plentiful at sea. The more he turned the matter over, the more he was nonplused, and made uneasy and discomfited. In his disgustful recoil from an overture which, though he but ill comprehended, he instinctively knew must involve evil of some sort, Billy Budd was like a young horse fresh from the pasture suddenly inhaling a vile whiff from some chemical factory, and by repeated snortings trying to get it out of his nostrils and lungs. This frame of mind barred all desire of holding further parley with the fellow, even were it but for the purpose of gaining some enlightenment as to his design in approaching him. And yet he was not without natural curiosity to see how such a visitor in the dark would look in broad day.

He espied him the following afternoon in his first dogwatch below, one

of the smokers on that forward part of the upper gun deck allotted to
the pipe. He recognized him by his general cut and build more than
by his round freckled face and glassy eyes of pale blue, veiled with lashes
all but white. And yet Billy was a bit uncertain whether indeed it were
he—yonder chap about his own age chatting and laughing in freehearted
way, leaning against a gun; a genial young fellow enough to look at, and
something of a rattlebrain, to all appearance. Rather chubby too for a
sailor, even an afterguardsman. In short, the last man in the world, one
would think, to be overburdened with thoughts, especially those
perilous thoughts that must needs belong to a conspirator in any serious
project, or even to the underling of such a conspirator.

Although Billy was not aware of it, the fellow, with a sidelong watchful glance, had perceived Billy first, and then noting that Billy was looking at him, thereupon nodded a familiar sort of friendly recognition as
to an old acquaintance, without interrupting the talk he was engaged in
with the group of smokers. A day or two afterwards, chancing in the
evening promenade on a gun deck to pass Billy, he offered a flying word
of good fellowship, as it were, which by its unexpectedness, and
equivocalness under the circumstances, so embarrassed Billy that he
knew not how to respond to it, and let it go unnoticed.

Billy was now left more at a loss than before. The ineffectual speculations into which he was led were so disturbingly alien to him that he did
his best to smother them. It never entered his mind that here was a matter which, from its extreme questionableness, it was his duty as a loyal
bluejacket to report in the proper quarter. And, probably, had such a step
been suggested to him, he would have been deterred from taking it by
the thought, one of novice magnanimity, that it would savor overmuch
of the dirty work of a telltale. He kept the thing to himself. Yet upon
one occasion he could not forbear a little disburdening himself to the old
Dansker, tempted thereto perhaps by the influence of a balmy night
when the ship lay becalmed; the twain, silent for the most part,
sitting together on deck, their heads propped against the bulwarks. But it
was only a partial and anonymous account that Billy gave, the un-
founded scruples above referred to preventing full disclosure to anybody.
Upon hearing Billy's version, the sage Dansker seemed to divine more
than he was told; and after a little meditation, during which his wrinkles
were pursed as into a point, quite effacing for the time that quizzing
expression his face sometimes wore: "Didn't I say so, Baby Budd?"

"Say what?" demanded Billy.

"Why, *Jemmy Legs* is *down* on you."

"And what," rejoined Billy in amazement, "has *Jemmy Legs* to do with that cracked afterguardsman?"

"Ho, it was an afterguardsman, then. A cat's-paw, a cat's-paw!" And with that exclamation, whether it had reference to a light puff of air just then coming over the calm sea, or a subtler relation to the afterguardsman, there is no telling, the old Merlin gave a twisting wrench with his black teeth at his plug of tobacco, vouchsafing no reply to Billy's impetuous question, though now repeated, for it was his wont to relapse into grim silence when interrogated in skeptical sort as to any of his sententious oracles, not always very clear ones, rather partaking of that obscurity which invests most Delphic deliverances from any quarter.

Long experience had very likely brought this old man to that bitter prudence which never interferes in aught and never gives advice.

Yes, despite the Dansker's pithy insistence as to the master-at-arms being at the bottom of these strange experiences of Billy on board the *Bellipotent,* the young sailor was ready to ascribe them to almost anybody but the man who, to use Billy's own expression, "always had a pleasant word for him." This is to be wondered at. Yet not so much to be wondered at. In certain matters, some sailors even in mature life remain unsophisticated enough. But a young seafarer of the disposition of our athletic foretopman is much of a child-man. And yet a child's utter innocence is but its blank ignorance, and the innocence more or less wanes as intelligence waxes. But in Billy Budd intelligence, such as it was, had advanced while yet his simple-mindedness remained for the most part unaffected. Experience is a teacher indeed; yet did Billy's years make his experience small. Besides, he had none of that intuitive knowledge of the bad which in natures not good or incompletely so foreruns experience, and therefore may pertain, as in some instances it too clearly does pertain, even to youth.

And what could Billy know of man except of man as a mere sailor? And the old-fashioned sailor, the veritable man before the mast, the sailor from boyhood up, he, though indeed of the same species as a landsman, is in some respects singularly distinct from him. The sailor is frankness, the landsman is finesse. Life is not a game with the sailor, demanding the long head—no intricate game of chess where few moves are made in straightforwardness and ends are attained by indirection, an oblique, tedious, barren game hardly worth that poor candle burned out in playing it.

Yes, as a class, sailors are in character a juvenile race. Even their deviations are marked by juvenility, this more especially holding true with the sailors of Billy's time. Then, too, certain things which apply to all sailors do more pointedly operate here and there upon the junior one. Every sailor, too, is accustomed to obey orders without debating them; his life afloat is externally ruled for him; he is not brought into that promiscuous commerce with mankind where unobstructed free agency on equal terms—equal superficially, at least—soon teaches one that unless upon occasion he exercise a distrust keen in proportion to the fairness of the appearance, some foul turn may be served him. A ruled undemonstrative distrustfulness is so habitual, not with businessmen so much as with men who know their kind in less shallow relations than business, namely, certain men of the world, that they come at last to employ it all but unconsciously; and some of them would very likely feel real surprise at being charged with it as one of their general characteristics.

But after the little matter at the mess Billy Budd no more found himself in strange trouble at times about his hammock or his clothes bag or what not. As to that smile that occasionally sunned him, and the pleasant passing word, these were, if not more frequent, yet if anything more pronounced than before.

But for all that, there were certain other demonstrations now. When Claggart's unobserved glance happened to light on belted Billy rolling along the upper gun deck in the leisure of the second dogwatch, exchanging passing broadsides of fun with other young promenaders in the crowd, that glance would follow the cheerful sea Hyperion with a settled meditative and melancholy expression, his eyes strangely suffused with incipient feverish tears. Then would Claggart look like the man of sorrows. Yes, and sometimes the melancholy expression would have in it a touch of soft yearning, as if Claggart could even have loved Billy but for fate and ban. But this was an evanescence, and quickly repented of, as it were, by an immitigable look, pinching and shriveling the visage into the momentary semblance of a wrinkled walnut. But sometimes catching sight in advance of the foretopman coming in his direction, he would, upon their nearing, step aside a little to let him pass, dwelling upon Billy for the moment with the glittering dental satire of a Guise. But upon any abrupt unforeseen encounter a red light would flash forth from his eye like a spark from an anvil in a dusk smithy. That quick, fierce light was a strange one, darted from orbs which in repose were of a color nearest approaching a deeper violet, the softest of shades.

Though some of these caprices of the pit could not but be observed by their object, yet were they beyond the construing of such a nature. And the thews of Billy were hardly compatible with that sort of sensitive spiritual organization which in some cases instinctively conveys to ignorant innocence an admonition of the proximity of the malign. He thought the master-at-arms acted in a manner rather queer at times. That was all. But the occasional frank air and pleasant word went for what they purported to be, the young sailor never having heard as yet of the "too fair-spoken man."

Had the foretopman been conscious of having done or said anything to provoke the ill will of the official, it would have been different with him, and his sight might have been purged if not sharpened. As it was, innocence was his blinder.

So was it with him in yet another matter. Two minor officers, the armorer and captain of the hold, with whom he had never exchanged a word, his position in the ship not bringing him into contact with them, these men now for the first began to cast upon Billy, when they chanced to encounter him, that peculiar glance which evidences that the man from whom it comes has been some way tampered with, and to the prejudice of him upon whom the glance lights. Never did it occur to Billy as a thing to be noted or a thing suspicious, though he well knew the fact that the armorer and captain of the hold, with the ship's yeoman, apothecary, and others of that grade, were by naval usage messmates of the master-at-arms, men with ears convenient to his confidential tongue.

But the general popularity that came from our Handsome Sailor's manly forwardness upon occasion and irresistible good nature, indicating no mental superiority tending to excite an invidious feeling, this good will on the part of most of his shipmates made him the less to concern himself about such mute aspects toward him as those whereto allusion has just been made, aspects he could not so fathom as to infer their whole import.

As to the afterguardsman, though Billy for reasons already given necessarily saw little of him, yet when the two did happen to meet, invariably came the fellow's offhand cheerful recognition, sometimes accompanied by a passing pleasant word or two. Whatever that equivocal young person's original design may really have been, or the design of which he might have been the deputy, certain it was from his manner upon these occasions that he had wholly dropped it.

It was as if his precocity of crookedness (and every vulgar villain is precocious) had for once deceived him, and the man he had sought to entrap as a simpleton had through his very simplicity ignominiously baffled him.

But shrewd ones may opine that it was hardly possible for Billy to refrain from going up to the afterguardsman and bluntly demanding to know his purpose in the initial interview so abruptly closed in the fore-chains. Shrewd ones may also think it but natural in Billy to set about sounding some of the other impressed men of the ship in order to discover what basis, if any, there was for the emissary's obscure suggestions as to plotting disaffection aboard. Yes, shrewd ones may so think. But something more, or rather something else, than mere shrewdness is perhaps needful for the due understanding of such a character as Billy Budd's.

As to Claggart, the monomania in the man—if that indeed it were—as involuntarily disclosed by starts in the manifestations detailed, yet in general covered over by his self-contained and rational demeanor; this, like a subterranean fire, was eating its way deeper and deeper in him. Something decisive must come of it.

After the mysterious interview in the fore-chains, the one so abruptly ended there by Billy, nothing especially germane to the story occurred until the events now about to be narrated.

Elsewhere it has been said that in the lack of frigates (of course better sailers than line-of-battle ships) in the English squadron up the Straits at that period, the *Bellipotent* 74 was occasionally employed not only as an available substitute for a scout but at times on detached service of more important kind. This was not alone because of her sailing qualities, not common in a ship of her rate, but quite as much, probably, that the character of her commander, it was thought, specially adapted him for any duty where under unforeseen difficulties a prompt initiative might have to be taken in some matter demanding knowledge and ability in addition to those qualities implied in good seamanship. It was on an expedition of the latter sort, a somewhat distant one, and when the *Bellipotent* was almost at her furthest remove from the fleet, that in the latter part of an afternoon watch she unexpectedly came in sight of a ship of the enemy. It proved to be a frigate. The latter, perceiving through the glass that the weight of men and metal would be heavily against her, invoking her light heels crowded sail to get away. After a chase urged almost against hope and lasting until about the middle of the first dogwatch, she signally succeeded in effecting her escape.

Not long after the pursuit had been given up, and ere the excitement incident thereto had altogether waned away, the master-at-arms, ascending from his cavernous sphere, made his appearance cap in hand by the mainmast respectfully waiting the notice of Captain Vere, then solitary walking the weather side of the quarter-deck, doubtless somewhat chafed at the failure of the pursuit. The spot where Claggart stood was the place allotted to men of lesser grades seeking some more particular interview either with the officer of the deck or the captain himself. But from the latter it was not often that a sailor or petty officer of those days would seek a hearing; only some exceptional cause would, according to established custom, have warranted that.

Presently, just as the commander, absorbed in his reflections, was on the point of turning aft in his promenade, he became sensible of Claggart's presence, and saw the doffed cap held in deferential expectancy. Here be it said that Captain Vere's personal knowledge of this petty officer had only begun at the time of the ship's last sailing from home, Claggart then for the first, in transfer from a ship detained for repairs, supplying on board the *Bellipotent* the place of a previous master-at-arms disabled and ashore.

No sooner did the commander observe who it was that now deferentially stood awaiting his notice than a peculiar expression came over him. It was not unlike that which uncontrollably will flit across the countenance of one at unawares encountering a person who, though known to him indeed, has hardly been long enough known for thorough knowledge, but something in whose aspect nevertheless now for the first provokes a vaguely repellent distaste. But coming to a stand and resuming much of his wonted official manner, save that a sort of impatience lurked in the intonation of the opening word, he said "Well? What is it, Master-at-arms?"

With the air of a subordinate grieved at the necessity of being a messenger of ill tidings, and while conscientiously determined to be frank yet equally resolved upon shunning overstatement, Claggart at this invitation, or rather summons, to disburden, spoke up. What he said, conveyed in the language of no uneducated man, was to the effect following, if not altogether in these words, namely, that during the chase and preparations for the possible encounter he had seen enough to convince him that at least one sailor aboard was a dangerous character in a ship mustering some who not only had taken a guilty part in the late serious troubles, but others also who, like the man in question, had entered His Majesty's service under another form than enlistment.

At this point Captain Vere with some impatience interrupted him: "Be direct, man; say *impressed men.*"

Claggart made a gesture of subservience, and proceeded. Quite lately he (Claggart) had begun to suspect that on the gun decks some sort of movement prompted by the sailor in question was covertly going on, but he had not thought himself warranted in reporting the suspicion so long as it remained indistinct. But from what he had that afternoon observed in the man referred to, the suspicion of something clandestine going on had advanced to a point less removed from certainty. He deeply felt, he added, the serious responsibility assumed in making a report involving such possible consequences to the individual mainly concerned, besides tending to augment those natural anxieties which every naval commander must feel in view of extraordinary outbreaks so recent as those which, he sorrowfully said it, it needed not to name.

Now at the first broaching of the matter Captain Vere, taken by surprise, could not wholly dissemble his disquietude. But as Claggart went on, the former's aspect changed into restiveness under something in the testifier's manner in giving his testimony. However, he refrained from interrupting him. And Claggart, continuing, concluded with this: "God forbid, your honor, that the *Bellipotent's* should be the experience of the——"

"Never mind that!" here peremptorily broke in the superior, his face altering with anger, instinctively divining the ship that the other was about to name, one in which the Nore Mutiny had assumed a singularly tragical character that for a time jeopardized the life of its commander. Under the circumstances he was indignant at the purposed allusion. When the commissioned officers themselves were on all occasions very heedful how they referred to the recent events in the fleet, for a petty officer unnecessarily to allude to them in the presence of his captain, this struck him as a most immodest presumption. Besides, to his quick sense of self-respect it even looked under the circumstances something like an attempt to alarm him. Nor at first was he without some surprise that one who so far as he had hitherto come under his notice had shown considerable tact in his function should in this particular evince such lack of it.

But these thoughts and kindred dubious ones flitting across his mind were suddenly replaced by an intuitional surmise which, though as yet obscure in form, served practically to affect his reception of the ill tidings. Certain it is that, long versed in everything pertaining to the complicated gun-deck life, which like every other form of life has its secret mines and dubious side, the side popularly disclaimed, Captain Vere did not permit himself to be unduly disturbed by the general tenor of his subordinate's report.

Furthermore, if in view of recent events prompt action should be taken at the first palpable sign of recurring insubordination, for all that, not judicious would it be, he thought, to keep the idea of lingering disaffection alive by undue forwardness in crediting an informer, even if his own subordinate and charged among other things with police surveillance of the crew. This feeling would not perhaps have so prevailed with him were it not that upon a prior occasion the patriotic zeal officially evinced by Claggart had somewhat irritated him as appearing rather supersensible and strained. Furthermore, something even in the official's self-possessed and somewhat ostentatious manner in making his specifications strangely reminded him of a bandsman, a perjurous witness in a capital case before a court-martial ashore of which when a lieutenant he (Captain Vere) had been a member.

Now the peremptory check given to Claggart in the matter of the arrested allusion was quickly followed up by this: "You say that there is at least one dangerous man aboard. Name him."

"William Budd, a foretopman, your honor."

"William Budd!" repeated Captain Vere with unfeigned astonishment. "And mean you the man that Lieutenant Ratcliffe took from the merchantman not very long ago, the young fellow who seems to be so popular with the men—Billy, the Handsome Sailor, as they call him?"

"The same, your honor; but for all his youth and good looks, a deep one. Not for nothing does he insinuate himself into the good will of his shipmates, since at the least they will at a pinch say—all hands will—a good word for him, and at all hazards. Did Lieutenant Ratcliffe happen to tell your honor of that adroit fling of Budd's, jumping up in the cutter's bow under the merchantman's stern when he was being taken off? It is even masked by that sort of good-humored air that at heart he resents his impressment. You have but noted his fair cheek. A mantrap may be under the ruddy-tipped daisies."

Now the Handsome Sailor as a signal figure among the crew had naturally enough attracted the captain's attention from the first. Though in general not very demonstrative to his officers, he had congratulated Lieutenant Ratcliffe upon his good fortune in lighting on such a fine specimen of the *genus homo*, who in the nude might have posed for a statue of young Adam before the Fall. As to Billy's adieu to the ship

Rights-of-Man, which the boarding lieutenant had indeed reported to him, but, in a deferential way, more as a good story than aught else, Captain Vere, though mistakenly understanding it as a satiric sally, had but thought so much the better of the impressed man for it; as a military sailor, admiring the spirit that could take an arbitrary enlistment so merrily and sensibly. The foretopman's conduct, too, so far as it had fallen under the captain's notice, had confirmed the first happy augury, while the new recruit's qualities as a "sailorman" seemed to be such that he had thought of recommending him to the executive officer for promotion to a place that would more frequently bring him under his own observation, namely, the captaincy of the mizzentop, replacing there in the starboard watch a man not so young whom partly for that reason he deemed less fitted for the post. Be it parenthesized here that since the mizzentopmen have not to handle such breadths of heavy canvas as the lower sails on the mainmast and foremast, a young man if of the right stuff not only seems best adapted to duty there, but in fact is generally selected for the captaincy of that top, and the company under him are light hands and often but striplings. In sum, Captain Vere had from the beginning deemed Billy Budd to be what in the naval parlance of the time was called a "King's bargain": that is to say, for His Britannic Majesty's navy a capital investment at small outlay or none at all.

After a brief pause, during which the reminiscences above mentioned passed vividly through his mind and he weighed the import of Claggart's last suggestion conveyed in the phrase "mantrap under the daisies," and the more he weighed it the less reliance he felt in the informer's good faith, suddenly he turned upon him and in a low voice demanded: "Do you come to me, Master-at-arms, with so foggy a tale? As to Budd, cite me an act or spoken word of his confirmatory of what you in general charge against him. Stay," drawing nearer to him; "heed what you speak. Just now, and in a case like this, there is a yardarm-end for the false witness."

"Ah, your honor!" sighed Claggart, mildly shaking his shapely head as in sad deprecation of such unmerited severity of tone. Then, bridling—erecting himself as in virtuous self-assertion—he circumstantially alleged certain words and acts which collectively, if credited, led to presumptions mortally inculpating Budd. And for some of these averments, he added, substantiating proof was not far.

With gray eyes impatient and distrustful essaying to fathom to the bottom Claggart's calm violet ones, Captain Vere again heard him out; then for the moment stood ruminating. The mood he evinced, Claggart—

himself for the time liberated from the other's scrutiny—steadily regarded with a look difficult to render: a look curious of the operation of his tactics, a look such as might have been that of the spokesman of the envious children of Jacob deceptively imposing upon the troubled patriarch the blood-dyed coat of young Joseph.

Though something exceptional in the moral quality of Captain Vere made him, in earnest encounter with a fellow man, a veritable touchstone of that man's essential nature, yet now as to Claggart and what was really going on in him his feeling partook less of intuitional conviction than of strong suspicion clogged by strange dubieties. The perplexity he evinced proceeded less from aught touching the man informed against—as Claggart doubtless opined—than from considerations how best to act in regard to the informer. At first, indeed, he was naturally for summoning that substantiation of his allegations which Claggart said was at hand. But such a proceeding would result in the matter at once getting abroad, which in the present stage of it, he thought, might undesirably affect the ship's company. If Claggart was a false witness—that closed the affair. And therefore, before trying the accusation, he would first practically test the accuser; and he thought this could be done in a quiet, undemonstrative way.

The measure he determined upon involved a shifting of the scene, a transfer to a place less exposed to observation than the broad quarterdeck. For although the few gun-room officers there at the time had, in due observance of naval etiquette, withdrawn to leeward the moment Captain Vere had begun his promenade on the deck's weather side; and though during the colloquy with Claggart they of course ventured not to diminish the distance; and though throughout the interview Captain Vere's voice was far from high, and Claggart's silvery and low; and the wind in the cordage and the wash of the sea helped the more to put them beyond earshot; nevertheless, the interview's continuance already had attracted observation from some topmen aloft and other sailors in the waist or further forward.

Having determined upon his measures, Captain Vere forthwith took action. Abruptly turning to Claggart, he asked, "Master-at-arms, is it now Budd's watch aloft?"

"No, your honor."

Whereupon, "Mr. Wilkes!" summoning the nearest midshipman. "Tell Albert to come to me." Albert was the captain's hammock boy, a sort of sea valet in whose discretion and fidelity his master had much confidence. The lad appeared.

"You know Budd, the foretopman?"

"I do, Sir."

"Go find him. It is his watch off. Manage to tell him out of earshot that he is wanted aft. Contrive it that he speaks to nobody. Keep him in talk yourself. And not till you get well aft here, not till then let him know that the place where he is wanted is my cabin. You understand. Go.— Master-at-arms, show yourself on the decks below, and when you think it time for Albert to be coming with his man, stand by quietly to follow the sailor in."

Now when the foretopman found himself in the cabin, closeted there, as it were, with the captain and Claggart, he was surprised enough. But it was a surprise unaccompanied by apprehension or distrust. To an immature nature essentially honest and humane, forewarning intimations of subtler danger from one's kind come tardily if at all. The only thing that took shape in the young sailor's mind was this: Yes, the captain, I have always thought, looks kindly upon me. Wonder if he's going to make me his coxswain. I should like that. And maybe now he is going to ask the master-at-arms about me.

"Shut the door there, sentry," said the commander; "stand without, and let nobody come in.—Now, Master-at-arms, tell this man to his face what you told of him to me," and stood prepared to scrutinize the mutually confronting visages.

With the measured step and calm collected air of an asylum physician approaching in the public hall some patient beginning to show indications of a coming paroxysm, Claggart deliberately advanced within short range of Billy and, mesmerically looking him in the eye, briefly recapitulated the accusation.

Not at first did Billy take it in. When he did, the rosetan of his cheek looked struck as by white leprosy. He stood like one impaled and gagged. Meanwhile the accuser's eyes, removing not as yet from the blue dilated ones, underwent a phenomenal change, their wonted rich violet color blurring into a muddy purple. Those lights of human intelligence, losing human expression, were gelidly protruding like the alien eyes of certain uncatalogued creatures of the deep. The first mesmeristic glance was one of serpent fascination; the last was as the paralyzing lurch of the torpedo fish.

"Speak, man!" said Captain Vere to the transfixed one, struck by his aspect even more than by Claggart's. "Speak! Defend yourself!" Which appeal caused but a strange dumb gesturing and gurgling in Billy;

amazement at such an accusation so suddenly sprung on inexperienced nonage; this, and, it may be, horror of the accuser's eyes, serving to bring out his lurking defect and in this instance for the time intensifying it into a convulsed tongue-tie; while the intent head and entire form straining forward in an agony of ineffectual eagerness to obey the injunction to speak and defend himself gave an expression to the face like that of a condemned vestal priestess in the moment of being buried alive, and in the first struggle against suffocation.

Though at the time Captain Vere was quite ignorant of Billy's liability to vocal impediment, he now immediately divined it, since vividly Billy's aspect recalled to him that of a bright young schoolmate of his whom he had once seen struck by much the same startling impotence in the act of eagerly rising in the class to be foremost in response to a testing question put to it by the master. Going close up to the young sailor, and laying a soothing hand on his shoulder, he said, "There is no hurry, my boy. Take your time, take your time." Contrary to the effect intended, these words so fatherly in tone, doubtless touching Billy's heart to the quick, prompted yet more violent efforts at utterance—efforts soon ending for the time in confirming the paralysis, and bringing to his face an expression which was as a crucifixion to behold. The next instant, quick as the flame from a discharged cannon at night, his right arm shot out, and Claggart dropped to the deck. Whether intentionally or but owing to the young athlete's superior height, the blow had taken effect full upon the forehead, so shapely and intellectual-looking a feature in the master-at-arms, so that the body fell over lengthwise, like a heavy plank tilted from erectness. A gasp or two, and he lay motionless.

"Fated boy," breathed Captain Vere in tone so low as to be almost a whisper, "what have you done! But here, help me."

The twain raised the felled one from the loins up into a sitting position. The spare form flexibly acquiesced, but inertly. It was like handling a dead snake. They lowered it back. Regaining erectness, Captain Vere with one hand covering his face stood to all appearance as impassive as the object at his feet. Was he absorbed in taking in all the bearings of the event and what was best not only now at once to be done, but also in the sequel? Slowly he uncovered his face; and the effect was as if the moon emerging from eclipse should reappear with quite another aspect than that which had gone into hiding. The father in him, manifested towards Billy thus far in the scene, was replaced by the military disciplinarian. In his official tone he bade the foretopman retire to a stateroom

aft (pointing it out), and there remain till thence summoned. This order
Billy in silence mechanically obeyed. Then going to the cabin door where
it opened on the quarter-deck, Captain Vere said to the sentry without,
"Tell somebody to send Albert here." When the lad appeared, his master so contrived it that he should not catch sight of the prone one. "Albert,"
he said to him, "tell the surgeon I wish to see him. You need not come
back till called."

When the surgeon entered—a self-poised character of that grave sense
and experience that hardly anything could take him aback—Captain
Vere advanced to meet him, thus unconsciously intercepting his view
of Claggart, and, interrupting the other's wonted ceremonious salutation,
said, "Nay. Tell me how it is with yonder man," directing his attention
to the prostrate one.

The surgeon looked, and for all his self-command somewhat started at
the abrupt revelation. On Claggart's always pallid complexion, thick black
blood was now oozing from nostril and ear. To the gazer's professional
eye it was unmistakably no living man that he saw.

"Is it so, then?" said Captain Vere, intently watching him. "I thought it.
But verify it." Whereupon the customary tests confirmed the surgeon's
first glance, who now, looking up in unfeigned concern, cast a look of intense inquisitiveness upon his superior. But Captain Vere, with one hand
to his brow, was standing motionless. Suddenly, catching the surgeon's
arm convulsively, he exclaimed, pointing down to the body, "It is the
divine judgment on Ananias! Look!"

Disturbed by the excited manner he had never before observed in
the *Bellipotent*'s captain, and as yet wholly ignorant of the affair, the
prudent surgeon nevertheless held his peace, only again looking an
earnest interrogatory as to what it was that had resulted in such a
tragedy.

But Captain Vere was now again motionless, standing absorbed in
thought. Again starting, he vehemently exclaimed, "Struck dead by an
angel of God! Yet the angel must hang!"

At these passionate interjections, mere incoherences to the listener as
yet unapprised of the antecedents, the surgeon was profoundly discom-
posed. But now, as recollecting himself, Captain Vere in less passionate
tone briefly related the circumstances leading up to the event. "But come;
we must dispatch," he added. "Help me to remove him" (meaning the
body) "to yonder compartment," designating one opposite that where
the foretopman remained immured. Anew disturbed by a request that, as

implying a desire for secrecy, seemed unaccountably strange to him, there was nothing for the subordinate to do but comply.

"Go now," said Captain Vere with something of his wonted manner. "Go now. I presently shall call a drumhead court. Tell the lieutenants what has happened, and tell Mr. Mordant" (meaning the captain of marines), "and charge them to keep the matter to themselves."

Full of disquietude and misgiving, the surgeon left the cabin. Was Captain Vere suddenly affected in his mind, or was it but a transient excitement, brought about by so strange and extraordinary a tragedy? As to the drumhead court, it struck the surgeon as impolitic, if nothing more. The thing to do, he thought, was to place Billy Budd in confinement, and in a way dictated by usage, and postpone further action in so extraordinary a case to such time as they should rejoin the squadron, and then refer it to the admiral. He recalled the unwonted agitation of Captain Vere and his excited exclamations, so at variance with his normal manner. Was he unhinged?

But assuming that he is, it is not so susceptible of proof. What then can the surgeon do? No more trying situation is conceivable than that of an officer subordinate under a captain whom he suspects to be not mad, indeed, but yet not quite unaffected in his intellects. To argue his order to him would be insolence. To resist him would be mutiny.

In obedience to Captain Vere, he communicated what had happened to the lieutenants and captain of marines, saying nothing as to the captain's state. They fully shared his own surprise and concern. Like him too, they seemed to think that such a matter should be referred to the admiral.

Who in the rainbow can draw the line where the violet tint ends and the orange tint begins? Distinctly we see the difference of the colors, but where exactly does the one first blendingly enter into the other? So with sanity and insanity. In pronounced cases there is no question about them. But in some supposed cases, in various degrees supposedly less pronounced, to draw the exact line of demarcation few will undertake, though for a fee becoming considerate some professional experts will. There is nothing namable but that some men will, or undertake to, do it for pay.

Whether Captain Vere, as the surgeon professionally and privately surmised, was really the sudden victim of any degree of aberration, everyone must determine for himself by such light as this narrative may afford.

That the unhappy event which has been narrated could not have happened at a worse juncture was but too true. For it was close on the heel of the suppressed insurrections, an aftertime very critical to naval authority, demanding from every English sea commander two qualities not readily interfusable—prudence and rigor. Moreover, there was something crucial in the case.

In the jugglery of circumstances preceding and attending the event on board the *Bellipotent,* and in the light of that martial code whereby it was formally to be judged, innocence and guilt personified in Claggart and Budd in effect changed places. In a legal view the apparent victim of the tragedy was he who had sought to victimize a man blameless; and the indisputable deed of the latter, navally regarded, constituted the most heinous of military crimes. Yet more. The essential right and wrong involved in the matter, the clearer that might be, so much the worse for the responsibility of a loyal sea commander, inasmuch as he was not authorized to determine the matter on that primitive basis.

Small wonder then that the *Bellipotent*'s captain, though in general a man of rapid decision, felt that circumspectness not less than promptitude was necessary. Until he could decide upon his course, and in each detail; and not only so, but until the concluding measure was upon the point of being enacted, he deemed it advisable, in view of all the circumstances, to guard as much as possible against publicity. Here he may or may not have erred. Certain it is, however, that subsequently in the confidential talk of more than one or two gun rooms and cabins he was not a little criticized by some officers, a fact imputed by his friends and vehemently by his cousin Jack Denton to professional jealousy of Starry Vere. Some imaginative ground for invidious comment there was. The maintenance of secrecy in the matter, the confining all knowledge of it for a time to the place where the homicide occurred, the quarter-deck cabin—in these particulars lurked some resemblance to the policy adopted in those tragedies of the palace which have occurred more than once in the capital founded by Peter the Barbarian.

The case indeed was such that fain would the *Bellipotent*'s captain have deferred taking any action whatever respecting it further than to keep the foretopman a close prisoner till the ship rejoined the squadron and then submitting the matter to the judgment of his admiral.

But a true military officer is in one particular like a true monk. Not with more of self-abnegation will the latter keep his vows of mo-

nastic obedience than the former his vows of allegiance to martial
duty.

Feeling that unless quick action was taken on it, the deed of the
foretopman, so soon as it should be known on the gun decks, would tend
to awaken any slumbering embers of the Nore among the crew, a sense of
the urgency of the case overruled in Captain Vere every other consideration. But though a conscientious disciplinarian, he was no lover
of authority for mere authority's sake. Very far was he from embracing
opportunities for monopolizing to himself the perils of moral responsibility, none at least that could properly be referred to an official superior
or shared with him by his official equals or even subordinates. So thinking,
he was glad it would not be at variance with usage to turn the matter over
to a summary court of his own officers, reserving to himself, as the one
on whom the ultimate accountability would rest, the right of maintaining
a supervision of it, or formally or informally interposing at need. Accordingly a drumhead court was summarily convened, he electing the
individuals composing it: the first lieutenant, the captain of marines, and
the sailing master.

In associating an officer of marines with the sea lieutenant and the sailing master in a case having to do with a sailor, the commander perhaps deviated from general custom. He was prompted thereto by the
circumstance that he took that soldier to be a judicious person, thoughtful,
and not altogether incapable of grappling with a difficult case unprecedented in his prior experience. Yet even as to him he was not without some latent misgiving, for withal he was an extremely good-natured
man, an enjoyer of his dinner, a sound sleeper, and inclined to obesity—
a man who though he would always maintain his manhood in battle
might not prove altogether reliable in a moral dilemma involving aught
of the tragic. As to the first lieutenant and the sailing master, Captain
Vere could not but be aware that though honest natures, of approved
gallantry upon occasion, their intelligence was mostly confined to the
matter of active seamanship and the fighting demands of their profession.

The court was held in the same cabin where the unfortunate affair had
taken place. This cabin, the commander's, embraced the entire area under the poop deck. Aft, and on either side, was a small stateroom, the
one now temporarily a jail and the other a deadhouse, and a yet smaller
compartment, leaving a space between expanding forward into a goodly
oblong of length coinciding with the ship's beam. A skylight of moderate
dimension was overhead, and at each end of the oblong space were two

sashed porthole windows easily convertible back into embrasures for short carronades.

All being quickly in readiness, Billy Budd was arraigned, Captain Vere necessarily appearing as the sole witness in the case, and as such temporarily sinking his rank, though singularly maintaining it in a matter apparently trivial, namely, that he testified from the ship's weather side, with that object having caused the court to sit on the lee side. Concisely he narrated all that had led up to the catastrophe, omitting nothing in Claggart's accusation and deposing as to the manner in which the prisoner had received it. At this testimony the three officers glanced with no little surprise at Billy Budd, the last man they would have suspected either of the mutinous design alleged by Claggart or the undeniable deed he himself had done. The first lieutenant, taking judicial primacy and turning toward the prisoner, said, "Captain Vere has spoken. Is it or is it not as Captain Vere says?"

In response came syllables not so much impeded in the utterance as might have been anticipated. They were these: "Captain Vere tells the truth. It is just as Captain Vere says, but it is not as the master-at-arms said. I have eaten the King's bread and I am true to the King."

"I believe you, my man," said the witness, his voice indicating a suppressed emotion not otherwise betrayed.

"God will bless you for that, your honor!" not without stammering said Billy, and all but broke down. But immediately he was recalled to self-control by another question, to which with the same emotional difficulty of utterance he said, "No, there was no malice between us. I never bore malice against the master-at-arms. I am sorry that he is dead. I did not mean to kill him. Could I have used my tongue I would not have struck him. But he foully lied to my face and in presence of my captain, and I had to say something, and I could only say it with a blow, God help me!"

In the impulsive aboveboard manner of the frank one the court saw confirmed all that was implied in words that just previously had perplexed them, coming as they did from the testifier to the tragedy and promptly following Billy's impassioned disclaimer of mutinous intent—Captain Vere's words, "I believe you, my man."

Next it was asked of him whether he knew of or suspected aught savoring of incipient trouble (meaning mutiny, though the explicit term was avoided) going on in any section of the ship's company.

The reply lingered. This was naturally imputed by the court to the same vocal embarrassment which had retarded or obstructed previous answers. But in main it was otherwise here, the question immediately recalling to Billy's mind the interview with the afterguardsman in the fore-chains. But an innate repugnance to playing a part at all approaching that of an informer against one's own shipmates—the same erring sense of uninstructed honor which had stood in the way of his reporting the matter at the time, though as a loyal man-of-war's man it was incumbent on him, and failure so to do, if charged against him and proven, would have subjected him to the heaviest of penalties; this, with the blind feeling now his that nothing really was being hatched, prevailed with him. When the answer came it was a negative.

"One question more," said the officer of marines, now first speaking and with a troubled earnestness. "You tell us that what the master-at-arms said against you was a lie. Now why should he have so lied, so maliciously lied, since you declare there was no malice between you?"

At that question, unintentionally touching on a spiritual sphere wholly obscure to Billy's thoughts, he was nonplussed, evincing a confusion indeed that some observers, such as can readily be imagined, would have construed into involuntary evidence of hidden guilt. Nevertheless, he strove some way to answer, but all at once relinquished the vain endeavor, at the same time turning an appealing glance towards Captain Vere as deeming him his best helper and friend. Captain Vere, who had been seated for a time, rose to his feet, addressing the interrogator. "The question you put to him comes naturally enough. But how can he rightly answer it?—or anybody else, unless indeed it be he who lies within there," designating the compartment where lay the corpse. "But the prone one there will not rise to our summons. In effect, though, as it seems to me, the point you make is hardly material. Quite aside from any conceivable motive actuating the master-at-arms, and irrespective of the provocation to the blow, a martial court must needs in the present case confine its attention to the blow's consequence, which consequence justly is to be deemed not otherwise than as the striker's deed."

This utterance, the full significance of which it was not at all likely that Billy took in, nevertheless caused him to turn a wistful interrogative look toward the speaker, a look in its dumb expressiveness not unlike that which a dog of generous breed might turn upon his master, seeking in his face some elucidation of a previous gesture ambiguous to the canine intelligence. Nor was the same utterance without marked effect upon the three officers, more especially the soldier. Couched in it seemed to them a meaning unanticipated, involving a prejudgment on the speaker's part. It served to augment a mental disturbance previously evident enough.

The soldier once more spoke, in a tone of suggestive dubiety addressing at once his associates and Captain Vere: "Nobody is present—none
of the ship's company, I mean—who might shed lateral light, if any is to
be had, upon what remains mysterious in this matter."

"That is thoughtfully put," said Captain Vere; "I see your drift. Ay,
there is a mystery; but, to use a scriptural phrase, it is a 'mystery of iniquity,' a matter for psychologic theologians to discuss. But what has a
military court to do with it? Not to add that for us any possible investiga-
tion of it is cut off by the lasting tongue-tie of—him—in yonder," again
designating the mortuary stateroom. "The prisoner's deed—with that
alone we have to do."

To this, and particularly the closing reiteration, the marine soldier,
knowing not how aptly to reply, sadly abstained from saying aught.
The first lieutenant, who at the outset had not unnaturally assumed
primacy in the court, now overrulingly instructed by a glance from Captain Vere, a glance more effective than words, resumed that primacy.
Turning to the prisoner, "Budd," he said, and scarce in equable tones,
"Budd, if you have aught further to say for yourself, say it now."

Upon this the young sailor turned another quick glance toward Captain Vere; then, as taking a hint from that aspect, a hint confirming his
own instinct that silence was now best, replied to the lieutenant, "I have
said all, Sir."

The marine—the same who had been the sentinel without the cabin
door at the time that the foretopman, followed by the master-at-arms,
entered it—he, standing by the sailor throughout these judicial proceedings, was now directed to take him back to the after compartment
originally assigned to the prisoner and his custodian. As the twain disappeared from view, the three officers, as partially liberated from some inward constraint associated with Billy's mere presence, simultaneously
stirred in their seats. They exchanged looks of troubled indecision, yet
feeling that decide they must and without long delay. For Captain Vere,
he for the time stood—unconsciously with his back toward them, apparently in one of his absent fits—gazing out from a sashed porthole to
windward upon the monotonous blank of the twilight sea. But the court's
silence continuing, broken only at moments by brief consultations, in low
earnest tones, this served to arouse him and energize him. Turning, he
to and fro paced the cabin athwart; in the returning ascent to windward
climbing the slant deck in the ship's lee roll, without knowing it symbolizing thus in his action a mind resolute to surmount difficulties even if
against primitive instincts strong as the wind and the sea. Presently he

came to a stand before the three. After scanning their faces he stood less
as mustering his thoughts for expression than as one inly deliberating how best to put them to well-meaning men not intellectually
mature, men with whom it was necessary to demonstrate certain principles that were axioms to himself. Similar impatience as to talking is
perhaps one reason that deters some minds from addressing any popular
assemblies.

When speak he did, something, both in the substance of what he said
and his manner of saying it, showed the influence of unshared studies
modifying and tempering the practical training of an active career. This,
along with his phraseology, now and then was suggestive of the grounds
whereon rested that imputation of a certain pedantry socially alleged
against him by certain naval men of wholly practical cast, captains who
nevertheless would frankly concede that His Majesty's navy mustered
no more efficient officer of their grade than Starry Vere.

What he said was to this effect: "Hitherto I have been but the witness,
little more; and I should hardly think now to take another tone, that of
your coadjutor for the time, did I not perceive in you—at the crisis too—a
troubled hesitancy, proceeding, I doubt not, from the clash of military
duty with moral scruple—scruple vitalized by compassion. For the compassion, how can I otherwise than share it? But, mindful of paramount
obligations, I strive against scruples that may tend to enervate decision.
Not, gentlemen, that I hide from myself that the case is an exceptional
one. Speculatively regarded, it well might be referred to a jury of
casuists. But for us here, acting not as casuists or moralists, it is a case
practical, and under martial law practically to be dealt with.

"But your scruples: do they move as in a dusk? Challenge them. Make
them advance and declare themselves. Come now; do they import something like this: If, mindless of palliating circumstances, we are bound to
regard the death of the master-at-arms as the prisoner's deed, then does
that deed constitute a capital crime whereof the penalty is a mortal
one? But in natural justice is nothing but the prisoner's overt act to be
considered? How can we adjudge to summary and shameful death a fellow creature innocent before God, and whom we feel to be so?—Does
that state it aright? You sign sad assent. Well, I too feel that, the full force
of that. It is Nature. But do these buttons that we wear attest that our allegiance is to Nature? No, to the King. Though the ocean, which is in-
violate Nature primeval, though this be the element where we move
and have our being as sailors, yet as the King's officers lies our duty in a
sphere correspondingly natural? So little is that true, that in receiv-

ing our commissions we in the most important regards ceased to be natural free agents. When war is declared are we the commissioned fighters previously consulted? We fight at command. If our judgments approve the war, that is but coincidence. So in other particulars. So now. For suppose condemnation to follow these present proceedings. Would it be so much we ourselves that would condemn as it would be martial law operating through us? For that law and the rigor of it, we are not responsible. Our vowed responsibility is in this: That however pitilessly that law may operate in any instances, we nevertheless adhere to it and administer it.

"But the exceptional in the matter moves the hearts within you. Even so too is mine moved. But let not warm hearts betray heads that should be cool. Ashore in a criminal case, will an upright judge allow himself off the bench to be waylaid by some tender kinswoman of the accused seeking to touch him with her tearful plea? Well, the heart here, sometimes the feminine in man, is as that piteous woman, and, hard though it be, she must here be ruled out."

He paused, earnestly studying them for a moment; then resumed.

"But something in your aspect seems to urge that it is not solely the heart that moves in you, but also the conscience, the private conscience. But tell me whether or not, occupying the position we do, private conscience should not yield to that imperial one formulated in the code under which alone we officially proceed?"

Here the three men moved in their seats, less convinced than agitated by the course of an argument troubling but the more the spontaneous conflict within.

Perceiving which, the speaker paused for a moment; then, abruptly changing his tone, went on.

"To steady us a bit, let us recur to the facts.—In wartime at sea a man-of-war's man strikes his superior in grade, and the blow kills. Apart from its effect the blow itself is, according to the Articles of War, a capital crime. Furthermore——"

"Ay, Sir," emotionally broke in the officer of marines, "in one sense it was. But surely Budd purposed neither mutiny nor homicide."

"Surely not, my good man. And before a court less arbitrary and more merciful than a martial one, that plea would largely extenuate. At the Last Assizes it shall acquit. But how here? We proceed under the law of the Mutiny Act. In feature no child can resemble his father more than that act resembles in spirit the thing from which it derives—War. In His Majesty's service—in this ship, indeed—there are Englishmen forced to fight for the King against their will. Against their conscience, for aught we know. Though as their fellow creatures some of us may appreciate their position, yet as navy officers what reck we of it? Still less recks the enemy. Our impressed men he would fain cut down in the same swath with our volunteers. As regards the enemy's naval conscripts, some of whom may even share our own abhorrence of the regicidal French Directory, it is the same on our side. War looks but to the frontage, the appearance. And the Mutiny Act, War's child, takes after the father. Budd's intent or nonintent is nothing to the purpose.

"But while, put to it by those anxieties in you which I cannot but respect, I only repeat myself—while thus strangely we prolong proceedings that should be summary—the enemy may be sighted and an engagement result. We must do; and one of two things must we do—condemn or let go."

"Can we not convict and yet mitigate the penalty?" asked the sailing master, here speaking, and falteringly, for the first.

"Gentlemen, were that clearly lawful for us under the circumstances, consider the consequences of such clemency. The people" (meaning the ship's company) "have native sense; most of them are familiar with our naval usage and tradition; and how would they take it? Even could you explain to them—which our official position forbids—they, long molded by arbitrary discipline, have not that kind of intelligent responsiveness that might qualify them to comprehend and discriminate. No, to the people the foretopman's deed, however it be worded in the announcement, will be plain homicide committed in a flagrant act of mutiny. What penalty for that should follow, they know. But it does not follow. Why? they will ruminate. You know what sailors are. Will they not revert to the recent outbreak at the Nore? Ay. They know the well-founded alarm —the panic it struck throughout England. Your clement sentence they would account pusillanimous. They would think that we flinch, that we are afraid of them—afraid of practicing a lawful rigor singularly demanded at this juncture, lest it should provoke new troubles. What shame to us such a conjecture on their part, and how deadly to discipline. You see then whither, prompted by duty and the law, I steadfastly drive. But I beseech you, my friends, do not take me amiss. I feel as you do for this unfortunate boy. But did he know our hearts, I take him to be of that generous nature that he would feel even for us on whom in this military necessity so heavy a compulsion is laid."

With that, crossing the deck he resumed his place by the sashed porthole, tacitly leaving the three to come to a decision. On the cabin's opposite side the troubled court sat silent. Loyal lieges, plain and practical, though at bottom they dissented from some points Captain Vere had put to them, they were without the faculty, hardly had the inclination, to gainsay one whom they felt to be an earnest man, one too not less their superior in mind than in naval rank. But it is not improbable that even such of his words as were not without influence over them less came home to them than his closing appeal to their instinct as sea officers: in the forethought he threw out as to the practical consequences to discipline, considering the unconfirmed tone of the fleet at the time, should a man-of-war's man's violent killing at sea of a superior in grade be allowed to pass for aught else than a capital crime demanding prompt infliction of the penalty.

Not unlikely they were brought to something more or less akin to that harassed frame of mind which in the year 1842 actuated the commander of the U.S. brig-of-war *Somers* to resolve, under the so-called Articles of War, articles modeled upon the English Mutiny Act, to resolve upon the execution at sea of a midshipman and two sailors as mutineers designing the seizure of the brig. Which resolution was carried out though in a time of peace and within not many days' sail of home: an act vindicated by a naval court of inquiry subsequently convened ashore. History, and here cited without comment. True, the circumstances on board the *Somers* were different from those on board the *Bellipotent*. But the urgency felt, well-warranted or otherwise, was much the same.

Says a writer whom few know, "Forty years after a battle it is easy for a noncombatant to reason about how it ought to have been fought. It is another thing personally and under fire to have to direct the fighting while involved in the obscuring smoke of it. Much so with respect to other emergencies involving considerations both practical and moral, and when it is imperative promptly to act. The greater the fog the more it imperils the steamer, and speed is put on though at the hazard of running somebody down. Little ween the snug card players in the cabin of the responsibilities of the sleepless man on the bridge."

In brief, Billy Budd was formally convicted and sentenced to be hung at the yardarm in the early morning watch, it being now night. Otherwise, as is customary in such cases, the sentence would forthwith have been carried out. In wartime on the field or in the fleet, a mortal punishment decreed by a drumhead court—on the field sometimes decreed by but a nod from the general—follows without delay on the heel of conviction, without appeal.

It was Captain Vere himself who of his own motion communicated the finding of the court to the prisoner, for that purpose going to the com-

partment where he was in custody and bidding the marine there to withdraw for the time.

Beyond the communication of the sentence, what took place at this
interview was never known. But in view of the character of the twain
briefly closeted in that stateroom, each radically sharing in the rarer
qualities of our nature—so rare indeed as to be all but incredible to
average minds however much cultivated—some conjectures may be ventured.

It would have been in consonance with the spirit of Captain Vere
should he on this occasion have concealed nothing from the condemned
one—should he indeed have frankly disclosed to him the part he himself
had played in bringing about the decision, at the same time revealing his
actuating motives. On Billy's side it is not improbable that such a confession would have been received in much the same spirit that prompted
it. Not without a sort of joy, indeed, he might have appreciated the brave
opinion of him implied in his captain's making such a confidant of him.
Nor, as to the sentence itself, could he have been insensible that it was
imparted to him as to one not afraid to die. Even more may have been.
Captain Vere in end may have developed the passion sometimes latent
under an exterior stoical or indifferent. He was old enough to have been
Billy's father. The austere devotee of military duty, letting himself melt
back into what remains primeval in our formalized humanity, may in end
have caught Billy to his heart, even as Abraham may have caught young
Isaac on the brink of resolutely offering him up in obedience to the exacting behest. But there is no telling the sacrament, seldom if in any case
revealed to the gadding world, wherever under circumstances at all akin
to those here attempted to be set forth two of great Nature's nobler order
embrace. There is privacy at the time, inviolable to the survivor; and
holy oblivion, the sequel to each diviner magnanimity, providentially
covers all at last.

The first to encounter Captain Vere in act of leaving the compartment
was the senior lieutenant. The face he beheld, for the moment one expressive of the agony of the strong, was to that officer, though a man of
fifty, a startling revelation. That the condemned one suffered less than he
who mainly had effected the condemnation was apparently indicated by
the former's exclamation in the scene soon perforce to be touched upon.

Of a series of incidents within a brief term rapidly following each other,
the adequate narration may take up a term less brief, especially if explanation or comment here and there seem requisite to the better under-

standing of such incidents. Between the entrance into the cabin of him who never left it alive, and him who when he did leave it left it as one condemned to die; between this and the closeted interview just given, less than an hour and a half had elapsed. It was an interval long enough, however, to awaken speculations among no few of the ship's company as to what it was that could be detaining in the cabin the master-at-arms and the sailor; for a rumor that both of them had been seen to enter it and neither of them had been seen to emerge, this rumor had got abroad upon the gun decks and in the tops, the people of a great warship being in one respect like villagers, taking microscopic note of every outward movement or nonmovement going on. When, therefore, in weather not at all tempestuous, all hands were called in the second dogwatch, a summons under such circumstances not usual in those hours, the crew were not wholly unprepared for some announcement extraordinary, one having connection too with the continued absence of the two men from their wonted haunts.

There was a moderate sea at the time; and the moon, newly risen and near to being at its full, silvered the white spar deck wherever not blotted by the clear-cut shadows horizontally thrown of fixtures and moving men. On either side the quarter-deck the marine guard under arms was drawn up; and Captain Vere, standing in his place surrounded by all the wardroom officers, addressed his men. In so doing, his manner showed neither more nor less than that properly pertaining to his supreme position aboard his own ship. In clear terms and concise he told them what had taken place in the cabin: that the master-at-arms was dead, that he who had killed him had been already tried by a summary court and condemned to death, and that the execution would take place in the early morning watch. The word *mutiny* was not named in what he said. He refrained too from making the occasion an opportunity for any preachment as to the maintenance of discipline, thinking perhaps that under existing circumstances in the navy the consequence of violating discipline should be made to speak for itself.

Their captain's announcement was listened to by the throng of standing sailors in a dumbness like that of a seated congregation of believers in hell listening to the clergyman's announcement of his Calvinistic text.

At the close, however, a confused murmur went up. It began to wax. All but instantly, then, at a sign, it was pierced and suppressed by shrill whistles of the boatswain and his mates. The word was given to about ship.

To be prepared for burial Claggart's body was delivered to certain petty officers of his mess. And here, not to clog the sequel with lateral matters, it may be added that, at a suitable hour, the master-at-arms was committed to the sea with every funeral honor properly belonging to his naval grade.

In this proceeding, as in every public one growing out of the tragedy, strict adherence to usage was observed. Nor in any point could it have been at all deviated from, either with respect to Claggart or Billy Budd, without begetting undesirable speculations in the ship's company, sailors, and more particularly men-of-war's men, being of all men the greatest sticklers for usage. For similar cause, all communication between Captain Vere and the condemned one ended with the closeted interview already given, the latter being now surrendered to the ordinary routine preliminary to the end. His transfer under guard from the captain's quarters was effected without unusual precautions—at least no visible ones. If possible, not to let the men so much as surmise that their officers anticipate aught amiss from them is the tacit rule in a military ship. And the more that some sort of trouble should really be apprehended, the more do the officers keep that apprehension to themselves, though not the less unostentatious vigilance may be augmented. In the present instance, the sentry placed over the prisoner had strict orders to let no one have communication with him but the chaplain. And certain unobtrusive measures were taken absolutely to insure this point.

In a seventy-four of the old order the deck known as the upper gun deck was the one covered over by the spar deck, which last, though not without its armament, was for the most part exposed to the weather. In general it was at all hours free from hammocks; those of the crew swinging on the lower gun deck and berth deck, the latter being not only a dormitory but also the place for the stowing of the sailors' bags, and on both sides lined with the large chests or movable pantries of the many messes of the men.

On the starboard side of the *Bellipotent's* upper gun deck, behold Billy Budd under sentry lying prone in irons in one of the bays formed by the regular spacing of the guns comprising the batteries on either side. All these pieces were of the heavier caliber of that period. Mounted on lumbering wooden carriages, they were hampered with cumbersome harness of breeching and strong side tackles for running them out. Guns and carriages, together with the long rammers and shorter linstocks lodged in loops overhead—all these, as customary, were painted black; and the heavy hempen breechings, tarred to the same tint, wore the like livery of the undertakers. In contrast with the funeral hue of these surroundings, the prone sailor's exterior apparel, white jumper and white duck trousers, each more or less soiled, dimly glimmered in the obscure light of the bay like a patch of discolored snow in early April lingering at some upland cave's black mouth. In effect he is already in his shroud, or the garments that shall serve him in lieu of one. Over him but scarce illuminating him. two battle lanterns swing from two massive beams of the deck above. Fed with the oil supplied by the war contractors (whose gains, honest or otherwise. are in every land an anticipated portion of the harvest of death), with flickering splashes of dirty yellow light they pollute the pale moonshine all but ineffectually struggling in obstructed flecks through the open ports from which the tampioned cannon protrude. Other lanterns at intervals serve but to bring out somewhat the obscurer bays which, like small confessionals or side chapels in a cathedral. branch from the long dim-vistaea broad aisle between the two batteries of that covered tier.

Such was the deck where now lay the Handsome Sailor. Through the rosetan of his complexion no pallor could have shown. It would have taken days of sequestration from the winds and the sun to have brought about the effacement of that. But the skeleton in the cheekbone at the point of its angle was just beginning delicately to be defined under the warm-tinted skin. In fervid hearts self-contained. some brief experiences devour our human tissue as secret fire in a ship's hold consumes cotton in the bale.

But now lying between the two guns, as nipped in the vice of fate, Billy's agony, mainly proceeding from a generous young heart's virgin experience of the diabolical incarnate and effective in some men—the tension of that agony was over now. It survived not the something healing in the closeted interview with Captain Vere. Without movement, he lay as in a trance, that adolescent expression previously noted as his taking on something akin to the look of a slumbering child in the cradle when the warm hearth glow of the still chamber at night plays on the dimples that at whiles mysteriously form in the cheek. silently coming and going there. For now and then in the gyved one s trance a serene happy light born of some wandering reminiscence or dream would diffuse itself over his face. and then wane away only anew to return.

The chaplain, coming to see him and finding him thus. and perceiving no sign that he was conscious of his presence. attentively regarded him for a space, then slipping aside. withdrew for the time, peradventure feeling that even he, the minister of Christ though receiving his stipend from Mars. had no consolation to proffer which could result in a peace transcending that which ne beheld. But in the small hours he came again.

And the prisoner, now awake to his surroundings, noticed his approach, and civilly, all but cheerfully, welcomed him. But it was to little purpose that in the interview following, the good man sought to bring Billy Budd to some godly understanding that he must die, and at dawn. True, Billy himself freely referred to his death as a thing close at hand; but it was something in the way that children will refer to death in general, who yet among their other sports will play a funeral with hearse and mourners.

Not that like children Billy was incapable of conceiving what death really is. No, but he was wholly without irrational fear of it. a fear more prevalent in highly civilized communities than those so-called barbarous ones which in all respects stand nearer to unadulterate Nature. And, as elsewhere said, a barbarian Billy radically was—as much so, for all the costume, as his countrymen the British captives, living trophies, made to march in the Roman triumph of Germanicus. Quite as much so as those later barbarians, young men probably, and picked specimens among the earlier British converts to Christianity, at least nominally such, taken to Rome (as today converts from lesser isles of the sea may be taken to London), of whom the Pope of that time, admiring the strangeness of their personal beauty so unlike the Italian stamp, their clear ruddy complexion and curled flaxen locks, exclaimed, "Angles" (meaning *English*, the modern derivative), "Angles, do you call them? And is it because they look so like angels?" Had it been later in time, one would think that the Pope had in mind Fra Angelico's seraphs, some of whom, plucking apples in gardens of the Hesperides. have the faint rosebud complexion of the more beautiful English girls.

If in vain the good chaplain sought to impress the young barbarian with ideas of death akin to those conveyed in the skull, dial, and cross-bones on old tombstones, equally futile to all appearance were his efforts to bring home to him the thought of salvation and a Savior. Billy listened, but less out of awe or reverence, perhaps. than from a certain natural politeness, doubtless at bottom regarding all that in much the same way that most mariners of his class take any discourse abstract or out of the common tone of the workaday world. And this sailor way of taking cleri-cal discourse is not wholly unlike the way in which the primer of Chris-tianity, full of transcendent miracles, was received long ago on tropic isles by any superior *savage*, so called—a Tahitian, say, of Captain Cook's time or shortly after that time. Out of natural courtesy he received, but did not appropriate. It was like a gift placed in the palm of an outreached hand upon which the fingers do not close.

But the *Bellipotent*'s chaplain was a discreet man possessing the good sense of a good heart. So he insisted not in his vocation here. At the instance of Captain Vere, a lieutenant had apprised him of pretty much everything as to Billy; and since he felt that innocence was even a better thing than religion wherewith to go to Judgment, he reluctantly withdrew; but in his emotion not without first performing an act strange enough in an Englishman, and under the circumstances yet more so in any regular priest. Stooping over, he kissed on the fair cheek his fellow man, a felon in martial law, one whom though on the confines of death he felt he could never convert to a dogma; nor for all that did he fear for his future.

Marvel not that having been made acquainted with the young sailor's essential innocence the worthy man lifted not a finger to avert the doom of such a martyr to martial discipline. So to do would not only have been as idle as invoking the desert but would also have been an audacious transgression of the bounds of his function, one as exactly prescribed to him by military law as that of the boatswain or any other naval officer. Bluntly put, a chaplain is the minister of the Prince of Peace serving in the host of the God of War—Mars. As such, he is as incongruous as a musket would be on the altar at Christmas. Why, then, is he there? Because he indirectly subserves the purpose attested by the cannon; because too he lends the sanction of the religion of the meek to that which practically is the abrogation of everything but brute force.

The night so luminous on the spar deck, but otherwise on the cavernous ones below, levels so like the tiered galleries in a coal mine—the luminous night passed away. But like the prophet in the chariot disappearing in heaven and dropping his mantle to Elisha, the withdrawing night transferred its pale robe to the breaking day. A meek, shy light appeared in the east, where stretched a diaphanous fleece of white furrowed vapor. That light slowly waxed. Suddenly *eight bells* was struck aft, responded to by one louder metallic stroke from forward. It was four o'clock in the morning. Instantly the silver whistles were heard summoning all hands to witness punishment. Up through the great hatchways rimmed with racks of heavy shot the watch below came pouring, overspreading with the watch already on deck the space between the mainmast and foremast including that occupied by the capacious launch and the black booms tiered on either side of it, boat and booms making a summit of observation for the powder boys and younger tars. A different group comprising one watch of topmen leaned over the rail of that sea balcony, no small one in a seventy-four, looking down on the crowd below. Man or boy, none spake but in whisper, and few spake at all. Captain Vere—as before, the central figure among the assembled commissioned officers—stood nigh the break of the poop deck facing forward. Just below him on the quarter-deck the marines in full equipment were drawn up much as at the scene of the promulgated sentence.

At sea in the old time, the execution by halter of a military sailor was generally from the foreyard. In the present instance, for special reasons the main yard was assigned. Under an arm of that yard the prisoner was presently brought up, the chaplain attending him. It was noted at the time, and remarked upon afterwards, that in this final scene the good man evinced little or nothing of the perfunctory. Brief speech indeed he had with the condemned one, but the genuine Gospel was less on his tongue than in his aspect and manner towards him. The final preparations personal to the latter being speedily brought to an end by two boatswain's mates, the consummation impended. Billy stood facing aft. At the penultimate moment, his words, his only ones, words wholly unobstructed in the utterance, were these: "God bless Captain Vere!" Syllables so unanticipated coming from one with the ignominious hemp about his neck—a conventional felon's benediction directed aft towards the quarters of honor; syllables, too, delivered in the clear melody of a singing bird on the point of launching from the twig—had a phenomenal effect, not unenhanced by the rare personal beauty of the young sailor, spiritualized now through late experiences so poignantly profound.

Without volition, as it were, as if indeed the ship's populace were but the vehicles of some vocal current electric, with one voice from alow and aloft came a resonant sympathetic echo: "God bless Captain Vere!" And yet at that instant Billy alone must have been in their hearts, even as in their eyes.

At the pronounced words and the spontaneous echo that voluminously rebounded them, Captain Vere, either through stoic self-control or a sort of momentary paralysis induced by emotional shock, stood erectly rigid as a musket in the shiparmorer's rack.

The hull, deliberately recovering from the periodic roll to leeward, was just regaining an even keel when the last signal, a preconcerted dumb one, was given. At the same moment it chanced that the vapory fleece hanging low in the east was shot through with a soft glory as of the fleece of the Lamb of God seen in mystical vision, and simultaneously therewith, watched by the wedged mass of upturned faces, Billy ascended; and, ascending, took the full rose of the dawn.

In the pinioned figure arrived at the yard-end, to the wonder of all no motion was apparent, none save that created by the slow roll of the hull in moderate weather, so majestic in a great ship ponderously cannoned.

When some days afterwards, in reference to the singularity just mentioned, the purser, a rather ruddy, rotund person more accurate as an accountant than profound as a philosopher, said at mess to the surgeon, "What testimony to the force lodged in will power," the latter, saturnine, spare, and tall, one in whom a discreet causticity went along with a manner less genial than polite, replied, "Your pardon, Mr. Purser. In a hanging scientifically conducted—and under special orders I myself directed how Budd's was to be effected—any movement following the completed suspension and originating in the body suspended, such movement indicates mechanical spasm in the muscular system. Hence the absence of that is no more attributable to will power, as you call it than to horsepower—begging your pardon."

"But this muscular spasm you speak of, is not that in a degree more or less invariable in these cases?"

"Assuredly so, Mr. Purser."

"How then, my good Sir, do you account for its absence in this instance?"

"Mr. Purser, it is clear that your sense of the singularity in this matter equals not mine. You account for it by what you call will power—a term not yet included in the lexicon of science. For me, I do not, with my present knowledge, pretend to account for it at all. Even should we assume the hypothesis that at the first touch of the halyards the action of Budd's heart, intensified by extraordinary emotion at its climax, abruptly stopped—much like a watch when in carelessly winding it up you strain at the finish, thus snapping the chain—even under that hypothesis how account for the phenomenon that followed?"

"You admit, then, that the absence of spasmodic movement was phenomenal."

"It was phenomenal, Mr. Purser. in the sense that it was an appearance the cause of which is not immediately to be assigned."

"But tell me, my dear Sir," pertinaciously continued the other, "was the man's death effected by the halter, or was it a species of euthanasia?"

"*Euthanasia* Mr. Purser, is something like your *will power*: I doubt its authenticity as a scientific term—begging your pardon again. It is at once imaginative and metaphysical—in short, Greek. But," abruptly changing his tone, "there is a case in the sick bay that I do not care to leave to my assistants. Beg your pardon, but excuse me." And rising from the mess he formally withdrew.

The silence at the moment of execution and for a moment or two continuing thereafter, a silence but emphasized by the regular wash of the sea against the hull or the flutter of a sail caused by the helmsman's eyes being tempted astray, this emphasized silence was gradually disturbed by a sound not easily to be verbally rendered. Whoever has heard the freshet wave of a torrent suddenly swelled by pouring showers in tropical mountains, showers not shared by the plain; whoever has heard the first muffled murmur of its sloping advance through precipitous woods may form some conception of the sound now heard. The seeming remoteness of its source was because of its murmurous indistinctness, since it came from close by, even from the men massed on the ship's open deck. Being inarticulate, it was dubious in significance further than it seemed to indicate some capricious revulsion of thought or feeling such as mobs ashore are liable to, in the present instance possibly implying a sullen revocation on the men's part of their involuntary echoing of Billy's benediction. But ere the murmur had time to wax into clamor it was met by a strategic command, the more telling that it came with abrupt unexpectedness: "Pipe down the starboard watch, Boatswain, and see that they go."

Shrill as the shriek of the sea hawk, the silver whistles of the boatswain and his mates pierced that ominous low sound, dissipating it; and yielding to the mechanism of discipline the throng was thinned by one-half. For the remainder, most of them were set to temporary employments connected with trimming the yards and so forth, business readily to be got up to serve occasion by any officer of the deck.

Now each proceeding that follows a mortal sentence pronounced at sea by a drumhead court is characterized by promptitude not perceptibly merging into hurry, though bordering that. The hammock, the one which had been Billy's bed when alive, having already been ballasted with shot and otherwise prepared to serve for his canvas coffin, the last offices of the sea undertakers, the sailmaker's mates, were now speedily completed. When everything was in readiness a second call for all hands, made necessary by the strategic movement before mentioned. was sounded, now to witness burial.

The details of this closing formality it needs not to give. But when the tilted plank let slide its freight into the sea, a second strange human murmur was heard, blended now with another inarticulate sound proceeding from certain larger seafowl who, their attention having been attracted by the peculiar commotion in the water resulting from the heavy sloped dive of the shotted hammock into the sea, flew screaming to the spot. So near the hull did they come that the stridor or bony creak of their gaunt double-jointed pinions was audible. As the ship under light airs passed on, leaving the burial spot astern, they still kept circling it low down with the moving shadow of their outstretched wings and the croaked requiem of their cries.

Upon sailors as superstitious as those of the age preceding ours, men-of-war's men too who had just beheld the prodigy of repose in the form suspended in air, and now foundering in the deeps; to such mariners the action of the seafowl, though dictated by mere animal greed for prey, was big with no prosaic significance. An uncertain movement began among them, in which some encroachment was made. It was tolerated but for a moment. For suddenly the drum beat to quarters, which familiar sound, happening at least twice every day, had upon the present occasion a signal peremptoriness in it. True martial discipline long continued superinduces in average man a sort of impulse whose operation at the official word of command much resembles in its promptitude the effect of an instinct.

The drumbeat dissolved the multitude, distributing most of them along the batteries of the two covered gun decks. There, as wonted, the guns' crews stood by their respective cannon erect and silent. In due course the first officer, sword under arm and standing in his place on the quarter-deck, formally received the successive reports of the sworded lieutenants commanding the sections of batteries below; the last of which reports being made, the summed report he delivered with the customary salute to the commander. All this occupied time, which in the present case was the object in beating to quarters at an hour prior to the customary one. That such variance from usage was authorized by an officer like Captain Vere, a martinet as some deemed him, was evidence of the necessity for unusual action implied in what he deemed to be temporarily the mood of his men. "With mankind," he would say, "forms, measured forms, are everything; and that is the import couched in the story of Orpheus with his lyre spellbinding the wild denizens of the wood." And this he once applied to the disruption of forms going on across the Channel and the consequences thereof.

At this unwonted muster at quarters, all proceeded as at the regular hour. The band on the quarter-deck played a sacred air, after which the chaplain went through the customary morning service. That done, the drum beat the retreat; and toned by music and religious rites subserving the discipline and purposes of war, the men in their wonted orderly manner dispersed to the places allotted them when not at the guns.

And now it was full day. The fleece of low-hanging vapor had vanished, licked up by the sun that late had so glorified it. And the circumambient air in the clearness of its serenity was like smooth white marble in the polished block not yet removed from the marble-dealer's yard.

The symmetry of form attainable in pure fiction cannot so readily be achieved in a narration essentially having less to do with fable than with fact. Truth uncompromisingly told will always have its ragged edges; hence the conclusion of such a narration is apt to be less finished than an architectural finial.

How it fared with the Handsome Sailor during the year of the Great Mutiny has been faithfully given. But though properly the story ends with his life, something in way of sequel will not be amiss. Three brief chapters will suffice.

In the general rechristening under the Directory of the craft originally forming the navy of the French monarchy, the *St. Louis* line-of-battle ship was named the *Athée* (the *Atheist*). Such a name, like some other substituted ones in the Revolutionary fleet, while proclaiming the infidel audacity of the ruling power, was yet, though not so intended to be, the aptest name, if one consider it, ever given to a warship; far more so indeed than the *Devastation,* the *Erebus* (the *Hell*), and similar names bestowed upon fighting ships.

On the return passage to the English fleet from the detached cruise during which occurred the events already recorded, the *Bellipotent* fell in with the *Athée*. An engagement ensued, during which Captain Vere, in the act of putting his ship alongside the enemy with a view of throwing his boarders across her bulwarks, was hit by a musket ball from a porthole of the enemy's main cabin. More than disabled, he dropped to the deck and was carried below to the same cockpit where some of his men already lay. The senior lieutenant took command. Under him the enemy was finally captured, and though much crippled was by rare good fortune successfully taken into Gibraltar, an English port not very distant from the scene of the fight. There, Captain Vere with the rest of the wounded was put ashore. He lingered for some days, but the end came. Unhappily he was cut off too early for the Nile and Trafalgar. The spirit that 'spite its philosophic austerity may yet have indulged in the most secret of all passions, ambition, never attained to the fullness of fame.

Not long before death, while lying under the influence of that magical drug which, soothing the physical frame, mysteriously operates on the subtler element in man, he was heard to murmur words inexplicable to his attendant: "Billy Budd, Billy Budd." That these were not the accents of remorse would seem clear from what the attendant said to the *Belli-potent's* senior officer of marines, who, as the most reluctant to condemn of the members of the drumhead court, too well knew, though here he kept the knowledge to himself, who Billy Budd was.

Some few weeks after the execution, among other matters under the head of "News from the Mediterranean," there appeared in a naval chronicle of the time, an authorized weekly publication, an account of the affair. It was doubtless for the most part written in good faith, though the medium, partly rumor, through which the facts must have reached the writer served to deflect and in part falsify them. The account was as follows:

"On the tenth of the last month a deplorable occurrence took place on board H.M.S. *Bellipotent.* John Claggart, the ship's master-at-arms, discovering that some sort of plot was incipient among an inferior section of the ship's company, and that the ringleader was one William Budd; he, Claggart, in the act of arraigning the man before the captain, was vindictively stabbed to the heart by the suddenly drawn sheath knife of Budd.

"The deed and the implement employed sufficiently suggest that though mustered into the service under an English name the assassin was no Englishman, but one of those aliens adopting English cognomens whom the present extraordinary necessities of the service have caused to be admitted into it in considerable numbers.

"The enormity of the crime and the extreme depravity of the criminal appear the greater in view of the character of the victim, a middle-aged man respectable and discreet, belonging to that minor official grade, the petty officers, upon whom, as none know better than the commissioned gentlemen, the efficiency of His Majesty's navy so largely depends. His function was a responsible one, at once onerous and thankless; and his fidelity in it the greater because of his strong patriotic impulse. In this instance as in so many other instances in these days, the character of this unfortunate man signally refutes, if refutation were needed, that peevish saying attributed to the late Dr. Johnson, that patriotism is the last refuge of a scoundrel.

"The criminal paid the penalty of his crime. The promptitude of the punishment has proved salutary. Nothing amiss is now apprehended aboard H.M.S. *Bellipotent.*"

The above, appearing in a publication now long ago superannuated and forgotten, is all that hitherto has stood in human record to attest what manner of men respectively were John Claggart and Billy Budd.

Everything is for a term venerated in navies. Any tangible object associated with some striking incident of the service is converted into a monument. The spar from which the foretopman was suspended was for some few years kept trace of by the bluejackets. Their knowledge followed it from ship to dockyard and again from dockyard to ship, still pursuing it even when at last reduced to a mere dockyard boom. To them a chip of it was as a piece of the Cross. Ignorant though they were of the secret facts of the tragedy, and not thinking but that the penalty was somehow unavoidably inflicted from the naval point of view, for all that, they instinctively felt that Billy was a sort of man as incapable of mutiny as of willful murder. They recalled the fresh young image of the Handsome Sailor, that face never deformed by a sneer or subtler vile freak of the heart within. This impression of him was doubtless deepened by the fact that he was gone, and in a measure mysteriously gone. On the gun decks of the *Bellipotent* the general estimate of his nature and its unconscious simplicity eventually found rude utterance from another foretopman, one of his own watch, gifted, as some sailors are, with an artless *poetic* temperament. The tarry hand made some lines which, after circulating among the shipboard crews for a while, finally got rudely printed at Portsmouth as a ballad. The title given to it was the sailor's.

BILLY IN THE DARBIES

Good of the chaplain to enter Lone Bay
And down on his marrowbones here and pray
For the likes just o' me, Billy Budd.—But, look:
Through the port comes the moonshine astray!
It tips the guard's cutlass and silvers this nook;
But 'twill die in the dawning of Billy's last day.
A jewel block they'll make of me tomorrow,
Pendant pearl from the yardarm-end
Like the eardrop I gave to Bristol Molly—
O, 'tis me, not the sentence they'll suspend.
Ay, ay, all is up; and I must up too,
Early in the morning, aloft from alow.
On an empty stomach now never it would do.
They'll give me a nibble—bit o' biscuit ere I go.
Sure, a messmate will reach me the last parting cup;
But, turning heads away from the hoist and the belay,

Heaven knows who will have the running of me up!
No pipe to those halyards.—But aren't it all sham?
A blur's in my eyes; it is dreaming that I am.
A hatchet to my hawser? All adrift to go?
The drum roll to grog, and Billy never know?
But Donald he has promised to stand by the plank;
So I'll shake a friendly hand ere I sink.
But—no! It is dead then I'll be, come to think.
I remember Taff the Welshman when he sank.
And his cheek it was like the budding pink.
But me they'll lash in hammock, drop me deep.
Fathoms down, fathoms down, how I'll dream fast asleep.
I feel it stealing now. Sentry, are you there?
Just ease these darbies at the wrist,
And roll me over fair!
I am sleepy, and the oozy weeds about me twist.

The foregoing text is from the definitive edition,
BILLY BUDD, SAILOR (AN INSIDE NARRATIVE),
edited with notes by Harrison Hayford and M. M. Sealts, Jr.,
University of Chicago Press, © *1962.*

Ivan Bunin

1870–1953

Ivan Bunin was born in Voronezh, Russia, October 10, 1870. His family belonged to the old landed nobility. Bunin grew up on his father's estates in central Russia. A painter at first, he turned early to writing. His first poems came out in 1889. He was twice awarded the Pushkin Prize, the second time for his translation of Longfellow's *Hiawatha*. In 1909 he was elected one of the Twelve Honorary Academicians of the Russian Academy. Leo Tolstoy was also one of the twelve.

In his youth Bunin was a Tolstoyan, dedicated to good works and making barrel hoops. He met the Master, a tall old man who came at him with a frighteningly quick stride and spoke gently. In Moscow Bunin was associated with the writers Leonid Andreev and Maxim Gorky and the singer Feodor Chaliapin. He was so thin that the painter Ilya Repin asked him to model for one of his angels.

Bunin traveled all over Russia and visited Syria, Palestine, Egypt, Algeria, Tunisia, and the tropics. At Yalta, he and Anton Chekhov were close friends. They had a game, each repeating to the other some solemn remark the critics had made about him. "You are 'a man of crystal purity,'" Chekhov would say. Bunin would reply by calling him "the singer of twilight moods."

Bunin's novel *The Village* appeared in 1910. It was one of the first books to break down the traditional idealization of the Russian people in literature. Dismayed by the "utterly intolerable spectacle" of the Revolution, Bunin moved to South Russia in May, 1918. He left the country for good in February, 1920. Such works as *The Gentleman from San Francisco, Suchodol, An Evening in the Spring,* and *The Dreams of Chang and Other Stories* made him known all over the world. He lived an exile's life in Paris and at Grasse in Provence. His later works include *The Well of Days, Dark Avenues,* and *Memories and Portraits.* In 1933 Bunin was awarded the Nobel Prize for literature. He died in Paris on November 8, 1953.

When we read *The Gentleman from San Francisco* for the first time, we are so enchanted by the shimmer of a multitude of details that we hardly notice anything else. Even so, we are aware that this detail is not simply piled up, as Zola might do it. Whether it refers to the snowy winter sea, a crystal chandelier, or a little Sicilian horse, it evokes whatever it touches. We can see it and feel it. It is *there.* The story is created out of it.

Then we notice that this detail is of two kinds, one continually played off against the other. The first is our actual world of work, hardship, and weather, but also of light on the sea, of that Italy where each island "has its especial aroma" after rain. The other is the luxury world of the transatlantic liners and the grand hotels, in which the traveler does not need to do anything at all. His whole duty consists in answering the gong—that ironic gong!—for dinner, like one of Pavlov's salivating dogs. For a moment, at the crisis of the story, the author brings these two worlds together.

Is it a period story? We feel that it is, that the author meant it to be that. Its time is easy to guess: the period not long before World War I. The travelers take tea, not cocktails, at five o'clock. Women are evidently not permitted in the ship's bar. The Chinese stewards wear queues. But the sense of period is conveyed to us by other and more subtle intimations—by the naïveté of that young couple aboard the *Atlantida* hired to "play at love," and by the general sense, displayed in the attitudes of everyone from the San Francisco gentleman to Luigi the bell-boy, that this dream world is completely insulated, permanent, and untouchable. No one knew better than Bunin that it was not.

Moreover, we are aware that these two contrasted worlds are also two exclusive worlds of people. Each is covertly hostile to the other. The Gentleman from San Francisco is offended by the sight of the fishermen's miserable stone huts; after his death, Luigi the waiter mocks him with his obsequious *"Ha sonato, Signore?"* at the door. Here are the two worlds of those who serve and those who are served.

Those who are served, the San Franciscan and his family, are nameless. The "hereditary prince of a certain Asiatic kingdom" is not merely nameless, he is "travelling incognito"—a double loss of identity. Symbolic figures moving in a dream have no need of identity. They are simply kinds of people: ticketed, consigned from one port to another, summoned by gongs, unobtrusively guarded to see that they do not get out of step. And it comes to us suddenly, in a kind of ironic reversal, that these travelers are servants too—of their schedules, of their arrangements, of the need to do and see everything, to get their money's worth.

They are servants, too, of their pleasure. They are going to Europe "for two whole years . . . solely for the sake of pleasure." Finally, the dead man is the servant of those forces—"the darkness, the ocean, the snow storm"—which govern and control all transient things.

The Gentleman
from San Francisco

Alas, alas that great city Babylon,
that mighty city!
The Apocalypse.

The gentleman from San Francisco—neither at Naples nor at Capri had any one remembered his name—was going to the Old World for two whole years, with wife and daughter, solely for the sake of pleasure.

He was firmly convinced that he was fully entitled to rest, to pleasure, to prolonged and comfortable travel, and to not a little else besides. For such a conviction he had his reasons—that, in the first place, he was rich, and, in the second, that he was only now beginning to live, despite his eight and fifty years. Until now he had not lived, but had merely existed—not at all badly, it is true, but nevertheless, putting all his hopes on the future. He had laboured with never a pause for rest [1]—the coolies, whom he had imported by whole thousands, well knew what this meant! —and finally he saw that much had already been accomplished, that he had almost come abreast of those whom he had at one time set out to emulate, and he decided to enjoy breathing space. It was a custom among the class of people to which he belonged to commence their enjoyment of life with a journey to Europe, to India, to Egypt. He, too, proposed to do the same. Of course he desired, first of all, to reward himself for his years of toil; however, he rejoiced on account of his wife and daughter as well. His wife had never been distinguished for any special sensitiveness to new impressions, but then, all elderly American women are fervid travellers. As for his daughter, a girl no longer in her first youth, and

---

1. More literal translation: "He worked without folding his hands" [Ed.].

somewhat sickly, travel was a downright necessity for her: to say nothing of the benefit to her health, were there no fortuitous encounters during travels? It is while travelling that one may at times sit at table with a *milliardaire,* or scrutinize frescos by his side.

The itinerary worked out by the gentleman from San Francisco was an extensive one. In December and January he hoped to enjoy the sun of southern Italy, the monuments of antiquity, the *tarantella,* the serenades of strolling singers, and that which men of his age relish with the utmost finesse: the love of little, youthful Neapolitaines, even though it be given not entirely without ulterior motives; he contemplated spending the Carnival in Nice, in Monte Carlo, whither the very pick of society gravitates at that time—that very society upon which all the benefits of civilization depend: not merely the cut of tuxedos, but, as well, the stability of thrones, and the declaration of wars, and the prosperity of hotels— Monte Carlo, where some give themselves up with passion to automobile and sail races; others to roulette; a third group to that which it is the custom to call flirting; a fourth, to trap-shooting, in which the pigeons, released from their cotes, soar up most gracefully above emerald-green swards, against the background of a sea that is the colour of forget-me-nots, only, in the same minute, to strike against the ground as little, crumpled clods of white. . . . The beginning of March he wanted to devote to Florence; about the time of the Passion of Our Lord to arrive at Rome, in order to hear the *Miserere* there; his plans also embraced Venice, and Paris, and bull-fighting in Seville, and sea-bathing in the British Islands, and Athens, and Constantinople, and Palestine, and Egypt, and even Japan—of course, be it understood, already on the return trip. . . . And everything went very well at first.

It was the end of November; almost as far as Gibraltar it was necessary to navigate now through an icy murk, now amidst a blizzard of wet snow; but the ship sailed in all safety and even without rolling; the passengers the steamer was carrying proved to be many, and all of them people of note; the ship—the famous *Atlantida*—resembled the most expensive of European hotels, with all conveniences: an all-night bar, Turkish baths, a newspaper of its own; and life upon it flowed in accordance with a most complicated system of regulations: people got up early, to the sounds of bugles, stridently resounding through the corridors at that dark hour when day was so slowly and inimically dawning over the greyish-green desert of waters, ponderously turbulent in the mist. Putting on their flannel pyjamas, the passengers drank coffee, chocolate, cocoa; then they got into marble baths, did their exercises, inducing an appetite and a sense of well-being, performed their toilet for the day, and went to breakfast. Until eleven one was supposed to promenade the decks vigorously, inhaling the fresh coolness of the ocean, or to play at shuffle-board and other games for the sake of arousing the appetite anew, and, at eleven, to seek sustenance in bouillon and sandwiches; having refreshed themselves, the passengers perused their newspaper with gusto and calmly awaited lunch, a meal still more nourishing and varied than the breakfast. The next two hours were sacred to repose—the decks were then encumbered with *chaises longues,* upon which the travellers reclined, covered up with plaids, contemplating the cloud-flecked sky and the foaming hummocks flashing by over the side, or else pleasantly dozing off; at five o'clock, refreshed and put in good spirits, they were drenched with strong fragrant tea, served with cookies; at seven they were apprized by bugle signals of a dinner of nine courses. . . . And thereupon the gentleman from San Francisco, in an access of animal spirits, would hurry to his resplendent *cabine de luxe,* to dress.

In the evening the tiers of the *Atlantida* gaped through the dusk as though they were fiery, countless eyes, and a great multitude of servants worked with especial feverishness in the kitchens, sculleries, and wine vaults. The ocean, heaving on the other side of the walls, was awesome; but none gave it a thought, firmly believing it under the sway of the captain, a red-haired man of monstrous bulk and ponderousness, always seeming sleepy, resembling, in his uniform frock-coat, with its golden chevrons, an enormous idol; it was only very rarely that he left his mysterious quarters to appear in public. A siren on the forecastle howled every minute in hellish sullenness and whined in frenzied malice, but not many of the diners heard the siren—it was drowned by the strains of a splendid stringed orchestra, playing exquisitely and ceaselessly in the two-tiered hall, decorated with marble; its floors covered with velvet rugs; festively flooded with the lights of crystal lustres and gilded girandoles; filled to overflowing with diamond-bedecked ladies in *décolleté* and men in tuxedos, graceful waiters and deferent *maîtres d'hôtel*—among whom one, who took orders for wines exclusively, even walked about with a chain around his neck, like a lord mayor. A tuxedo and perfect linen made the gentleman from San Francisco appear very much younger. Spare, not tall, clumsily but strongly built, groomed until he shone and moderately animated, he sat in the aureate-pearly refulgence of this palatial room, at a table with a bottle of amber Johannesberg, with countless goblets, small and large, of the thinnest glass, with a curly bouquet of curly hyacinths. There was something of the Mongol about his yellowish face with clipped silvery moustache; his large teeth gleamed with gold fillings; his stalwart, bald head glistened like old ivory. Rich, yet in keeping with her years, was the dress of his wife—a big woman, expansive and calm; elaborate, yet light and diaphanous, with an innocent frankness, was that of his daughter—tall, slender, with magnificent hair, exquisitely dressed, with breath aromatic from violet *cachou* and with the tenderest of tiny, rosy pimples about her lips and between her shoulder blades, just the least bit powdered. . . . The dinner lasted for two whole hours, while after dinner there was dancing in the ball-room, during which the men—the gentleman from San Francisco among their number, of course—with their feet cocked up, determined, upon the basis of the latest political and stock-exchange news, the destinies of nations, smoking Havana cigars and drinking *liqueurs* until they were crimson in the face, seated in the bar, where the waiters were Negroes in red jackets, the whites of their eyes resembling hard-boiled eggs with the shell off. The ocean, with a dull roar, was moiling in black mountains on the other side of the wall; the snow-gale whistled mightily through the sodden rigging; the whole steamer quivered as it mastered both the gale and the mountains, sundering to either side, as though with a plough, their shifting masses, that again and again boiled up and reared high, with tails of foam; the siren, stifled by the fog, was moaning with a deathly anguish; the look-outs up in their crow's nest froze from the cold and grew dazed from straining their attention beyond their strength. Like to the grim and sultry depths of the infernal regions, like to their ultimate, their ninth circle, was the womb of the steamer, below the water-line—that womb where dully gurgled the gigantic furnaces, devouring with their incandescent maws mountains of hard coal, cast into them by men stripped to the waist, purple from the flames, and with smarting, filthy sweat pouring over them; whereas here, in the bar, men threw their legs over the arms of their chairs with never a care, sipping cognac and *liqueurs,* and were wafted among clouds of spicy smoke as they indulged in well-turned conversation; in the ball-room everything was radiant with light and warmth and joy; the dancing couples were now a-whirl in waltzes, now twisting in the tango, and the music insistently, in some delectably shameless melancholy, was suppliant always of the one, always of the same thing. . . . There was an ambassador among this brilliant throng—a lean, modest little old man; there was a great man of riches—clean-shaven, lanky, of indeterminate years, and with the appearance of a prelate, in his dress-coat of an old-fashioned cut; there was a well-known Spanish writer; there was a world-celebrated beauty, already just the very least trifle faded and of an unenviable morality; there was an exquisite couple in love with each other, whom all watched with curiosity and whose happiness was unconcealed: *he* danced only with *her;* sang—and with great ability—only to *her* accompaniment; and everything they did was carried out so charmingly that the captain was the only one who knew that this pair was hired by Lloyd's to play at love for a good figure, and that they had been sailing for a long time, now on one ship, now on another.

At Gibraltar everybody was gladdened by the sun—it seemed to be early spring; a new passenger, whose person aroused the general interest, made his appearance on board the *Atlantida*—he was the hereditary prince of a certain Asiatic kingdom, travelling incognito; a little man who somehow seemed to be all made of wood, even though he was alert in his movements; broad of face, with narrow eyes, in gold-rimmed spectacles; a trifle unpleasant through the fact that his skin showed through his coarse black moustache like that of a cadaver; on the whole, however, he was charming, unpretentious, and modest. On the Mediterranean Sea there was a whiff of winter again; the billows ran high, and were as multi-coloured as the tail of a peacock; they had snowy-white crests, lashed up—although the sun was sparkling brightly and the sky was perfectly clear—by a *tramontana,* a chill northern wind from beyond the mountains, that was joyously and madly rushing to meet the ship. . . . Then, on the second day, the sky began to pale, the horizon became covered with mist, land was nearing; Ischia, Capri appeared; through the binoculars Naples—lumps of sugar strewn at the foot of some dove-coloured mass—could be seen; while over it and this dove-coloured thing were visible the ridges of distant mountains, vaguely glimmering with the dead whiteness of snows. There was a great number of people on deck; many of the ladies and gentlemen had already put on short, light fur coats, with the fur outside; Chinese boys, never contradictory and never speaking above a whisper, bow-legged striplings with pitch-black queues reaching to their heels and with eye-lashes as long and thick as those of young girls, were already dragging, little by little, sundry plaids, canes, and portmanteaux and grips of alligator hide toward the companionways. . . . The daughter of the gentleman from San Francisco was standing beside the prince, who had been, through a fortuitous circumstance, presented to her yesterday evening, and she pretended to be looking intently into the distance, in a direction he was pointing out to her, telling, explaining something or other to her, hurriedly and quietly. On account of his height he seemed a boy by contrast with others—he was queer and not at all prepossessing of person, with his spectacles, his derby, his English great-coat, while his scanty moustache looked just as if it were of horsehair, and the swarthy, thin skin seemed to be drawn tightly over his face, and somehow had the appearance of being lacquered—but the young girl was listening to him, without understanding, in her agitation, what he was saying; her heart was thumping from an incomprehensible rapture before his presence and from pride that he was speaking with her, and not some other; everything about him that was different from others—his lean hands, his clear skin, under which flowed the ancient blood of kings, even his altogether unpretentious, yet somehow distinctively neat, European dress—everything held a secret, inexplicable charm, evoked a feeling of amorousness. As for the gentleman from San Francisco himself, he, in a high silk hat, in grey spats over patent-leather shoes, kept on glancing at the famous beauty, who was standing beside him—a tall blonde of striking figure, her eyes painted in the latest Parisian fashion; she was holding a diminutive, hunched-up, mangy lap-dog on a silver chain and was chattering to it without cease. And the daughter, in some vague embarrassment, tried not to notice her father.

Like all Americans of means, he was very generous on his travels, and, like all of them, believed in the full sincerity and goodwill of those who brought him food and drink with such solicitude, who served him from morn till night, forestalling his least wish; of those who guarded his cleanliness and rest, lugged his things around, summoned porters for him, delivered his trunks to hotels. Thus had it been everywhere, thus had it been on the ship, and thus was it to be in Naples as well. Naples grew, and drew nearer; the musicians, the brass of their instruments flashing, had already clustered upon the deck, and suddenly deafened everybody with the triumphant strains of a march; the gigantic captain, in his full-dress uniform, appeared upon his stage, and, like a condescending heathen god, waved his hand amiably to the passengers—and to the gentleman from San Francisco it seemed that it was for him alone that the march so beloved by proud America was thundering, that it was he whom the captain was felicitating upon a safe arrival. And every other passenger felt similarly about himself—or herself. And when the *Atlantida* did finally enter the harbour, had heaved to at the wharf with her many-tiered mass, black with people, and the gang-planks clattered down—what a multitude of porters and their helpers in caps with gold braid, what a multitude of different *commissionaires*, whistling gamins, and strapping ragamuffins with packets of coloured postal cards in their hands made a

rush toward the gentleman from San Francisco, with offers of their services! And he smiled, with a kindly contemptuousness, at these ragamuffins,
as he went toward the automobile of precisely that hotel where there was
a possibility of the prince's stopping as well, and drawled through his
teeth, now in English, now in Italian:

"Go away! *Via!*"

Life at Naples at once assumed its wonted, ordered current: in the
early morning, breakfast in the sombre dining-room with its damp
draught from windows opening on some sort of a stony little garden; the
sky was usually overcast, holding out but little promise, and there was
the usual crowd of guides at the door of the vestibule; then came the first
smiles of a warm, rosy sun; there was, from the high hanging balcony, a
view of Vesuvius, enveloped to its foot by radiant morning mists, and of
silver and pearl eddies on the surface of the bay, and of the delicate contour of Capri against the horizon; one could see tiny burros, harnessed in
twos to little carts, running down below over the quay, sticky with mire,
and detachments of diminutive soldiers, marching off to somewhere or
other to lively and exhilarating music. Next came the procession to the
waiting automobile and the slow progress through populous, narrow, and
damp corridors of streets, between tall, many-windowed houses; the inspection of lifelessly clean museums, evenly and pleasantly, yet bleakly,
lit, seemingly illuminated by snow; or of cool churches, smelling of wax,
which everywhere and always contain the same things: a majestic portal,
screened by a heavy curtain of leather, and inside—silence, empty vast-
ness, unobtrusive little flames of a seven-branched candlestick glowing
redly in the distant depths, on an altar bedecked with laces; a solitary old
woman among the dark wooden pews; slippery tombstones underfoot;
and somebody's *Descent from the Cross*—inevitably a celebrated one. At
one o'clock there was luncheon upon the mountain of San Martino,
where, toward noon, gathered not a few people of the very first quality,
and where the daughter of the gentleman from San Francisco had once
almost fainted away for joy, because she thought she saw the prince
sitting in the hall, although she already knew through the newspapers
that he had left for a temporary stay at Rome. At five came tea at the
hotel, in the showy salon, so cosy with its rugs and flaming fire-places;
and after that it was already time to get ready for dinner, and once more
came the mighty, compelling reverberation of the gong through all the
stories; once more the processions in Indian file of ladies in *décolleté*,
rustling in their silks upon the staircases and reflected in all the mirrors;
once more the palatial dining-room, widely and hospitably opened, and

the red jackets of the musicians upon their platform, and the black cluster of waiters about the *maître d'hôtel*, who, with a skill out of the ordinary, was ladling some sort of a thick, roseate soup into plates. . . . The dinners, as everywhere else, were the crowning glory of each day; the guests dressed for them as for a rout, and these dinners were so abundant in edibles, and wines, and mineral waters, and sweets, and fruits that toward eleven o'clock at night the chambermaids were distributing through all the corridors rubber bags with hot water to warm sundry stomachs.

However, the December of that year proved to be not altogether a successful one for Naples; the porters grew confused when one talked with them of the weather, and merely shrugged their shoulders guiltily, muttering that they could not recall such another year, although it was not the first year that they had been forced to mutter this, and to urge in extenuation that "something terrible is happening everywhere"; there were unheard of storms and torrents of rain on the Riviera; there was snow in Athens; Etna was also all snowed over and was aglow of nights; tourists were fleeing from Palermo in all directions, escaping from the cold. The morning sun deceived the Neapolitans every day that winter: toward noon the sky became grey and a fine rain began falling, but growing heavier and colder all the time; at such times the palms near the entrance of the hotel glistened as though they were of tin, the town seemed especially dirty and cramped, the museums exceedingly alike; the cigar stumps of the corpulent cabmen, whose rubber coats flapped in the wind like wings, seemed to have an insufferable stench, while the energetic snapping of their whips over their scrawny-necked nags was patently false; the foot-gear of the *signori* sweeping the rails of the tram-ways seemed horrible; the women, splashing through the mud, their black-haired heads bared to the rain, appeared hideously short legged; as for the dampness, and the stench of putrid fish from the sea foaming at the quay, they were a matter of course. The gentleman and the lady from San Francisco began quarrelling in the morning; their daughter either walked about pale, with a headache, or, coming to life again, went into raptures over everything, and was, at such times, both charming and beautiful: beautiful were those tender and complex emotions which had been awakened within her by meeting that homely man through whose veins flowed uncommon blood; for, after all is said and done, per-haps it is of no real importance just what it is, precisely, that awakens a maiden's soul—whether it be money, or fame, or illustrious ances-try. . . .

Everybody affirmed that things were entirely different in Sorrento, in Capri—there it was both warmer and sunnier, and the lemons were in blossom, and the customs were more honest, and the wine was more natural. And so the family from San Francisco determined to set out with all its trunks to Capri, and, after seeing it all, after treading the stones where the palace of Tiberius had once stood, after visiting the fairylike caverns of the Azure Grotto, and hearing the bagpipers of Abruzzi, who for a whole month preceding Christmas wander over the island and sing the praises of the Virgin Mary, they meant to settle in Sorrento.

On the day of departure—a most memorable one for the family from San Francisco!—there was no sun from the early morning. A heavy fog hid Vesuvius to the very base; this grey fog spread low over the leaden heaving of the sea that was lost to the eye at a distance of a half a mile. Capri was entirely invisible, as though there had never been such a thing in the world. And the little steamer that set out for it was so tossed from side to side that the family from San Francisco was laid prostrate upon the divans in the sorry general cabin of this tub, their feet wrapped up in plaids, and their eyes closed from nausea. Mrs. suffered, so she thought, more than anybody; she was overcome by sea-sickness several times; it seemed to her that she was dying, whereas the stewardess, who always ran up to her with a small basin—she had been, for many years, day in and day out, rolling on these waves, in freezing weather and in torrid, and yet was still tireless and kind to everybody—merely laughed. Miss was dreadfully pale and held a slice of lemon between her teeth; now she could not have been cheered even by the hope of a chance encounter with the prince at Sorrento, where he intended to be about Christmas. Mr., who was lying on his back, in roomy overcoat and large cap, never unlocked his jaws all the way over; his face had grown darker and his moustache whiter, and his head ached dreadfully: during the last days, thanks to the bad weather, he had been drinking too heavily of evenings, and had too much admired the "living pictures" in dives of *recherché* libertinage. But the rain kept on lashing against the jarring windows, the water from them running down on the divans; the wind, howling, bent the masts, and at times, aided by the onslaught of a wave, careened the little steamer entirely to one side, and then something in the hold would roll with a rumble. During the stops, at Castellammare, at Sorrento, things were a trifle more bearable, but even then the rocking was fearful—the shore, with all its cliffs, gardens, *pigin,* its pink and white hotels and hazy mountains clad in curly greenery, swayed up and down as if on a swing; boats bumped up against the sides of the ship; sailors and steerage passengers were yelling vehemently; somewhere, as though it had been crushed, a baby was wailing and smothering; a raw wind was blowing in at the door; and, from a swaying boat with a flag of the Hotel Royal, a lisping gamin was screaming, luring travellers: "Kgoya-al! Hôtel Kgoya-al! . . ." And the gentleman from San Francisco, feeling that he was an old man, which was but proper, was already thinking with sadness and melancholy of all these Royals, Splendids, Excelsiors, and of these greedy, insignificant manikins, reeking of garlic, that are called Italians. Once, having opened his eyes and raised himself from the divan, he saw, underneath the craggy steep of the shore, a cluster of stone hovels, mouldy through and through, stuck one on top of another near the very edge of the water, near boats, near all sorts of rags, tins, and brown nets—hovels so miserable that, at the recollection that this was that very Italy he had come hither to enjoy, he felt despair. . . . Finally, at twilight, the dark mass of the island began to draw near, seemingly bored through and through by little red lights near its base; the wind became softer, warmer, more fragrant; over the abating waves, as opalescent as black oil, golden pythons flowed from the lanterns on the wharf. . . . Then came the sudden rumble of the anchor, and it fell with a splash into the water; the ferocious yells of the boatmen, vying with one another, floated in from all quarters—and at once the heart grew lighter, the lights in the general cabin shone more brightly, a desire arose to eat, to drink, to smoke, to be stirring. . . . Ten minutes later the family from San Francisco had descended into a large boat; within fifteen minutes it had set foot upon the stones of the wharf, and had then got into a bright little railway car and to its buzzing started the ascent of the slope, amid the stakes of the vineyards, half-crumbled stone enclosures, and wet, gnarled orange-trees, some of them under coverings of straw—trees with thick, glossy foliage, and aglimmer with the orange fruits; all these objects were sliding downward, past the open windows of the little car, toward the base of the mountain. . . . Sweetly smells the earth of Italy after rain, and her every island has its own, its especial aroma!

The island of Capri was damp and dark on this evening. But now it came into life for an instant; lights sprang up here and there, as always on the steamer's arrival. At the top of the mountain, where stood the station of the funicular, there was another throng of those whose duty lay in receiving fittingly the gentleman from San Francisco. There were other arrivals also, but they merited no attention—several Russians, who had taken up their abode in Capri, absent-minded because of their bookish meditations, unkempt, bearded, spectacled, the collars of their old drab overcoats turned up; and a group of long-legged, long-necked, round-headed German youths in Tyrolean costumes, with canvas knapsacks slung over their shoulders—these latter stood in need of nobody's services, feeling themselves at home everywhere, and were not at all generous in their expenditures. The gentleman from San Francisco, on the other hand, who was calmly keeping aloof from both the one group and the other, was immediately noticed. He and his ladies were bustlingly assisted to get out, some men running ahead of him to show him the way: he was surrounded anew by urchins, and by those robust Caprian wives who carry on their heads the portmanteaux and trunks of respectable travellers. The wooden pattens of these women clattered over a *piazzetta* that seemed to belong to some opera, an electric globe swaying above it in the damp wind; the rabble of urchins burst into sharp, bird-like whistles, and, as though on a stage, the gentleman from San Francisco proceeded in their midst toward some mediaeval arch, underneath houses that had become welded into one mass, beyond which a little echoing street—with the tuft of a palm above flat roofs on its left, and with blue stars in the black sky overhead—led slopingly to the grand entrance of the hotel, glittering ahead. . . . And again it seemed that it was in honour of the guests from San Francisco that this damp little town of stone on a craggy little island of the Mediterranean Sea had come to life, that it was they who had made so happy and affable the proprietor of the hotel, that it was they only who had been waited for by the Chinese gong that now began wailing the summons to dinner through all the stories of the hotel, the instant they had set foot in the vestibule.

The proprietor, a young man of haughty elegance, who had met them with a polite and exquisite bow, for a minute dumbfounded the gentleman from San Francisco: having glanced at him, the gentleman from San Francisco suddenly recalled that just the night before, among the rest of the confusion of images that had beset him in his sleep, he had seen precisely this gentleman—just like him, down to the least detail: in the same sort of frock with rounded skirts, and with the same pomaded and painstakingly combed head. Startled, he was almost taken aback; but since, from long, long before, there was not even a mustard seed of any sort of so-called mystical emotions left in his soul, his astonishment was dimmed the same instant, passing through a corridor of the hotel, he spoke jestingly to his wife and daughter of this strange coincidence of dream and reality. And only his daughter glanced at him with alarm at that moment: her heart suddenly contracted from sadness, from a feeling of their loneliness upon this foreign, dark island—a feeling so strong that she almost burst into tears. But still she said nothing of her feelings to her father—as always.

An exalted personage—Rais [Rex] XVII—who had been visiting Capri, had just taken his departure, and the guests from San Francisco were given the same apartments that he had occupied. To them was assigned the handsomest and most expert chambermaid, a Belgian, whose waist was slenderly and firmly corseted, and who wore a little starched cap that looked like a pronged crown; also, the stateliest and most dignified of flunkies, a fiery-eyed Sicilian, swarthy as coal; and the nimblest of bell-boys, the short and stout Luigi, a fellow who was very fond of a joke, and who had changed many places in his time. And a minute later there was a slight tap at the door of the room of the gentleman from San Francisco—the French *maître d'hôtel* had come to find out if the newly arrived guests would dine, and, in the event of an answer in the affirmative—of which, however, there was no doubt—to inform them that the *carte de jour* consisted of crawfish, roast beef, asparagus, pheasants, and so forth. The floor was still rocking under the gentleman from San Francisco—so badly had the atrocious little Italian steamer tossed him about —but, without hurrying, with his own hands, although somewhat clumsily from being unaccustomed to such things, he shut a window that had banged upon the entrance of the *maître d'hôtel* and had let in the odours of the distant kitchen and of the wet flowers in the garden, and with a leisurely precision replied that they would dine, that their table must be placed at a distance from the door, at the farthest end of the dining-room, that they would drink local wine and champagne, moderately dry and only slightly chilled. The *maître d'hôtel* concurred in every word of his, in intonations most varied, having, however, but one significance—that there was never a doubt, nor could there possibly be any, about the correctness of the wishes of the gentleman from San Francisco, and that everything would be carried out punctiliously. In conclusion he inclined his head, and asked deferentially:

"Will that be all, Sir?"

And, having received a long-drawn-out "Yes" in answer, he added that the *tarantella* would be danced in the vestibule to-day—the dancers would be Carmella and Giuseppe, known to all Italy, and to "the entire world of tourists."

"I have seen her on post cards," said the gentleman from San Francisco in a voice devoid of all expression. "About this Giuseppe, now—is he her husband?"

"Her cousin, Sir," answered the *maître d'hôtel.*

And, after a little wait, after considering something, the gentleman from San Francisco dismissed him with a nod.

And then he began his preparations anew, as though for a wedding ceremony: he turned on all the electric lights, filling all the mirrors with reflections of light and glitter, of furniture and opened trunks; he began shaving and washing, ringing the bell every minute, while other impatient rings from his wife's and daughter's rooms floated through the entire corridor and interrupted his. And Luigi, in his red apron, was rushing headlong to answer the bell, with an ease peculiar to many stout men, the while he made grimaces of horror that made the chambermaids, running by with glazed porcelain pails in their hands, laugh till they cried. Having knocked on the door with his knuckles, he asked with an assumed timidity, with a respectfulness that verged on idiocy:

"*Ha sonato, Signore?* [Did you ring, Sir?]"

And from the other side of the door came an unhurried, grating voice, insultingly polite:

"Yes, come in. . . ."

What were the thoughts, what were the emotions of the gentleman from San Francisco on this evening that was of such portent to him? He felt nothing exceptional, for the trouble in this world is just that everything is apparently all too simple! And even if he had sensed within his soul that something was impending, he would, nevertheless, have thought that this thing would not occur for some time to come—in any case, not immediately. Besides that, like everyone who has gone through the rocking of a ship, he wanted very much to eat, was anticipating with enjoyment the first spoonful of soup, the first mouthful of wine, and performed the usual routine of dressing even with a certain degree of exhilaration that left no time for reflections.

Having shaved and washed himself, having inserted several artificial teeth properly, he, standing before a mirror, wetted the remnants of his thick, pearly-grey hair and plastered it down around his swarthy-yellow skull, with brushes set in silver; drew a suit of cream-coloured silk underwear over his strong old body, beginning to be full at the waist from excesses in food, and put on silk socks and dancing slippers on his shrivelled, splayed feet; sitting down, he put in order his black trousers, drawn high by black silk braces, as well as his snowy-white shirt, with the bosom bulging out; put the links through the glossy cuffs, and began the torturous pursuit of the collar-button underneath the stiffly starched collar. The floor was still swaying beneath him, the tips of his fingers pained him greatly, the collar-button at times nipped hard the flabby skin in the hollow under his Adam's-apple, but he was persistent and finally, his eyes glittering from the exertion, his face all livid from the collar that was choking his throat—a collar far too tight—he did contrive to accomplish his task, and sat down in exhaustion in front of the pier-glass, reflected in it from head to foot, a reflection that was repeated in all the other mirrors.

"Oh, this is dreadful!" he muttered, letting his strong bald head drop, and without trying to understand, without reflecting, just what, precisely, was dreadful; then, with an accustomed and attentive glance, he inspected his stubby fingers, with gouty hardenings at the joints, and his convex nails of an almond colour, repeating, with conviction: "This is dreadful. . . ."

But at this point the second gong, sonorously, as in some heathen temple, reverberated through the entire house. And, getting up quickly from his seat, the gentleman from San Francisco drew his collar still tighter with the neck-tie and his stomach by means of the low-cut vest, put on his tuxedo, drew out his cuffs, scrutinized himself once more in the mirror. . . . This Carmella, swarthy, with eyes which she knew well how to use most effectively, resembling a mulatto woman, clad in a dress of many colours, with the colour of orange predominant, must dance exceptionally, he reflected. And, stepping briskly out of his room and walking over the carpet to the next one—his wife's—he asked, loudly, if they would be ready soon?

"In five minutes, Dad!" a girl's voice, ringing and by now gay, responded from the other side of the door.

"Very well," said the gentleman from San Francisco.

And, leisurely, he walked down red-carpeted corridors and staircases, descending in search of the reading room. The servants he met stood aside and hugged the wall to let him pass, but he kept on his way as though he had never even noticed them. An old woman who was late for dinner, already stooping, with milky hair but décolleté in a light-grey gown of silk, was hurrying with all her might, but drolly, in a hen-like manner, and he easily outstripped her. Near the glass doors of the dining-room, where all the guests had already assembled, and were beginning their dinner, he stopped before a little table piled with boxes of cigars and Egyptian cigarettes, took a large Manila cigar, and tossed three lire upon the little table; upon the closed veranda he glanced, in passing, through the open window: out of the darkness he felt a breath of the balmy air upon him, thought he saw the tip of an ancient palm that had flung wide across the stars its fronds, which seemed gigantic, heard the distant, even noise of the sea floating in to him. . . . In the reading room, snug, quiet, and illuminated only above the tables, some grey-haired German was standing, rustling the newspapers—unkempt, resembling Ibsen, in round silver spectacles and with the astonished eyes of a madman. Having scrutinized him coldly, the gentleman from San Francisco sat down in a deep leather chair in a corner near a green-shaded lamp, put on his *pince-nez*, twitching his head because his collar was choking him, and hid himself completely behind the newspaper sheet. He rapidly ran through the headlines of certain items, read a few lines about the never ceasing Balkan War, with an accustomed gesture turned the newspaper over—when suddenly the lines flared up before him with a glassy glare, his neck became taut, his eyes bulged out, the *pince-nez* flew off his nose. . . . He lunged forward, tried to swallow some air, and gasped wildly; his lower jaw sank, lighting up his entire mouth with the reflection of the gold fillings; his head dropped back on his shoulder and began to sway; the bosom of his shirt bulged out like a basket—and his whole body, squirming, his heels catching the carpet, slid downward to the floor, desperately struggling with someone.

Had the German not been in the reading room, the personnel of the hotel would have managed, quickly and adroitly, to hush up this dreadful occurrence; instantly, through back passages, seizing him by the head and feet, they would have rushed off the gentleman from San Francisco as far away as possible—and never a soul among the guests would have found out what he had been up to. But the German had dashed out of the reading room with a scream—he had aroused the entire house, the entire dining-room. And many jumped up from their meal, overturning their chairs; many, paling, ran toward the reading room. "What—what has happened?" was heard in all languages—and no one gave a sensible answer, no one comprehended anything, since even up to now men are amazed most of all by death, and will not, under any circumstances, believe in it. The proprietor dashed from one guest to another, trying to detain those who were running away and to pacify them with hasty assurances that this was just a trifling occurrence, a slight fainting spell of a certain gentleman from San Francisco. . . . But no one listened to him; many had seen the waiters and bell-boys tearing the neck-tie, the vest, and the rumpled tuxedo off this gentleman, and even, for some reason or other, the dancing slippers off his splayed feet, clad in black silk.

But he was still struggling. He was still obdurately wrestling with death; he absolutely refused to yield to her, who had so unexpectedly and churlishly fallen upon him. His head was swaying, he rattled hoarsely, like one with his throat cut; his eyes had rolled up, like a drunkard's. . . . When he was hurriedly carried in and laid upon a bed in room number forty-three—the smallest, the poorest, the dampest and the coldest, situated at the end of the bottom corridor—his daughter ran in, with her hair down, in a little dressing gown that had flown open, her bosom, raised up by the corset, uncovered; then his wife, big and ponderous, already dressed for dinner, her mouth rounded in terror. . . . But by now he had ceased even to bob his head.

A quarter of an hour later everything in the hotel had assumed some semblance of order. But the evening was irreparably spoiled. Some guests, returning to the dining-room, finished their dinner, but in silence, with aggrieved countenances, while the proprietor would approach now one group, now another, shrugging his shoulders in polite yet impotent irritation, feeling himself guilty without guilt, assuring everybody that he understood very well "how unpleasant all this was," and pledging his word that he would take "all measures within his power" to remove this unpleasantness. It was necessary to call off the *tarantella*, all unnecessary electric lights were switched off, the majority of the guests withdrew into the bar, and it became so quiet that one heard distinctly the ticking of the clock in the vestibule, whose sole occupant was a parrot, dully muttering something, fussing in his cage before going to sleep, contriving to doze off at last with one claw ludicrously stretched up to the upper perch. . . . The gentleman from San Francisco was lying upon a cheap iron bed, under coarse woollen blankets, upon which the dull light of a single bulb beat down from the ceiling. An ice-bag hung down to his moist and cold forehead. The livid face, already dead, was gradually growing cold; the hoarse rattling, expelled from the open mouth, illuminated by the reflection of gold, was growing fainter. This was no longer the gentleman from San Francisco rattling—he no longer existed—but some other. His wife, his daughter, the doctor and the servants were standing, gazing at him dully. Suddenly, that which they awaited and feared was consummated—the rattling ceased abruptly. And slowly, slowly, before the eyes of all, a pallor flowed over the face of the man who had died, and his features seemed to grow finer, to become irradiated, with a beauty which had been rightfully his in the long ago. . . .

The proprietor entered. *"Già è morto* [He's dead now]," said the doctor to him in a whisper. The proprietor, his face dispassionate, shrugged his shoulders. The wife, down whose cheeks the tears were quietly coursing, walked up to him and timidly said that the deceased ought now to be carried to his own room.

"Oh, no, Madam," hastily, correctly, but now without any amiability and not in English, but in French, retorted the proprietor, who was not at all interested now in such trifling sums as the arrivals from San Francisco might leave in his coffers. "That is absolutely impossible, Madam," said he, and added in explanation that he valued the apartments occupied by them very much; that, were he to carry out her wishes, everybody in Capri would know it and the tourists would shun those apartments.

The young lady, who had been gazing at him strangely, sat down on a chair, and, stuffing her mouth with a handkerchief, burst into sobs. The wife dried her tears immediately, her face flaring up. She adopted a louder tone, making demands in her own language, and still incredulous of the fact that all respect for them had been completely lost. The proprietor, with a polite dignity, cut her short: if madam was not pleased with the customs of the hotel, he would not venture to detain her; and he firmly announced that the body must be gotten away this very day, at dawn, that the police had already been notified, and one of the police officers would be here very soon and would carry out all the necessary formalities. Was it possible to secure even a common coffin in Capri, madam asks? Regrettably, no—it was beyond possibility, and no one would be able to make one in time. It would be necessary to have recourse to something else. . . . For instance, English soda water came in large and long boxes. . . . It was possible to knock the partitions out of such a box. . . .

At night the whole hotel slept. The window in room number forty-three was opened—it gave out upon a corner of the garden where, near a high stone wall with broken glass upon its crest, a phthisic banana-tree was growing; the electric light was switched off; the key was turned in the door, and everybody went away. The dead man remained in the darkness—the blue stars looked down upon him from the sky, a cricket with a pensive insouciance began his song in the wall. . . . In the dimly lit corridor two chambermaids were seated on a window-sill, at some darning. Luigi, in slippers, entered with a pile of clothing in his arms.

"*Pronto?* [All ready?]" he asked solicitously, in a ringing whisper, indicating with his eyes the fearsome door at the end of the corridor. And, he waved his hand airily in that direction. . . . "*Partenza!*" he called out in a whisper, as though he were speeding a train, the usual phrase used in Italian depots at the departure of trains, and the chambermaids, choking with silent laughter, let their heads sink on each other's shoulder.

Thereupon, hopping softly, he ran up to the very door, gave it the merest tap, and, inclining his head to one side, in a low voice, asked with the utmost deference:

"*Ha sonato, Signore?*"

And, squeezing his throat, thrusting out his lower jaw, in a grating voice, slowly and sadly, he answered his own question, as though from the other side of the door:

"Yes, come in. . . ."

And at dawn, when it had become light beyond the window of room number forty-three, and a humid wind had begun to rustle the tattered leaves of the banana-tree; when the blue sky of morning had lifted and spread out over the Island of Capri, and the pure and clear-cut summit of Monte Solaro had grown aureate against the sun that was rising beyond the distant blue mountains of Italy; when the stonemasons, who were repairing the tourists' paths on the island, had set out to work—a long box that had formerly been used for soda water was brought to room number forty-three. Soon it became very heavy, and was pressing hard against the knees of the junior porter, who bore it off briskly on a one-horse cab over the white paved highway that was sinuously winding to and fro over the slopes of Capri, among the stone walls and the vineyards, ever downwards, to the very sea. The cabby, a puny little man with reddened eyes, in an old, wretched jacket with short sleeves and in trodden-down shoes, was undergoing the after-effects of drink—he had diced the whole night through in a *trattoria*, and kept on lashing his sturdy little horse, tricked out in the Sicilian fashion, with all sorts of little bells livelily jingling upon the bridle with its tufts of coloured wool, and upon the brass points of its high pad; with a yard-long feather stuck in its cropped forelock, a feather that shook as the horse ran. The cabby kept silent; he was oppressed by his shiftlessness, his vices, by the fact that he had, that night, lost to the last mite all those coppers with which his pockets had been filled. But the morning was fresh; in air such as this, with the sea all around, under the morning sky, the after-effects of drink quickly evaporate, and a man is soon restored to a carefree mood, and the cabby was furthermore consoled by that unexpected sum, the opportunity to earn which had been granted him by some gentleman from San Francisco whose lifeless head was bobbing from side to side in the box at his back. . . . The little steamer—a beetle lying far down below, against the tender and vivid deep-blue with which the Bay of

Naples is so densely and highly flooded—was already blowing its final whistles, which reverberated loudly all over the island, whose every bend, every ridge, every stone was as distinctly visible from every point as if there were absolutely no such thing as atmosphere. Near the wharf the junior porter was joined by the senior, who was speeding with the daughter and wife of the gentleman from San Francisco in his automobile—they were pale, with eyes hollow from tears and a sleepless night. And ten minutes later the little steamer was again chugging through the water, again running toward Sorrento, toward Castellammare, carrying away from Capri, for all time, the family from San Francisco. . . . And again peace and quiet resumed their reign upon the island.

Upon this island, two thousand years ago, had lived a man who had become completely enmeshed in his cruel and foul deeds, who had for some reason seized the power over millions of people in his hands, and who, having himself lost his head at the senselessness of this power and from the fear of death by assassination. lurking in ambush behind every corner, had committed cruelties beyond all measure—and humankind has remembered him for all time; and those who. in their collusion. just as incomprehensively and, in substance, just as cruelly as he, reign at present in power over this world gather from all over the earth to gaze upon the ruins of that stone villa where he had dwelt on one of the steepest ascents of the island. On this splendid morning all those who had come to Capri for just this purpose were still sleeping in the hotels, although, toward their entrances, were already being led little mouse-grey burros with red saddles, upon which, after awaking and sating themselves with food, Americans and Germans, men and women, young and old, would again clamber up ponderously this day, and after whom would again run the old Caprian beggar women, with sticks in their gnarled hands—would run over stony paths, and always uphill, up to the very summit of Mount Tiberio. Set at rest by the fact that the dead old man from San Francisco, who had likewise been planning to go with them but instead of that had only frightened them with a *memento mori,* had already been shipped off to Naples, the travellers slept on heavily, and the quiet of the island was still undisturbed, the shops in the city were still shut. The market-place on the *piazzetta* alone was carrying on traffic—in fish and greens; and the people there were all simple folk, among whom, without anything to do, as always, was standing Lorenzo the boatman, famous all over Italy, a tall old man, a carefree rake and a handsome fellow, who had served more than once as a model to many artists; he had brought, and had already sold for a song, two lobsters that he had caught that night and which were already rustling in the apron of the cook of that very hotel where the family from San Francisco had passed the night, and now he could afford to stand in calm idleness even until the evening, looking about him with a kingly bearing (a little trick of his), consciously picturesque with his tatters, clay pipe, and a red woollen *berretta* drooping over one ear.

And, along the precipices of Monte Solaro, upon the ancient Phoenician road, hewn out of the crags, down its stone steps, two mountaineers of Abruzzi were descending from Anacapri. One had bagpipes under his leathern mantle, a large bag made from the skin of a she-goat, with two pipes; the other had something in the nature of wooden Pan's-reeds. They went on, and all the land, joyous, splendid, sun-flooded, spread out below them: the stony humps of the island, which was lying almost in its entirety at their feet; and that fairy-like deep-blue in which it was a-swim; and the radiant morning vapours over the sea, toward the east, under the blinding sun, which was now beating down hotly, rising ever higher and higher; and, still in their morning vagueness, the mistily azure massive outlines of Italy, of her mountains near and far, whose beauty human speech is impotent to express. . . . Half-way down the pipers slackened their pace: over the path, within a grotto in the craggy side of Monte Solaro, all illumed by the sun, all bathed in its warmth and glow, in snowy-white raiment of gypsum, and in a royal crown, golden-rusty from inclement weathers, stood the Mother of God, meek and gracious, her orbs lifted up to heaven, to the eternal and happy abodes of Her thrice-blessed Son. The pipers bared their heads, put their reeds to their lips, and there poured forth their naïve and humbly jubilant praises to the sun, to the morning, to Her, the Immaculate Intercessor for all those who suffer in this evil and beautiful world, and to Him Who had been born of Her womb in a cavern at Bethlehem, in a poor shepherd's shelter in the distant land of Judaea. . . .

Meanwhile, the body of the dead old man from San Francisco was returning to its home, to a grave on the shores of the New World. Having gone through many humiliations, through much human neglect, having wandered for a week from one port warehouse to another, it had finally gotten once more on board that same famous ship upon which but so recently, with so much deference, he had been borne to the Old World. But now he was already being concealed from the quick—he was lowered in his tarred coffin deep into the black hold. And once more the ship was sailing on and on upon its long sea voyage. In the night-time it sailed past the Island of Capri, and, to one watching them from the island, there was something sad about the ship's lights, slowly disappearing over the dark sea. But, upon the ship itself, in its brilliant *salons* resplendent with lustres and marbles, there was a crowded ball that night, as usual.

There was a ball on the second night also, and on the third—again in the midst of a raging snow storm, whirling over an ocean booming like a funeral mass, and heaving in mountains trapped out in mourning by the silver spindrift. The innumerable fiery eyes of the ship that was retreating into the night and the snow-gale were barely visible for the snow to the Devil watching from the crags of Gibraltar, from the stony gateway of two worlds. The Devil was as enormous as a cliff, but the ship was still more enormous than he; many-tiered, many-funnelled, created by the pride of the New Man with an ancient heart. The snow-gale smote upon its rigging and wide-throated funnels, hoary from the snow, but the ship was steadfast, firm, majestic—and awesome. Upon its topmost deck were reared, in their solitude among the snowy whirlwinds, those snug, dimly lit chambers where, plunged in a light and uneasy slumber, was its ponderous guide who resembled a heathen idol, reigning over the entire ship. He heard the pained howlings and the ferocious squealings of the storm-stifled siren, but soothed himself by the proximity of that which, in the final summing up, was incomprehensible even to himself, that which was on the other side of his wall: that large cabin, which had the appearance of being armoured, and was being constantly filled by the mysterious rumbling, quivering, and crisp sputtering of blue flames, flaring up and exploding around the pale-faced operator with a metal half-hoop upon his head. In the very depths, in the underwater womb of the *Atlantida*, were the thirty-thousand-pound masses of boilers and of all sorts of other machinery—dully glittering with steel, hissing out steam and exuding oil and boiling water—of that kitchen, made red-hot from infernal furnaces underneath, wherein was brewing the motion of the ship. Forces, fearful in their concentration, were bubbling, were being transmitted to its very keel, into an endlessly long catacomb, into a tunnel, illuminated by electricity, wherein slowly, with an inexorability that was crushing to the human soul, was revolving within its oily couch the gigantean shaft, exactly like a living monster that had stretched itself out in this tunnel. Meanwhile, amidship the *Atlantida*, its warm and luxurious cabins, its dining-halls and ball-rooms poured forth radiance and joyousness, were humming with the voices of a well-dressed gathering, were sweetly odorous with fresh flowers, and the strains of the stringed orchestra were their song. And again excruciatingly writhed and at intervals came together among this throng, among this glitter of lights, silks, diamonds and bared feminine shoulders, the supple pair of hired lovers: the sinfully modest, very pretty young woman, with eye-lashes cast down, with a chaste coiffure, and the well-built young man, with black hair that seemed to be pasted on, with his face pale from powder, shod in the most elegant of patent-leather foot-gear, clad in a tight-fitting dress-coat with long tails—an Adonis who resembled a huge leech. And none knew that, already for a long time, this pair had grown wearied of languishing dissemblingly in their blissful torment to the sounds of the shamelessly sad music, nor that far, far below, at the bottom of the black hold, stood a tarred coffin, in close proximity to the sombre and sultry depths of the ship that was toilsomely overpowering the darkness, the ocean, the snow storm. . . .

Translated by Bernard Guilbert Guerney.

Nathaniel Hawthorne

1804–1864

Nathaniel Hawthorne (he added a *w* to the family name of Hathorne) was born in Salem, Massachusetts, on July 4, 1804. His father was a shipmaster, and one of his ancestors had been a judge in the Salem witch trials. Young Hawthorne was graduated from Bowdoin College in 1825. He went back to Salem to learn how to write. Two years later he paid for the printing of his first novel, *Fanshawe*, but burned all the copies he could find.

His stories began to appear in many periodicals. In 1837 he published a first edition of *Twice-Told Tales* and enlarged it in 1842. He worked in the Boston Customhouse. For about six months in 1841, he was a founding member of Brook Farm, a Utopian community near Boston. Out of this experience came a novel, *The Blithedale Romance*, written eleven years later. In 1842 Hawthorne married Sophia Peabody of Salem. They settled in the Old Manse in Concord, where Emerson and Thoreau often came to visit.

Their life in the gray seventeenth-century house was commemorated in an essay, *The Old Manse*, and in *Mosses from an Old Manse*, a collection of stories published in 1846. In 1845, when he could not pay the rent, Hawthorne moved to his mother's house in Salem. The following year he was given a political appointment in

---

Notes from the artist: ". . . Hawthorne at age thirty-six, before he grew his mustache. The basic construction is derived from the letter A, the 'scarlet' letter . . . at the top, on the pillory scaffold, is Hester Prynne of The Scarlet Letter*."*

the Salem Customhouse. Three years later he was dropped when the Whigs returned to power.

At first he tried to fight his dismissal. Then, in grim anger, he sat down to write his best-known work, *The Scarlet Letter,* which appeared in 1850. At long last he was famous. In the following year he produced *The House of the Seven Gables* and *The Snow-Image and Other Twice-Told Tales;* in 1852 *The Blithedale Romance, A Wonder-Book for Boys and Girls,* and a campaign biography of Franklin Pierce, his schoolmate at Bowdoin. In 1853 came *Tanglewood Tales for Girls and Boys.*

During this period he lived for a while at Lenox in western Massachusetts. In nearby Pittsfield, Herman Melville was writing *Moby Dick.* They became mutually admiring friends. Hawthorne bought "The Wayside" house at Concord in 1852. The following year President Pierce appointed him American consul at Liverpool. He served four years there, spent most of 1858 to 1859 in Rome and Florence, and returned to England to write *The Marble Faun.*

Back in Concord by the middle of 1860, his health "rapidly and mysteriously" worsened. In 1862 he visited the Civil War battlefields and wrote an article that contains a striking picture of Lincoln.[1] On a trip with ex-President Pierce, he died at Plymouth, New Hampshire, on May 19, 1864.

Hawthorne, as Newton Arvin writes, felt "a cloudy and obfuscating sense of guilt at the heart of all human relations. . . ." It is perhaps the most profound thing that can be said about him, as man or writer. The testimony comes to us in a hundred voices. Henry James, Sr. said that Hawthorne had "the look all the time . . . of a rogue who suddenly finds himself in a company of detectives." Hawthorne himself was well aware of this quality. He once remarked, putting it lightly, that he was a "lover of the moral picturesque."

How can we help but find him one of the most puzzling of nineteenth-century writers? We hardly need to be told that *Pilgrim's Progress* was a favorite of his. In certain ways he seems more a man of Bunyan's century than of Balzac's. Few of his stories remain plausible under any sort of hard scrutiny. They are "romance" and claim the privileges of romance. But they are *moral* "romance." Like

---

[1] See Vol. 6, pp. 168–171, in this set.

an eighteenth-century writer, he states or implies a moral judgment on each of his characters. Who could guess that he was Flaubert's contemporary? And even on his home ground, New England history, we get the sense that he is often uninformed, confused, or prejudiced.

Why then do we read him? Because he is a powerful writer who can build a story stone by stone to its full height. Because he was perhaps the greatest historian of the Puritan conscience in America. He knew it in its darkest depth, in its involvement with every other human feeling. He came to it at that point in time when it was most in conflict with itself, when it was reaching out toward a larger and more humane life. He endured that conflict in himself and wrote it out of himself. In him, as in Melville, the sense of sin and guilt was still powerful. Like Melville, he said no to American free will, to Emerson's optimism and his call to the self.

Rappaccini's Daughter, like *The Marble Faun,* may be said to have come out of his two-year sojourn in Italy. But in it the "sunny Italy" of the ballads turns "desolate" and "gloomy." Perhaps it resembles the real Italy as little as the setting of some of his other tales resembles the New England of his own time. We cannot help but feel that all his stories take place in the Country of Hawthorne, an allegorical region as unmapped as Erewhon or Bluebeard's domain. Through it runs the dark River of Predestination, and the Mountains of Evil are never far off.

As we read *Rappaccini's Daughter,* we catch ourselves asking questions. How does Giovanni, alone among unpoisonous things, escape death in Rappaccini's garden? Why is the innocent and vital Beatrice made the carrier of evil and guilt? Is this meant to suggest the old Christian association between woman and sexual "evil"? Why are we—and Giovanni—not warned that Dr. Baglioni's antidote may not have the effect he intended? But we concede the author's freedom in his fable and pass on to the allegory. It stands out bold and plain: the scientist who puts himself beyond good and evil may also put himself outside the human community and work great evil in his pride of power.

Rappaccini's Daughter

A young man, named Giovanni Guasconti, came, very long ago, from the more southern region of Italy to pursue his studies at the University of Padua. Giovanni, who had but a scanty supply of gold ducats in his pocket, took lodgings in a high and gloomy chamber of an old edifice which looked not unworthy to have been the palace of a Paduan noble, and which, in fact, exhibited over its entrance the armorial bearings of a family long since extinct. The young stranger, who was not unstudied in the great poem of his country, recollected that one of the ancestors of this family, and perhaps an occupant of this very mansion, had been pictured by Dante as a partaker of the immortal agonies of his Inferno. These reminiscences and associations, together with the tendency to heartbreak natural to a young man for the first time out of his native sphere, caused Giovanni to sigh heavily as he looked around the desolate and ill-furnished apartment.

"Holy Virgin, signor!" cried old Dame Lisabetta, who, won by the youth's remarkable beauty of person, was kindly endeavoring to give the chamber a habitable air, "what a sigh was that to come out of a young man's heart! Do you find this old mansion gloomy? For the love of Heaven, then, put your head out of the window, and you will see as bright sunshine as you have left in Naples."

Guasconti mechanically did as the old woman advised, but could not quite agree with her that the Paduan sunshine was as cheerful as that of southern Italy. Such as it was, however, it fell upon a garden beneath the window and expended its fostering influences on a variety of plants, which seemed to have been cultivated with exceeding care.

"Does this garden belong to the house?" asked Giovanni.

"Heaven forbid, signor, unless it were fruitful of better pot herbs than any that grow there now," answered old Lisabetta. "No; that garden is cultivated by the own hands of Signor Giacomo Rappaccini, the famous doctor, who, I warrant him, has been heard of as far as Naples. It is said that he distills these plants into medicines that are as potent as a charm. Oftentimes you may see the signor doctor at work, and perchance the signora, his daughter, too, gathering the strange flowers that grow in the garden."

The old woman had now done what she could for the aspect of the chamber; and, commending the young man to the protection of the saints, took her departure.

Giovanni still found no better occupation than to look down into the garden beneath his window. From its appearance, he judged it to be one of those botanic gardens which were of earlier date in Padua than elsewhere in Italy or in the world. Or, not improbably, it might once have been the pleasure place of an opulent family; for there was the ruin of a marble fountain in the center, sculptured with rare art, but so woefully shattered that it was impossible to trace the original design from the chaos of remaining fragments. The water, however, continued to gush and sparkle into the sunbeams as cheerfully as ever. A little gurgling sound ascended to the young man's window, and made him feel as if the fountain were an immortal spirit that sung its song unceasingly and without heeding the vicissitudes around it, while one century embodied it in marble and another scattered the perishable garniture on the soil. All about the pool into which the water subsided grew various plants that seemed to require a plentiful supply of moisture for the nourishment of gigantic leaves, and, in some instances, flowers gorgeously magnificent. There was one shrub in particular, set in a marble vase in the midst of the pool, that bore a profusion of purple blossoms, each of which had the luster and richness of a gem; and the whole together made a show so resplendent that it seemed enough to illuminate the garden, even had there been no sunshine. Every portion of the soil was peopled with plants and herbs, which, if less beautiful, still bore tokens of assiduous care, as if all had their individual virtues, known to the scientific mind that fostered them. Some were placed in urns, rich with old carving, and others in common garden pots; some crept serpentlike along the ground or climbed on high, using whatever means of ascent was offered them. One plant had wreathed itself round a statue of Vertumnus, which was thus quite veiled and shrouded in a drapery of hanging foliage, so happily arranged that it might have served a sculptor for a study.

While Giovanni stood at the window he heard a rustling behind a screen of leaves, and became aware that a person was at work in the garden. His figure soon emerged into view, and showed itself to be that of no common laborer, but a tall, emaciated, sallow, and sickly looking man, dressed in a scholar's garb of black. He was beyond the middle term of life, with gray hair, a thin, gray beard, and a face singularly marked with intellect and cultivation, but which could never, even in his more youthful days, have expressed much warmth of heart.

Nothing could exceed the intentness with which this scientific gardener examined every shrub which grew in his path: it seemed as if he was looking into their inmost nature, making observations in regard to their creative essence, and discovering why one leaf grew in this shape and another in that, and wherefore such and such flowers differed among themselves in hue and perfume. Nevertheless, in spite of this deep intelligence on his part, there was no approach to intimacy between himself and these vegetable existences. On the contrary, he avoided their actual touch or the direct inhaling of their odors with a caution that impressed Giovanni most disagreeably; for the man's demeanor was that of one walking among malignant influences, such as savage beasts, or deadly snakes, or evil spirits, which, should he allow them one moment of license, would wreak upon him some terrible fatality. It was strangely frightful to the young man's imagination to see this air of insecurity in a person cultivating a garden, that most simple and innocent of human toils, and which had been alike the joy and labor of the unfallen parents of the race. Was this garden, then, the Eden of the present world? And this man, with such a perception of harm in what his own hands caused to grow—was he the Adam?

The distrustful gardener, while plucking away the dead leaves or pruning the too luxuriant growth of the shrubs, defended his hands with a pair of thick gloves. Nor were these his only armor. When, in his walk through the garden, he came to the magnificent plant that hung its purple gems beside the marble fountain, he placed a kind of mask over his mouth and nostrils, as if all this beauty did but conceal a deadlier malice; but, finding his task still too dangerous, he drew back, removed the mask, and called loudly, but in the infirm voice of a person affected with inward disease, "Beatrice! Beatrice!"

"Here am I, my father. What would you?" cried a rich and youthful voice from the window of the opposite house—a voice as rich as a tropical sunset, and which made Giovanni, though he knew not why, think of deep hues of purple or crimson and of perfumes heavily delectable. "Are you in the garden?"

"Yes, Beatrice," answered the gardener, "and I need your help."

Soon there emerged from under a sculptured portal the figure of a young girl, arrayed with as much richness of taste as the most splendid of the flowers, beautiful as the day, and with a bloom so deep and vivid that one shade more would have been too much. She looked redundant with life, health, and energy; all of which attributes were bound down and compressed, as it were, and girdled tensely, in their luxuriance, by her virgin zone. Yet Giovanni's fancy must have grown morbid while he looked down into the garden; for the impression which the fair stranger made upon him was as if here were another flower, the human sister of those vegetable ones, as beautiful as they, more beautiful than the richest of them, but still to be touched only with a glove, nor to be approached without a mask. As Beatrice came down the garden path, it was observable that she handled and inhaled the odor of several of the plants which her father had most sedulously avoided.

"Here, Beatrice," said the latter, "see how many needful offices require to be done to our chief treasure. Yet, shattered as I am, my life might pay the penalty of approaching it so closely as circumstances demand. Henceforth, I fear, this plant must be consigned to your sole charge."

"And gladly will I undertake it," cried again the rich tones of the young lady, as she bent towards the magnificent plant and opened her arms as if to embrace it. "Yes, my sister, my splendor, it shall be Beatrice's task to nurse and serve thee; and thou shalt reward her with thy kisses and perfumed breath, which to her is as the breath of life."

Then, with all the tenderness in her manner that was so strikingly expressed in her words, she busied herself with such attentions as the plant seemed to require; and Giovanni, at his lofty window, rubbed his eyes and almost doubted whether it were a girl tending her favorite flower, or one sister performing the duties of affection to another. The scene soon terminated. Whether Dr. Rappaccini had finished his labors in the garden, or that his watchful eye had caught the stranger's face, he now took his daughter's arm and retired. Night was already closing in; oppressive exhalations seemed to proceed from the plants and steal upward past the open window; and Giovanni, closing the lattice, went to his couch and dreamed of a rich flower and beautiful girl. Flower and maiden were different, and yet the same, and fraught with some strange peril in either shape.

But there is an influence in the light of morning that tends to rectify whatever errors of fancy, or even of judgment, we may have incurred during the sun's decline, or among the shadows of the night, or in the less wholesome glow of moonshine. Giovanni's first movement, on starting from sleep, was to throw open the window and gaze down into the garden which his dreams had made so fertile of mysteries. He was surprised and a little ashamed to find how real and matter-of-fact an affair it proved to be, in the first rays of the sun which gilded the dewdrops that hung upon leaf and blossom, and, while giving a brighter beauty to each rare flower, brought everything within the limits of ordinary experience. The young man rejoiced that, in the heart of the barren city, he had the privilege of overlooking this spot of lovely and luxuriant vegetation. It would serve, he said to himself, as a symbolic language to keep him in communion with Nature. Neither the sickly and thought-worn Dr. Giacomo Rappaccini, it is true, nor his brilliant daughter, were now visible; so that Giovanni could not determine how much of the singularity which he attributed to both was due to their own qualities and how much to his wonder-working fancy; but he was inclined to take a most rational view of the whole matter. In the course of the day he paid his respects to Signor Pietro Baglioni, professor of medicine in the university, a physician of eminent repute, to whom Giovanni had brought a letter of introduction. The professor was an elderly personage, apparently of genial nature, and habits that might almost be called jovial. He kept the young man to dinner, and made himself very agreeable by the freedom and liveliness of his conversation, especially when warmed by a flask or two of Tuscan wine. Giovanni, conceiving that men of science, inhabitants of the same city, must needs be on familiar terms with one another, took an opportunity to mention the name of Dr. Rappaccini. But the professor did not respond with so much cordiality as he had anticipated.

"Ill would it become a teacher of the divine art of medicine," said Professor Pietro Baglioni, in answer to a question of Giovanni, "to withhold due and well-considered praise of a physician so eminently skilled as Rappaccini; but, on the other hand, I should answer it but scantily to my conscience were I to permit a worthy youth like yourself, Signor Giovanni, the son of an ancient friend, to imbibe erroneous ideas respecting a man who might hereafter chance to hold your life and death in his hands. The truth is, our worshipful Dr. Rappaccini has as much science as any member of the faculty—with perhaps one single exception—in Padua, or all Italy; but there are certain grave objections to his professional character."

"And what are they?" asked the young man.

"Has my friend Giovanni any disease of body or heart, that he is so inquisitive about physicians?" said the professor, with a smile. "But as for

Rappaccini, it is said of him—and I, who know the man well, can answer for its truth—that he cares infinitely more for science than for mankind. His patients are interesting to him only as subjects for some new experiment. He would sacrifice human life, his own among the rest, or whatever else was dearest to him, for the sake of adding so much as a grain of mustard seed to the great heap of his accumulated knowledge."

"Methinks he is an awful man indeed," remarked Guasconti, mentally recalling the cold and purely intellectual aspect of Rappaccini. "And yet, worshipful professor, is it not a noble spirit? Are there many men capable of so spiritual a love of science?"

"God forbid," answered the professor, somewhat testily; "at least, unless they take sounder views of the healing art than those adopted by Rappaccini. It is his theory that all medicinal virtues are comprised within those substances which we term vegetable poisons. These he cultivates with his own hands, and is said even to have produced new varieties of poison, more horribly deleterious than Nature, without the assistance of this learned person, would ever have plagued the world withal. That the signor doctor does less mischief than might be expected with such dangerous substances is undeniable. Now and then, it must be owned, he has effected, or seemed to effect, a marvellous cure; but, to tell you my private mind, Signor Giovanni, he should receive little credit for such instances of success—they being probably the work of chance—but should be held strictly accountable for his failures, which may justly be considered his own work."

The youth might have taken Baglioni's opinions with many grains of allowance had he known that there was a professional warfare of long continuance between him and Dr. Rappaccini, in which the latter was generally thought to have gained the advantage. If the reader be inclined to judge for himself, we refer him to certain black-letter tracts on both sides, preserved in the medical department of the University of Padua.

"I know not, most learned professor," returned Giovanni, after musing on what had been said of Rappaccini's exclusive zeal for science. "I know not how dearly this physician may love his art; but surely there is one object more dear to him. He has a daughter."

"Aha!" cried the professor, with a laugh. "So now our friend Giovanni's secret is out. You have heard of this daughter, whom all the young men in Padua are wild about, though not half a dozen have ever had the good hap to see her face. I know little of the Signora Beatrice save that Rappaccini is said to have instructed her deeply in his science, and that, young and beautiful as fame reports her, she is already qualified to fill a professor's chair. Perchance her father destines her for mine! Other absurd rumors there be, not worth talking about or listening to. So now, Signor Giovanni, drink off your glass of lachryma."

Guasconti returned to his lodgings somewhat heated with the wine he had quaffed, and which caused his brain to swim with strange fantasies in reference to Dr. Rappaccini and the beautiful Beatrice. On his way, happening to pass by a florist's, he bought a fresh bouquet of flowers.

Ascending to his chamber, he seated himself near the window, but within the shadow thrown by the depth of the wall, so that he could look down into the garden with little risk of being discovered. All beneath his eye was a solitude. The strange plants were basking in the sunshine, and now and then nodding gently to one another, as if in acknowledgment of sympathy and kindred. In the midst, by the shattered fountain, grew the magnificent shrub, with its purple gems clustering all over it; they glowed in the air, and gleamed back again out of the depths of the pool, which thus seemed to overflow with colored radiance from the rich reflection that was steeped in it. At first, as we have said, the garden was a solitude. Soon, however—as Giovanni had half hoped, half feared, would be the case—a figure appeared beneath the antique sculptured portal, and came down between the rows of plants, inhaling their various perfumes as if she were one of those beings of old classic fable that lived upon sweet odors. On again beholding Beatrice, the young man was even startled to perceive how much her beauty exceeded his recollection of it; so brilliant, so vivid, was its character, that she glowed amid the sunlight, and, as Giovanni whispered to himself, positively illuminated the more shadowy intervals of the garden path. Her face being now more revealed than on the former occasion, he was struck by its expression of simplicity and sweetness—qualities that had not entered into his idea of her character, and which made him ask anew what manner of mortal she might be. Nor did he fail again to observe, or imagine, an analogy between the beautiful girl and the gorgeous shrub that hung its gemlike flowers over the fountain—a resemblance which Beatrice seemed to have indulged a fantastic humor in heightening, both by the arrangement of her dress and the selection of its hues.

Approaching the shrub, she threw open her arms, as with a passionate ardor, and drew its branches into an intimate embrace—so intimate that her features were hidden in its leafy bosom and her glistening ringlets all intermingled with the flowers.

"Give me thy breath, my sister," exclaimed Beatrice; "for I am faint with common air. And give me this flower of thine, which I separate with gentlest fingers from the stem and place it close beside my heart."

With these words the beautiful daughter of Rappaccini plucked one of the richest blossoms of the shrub, and was about to fasten it in her bosom. But now, unless Giovanni's draughts of wine had bewildered his senses, a singular incident occurred. A small orange-colored reptile, of the lizard or chameleon species, chanced to be creeping along the path, just at the feet of Beatrice. It appeared to Giovanni—but, at the distance from which he gazed, he could scarcely have seen anything so minute—it appeared to him, however, that a drop or two of moisture from the broken stem of the flower descended upon the lizard's head. For an instant the reptile contorted itself violently, and then lay motionless in the sunshine. Beatrice observed this remarkable phenomenon, and crossed herself, sadly, but without surprise; nor did she therefore hesitate to arrange the fatal flower in her bosom. There it blushed, and almost glimmered with the dazzling effect of a precious stone, adding to her dress and aspect the one appropriate charm which nothing else in the world could have supplied. But Giovanni, out of the shadow of his window, bent forward and shrank back, and murmured and trembled.

"Am I awake? Have I my senses?" said he to himself. "What is this being? Beautiful shall I call her, or inexpressibly terrible?"

Beatrice now strayed carelessly through the garden, approaching closer beneath Giovanni's window, so that he was compelled to thrust his head quite out of its concealment in order to gratify the intense and painful curiosity which she excited. At this moment there came a beautiful insect over the garden wall; it had, perhaps, wandered through the city, and found no flowers or verdure among those antique haunts of men until the heavy perfumes of Dr. Rappaccini's shrubs had lured it from afar. Without alighting on the flowers, this winged brightness seemed to be attracted by Beatrice, and lingered in the air and fluttered about her head. Now, here it could not be but that Giovanni Guasconti's eyes deceived him. Be that as it might, he fancied that, while Beatrice was gazing at the insect with childish delight, it grew faint and fell at her feet; its bright wings shivered; it was dead—from no cause that he could discern, unless it were the atmosphere of her breath. Again Beatrice crossed herself and sighed heavily as she bent over the dead insect.

An impulsive movement of Giovanni drew her eyes to the window. There she beheld the beautiful head of the young man—rather a Grecian than an Italian head, with fair, regular features, and a glistening of gold among his ringlets—gazing down upon her like a being that hovered in mid air. Scarcely knowing what he did, Giovanni threw down the bouquet which he had hitherto held in his hand.

"Signora," said he, "there are pure and healthful flowers. Wear them for the sake of Giovanni Guasconti."

"Thanks, signor," replied Beatrice, with her rich voice, that came forth as it were like a gush of music, and with a mirthful expression half childish and half womanlike. "I accept your gift, and would fain recompense it with this precious purple flower; but if I toss it into the air it will not reach you. So Signor Guasconti must even content himself with my thanks."

She lifted the bouquet from the ground, and then, as if inwardly ashamed at having stepped aside from her maidenly reserve to respond to a stranger's greeting, passed swiftly homeward through the garden. But few as the moments were, it seemed to Giovanni, when she was on the point of vanishing beneath the sculptured portal, that his beautiful bouquet was already beginning to wither in her grasp. It was an idle thought; there could be no possibility of distinguishing a faded flower from a fresh one at so great a distance.

For many days after this incident the young man avoided the window that looked into Dr. Rappaccini's garden, as if something ugly and monstrous would have blasted his eyesight had he been betrayed into a glance. He felt conscious of having put himself, to a certain extent, within the influence of an unintelligible power by the communication which he had opened with Beatrice. The wisest course would have been, if his heart were in any real danger, to quit his lodgings and Padua itself at once; the next wiser, to have accustomed himself, as far as possible, to the familiar and daylight view of Beatrice—thus bringing her rigidly and systematically within the limits of ordinary experience. Least of all, while avoiding her sight, ought Giovanni to have remained so near this extraordinary being that the proximity and possibility even of intercourse should give a kind of substance and reality to the wild vagaries which his imagination ran riot continually in producing. Guasconti had not a deep heart—or, at all events, its depths were not sounded now; but he had a quick fancy, and an ardent southern temperament, which rose every instant to a higher fever pitch. Whether or no Beatrice possessed those terrible attributes, that fatal breath, the affinity with those so beautiful and deadly flowers which were indicated by what Giovanni had witnessed, she had at least instilled a fierce and subtle poison into his system. It was not love, although her rich beauty was a madness to him; nor horror, even while he fancied her spirit to be imbued with the same baneful essence that seemed to pervade her physical frame; but a wild offspring of both love and horror that had each parent in it, and burned like one and shivered like the other. Giovanni knew not what to dread; still less did he know what to hope; yet hope and dread kept a continual warfare in his breast, alternately vanquishing one another and starting up afresh to renew the contest. Blessed are all simple emotions, be they dark or bright! It is the lurid inter-mixture of the two that produces the illuminating blaze of the infernal regions.

Sometimes he endeavored to assuage the fever of his spirit by a rapid walk through the streets of Padua or beyond its gates: his footsteps kept time with the throbbings of his brain, so that the walk was apt to accelerate itself to a race. One day he found himself arrested; his arm was seized by a portly personage, who had turned back on recognizing the young man and expended much breath in overtaking him.

"Signor Giovanni! Stay, my young friend!" cried he. "Have you forgotten me? That might well be the case if I were as much altered as yourself."

It was Baglioni, whom Giovanni had avoided ever since their first meeting, from a doubt that the professor's sagacity would look too deeply into his secrets. Endeavoring to recover himself, he stared forth wildly from his inner world into the outer one and spoke like a man in a dream.

"Yes; I am Giovanni Guasconti. You are Professor Pietro Baglioni. Now let me pass!"

"Not yet, not yet, Signor Giovanni Guasconti," said the professor, smiling, but at the same time scrutinizing the youth with an earnest glance. "What! did I grow up side by side with your father? and shall his son pass me like a stranger in these old streets of Padua? Stand still, Signor Giovanni; for we must have a word or two before we part."

"Speedily, then, most worshipful professor, speedily," said Giovanni, with feverish impatience. "Does not your worship see that I am in haste?"

Now, while he was speaking there came a man in black along the street, stooping and moving feebly like a person in inferior health. His face was all overspread with a most sickly and sallow hue, but yet so pervaded with an expression of piercing and active intellect that an observer might easily have overlooked the merely physical attributes and have seen only this wonderful energy. As he passed, this person exchanged a cold and distant salutation with Baglioni, but fixed his eyes upon Giovanni with an intentness that seemed to bring out whatever was within him worthy of notice. Nevertheless, there was a peculiar quietness in the look, as if taking merely a speculative, not a human, interest in the young man.

"It is Dr. Rappaccini!" whispered the professor when the stranger had passed. "Has he ever seen your face before?"

"Not that I know," answered Giovanni, starting at the name.

"He *has* seen you! he must have seen you!" said Baglioni, hastily. "For some purpose or other, this man of science is making a study of you. I know that look of his! It is the same that coldly illuminates his face as he bends over a bird, a mouse, or a butterfly, which, in pursuance of some experiment, he has killed by the perfume of a flower; a look as deep as Nature itself, but without Nature's warmth of love. Signor Giovanni, I will stake my life upon it, you are the subject of one of Rappaccini's experiments!"

"Will you make a fool of me?" cried Giovanni, passionately. "*That*, signor professor, were an untoward experiment."

"Patience! patience!" replied the imperturbable professor. "I tell thee, my poor Giovanni, that Rappaccini has a scientific interest in thee. Thou hast fallen into fearful hands! And the Signora Beatrice—what part does she act in this mystery?"

But Guasconti, finding Baglioni's pertinacity intolerable, here broke away, and was gone before the professor could again seize his arm. He looked after the young man intently and shook his head.

"This must not be," said Baglioni to himself. "The youth is the son of my old friend, and shall not come to any harm from which the arcana of medical science can preserve him. Besides, it is too insufferable an impertinence in Rappaccini, thus to snatch the lad out of my own hands, as I may say, and make use of him for his infernal experiments. This daughter of his! It shall be looked to. Perchance, most learned Rappaccini, I may foil you where you little dream of it!"

Meanwhile Giovanni had pursued a circuitous route, and at length found himself at the door of his lodgings. As he crossed the threshold he was met by old Lisabetta, who smirked and smiled, and was evidently desirous to attract his attention; vainly, however, as the ebullition of his feelings had momentarily subsided into a cold and dull vacuity. He turned his eyes full upon the withered face that was puckering itself into a smile, but seemed to behold it not. The old dame, therefore, laid her grasp upon his cloak.

"Signor! signor!" whispered she, still with a smile over the whole breadth of her visage, so that it looked not unlike a grotesque carving in wood, darkened by centuries. "Listen, signor! There is a private entrance into the garden!"

"What do you say?" exclaimed Giovanni, turning quickly about, as if an inanimate thing should start into feverish life. "A private entrance into Dr. Rappaccini's garden?"

"Hush! hush! not so loud!" whispered Lisabetta, putting her hand over his mouth. "Yes; into the worshipful doctor's garden, where you may see all his fine shrubbery. Many a young man in Padua would give gold to be admitted among those flowers."

Giovanni put a piece of gold into her hand.

"Show me the way," said he.

A surmise, probably excited by his conversation with Baglioni, crossed his mind, that this interposition of old Lisabetta might perchance be connected with the intrigue, whatever were its nature, in which the professor seemed to suppose that Dr. Rappaccini was involving him. But such a suspicion, though it disturbed Giovanni, was inadequate to restrain him. The instant that he was aware of the possibility of approaching Beatrice, it seemed an absolute necessity of his existence to do so. It mattered not whether she were angel or demon; he was irrevocably within her sphere, and must obey the law that whirled him onward, in ever-lessening circles, toward a result which he did not attempt to foreshadow; and yet, strange to say, there came across him a sudden doubt whether this intense interest on his part were not delusory; whether it were really of so deep and positive a nature as to justify him in now thrusting himself into an incalculable position; whether it were not merely the fantasy of a young man's brain, only slightly or not at all connected with his heart.

He paused, hesitated, turned half about, but again went on. His withered guide led him along several obscure passages, and finally undid a door, through which, as it was opened, there came the sight and sound of rustling leaves, with the broken sunshine glimmering among them. Giovanni stepped forth, and, forcing himself through the entanglement of a shrub that wreathed its tendrils over the hidden entrance, stood beneath his own window in the open area of Dr. Rappaccini's garden.

How often is it the case that, when impossibilities have come to pass and dreams have condensed their misty substance into tangible realities, we find ourselves calm, and even coldly self-possessed, amid circumstances which it would have been a delirium of joy or agony to anticipate! Fate delights to thwart us thus. Passion will choose his own time to rush upon the scene, and lingers sluggishly behind when an appropriate adjustment of events would seem to summon his appearance. So was it now with Giovanni. Day after day his pulses had throbbed with feverish blood at the improbable idea of an interview with Beatrice, and of standing with her, face to face, in this very garden, basking in the Oriental sunshine of her beauty, and snatching from her full gaze the mystery which he deemed the riddle of his own existence. But now there was a singular and untimely equanimity within his breast. He threw a glance around the garden to discover if Beatrice or her father were present, and, perceiving that he was alone, began a critical observation of the plants.

The aspect of one and all of them dissatisfied him; their gorgeousness seemed fierce, passionate, and even unnatural. There was hardly an individual shrub which a wanderer, straying by himself through a forest, would not have been startled to find growing wild, as if an unearthly face had glared at him out of the thicket. Several also would have shocked a delicate instinct by an appearance of artificialness indicating that there had been such commixture, and, as it were, adultery, of various vegetable species, that the production was no longer of God's making, but the monstrous offspring of man's depraved fancy, glowing with only an evil mockery of beauty. They were probably the result of experiment, which in one or two cases had succeeded in mingling plants individually lovely into a compound possessing the questionable and ominous character that distinguished the whole growth of the garden. In fine, Giovanni recognized but two or three plants in the collection, and those of a kind that he well knew to be poisonous. While busy with these contemplations he heard the rustling of a silken garment, and, turning, beheld Beatrice emerging from beneath the sculptured portal.

Giovanni had not considered with himself what should be his deportment; whether he should apologize for his intrusion into the garden, or assume that he was there with the privity at least, if not by the desire, of Dr. Rappaccini or his daughter; but Beatrice's manner placed him at his ease, though leaving him still in doubt by what agency he had gained admittance. She came lightly along the path and met him near the broken fountain. There was surprise in her face, but brightened by a simple and kind expression of pleasure.

"You are a connoisseur in flowers, signor," said Beatrice, with a smile, alluding to the bouquet which he had flung her from the window. "It is no marvel, therefore, if the sight of my father's rare collection has tempted you to take a nearer view. If he were here, he could tell you many strange and interesting facts as to the nature and habits of these shrubs; for he has spent a lifetime in such studies, and this garden is his world."

"And yourself, lady," observed Giovanni, "if fame says true, you likewise are deeply skilled in the virtues indicated by these rich blossoms and these spicy perfumes. Would you deign to be my instructress, I should prove an apter scholar than if taught by Signor Rappaccini himself."

"Are there such idle rumors?" asked Beatrice, with the music of a pleasant laugh. "Do people say that I am skilled in my father's science of plants? What a jest is there! No; though I have grown up among these flowers, I know no more of them than their hues and perfume; and sometimes methinks I would fain rid myself of even that small knowledge. There are many flowers here, and those not the least brilliant, that shock and offend me when they meet my eye. But pray, signor, do not believe these stories about my science. Believe nothing of me save what you see with your own eyes."

"And must I believe all that I have seen with my own eyes?" asked Giovanni, pointedly, while the recollection of former scenes made him shrink. "No, signora; you demand too little of me. Bid me believe nothing save what comes from your own lips."

It would appear that Beatrice understood him. There came a deep flush to her cheek; but she looked full into Giovanni's eyes, and responded to his gaze of uneasy suspicion with a queenlike haughtiness.

"I do so bid you, signor," she replied. "Forget whatever you may have fancied in regard to me. If true to the outward senses, still it may be false in its essence; but the words of Beatrice Rappaccini's lips are true from the depths of the heart outward. Those you may believe."

A fervor glowed in her whole aspect and beamed upon Giovanni's consciousness like the light of truth itself; but while she spoke there was a fragrance in the atmosphere around her, rich and delightful, though evanescent, yet which the young man, from an indefinable reluctance, scarcely dared to draw into his lungs. It might be the odor of the flowers. Could it be Beatrice's breath which thus embalmed her words with a strange richness, as if by steeping them in her heart? A faintness passed like a shadow over Giovanni and flitted away; he seemed to gaze through the beautiful girl's eyes into her transparent soul, and felt no more doubt or fear.

The tinge of passion that had colored Beatrice's manner vanished; she became gay, and appeared to derive a pure delight from her communion with the youth, not unlike what the maiden of a lonely island might have felt conversing with a voyager from the civilized world. Evidently her experience of life had been confined within the limits of that garden. She talked now about matters as simple as the daylight or summer clouds, and now asked questions in reference to the city, or Giovanni's distant home, his friends, his mother, and his sisters—questions indicating such seclusion, and such lack of familiarity with modes and forms, that Giovanni responded as if to an infant. Her spirit gushed out before him like a fresh rill that was just catching its first glimpse of the sunlight and wondering at the reflections of earth and sky which were flung into its bosom. There came thoughts, too, from a deep source, and fantasies of a gemlike brilliancy, as if diamonds and rubies sparkled upward among the bubbles of the fountain. Ever and anon there gleamed across the young man's mind a sense of wonder that he should be walking side by side with the being who had so wrought upon his imagination, whom he had idealized in such hues of terror, in whom he had positively witnessed such manifestations of dreadful attributes—that he should be conversing with Beatrice like a brother, and should find her so human and so maidenlike. But such reflections were only momentary; the effect of her character was too real not to make itself familiar at once.

In this free intercourse they had strayed through the garden, and now, after many turns among its avenues, were come to the shattered fountain, beside which grew the magnificent shrub, with its treasury of glowing blossoms. A fragrance was diffused from it which Giovanni recognized as identical with that which he had attributed to Beatrice's breath, but incomparably more powerful. As her eyes fell upon it, Giovanni beheld her press her hand to her bosom as if her heart were throbbing suddenly and painfully.

"For the first time in my life," murmured she, addressing the shrub, "I had forgotten thee."

"I remember, signora," said Giovanni, "that you once promised to reward me with one of these living gems for the bouquet which I had the happy boldness to fling at your feet. Permit me now to pluck it as a memorial of this interview."

He made a step towards the shrub with extended hand; but Beatrice darted forward, uttering a shriek that went through his heart like a dagger. She caught his hand and drew it back with the whole force of her slender figure. Giovanni felt her touch thrilling through his fibers.

"Touch it not!" exclaimed she, in a voice of agony. "Not for thy life! It is fatal!"

Then, hiding her face, she fled from him and vanished beneath the sculptured portal. As Giovanni followed her with his eyes, he beheld the emaciated figure and pale intelligence of Dr. Rappaccini, who had been watching the scene, he knew not how long, within the shadow of the entrance.

No sooner was Guasconti alone in his chamber than the image of Beatrice came back to his passionate musings, invested with all the witchery that had been gathering around it ever since his first glimpse of her, and now likewise imbued with a tender warmth of girlish womanhood. She was human; her nature was endowed with all gentle and feminine qualities; she was worthiest to be worshiped; she was capable, surely, on her part, of the height and heroism of love. Those tokens which he had hitherto considered as proofs of a frightful peculiarity in her physical and moral system were now either forgotten or, by the subtle sophistry of passion, transmitted into a golden crown of enchantment, rendering Beatrice the more admirable by so much as she was the more unique. Whatever had looked ugly was now beautiful; or, if incapable of such a change, it stole away and hid itself among those shapeless half ideas which throng the dim region beyond the daylight of our perfect consciousness. Thus did he spend the night, nor fell asleep until the dawn had begun to awake the slumbering flowers in Dr. Rappaccini's garden, whither Giovanni's dreams doubtless led him. Up rose the sun in his due season, and, flinging his beams upon the young man's eyelids, awoke him to a sense of pain. When thoroughly aroused, he became sensible of a burning and tingling agony in his hand—in his right hand—the very hand which Beatrice had grasped in her own when he was on the point of plucking one of the gemlike flowers. On the back of that hand there was now a purple print like that of four small fingers, and the likeness of a slender thumb upon his wrist.

Oh, how stubbornly does love—or even that cunning semblance of love which flourishes in the imagination, but strikes no depth of root into the heart—how stubbornly does it hold its faith until the moment comes when it is doomed to vanish into thin mist! Giovanni wrapped a handkerchief about his hand and wondered what evil thing had stung him, and soon forgot his pain in a reverie of Beatrice.

After the first interview, a second was in the inevitable course of what we call fate. A third; a fourth; and a meeting with Beatrice in the garden was no longer an incident in Giovanni's daily life, but the whole space in which he might be said to live; for the anticipation and memory of that ecstatic hour made up the remainder. Nor was it otherwise with the daughter of Rappaccini. She watched for the youth's appearance, and flew to his side with confidence as unreserved as if they had been playmates from early infancy—as if they were such playmates still. If, by any unwonted chance, he failed to come at the appointed moment, she stood beneath the window and sent up the rich sweetness of her tones to float around him in his chamber and echo and reverberate throughout his heart: "Giovanni! Giovanni! Why tarriest thou? Come down!" And down he hastened into that Eden of poisonous flowers.

But, with all this intimate familiarity, there was still a reserve in Beatrice's demeanor, so rigidly and invariably sustained that the idea of infringing it scarcely occurred to his imagination. By all appreciable signs, they loved; they had looked love with eyes that conveyed the holy secret from the depths of one soul into the depths of the other, as if it were too sacred to be whispered by the way; they had even spoken love in those gushes of passion when their spirits darted forth in articulated breath like tongues of long-hidden flame; and yet there had been no seal of lips, no clasp of hands, nor any slightest caress such as love claims and hallows. He had never touched one of the gleaming ringlets of her hair; her garment—so marked was the physical barrier between them—had never been waved against him by a breeze. On the few occasions when Giovanni had seemed tempted to overstep the limit, Beatrice grew so sad, so stern, and withal wore such a look of desolate separation, shuddering at itself, that not a spoken word was requisite to repel him. At such times he was startled at the horrible suspicions that rose, monsterlike, out of the caverns of his heart and stared him in the face; his love grew thin and faint as the morning mist, his doubts alone had substance. But, when Beatrice's face brightened again after the momentary shadow, she was transformed at once from the mysterious, questionable being whom he had watched with so much awe and horror; she was now the beautiful and unsophisticated girl whom he felt that his spirit knew with a certainty beyond all other knowledge.

A considerable time had now passed since Giovanni's last meeting with Baglioni. One morning, however, he was disagreeably surprised by a visit from the professor, whom he had scarcely thought of for whole weeks, and would willingly have forgotten still longer. Given up as he had long been to a pervading excitement, he could tolerate no companions except upon condition of their perfect sympathy with his present state of feeling. Such sympathy was not to be expected from Professor Baglioni.

The visitor chatted carelessly for a few moments about the gossip of the city and the university, and then took up another topic.

"I have been reading an old classic author lately," said he, "and met with a story that strangely interested me. Possibly you may remember it. It is of an Indian prince, who sent a beautiful woman as a present to Alexander the Great. She was as lovely as the dawn and gorgeous as the sunset; but what especially distinguished her was a certain rich perfume in her breath—richer than a garden of Persian roses. Alexander, as was natural to a youthful conqueror, fell in love at first sight with this magnificent stranger; but a certain sage physician, happening to be present, discovered a terrible secret in regard to her."

"And what was that?" asked Giovanni, turning his eyes downward to avoid those of the professor.

"That this lovely woman," continued Baglioni, with emphasis, "had been nourished with poisons from her birth upward, until her whole nature was so imbued with them that she herself had become the deadliest poison in existence. Poison was her element of life. With that rich perfume of her breath she blasted the very air. Her love would have been poison—her embrace death. Is not this a marvellous tale?"

"A childish fable," answered Giovanni, nervously starting from his chair. "I marvel how your worship finds time to read such nonsense among your graver studies."

"By the by," said the professor, looking uneasily about him, "what singular fragrance is this in your apartment? Is it the perfume of your gloves? It is faint, but delicious; and yet, after all, by no means agreeable. Were I to breathe it long, methinks it would make me ill. It is like the breath of a flower; but I see no flowers in the chamber."

"Nor are there any," replied Giovanni, who had turned pale as the professor spoke; "nor, I think, is there any fragrance except in your worship's imagination. Odors, being a sort of element combined of the sensual and the spiritual, are apt to deceive us in this manner. The recollection of a perfume, the bare idea of it, may easily be mistaken for a present reality."

"Ay; but my sober imagination does not often play such tricks," said Baglioni; "and, were I to fancy any kind of odor, it would be that of some vile apothecary drug, wherewith my fingers are likely enough to be imbued. Our worshipful friend Rappaccini, as I have heard, tinctures his medicaments with odors richer than those of Araby. Doubtless, likewise, the fair and learned Signora Beatrice would minister to her patients with draughts as sweet as a maiden's breath; but woe to him that sips them!"

Giovanni's face evinced many contending emotions. The tone in which the professor alluded to the pure and lovely daughter of Rappaccini was a torture to his soul; and yet the intimation of a view of her character, opposite to his own, gave instantaneous distinctness to a thousand dim suspicions, which now grinned at him like so many demons. But he strove hard to quell them and to respond to Baglioni with a true lover's perfect faith.

"Signor professor," said he, "you were my father's friend; perchance, too, it is your purpose to act a friendly part towards his son. I would fain feel nothing toward you save respect and deference; but I pray you to observe, signor, that there is one subject on which we must not speak. You know not the Signora Beatrice. You cannot, therefore, estimate the wrong—the blasphemy, I may even say that is offered to her character by a light or injurious word."

"Giovanni! my poor Giovanni!" answered the professor, with a calm expression of pity, "I know this wretched girl far better than yourself. You shall hear the truth in respect to the poisoner Rappaccini and his poisonous daughter; yes, poisonous as she is beautiful. Listen; for, even should you do violence to my gray hairs, it shall not silence me. That old fable of the Indian woman has become a truth by the deep and deadly science of Rappaccini and in the person of the lovely Beatrice."

Giovanni groaned and hid his face.

"Her father," continued Baglioni, "was not restrained by natural affection from offering up his child in this horrible manner as the victim of his insane zeal for science; for, let us do him justice, he is as true a man of science as ever distilled his own heart in an alembic. What, then, will be your fate? Beyond a doubt you are selected as the material of some new experiment. Perhaps the result is to be death; perhaps a fate more awful still. Rappaccini, with what he calls the interest of science before his eyes, will hesitate at nothing."

"It is a dream," muttered Giovanni to himself; "surely it is a dream."

"But," resumed the professor, "be of good cheer, son of my friend. It is not yet too late for the rescue. Possibly we may even succeed in bringing back this miserable child within the limits of ordinary nature, from which her father's madness has estranged her. Behold this little silver vase! It was wrought by the hands of the renowned Benvenuto Cellini, and is well worthy to be a love gift to the fairest dame in Italy. But its contents are invaluable. One little sip of this antidote would have rendered the most virulent poisons of the Borgias innocuous. Doubt not that it will be as efficacious against those of Rappaccini. Bestow the vase, and the precious liquid within it, on your Beatrice, and hopefully await the result."

Baglioni laid a small, exquisitely wrought silver vial on the table and withdrew, leaving what he had said to produce its effect upon the young man's mind.

"We will thwart Rappaccini yet," thought he, chuckling to himself, as he descended the stairs; "but, let us confess the truth of him, he is a wonderful man—a wonderful man indeed; a vile empiric, however, in his practice, and therefore not to be tolerated by those who respect the good old rules of the medical profession."

Throughout Giovanni's whole acquaintance with Beatrice, he had occasionally, as we have said, been haunted by dark surmises as to her character; yet so thoroughly had she made herself felt by him as a simple, natural, most affectionate, and guileless creature, that the image now held up by Professor Baglioni looked as strange and incredible as if it were not in accordance with his own original conception. True, there were ugly recollections connected with his first glimpses of the beautiful girl; he could not quite forget the bouquet that withered in her grasp, and the insect that perished amid the sunny air, by no ostensible agency save the fragrance of her breath. These incidents, however, dissolving in the pure light of her character, had no longer the efficacy of facts, but were acknowledged as mistaken fantasies, by whatever testimony of the senses they might appear to be substantiated. There is something truer and more real than what we can see with the eyes and touch with the finger. On such better evidence had Giovanni founded his confidence in Beatrice, though rather by the necessary force of her high attributes than by any deep and generous faith on his part. But now his spirit was incapable of sustaining itself at the height to which the early enthusiasm of passion had exalted it; he fell down, groveling among earthly doubts, and defiled therewith the pure whiteness of Beatrice's image. Not that he gave her up; he did but distrust. He resolved to institute some decisive test that should satisfy him, once for all, whether there were those dreadful peculiarities in her physical nature which could not be supposed to exist without some corresponding monstrosity of soul. His eyes, gazing down afar, might have deceived him as to the lizard, the insect, and the flowers; but if he could witness, at the distance of a few paces, the sudden blight of one fresh and healthful flower in Beatrice's hand, there would be room for no further question. With this idea he hastened to the florist's and purchased a bouquet that was still gemmed with the morning dewdrops.

It was now the customary hour of his daily interview with Beatrice. Before descending into the garden, Giovanni failed not to look at his figure in the mirror—a vanity to be expected in a beautiful young man, yet, as displaying itself at that troubled and feverish moment, the token of a certain shallowness of feeling and insincerity of character. He did gaze, however, and said to himself that his features had never before possessed so rich a grace, nor his eyes such vivacity, nor his cheeks so warm a hue of superabundant life.

"At least," thought he, "her poison has not yet insinuated itself into my system. I am no flower to perish in her grasp."

With that thought he turned his eyes on the bouquet, which he had never once laid aside from his hand. A thrill of indefinable horror shot through his frame on perceiving that those dewy flowers were already beginning to droop; they wore the aspect of things that had been fresh and lovely yesterday. Giovanni grew white as marble, and stood motionless before the mirror, staring at his own reflection there as at the likeness of something frightful. He remembered Baglioni's remark about the fragrance that seemed to pervade the chamber. It must have been the poison in his breath! Then he shuddered—shuddered at himself. Recovering from his stupor, he began to watch with curious eye a spider that was busily at work hanging its web from the antique cornice of the apartment, crossing and recrossing the artful system of interwoven lines—as vigorous and active a spider as ever dangled from an old ceiling. Giovanni bent toward the insect, and emitted a deep, long breath. The spider suddenly ceased its toil; the web vibrated with a tremor originating in the body of the small artisan. Again Giovanni sent forth a breath, deeper, longer, and imbued with a venomous feeling out of his heart: he knew not whether he were wicked, or only desperate. The spider made a convulsive gripe with his limbs and hung dead across the window.

"Accursed! accursed!" muttered Giovanni, addressing himself. "Hast thou grown so poisonous that this deadly insect perishes by thy breath?"

At that moment a rich, sweet voice came floating up from the garden.

"Giovanni! Giovanni! It is past the hour! Why tarriest thou? Come down!"

"Yes," muttered Giovanni again. "She is the only being whom my breath may not slay! Would that it might!"

He rushed down, and in an instant was standing before the bright and loving eyes of Beatrice. A moment ago his wrath and despair had been so fierce that he could have desired nothing so much as to wither her by a glance; but with her actual presence there came influences which had too real an existence to be at once shaken off: recollections of the delicate and benign power of her feminine nature, which had so often enveloped him in a religious calm; recollections of many a holy and passionate outgush of her heart, when the pure fountain had been unsealed from its depths and made visible in its transparency to his mental eye; recollections which, had Giovanni known how to estimate them, would have assured him that all this ugly mystery was but an earthly illusion, and that, whatever mist of evil might seem to have gathered over her, the real Beatrice was a heavenly angel. Incapable as he was of such high faith, still her presence had not utterly lost its magic. Giovanni's rage was quelled into an aspect of sullen insensibility. Beatrice, with a quick spiritual sense, immediately felt that there was a gulf of blackness between them which neither he nor she could pass. They walked on together, sad and silent, and came thus to the marble fountain and to its pool of water on the ground, in the midst of which grew the shrub that bore gemlike blossoms. Giovanni was affrighted at the eager enjoyment— the appetite, as it were—with which he found himself inhaling the fragrance of the flowers.

"Beatrice," asked he, abruptly, "whence came this shrub?"

"My father created it," answered she, with simplicity.

"Created it! created it!" repeated Giovanni. "What mean you, Beatrice?"

"He is a man fearfully acquainted with the secrets of Nature," replied Beatrice; "and, at the hour when I first drew breath, this plant sprang from the soil, the offspring of his science, of his intellect, while I was but his earthly child. Approach it not!" continued she, observing with terror that Giovanni was drawing nearer to the shrub. "It has qualities that you little dream of. But I, dearest Giovanni, I grew up and blossomed with the plant and was nourished with its breath. It was my sister, and I loved it with a human affection; for, alas!—hast thou not suspected it?— there was an awful doom."

Here Giovanni frowned so darkly upon her that Beatrice paused and trembled. But her faith in his tenderness reassured her, and made her blush that she had doubted for an instant.

"There was an awful doom," she continued, "the effect of my father's fatal love of science, which estranged me from all society of my kind. Until Heaven sent thee, dearest Giovanni, oh, how lonely was thy poor Beatrice!"

"Was it a hard doom?" asked Giovanni, fixing his eyes upon her.

"Only of late have I known how hard it was," answered she, tenderly. "Oh, yes; but my heart was torpid, and therefore quiet."

Giovanni's rage broke forth from his sullen gloom like a lightning flash out of a dark cloud.

"Accursed one!" cried he, with venomous scorn and anger. "And, finding thy solitude wearisome, thou hast severed me likewise from all the warmth of life and enticed me into thy region of unspeakable horror!"

"Giovanni!" exclaimed Beatrice, turning her large bright eyes upon his face. The force of his words had not found its way into her mind; she was merely thunderstruck.

"Yes, poisonous thing!" repeated Giovanni, beside himself with passion. "Thou hast done it! Thou hast blasted me! Thou hast filled my veins with poison! Thou hast made me as hateful, as ugly, as loathsome and deadly a creature as thyself—a world's wonder of hideous monstrosity! Now, if our breath be happily as fatal to ourselves as to all others, let us join our lips in one kiss of unutterable hatred, and so die!"

"What has befallen me?" murmured Beatrice, with a low moan out of her heart. "Holy Virgin, pity me, a poor heart broken child!"

"Thou—dost thou pray?" cried Giovanni, still with the same fiendish scorn. "Thy very prayers, as they come from thy lips, taint the atmosphere with death. Yes, yes; let us pray! Let us to church and dip our fingers in the holy water at the portal! They that come after us will perish as by a pestilence! Let us sign crosses in the air! It will be scattering curses abroad in the likeness of holy symbols!"

"Giovanni," said Beatrice, calmly, for her grief was beyond passion, "why dost thou join thyself with me thus in those terrible words? I, it is true, am the horrible thing thou namest me. But thou—what hast thou to do, save with one other shudder of my hideous misery to go forth out of the garden and mingle with thy race, and forget that there ever crawled on earth such a monster as poor Beatrice?"

"Dost thou pretend ignorance?" asked Giovanni, scowling upon her. "Behold! this power have I gained from the pure daughter of Rappaccini."

There was a swarm of summer insects flitting through the air in search of the food promised by the flower odors of the fatal garden. They circled round Giovanni's head, and were evidently attracted toward him by the same influence which had drawn them for an instant within the sphere of several of the shrubs. He sent forth a breath among them, and smiled bitterly at Beatrice as at least a score of the insects fell dead upon the ground.

"I see it! I see it!" shrieked Beatrice. "It is my father's fatal science! No, no, Giovanni; it was not I! Never! never! I dreamed only to love thee and be with thee a little time, and so to let thee pass away, leaving but thine image in mine heart; for, Giovanni, believe it, though my body be nourished with poison, my spirit is God's creature, and craves love as its daily food. But my father, he has united us in this fearful sympathy. Yes; spurn me, tread upon me, kill me! Oh, what is death after such words as thine? But it was not I. Not for a world of bliss would I have done it."

Giovanni's passion had exhausted itself in its outburst from his lips.

There now came across him a sense, mournful, and not without tenderness, of the intimate and peculiar relationship between Beatrice and
himself. They stood, as it were, in an utter solitude, which would be made
none the less solitary by the densest throng of human life. Ought not,
then, the desert of humanity around them to press this insulated pair
closer together? If they should be cruel to one another, who was there to
be kind to them? Besides, thought Giovanni, might there not still be a
hope of his returning within the limits of ordinary nature, and leading
Beatrice, the redeemed Beatrice, by the hand? O, weak, and selfish, and
unworthy spirit, that could dream of an earthly union and earthly happiness as possible, after such deep love had been so bitterly wronged as
was Beatrice's love by Giovanni's blighting words! No, no; there could be
no such hope. She must pass heavily, with that broken heart, across the
borders of Time—she must bathe her hurts in some fount of paradise,
and forget her grief in the light of immortality, and *there* be well.

But Giovanni did not know it.

"Dear Beatrice," said he, approaching her, while she shrank away as
always at his approach, but now with a different impulse, "dearest
Beatrice, our fate is not yet so desperate. Behold! there is a medicine,
potent, as a wise physician has assured me, and almost divine in its
efficacy. It is composed of ingredients the most opposite to those by
which thy awful father has brought this calamity upon thee and me.
It is distilled of blessed herbs. Shall we not quaff it together, and thus be
purified from evil?"

"Give it me!" said Beatrice, extending her hand to receive the little
silver vial which Giovanni took from his bosom. She added, with a peculiar emphasis, "I will drink; but do thou await the result."

She put Baglioni's antidote to her lips; and, at the same moment, the
figure of Rappaccini emerged from the portal and came slowly towards
the marble fountain. As he drew near, the pale man of science seemed to
gaze with a triumphant expression at the beautiful youth and maiden,
as might an artist who should spend his life in achieving a picture or a
group of statuary and finally be satisfied with his success. He paused;
his bent form grew erect with conscious power; he spread out his hands
over them in the attitude of a father imploring a blessing upon his children; but those were the same hands that had thrown poison into the
stream of their lives. Giovanni trembled. Beatrice shuddered nervously,
and pressed her hand upon her heart.

"My daughter," said Rappaccini, "thou art no longer lonely in the world.
Pluck one of those precious gems from thy sister shrub and bid thy
bridegroom wear it in his bosom. It will not harm him now. My science

and the sympathy between thee and him have so wrought within his system that he now stands apart from common men, as thou dost, daughter of my pride and triumph, from ordinary women. Pass on, then, through the world, most dear to one another and dreadful to all besides!"

"My father," said Beatrice, feebly,—and still as she spoke she kept her hand upon her heart—"wherefore didst thou inflict this miserable doom upon thy child?"

"Miserable!" exclaimed Rappaccini. "What mean you, foolish girl? Dost thou deem it misery to be endowed with marvellous gifts against which no power nor strength could avail an enemy—misery, to be able to quell the mightiest with a breath—misery, to be as terrible as thou art beautiful? Wouldst thou, then, have preferred the condition of a weak woman, exposed to all evil and capable of none?"

"I would fain have been loved, not feared," murmured Beatrice, sinking down upon the ground. "But now it matters not. I am going, father, where the evil which thou hast striven to mingle with my being will pass away like a dream—like the fragrance of these poisonous flowers, which will no longer taint my breath among the flowers of Eden. Farewell, Giovanni! Thy words of hatred are like lead within my heart; but they, too, will fall away as I ascend. Oh, was there not, from the first, more poison in thy nature than in mine?"

To Beatrice—so radically had her earthly part been wrought upon by Rappaccini's skill—as poison had been life, so the powerful antidote was death; and thus the poor victim of man's ingenuity and of thwarted nature, and of the fatality that attends all such efforts of perverted wisdom, perished there, at the feet of her father and Giovanni. Just at that moment Professor Pietro Baglioni looked forth from the window, and called loudly, in a tone of triumph mixed with horror, to the thunder-stricken man of science—

"Rappaccini! Rappaccini! and is *this* the upshot of your experiment!"

"Rappaccini's Daughter" is from a collection of Hawthorne's stories entitled
MOSSES FROM AN OLD MANSE.

George Eliot

1819–1880

Georg Eliot (the pen name of Mary Ann or Marian Evans) was born at Chilvers Coton, Warwickshire, England, November 22, 1819. Limited by an extremely narrow religious upbringing, she managed to school herself in German, Italian, music and literature. When she was twenty-two she made new philosophic friends in Coventry and became a rationalist for the rest of her life. In 1844 she began to translate Strauss's *The Life of Jesus.* After her father died in 1849, she lived abroad for a while.

From 1851 to 1853 she served as assistant editor of the *Westminster Review.* This led to an acquaintance with Herbert Spencer, Carlyle, Francis Newman, and others. In 1851 she met the philosopher George Henry Lewes, who was separated from his wife. He and the future novelist traveled together on the continent. Later they settled in London, in a "singularly happy" union both regarded as a marriage. Their receptions were select and famous.

She published *Scenes of Clerical Life* in 1858. With *Adam Bede,* in the next year, the tremendous reputation of "George Eliot" was made. She brought out *The Mill on the Floss* in 1860 and *Silas Marner* in 1861. That year she spent a month in Florence preparing to write *Romola.* She was offered £10,000 for the copyright and *Cornhill Magazine* paid £7,000 for its serialization.

Between 1866 and 1879, she published *Felix Holt, The Spanish Gypsy* (a blank-verse play), *Middlemarch, Daniel Deronda* (a strong argument against anti-Semitism) and a book of essays, *Impressions of Theophrastus Such.* Her work grew more and more intellectual. Like Tolstoy's later books, it was increasingly weighted with moral pleading.

In 1876 Lewes and George Eliot moved to Witley, near Godalming. Lewes died on November 28, 1878. "Here I and sorrow sit," she wrote in her journal. John W. Cross, a friend since 1869, helped to settle her affairs. In 1880—he forty and she sixty-one—she married him. That same year, on December 22, she died in London.

T*he Lifted Veil* is a fascinating story on several counts. About the middle of the nineteenth century, psychic phenomena of all kinds were so popular that they became half serious parlor games. The spiritualist Fox sisters bewitched New York. A medium from Connecticut, D. D. Home, excited the foreign colony in Florence, where George Eliot studied Savonarola and his times in 1861. Ruskin asked Home to help him get in touch with the sixteenth-century painter Paolo Veronese.

Against this background, Latimer, the narrator in *The Lifted Veil,* might have been a fashionable hero of his time. He is both telepathic and clairvoyant—that is, he can receive and read other people's streams of consciousness, and he has accurate visions of future events and scenes not otherwise known to him. Both talents, verified or not, are included under the current term ESP or psi cognition.

Given these talents, plus a sensibility so acute that he can hardly bear the ordinary stresses of life, and Latimer becomes one of the most exasperating characters in English fiction. What does he do? Nothing—or as nearly nothing as any man can and still remain alive. No character in a Russian novel is so helplessly inert. He has a taste for poetry, perhaps some gift. How can he know unless he tries? He does not try. His qualifications as a mind reader and clairvoyant might have made him the most sought-after man in London. Instead, they remain his secret terror. He makes no use of them.

His one positive act is his marriage to Bertha. On this the story revolves. Cautiously enough, the author makes Latimer's psychic powers stop short of penetrating his wife's thoughts. There he draws a blank, or shows only the most ordinary awareness. We grant the

---

Notes from the artist: ". . . the profile of George Eliot is superimposed over a facsimile of the original manuscript of her novel Adam Bede.*"*

Page of the MS. of "Adam Bede"

George Eliot

ironic rightness of this. He is not the first or last husband whose insight fails to include his wife. But what if the author had not done this? What if she had allowed Latimer to see into his wife's mind? And what if their hostility to each other had become a duel—his psychic powers against her feminine penetration?

But we see at once that Latimer is not the man for it. If we allow for his limitations, as the author intended we should, he becomes the center of a solidly written story. His psychic gift works as a technical device. It allows the author to foretell each crisis in his life, even the last, but with one exception: Bertha's plot against him. This is revealed, almost by chance, in the doctor's experiment. Only then does Latimer—and the reader—understand the depth of her hatred.

The Lifted Veil

CHAPTER I

T he time of my end approaches. I have lately been subject to attacks of angina pectoris; and in the ordinary course of things, my physician tells me, I may fairly hope that my life will not be protracted many months. Unless, then, I am cursed with an exceptional physical constitution, as I am cursed with an exceptional mental character, I shall not much longer groan under the wearisome burden of this earthly existence. If it were to be otherwise—if I were to live on to the age most men desire and provide for—I should for once have known whether the miseries of delusive expectation can outweigh the miseries of true prevision. For I foresee when I shall die, and everything that will happen in my last moments.

Just a month from this day, on September 20, 1850, I shall be sitting in this chair, in this study, at ten o'clock at night, longing to die, weary of incessant insight and foresight, without delusions and without hope. Just as I am watching a tongue of blue flame rising in the fire, and my lamp is burning low, the horrible contraction will begin at my chest. I shall only have time to reach the bell, and pull it violently, before the sense of suffocation will come. No one will answer my bell. I know why. My two servants are lovers, and will have quarrelled. My housekeeper will have rushed out of the house in a fury, two hours before, hoping that Perry will believe she has gone to drown herself. Perry is alarmed at last, and is gone out after her. The little scullery-maid is asleep on a bench: she never answers the bell; it does not wake her. The sense of suffocation increases: my lamp goes out with a horrible stench: I make a great effort, and snatch at the bell again. I long for life, and there is no help. I thirsted for the unknown: the thirst is gone. O God, let me stay with

the known, and be weary of it: I am content. Agony of pain and suffocation—and all the while the earth, the fields, the pebbly brook at the bottom of the rookery, the fresh scent after the rain, the light of the morning through my chamber-window, the warmth of the hearth after the
frosty air—will darkness close over them forever?

Darkness—darkness—no pain—nothing but darkness: but I am passing on and on through the darkness: my thought stays in the darkness,
but always with a sense of moving onward. . . .

Before that time comes, I wish to use my last hours of ease and
strength in telling the strange story of my experience. I have never fully
unbosomed myself to any human being; I have never been encouraged
to trust much in the sympathy of my fellow-men. But we have all a chance
of meeting with some pity, some tenderness, some charity, when we are
dead: it is the living only who cannot be forgiven—the living only from
whom men's indulgence and reverence are held off, like the rain by the
hard east wind. While the heart beats, bruise it—it is your only opportunity; while the eye can still turn towards you with moist, timid entreaty, freeze it with an icy unanswering gaze; while the ear, that delicate
messenger to the inmost sanctuary of the soul, can still take in the tones of
kindness, put it off with hard civility, or sneering compliment, or envious
affectation of indifference; while the creative brain can still throb with
the sense of injustice, with the yearning for brotherly recognition—make
haste—oppress it with your ill-considered judgements, your trivial comparisons, your careless misrepresentations. The heart will by and by be
still—*ubi saeva indignatio ulterius cor lacerare nequit* [Where fierce indignation can no longer tear his heart] [1]; the eye will cease to entreat;
the ear will be deaf; the brain will have ceased from all wants as well as
from all work. Then your charitable speeches may find vent; then you
may remember and pity the toil and the struggle and the failure; then
you may give due honour to the work achieved; then you may find extenuation for errors, and may consent to bury them.

That is a trivial schoolboy text; why do I dwell on it? It has little reference to me, for I shall leave no works behind me for men to honour. I
have no near relatives who will make up, by weeping over my grave,
for the wounds they inflicted on me when I was among them. It is only
the story of my life that will perhaps win a little more sympathy from
strangers when I am dead, than I ever believed it would obtain from
my friends while I was living.

---

1. Jonathan Swift's epitaph, written by himself.

My childhood perhaps seems happier to me than it really was, by contrast with all the after-years. For then the curtain of the future was as impenetrable to me as to other children: I had all their delight in the present hour, their sweet indefinite hopes for the morrow; and I had a tender mother: even now, after the dreary lapse of long years, a slight trace of sensation accompanies the remembrance of her caress as she held me on her knee—her arms round my little body, her cheek pressed on mine. I had a complaint of the eyes that made me blind for a little while, and she kept me on her knee from morning till night. That unequalled love soon vanished out of my life, and even to my childish consciousness it was as if that life had become more chill. I rode my little white pony with the groom by my side as before, but there were no loving eyes looking at me as I mounted, no glad arms opened to me when I came back. Perhaps I missed my mother's love more than most children of seven or eight would have done, to whom the other pleasures of life remained as before; for I was certainly a very sensitive child. I remember still the mingled trepidation and delicious excitement with which I was affected by the tramping of the horses on the pavement in the echoing stables, by the loud resonance of the grooms' voices, by the booming bark of the dogs as my father's carriage thundered under the archway of the courtyard, by the din of the gong as it gave notice of luncheon and dinner. The measured tramp of soldiery which I sometimes heard—for my father's house lay near a county town where there were large barracks —made me sob and tremble; and yet when they were gone past, I longed for them to come back again.

I fancy my father thought me an odd child, and had little fondness for me; though he was very careful in fulfilling what he regarded as a parent's duties. But he was already past the middle of life, and I was not his only son. My mother had been his second wife, and he was five-and-forty when he married her. He was a firm, unbending, intensely orderly man, in root and stem a banker, but with a flourishing graft of the active landholder, aspiring to county influence: one of those people who are always like themselves from day to day, who are uninfluenced by the weather, and neither know melancholy nor high spirits. I held him in great awe, and appeared more timid and sensitive in his presence than at other times; a circumstance which, perhaps, helped to confirm him in the intention to educate me on a different plan from the prescriptive one with which he had complied in the case of my elder brother, already a tall youth at Eton. My brother was to be his representative and successor; he must go to Eton and Oxford, for the sake of making connections, of course: my father was not a man to underrate the bearing of Latin satirists or Greek dramatists on the attainment of an aristocratic position. But, intrinsically, he had slight esteem for "those dead but sceptred spirits"; having qualified himself for forming an independent opinion by reading Potter's *Aeschylus,* and dipping into Francis's *Horace.* To this negative view he added a positive one, derived from a recent connection with mining speculations; namely, that a scientific education was the really useful training for a younger son. Moreover, it was clear that a shy, sensitive boy like me was not fit to encounter the rough experience of a public school. Mr. Letherall had said so very decidedly. Mr. Letherall was a large man in spectacles, who one day took my small head between his large hands, and pressed it here and there in an exploratory, suspicious manner—then placed each of his great thumbs on my temples, and pushed me a little way from him, and stared at me with glittering spectacles. The contemplation appeared to displease him, for he frowned sternly, and said to my father, drawing his thumbs across my eyebrows—

"The deficiency is there, sir—there; and here," he added, touching the upper sides of my head, "here is the excess. That must be brought out, sir, and this must be laid to sleep."

I was in a state of tremor, partly at the vague idea that I was the object of reprobation, partly in the agitation of my first hatred—hatred of this big, spectacled man, who pulled my head about as if he wanted to buy and cheapen it.

I am not aware how much Mr. Letherall had to do with the system afterwards adopted towards me, but it was presently clear that private tutors, natural history, science, and the modern languages, were the appliances by which the defects of my organization were to be remedied. I was very stupid about machines, so I was to be greatly occupied with them; I had no memory for classification, so it was particularly necessary that I should study systematic zoology and botany; I was hungry for human deeds and humane motions, so I was to be plentifully crammed with the mechanical powers, the elementary bodies, and the phenomena of electricity and magnetism. A better-constituted boy would certainly have profited under my intelligent tutors, with their scientific apparatus; and would, doubtless, have found the phenomena of electricity and magnetism as fascinating as I was, every Thursday, assured they were. As it was, I could have paired off, for ignorance of whatever was taught me, with the worst Latin scholar that was ever turned out of a classical academy. I read Plutarch, and Shakespeare, and Don Quixote by the sly, and supplied myself in that way with wandering thoughts, while my tutor was assuring me that "an improved man, as distinguished from an ignorant one, was a man who knew the reason why water ran downhill." I had no desire to be this improved man; I was glad of the running water; I could watch it and listen to it gurgling among the pebbles, and bathing the bright green water-plants, by the hour together. I did not want to know *why* it ran; I had perfect confidence that there were good reasons for what was so very beautiful.

There is no need to dwell on this part of my life. I have said enough to indicate that my nature was of the sensitive, unpractical order, and that it grew up in an uncongenial medium, which could never foster it into happy, healthy development. When I was sixteen I was sent to Geneva to complete my course of education; and the change was a very happy one to me, for the first sight of the Alps, with the setting sun on them, as we descended the Jura, seemed to me like an entrance into heaven; and the three years of my life there were spent in a perpetual sense of exaltation, as if from a draught of delicious wine, at the presence of Nature in all her awful loveliness. You will think, perhaps, that I must have been a poet, from this early sensibility to Nature. But my lot was not so happy as that. A poet pours forth his song and *believes* in the listening ear and answering soul, to which his song will be floated sooner or later. But the poet's sensibility without his voice—the poet's sensibility that finds no vent but in silent tears on the sunny bank, when the noonday light sparkles on the water, or in an inward shudder at the sound of harsh human tones, the sight of a cold human eye—this dumb passion brings with it a fatal solitude of soul in the society of one's fellow-men. My least solitary moments were those in which I pushed off in my boat, at evening, towards the centre of the lake; it seemed to me that the sky, and the glowing mountain tops, and the wide blue water, surrounded me with a cherishing love such as no human face had shed on me since my mother's love had vanished out of my life. I used to do as Jean Jacques did— lie down in my boat and let it glide where it would, while I looked up at the departing glow leaving one mountain top after the other, as if the prophet's chariot of fire were passing over them on its way to the home of light. Then, when the white summits were all sad and corpse-like, I had to push homeward, for I was under careful surveillance, and was allowed no late wanderings. This disposition of mine was not favourable to the formation of intimate friendships among the numerous youths of my own age who are always to be found studying at Geneva. Yet I made *one* such friendship; and, singularly enough, it was with a youth whose intellectual tendencies were the very reverse of my own. I shall call him

Charles Meunier; his real surname—an English one, for he was of English extraction—having since become celebrated. He was an orphan, who lived on a miserable pittance while he pursued the medical studies for which he had a special genius. Strange! that with my vague mind, susceptible and unobservant, hating inquiry and given up to contemplation, I should have been drawn towards a youth whose strongest passion was science. But the bond was not an intellectual one; it came from a source that can happily blend the stupid with the brilliant, the dreamy with the practical; it came from community of feeling. Charles was poor and ugly, derided by Genevese gamins, and not acceptable in drawing-rooms. I saw that he was isolated, as I was, though from a different cause, and, stimulated by a sympathetic resentment, I made timid advances towards him. It is enough to say that there sprang up as much comradeship between us as our different habits would allow; and in Charles's rare holidays we went up the Salève together, or took the boat to Vevey, while I listened dreamily to the monologues in which he unfolded his bold conceptions of future experiment and discovery. I mingled them confusedly in my thought with glimpses of blue water and delicate floating cloud, with the notes of birds and the distant glitter of the glacier. He knew quite well that my mind was half absent, yet he liked to talk to me in this way; for don't we talk of our hopes and our projects even to dogs and birds, when they love us? I have mentioned this one friendship because of its connection with a strange and terrible scene which I shall have to narrate in my subsequent life.

This happier life at Geneva was put an end to by a severe illness, which is partly a blank to me, partly a time of dimly-remembered suffering, with the presence of my father by my bed from time to time. Then came the languid monotony of convalescence, the days gradually breaking into variety and distinctness as my strength enabled me to take longer and longer drives. On one of these more vividly remembered days, my father said to me, as he sat beside my sofa—

"When you are quite well enough to travel, Latimer, I shall take you home with me. The journey will amuse you and do you good, for I shall go through the Tirol and Austria, and you will see many new places. Our neighbours, the Filmores, are come; Alfred will join us at Basel, and we shall all go together to Vienna, and back by Prague. . . ."

My father was called away before he had finished his sentence, and he left my mind resting on the word *Prague*, with a strange sense that a new and wondrous scene was breaking upon me: a city under the broad sunshine, that seemed to me as if it were the summer sunshine of a long-past century arrested in its course—unrefreshed for ages by dews of night, or the rushing rain-cloud; scorching the dusty, weary, time-eaten grandeur of a people doomed to live on in the stale repetition of memories, like deposed and superannuated kings in their regal gold-inwoven tatters. The city looked so thirsty that the broad river seemed to me a sheet of metal; and the blackened statues, as I passed under their blank gaze, along the unending bridge, with their ancient garments and their saintly crowns, seemed to me the real inhabitants and owners of this place, while the busy, trivial men and women, hurrying to and fro, were a swarm of ephemeral visitants infesting it for a day. It is such grim, stony beings as these, I thought, who are the fathers of ancient faded children, in those tanned time-fretted dwellings that crowd the steep before me; who pay their court in the worn and crumbling pomp of the palace which stretches its monotonous length on the height; who worship wearily in the stifling air of the churches, urged by no fear or hope, but compelled by their doom to be ever old and undying, to live on in the rigidity of habit, as they live on in perpetual midday, without the repose of night or the new birth of morning.

A stunning clang of metal suddenly thrilled through me, and I became conscious of the objects in my room again: one of the fire-irons had fallen as Pierre opened the door to bring me my draught. My heart was palpitating violently, and I begged Pierre to leave my draught beside me; I would take it presently.

As soon as I was alone again, I began to ask myself whether I had been sleeping. Was this a dream—this wonderfully distinct vision—minute in its distinctness down to a patch of rainbow light on the pavement, transmitted through a coloured lamp in the shape of a star—of a strange city, quite unfamiliar to my imagination? I had seen no picture of Prague: it lay in my mind as a mere name, with vaguely-remembered historical associations—ill-defined memories of imperial grandeur and religious wars.

Nothing of this sort had ever occurred in my dreaming experience before, for I had often been humiliated because my dreams were only saved from being utterly disjointed and commonplace by the frequent terrors of nightmare. But I could not believe that I had been asleep, for I remembered distinctly the gradual breaking in of the vision upon me, like the new images in a dissolving view, or the growing distinctness of the landscape as the sun lifts up the veil of the morning mist. And while I was conscious of this incipient vision, I was also conscious that Pierre came to tell my father Mr. Filmore was waiting for him, and that my father hurried out of the room. No, it was not a dream; was it—the thought was full of tremulous exultation—was it the poet's nature in me, hitherto only a troubled yearning sensibility, now manifesting itself suddenly as spontaneous creation? Surely it was in this way that Homer saw the plain of Troy, that Dante saw the abodes of the departed, that Milton saw the earthward flight of the Tempter. Was it that my illness had wrought some happy change in my organization—given a firmer tension to my nerves—carried off some dull obstruction? I had often read of such effects—in works of fiction at least. Nay; in genuine biographies I had read of the subtilizing or exalting influence of some diseases on the mental powers. Did not Novalis feel his inspiration intensified under the progress of consumption?

When my mind had dwelt for some time on this blissful idea, it seemed to me that I might perhaps test it by an exertion of my will. The vision had begun when my father was speaking of our going to Prague. I did not for a moment believe it was really a representation of that city; I believed—I hoped it was a picture that my newly liberated genius had painted in fiery haste, with the colours snatched from lazy memory. Suppose I were to fix my mind on some other place—Venice, for example, which was far more familiar to my imagination than Prague: perhaps the same sort of result would follow. I concentrated my thoughts on Venice; I stimulated my imagination with poetic memories, and strove to feel myself present in Venice, as I had felt myself present in Prague. But in vain. I was only colouring the Canaletto engravings that hung in my old bedroom at home; the picture was a shifting one, my mind wandering uncertainly in search of more vivid images; I could see no accident of form or shadow without conscious labour after the necessary conditions. It was all prosaic effort, not rapt passivity, such as I had experienced half an hour before. I was discouraged; but I remembered that inspiration was fitful.

For several days I was in a state of excited expectation, watching for a recurrence of my new gift. I sent my thoughts ranging over my world of knowledge, in the hope that they would find some object which would send a reawakening vibration through my slumbering genius. But no; my world remained as dim as ever, and that flash of strange light refused to come again, though I watched for it with palpitating eagerness.

My father accompanied me every day in a drive, and a gradually lengthening walk as my powers of walking increased; and one evening he had agreed to come and fetch me at twelve the next day, that we might go together to select a musical box, and other purchases rigorously demanded of a rich Englishman visiting Geneva. He was one of the most punctual of men and bankers, and I was always nervously anxious to be quite ready for him at the appointed time. But, to my surprise, at a quarter past twelve he had not appeared. I felt all the impatience of a convalescent who has nothing particular to do, and who has just taken a tonic in the prospect of immediate exercise that would carry off the stimulus.

Unable to sit still and reserve my strength, I walked up and down the room, looking out on the current of the Rhône, just where it leaves the dark-blue lake; but thinking all the while of the possible causes that could detain my father.

Suddenly I was conscious that my father was in the room, but not alone: there were two persons with him. Strange! I had heard no footstep, I had not seen the door open; but I saw my father, and at his right hand our neighbour Mrs. Filmore, whom I remembered very well, though I had not seen her for five years. She was a commonplace middle-aged woman, in silk and cashmere; but the lady on the left of my father was not more than twenty, a tall, slim, willowy figure, with luxuriant blond hair, arranged in cunning braids and folds that looked almost too massive for the slight figure and the small-featured, thin-lipped face they crowned. But the face had not a girlish expression: the features were sharp, the pale grey eyes at once acute, restless, and sarcastic. They were fixed on me in half-smiling curiosity, and I felt a painful sensation as if a sharp wind were cutting me. The pale-green dress, and the green leaves that seemed to form a border about her pale blond hair, made me think of a Water-Nixie—for my mind was full of German lyrics, and this pale, fatal-eyed woman, with the green weeds, looked like a birth from some cold sedgy stream, the daughter of an aged river.

"Well Latimer, you thought me long," my father said. . . .

But while the last word was in my ears, the whole group vanished, and there was nothing between me and the Chinese painted folding-screen that stood before the door. I was cold and trembling; I could only totter forward and throw myself on the sofa. This strange new power had manifested itself again. . . . But *was* it a power? Might it not rather be a disease—a sort of intermittent delirium, concentrating my energy of brain into moments of unhealthy activity, and leaving my saner hours all the more barren? I felt a dizzy sense of unreality in what my eye rested on; I grasped the bell convulsively, like one trying to free himself from nightmare, and rang it twice. Pierre came with a look of alarm in his face.

"*Monsieur ne se trouve pas bien?*" he said anxiously.

"I'm tired of waiting, Pierre," I said, as distinctly and emphatically as I could, like a man determined to be sober in spite of wine; "I'm afraid something has happened to my father—he's usually so punctual. Run to the Hôtel des Bergues and see if he is there."

Pierre left the room at once, with a soothing "Bien, Monsieur"; and I felt the better for this scene of simple, waking prose. Seeking to calm myself still further, I went into my bedroom, adjoining the *salon*, and opened a case of eau-de-Cologne; took out a bottle; went through the process of taking out the cork very neatly, and then rubbed the reviving spirit over my hands and forehead, and under my nostrils, drawing a new delight from the scent because I had procured it by slow details of labour, and by no strange sudden madness. Already I had begun to taste something of the horror that belongs to the lot of a human being whose nature is not adjusted to simple human conditions.

Still enjoying the scent, I returned to the *salon*, but it was not unoccupied, as it had been before I left it. In front of the Chinese folding-screen there was my father, with Mrs. Filmore on his right hand, and on his left —the slim, blond-haired girl, with the keen face and the keen eyes fixed on me in half-smiling curiosity.

"Well, Latimer, you thought me long," my father said. . . .

I heard no more, felt no more, till I became conscious that I was lying with my head low on the sofa, Pierre, and my father by my side. As soon as I was thoroughly revived, my father left the room, and presently returned, saying—

"I've been to tell the ladies how you are, Latimer. They were waiting in the next room. We shall put off our shopping expedition to-day."

Presently he said, "That young lady is Bertha Grant, Mrs. Filmore's orphan niece. Filmore has adopted her, and she lives with them, so you will have her for a neighbour when we go home—perhaps for a near relation; for there is a tenderness between her and Alfred, I suspect, and I should be gratified by the match, since Filmore means to provide for her in every way as if she were his daughter. It had not occurred to me that you knew nothing about her living with the Filmores."

He made no further allusion to the fact of my having fainted at the moment of seeing her, and I would not for the world have told him the reason: I shrank from the idea of disclosing to any one what might be regarded as a pitiable peculiarity, most of all from betraying it to my father, who would have suspected my sanity ever after.

I do not mean to dwell with particularity on the details of my experience. I have described these two cases at length, because they had definite, clearly traceable results in my afterlot.

Shortly after this last occurrence—I think the very next day—I began to be aware of a phase in my abnormal sensibility, to which, from the languid and slight nature of my intercourse with others since my illness, I had not been alive before. This was the obtrusion on my mind of the mental process going forward in first one person, and then another, with whom I happened to be in contact: the vagrant, frivolous ideas and emotions of some uninteresting acquaintance—Mrs. Filmore, for example—would force themselves on my consciousness like an importunate, ill-played musical instrument, or the loud activity of an imprisoned insect. But this unpleasant sensibility was fitful, and left me moments of rest, when the souls of my companions were once more shut out from me, and I felt a relief such as silence brings to wearied nerves. I might have believed this importunate insight to be merely a diseased activity of the imagination, but that my prevision of incalculable words and actions proved it to have a fixed relation to the mental process in other minds. But this superadded consciousness, wearying and annoying enough when it urged on me the trivial experience of indifferent people, became an intense pain and grief when it seemed to be opening to me the souls of those who were in a close relation to me—when the rational talk, the graceful attentions, the wittily-turned phrases, and the kindly deeds, which used to make the web of their characters, were seen as if thrust asunder by a microscopic vision, that showed all the intermediate frivolities, all the suppressed egoism, all the struggling chaos of puerilities, meanness, vague capricious memories, and indolent make-shift thoughts, from which human words and deeds emerge like leaflets covering a fermenting heap.

At Basel we were joined by my brother Alfred, now a handsome, self-confident man of six-and-twenty—a thorough contrast to my fragile, nervous, ineffectual self. I believe I was held to have a sort of half-womanish, half-ghostly beauty; for the portrait-painters, who are thick as weeds at Geneva, had often asked me to sit to them, and I had been the model of a dying minstrel in a fancy picture. But I thoroughly disliked my own physique and nothing but the belief that it was a condition of poetic genius would have reconciled me to it. That brief hope was quite fled, and I saw in my face now nothing but the stamp of a morbid organization, framed for passive suffering—too feeble for the sublime resistance of poetic production. Alfred, from whom I had been almost constantly separated, and who, in his present stage of character and appearance, came before me as a perfect stranger, was bent on being extremely friendly and brotherlike to me. He had the superficial kindness of a good-humoured, self-satisfied nature, that fears no rivalry, and has encountered no contrarieties. I am not sure that my disposition was good enough for me to have been quite free from envy towards him, even if our desires had not clashed, and if I had been in the healthy human condition which admits of generous confidence and charitable construction. There must always have been an antipathy between our natures. As it was, he became in a few weeks an object of intense hatred to me; and when he entered the room, still more when he spoke, it was as if a sensation of grating metal had set my teeth on edge. My diseased consciousness was more intensely and continually occupied with his thoughts and emotions, than with those of any other person who came in my way. I was perpetually exasperated with the petty promptings of his conceit and his love of patronage, with his self-complacent belief in Bertha Grant's passion for him, with his half-pitying contempt for me—seen not in the ordinary indications of intonation and phrase and slight action, which an acute and suspicious mind is on the watch for, but in all their naked skinless complication.

For we were rivals, and our desires clashed, though he was not aware of it. I have said nothing yet of the effect Bertha Grant produced in me on a nearer acquaintance. That effect was chiefly determined by the fact that she made the only exception, among all the human beings about me, to my unhappy gift of insight. About Bertha I was always in a state of uncertainty: I could watch the expression of her face, and speculate on its meaning; I could ask for her opinion with the real interest of ignorance; I could listen for her words and watch for her smile with hope and fear: she had for me the fascination of an unravelled destiny. I say it was this fact that chiefly determined the strong effect she produced on me: for, in the abstract, no womanly character could seem to have less affinity for that of a shrinking, romantic, passionate youth than Bertha's. She was keen, sarcastic, unimaginative, prematurely cynical, remaining critical and unmoved in the most impressive scenes, inclined to dissect all my favourite poems, and especially contemptuous towards the German lyrics which were my pet literature at that time. To this moment I am unable to define my feeling towards her: it was not ordinary boyish admiration, for she was the very opposite, even to the colour of her hair, of the ideal woman who still remained to me the type of loveliness; and she was without that enthusiasm for the great and good, which, even at the moment of her strongest dominion over me, I should have declared to be the highest element of character. But there is no tyranny more complete than that which a self-centred negative nature exercises over a morbidly sensitive nature perpetually craving sympathy and support. The most independent people feel the effect of a man's silence in heightening their value for his opinion—feel an additional triumph in conquering the reverence of a critic habitually captious and satirical: no wonder, then, that an enthusiastic self-distrusting youth should watch and wait before the closed secret of a sarcastic woman's face, as if it were the shrine of the doubtfully benignant deity who ruled his destiny. For a young enthusiast is unable to imagine the total negation in another mind of the emotions which are stirring his own: they may be feeble, latent, inactive, he thinks, but they are there—they may be called forth; sometimes, in moments of happy hallucination, he believes they may be there in all the greater strength because he sees no outward sign of them. And this effect, as I have intimated, was heightened to its utmost intensity in me, because Bertha was the only being who remained for me in the mysterious seclusion of soul that renders such youthful delusion possible. Doubtless there was another sort of fascination at work—that subtle physical attraction which delights in cheating our psychological predictions, and in compelling the men who paint sylphs, to fall in love with some *bonne et brave femme,* heavy-heeled and freckled.

Bertha's behaviour towards me was such as to encourage all my illusions, to heighten my boyish passion, and make me more and more dependent on her smiles. Looking back with my present wretched knowledge, I conclude that her vanity and love of power were intensely gratified by the belief that I had fainted on first seeing her purely from the strong impression her person had produced on me. The most prosaic woman likes to believe herself the object of a violent, a poetic passion; and without a grain of romance in her, Bertha had that spirit of intrigue which gave piquancy to the idea that the brother of the man she meant to marry was dying with love and jealousy for her sake. That she meant to marry my brother was what at that time I did not believe; for though he was assiduous in his attentions to her, and I knew well enough that both he and my father had made up their minds to this result, there was not yet an understood engagement—there had been no explicit declaration; and Bertha habitually, while she flirted with my brother, and accepted his homage in a way that implied to him a thorough recognition of its intention, made me believe, by the subtlest looks and phrases —feminine nothings which could never be quoted against her—that he was really the object of her secret ridicule; that she thought him, as I did, a coxcomb, whom she would have pleasure in disappointing. Me she openly petted in my brother's presence, as if I were too young and sickly ever to be thought of as a lover; and that was the view he took of me. But I believe she must inwardly have delighted in the tremors into which she threw me by the coaxing way in which she patted my curls, while she laughed at my quotations. Such caresses were always given in the presence of our friends; for when we were alone together, she affected a much greater distance towards me, and now and then took the opportunity, by words or slight actions, to stimulate my foolish timid hope that she really preferred me. And why should she not follow her inclination? I was not in so advantageous a position as my brother, but I had fortune, I was not a year younger than she was, and she was an heiress, who would soon be of age to decide for herself.

The fluctuations of hope and fear, confined to this one channel, made each day in her presence a delicious torment. There was one deliberate act of hers which especially helped to intoxicate me. When we were at Vienna her twentieth birthday occurred, and as she was very fond of ornaments, we all took the opportunity of the splendid jewellers' shops in that Teutonic Paris to purchase her a birthday present of jewellery. Mine, naturally, was the least expensive; it was an opal ring—the opal was my favourite stone, because it seems to blush and turn pale as if it had a soul. I told Bertha so when I gave it her, and said that it was an emblem of the poetic nature, changing with the changing light of heaven and of woman's eyes. In the evening she appeared elegantly dressed, and wearing conspicuously all the birthday presents except mine. I looked eagerly at her fingers, but saw no opal. I had no opportunity of noticing this to her during the evening; but the next day, when I found her seated near the window alone, after breakfast, I said, "You scorn to wear my poor opal. I should have remembered that you despised poetic natures, and should have given you coral, or turquoise, or some other opaque unresponsive stone." "Do I despise it?" she answered, taking hold of a delicate gold chain which she always wore round her neck and drawing out the end from her bosom with my ring hanging to it; "it hurts me a little, I can tell you," she said, with her usual dubious smile, "to wear it in that secret place; and since your poetical nature is so stupid as to prefer a more public position, I shall not endure the pain any longer."

She took off the ring from the chain and put it on her finger, smiling still, while the blood rushed to my cheeks, and I could not trust myself to say a word of entreaty that she would keep the ring where it was before.

I was completely fooled by this, and for two days shut myself up in my own room whenever Bertha was absent, that I might intoxicate myself afresh with the thought of this scene and all it implied.

I should mention that during these two months—which seemed a long life to me from the novelty and intensity of the pleasures and pains I underwent—my diseased participation in other people's consciousness continued to torment me; now it was my father, and now my brother, now Mrs. Filmore or her husband, and now our German courier, whose stream of thought rushed upon me like a ringing in the ears not to be got rid of, though it allowed my own impulses and ideas to continue their uninterrupted course. It was like a preternaturally heightened sense of hearing, making audible to one a roar of sound where others find perfect stillness. The weariness and disgust of this involuntary intrusion into other souls was counteracted only by my ignorance of Bertha, and my growing passion for her; a passion enormously stimulated, if not produced, by that ignorance. She was my oasis of mystery in the dreary desert of knowledge. I had never allowed my diseased condition to betray itself, or to drive me into any unusual speech or action, except once, when, in a moment of peculiar bitterness against my brother, I had forestalled some words which I knew he was going to utter—a clever observation, which he had prepared beforehand. He had occasionally a slightly-affected hesitation in his speech, and when he paused an instant after the second word, my impatience and jealousy impelled me to continue the speech for him, as if it were something we had both learned by rote. He coloured and looked astonished, as well as annoyed; and the words had no sooner escaped my lips than I felt a shock of alarm lest such an anticipation of words—very far from being words of course, easy to divine—should have betrayed me as an exceptional being, a sort of quiet energumen, whom every one, Bertha above all, would shudder at and avoid. But I magnified, as usual, the impression any word or deed of mine could produce on others; for no one gave any sign of having noticed my interruption as more than a rudeness, to be forgiven me on the score of my feeble nervous condition.

While this superadded consciousness of the actual was almost constant with me, I had never had a recurrence of that distinct prevision which I have described in relation to my first interview with Bertha; and I was waiting with eager curiosity to know whether or not my vision of Prague would prove to have been an instance of the same kind. A few days after the incident of the opal ring, we were paying one of our frequent visits to the Lichtenberg Palace. I could never look at many pictures in succession; for pictures, when they are at all powerful, affect me so strongly that one or two exhaust all my capability of contemplation. This morning I had been looking at Giorgione's picture of the cruel-eyed woman, said to be a likeness of Lucrezia Borgia. I had stood long alone before it, fascinated by the terrible reality of that cunning, relentless face, till I felt a strange poisoned sensation, as if I had long been inhaling a fatal odour, and was just beginning to be conscious of its effects. Perhaps even then I should not have moved away, if the rest of the party had not returned to this room, and announced that they were going to the Belvedere Gallery to settle a bet which had arisen between my brother and Mr. Filmore about a portrait. I followed them dreamily, and was hardly alive to what occurred till they had all gone up to the gallery, leaving me below; for I refused to come within sight of another picture that day. I made my way to the Grand Terrace, since it was agreed that we should saunter in the gardens when the dispute had been decided. I had been sitting here a short space, vaguely conscious of trim gardens, with a city and green hills in the distance, when, wishing to avoid the proximity of the sentinel, I rose and walked down the broad stone steps, intending to seat myself farther on in the gardens. Just as I reached the gravel-walk, I felt an arm slipped within mine, and a light hand gently pressing my wrist. In the same instant a strange intoxicating numbness passed over me, like the continuance or climax of the sensation I was still feeling from the gaze of Lucrezia Borgia. The gardens, the summer sky, the consciousness of Bertha's arm being within mine, all vanished, and I seemed to be suddenly in darkness, out of which there gradually broke a dim firelight, and I felt myself sitting in my father's leather chair in the library at home. I knew the fireplace—the dogs for the wood-fire—the black marble chimneypiece with the white marble medallion of the dying Cleopatra in the centre. Intense and hopeless misery was pressing on my soul; the light became stronger, for Bertha was entering with a candle in her hand—Bertha, my wife—with cruel eyes, with green jewels and green leaves on her white ball-dress; every hateful thought within her present to me. . . . "Madman, idiot! Why don't you kill yourself, then?" It was a moment of hell. I saw into her pitiless soul—saw its barren worldliness, its scorching hate—and felt it clothe me round like an air I was obliged to breathe. She came with her candle and stood over me with a bitter smile of contempt; I saw the great emerald brooch on her bosom, a studded serpent with diamond eyes. I shuddered—I de-spised this woman with the barren soul and mean thoughts; but I felt helpless before her, as if she clutched my bleeding heart, and would clutch it till the last drop of life-blood ebbed away. She was my wife, and we hated each other. Gradually the hearth, the dim library, the candle-light disappeared—seemed to melt away into a background of light, the green serpent with the diamond eyes remaining a dark image on the retina. Then I had a sense of my eyelids quivering, and the living daylight broke in upon me; I saw gardens, and heard voices; I was seated on the steps of the Belvedere Terrace, and my friends were round me.

The tumult of mind into which I was thrown by this hideous vision made me ill for several days, and prolonged our stay at Vienna. I shud-dered with horror as the scene recurred to me; and it recurred constantly, with all its minutiae, as if they had been burnt into my memory; and yet, such is the madness of the human heart under the influence of its immediate desires, I felt a wild hell-braving joy that Bertha was to be mine; for the fulfilment of my former prevision concerning her first ap-pearance before me, left me little hope that this last hideous glimpse of the future was the mere diseased play of my own mind, and had no re-lation to external realities. One thing alone I looked towards as a possible means of casting doubt on my terrible conviction—the discovery that my vision of Prague had been false—and Prague was the next city on our route.

Meanwhile, I was no sooner in Bertha's society again, than I was as completely under her sway as before. What if I saw into the heart of Bertha, the matured woman—Bertha, my wife? Bertha, the *girl*, was a fascinating secret to me still: I trembled under her touch; I felt the witch-ery of her presence; I yearned to be assured of her love. The fear of poi-son is feeble against the sense of thirst. Nay, I was just as jealous of my brother as before—just as much irritated by his small patronizing ways; for my pride, my diseased sensibility, were there as they had always been, and winced as inevitably under every offence as my eye winced from an intruding mote. The future, even when brought within the com-pass of feeling by a vision that made me shudder, had still no more than the force of an idea, compared with the force of present emotion—of my love for Bertha, of my dislike and jealousy towards my brother.

It is an old story, that men sell themselves to the tempter, and sign a bond with their blood, because it is only to take effect at a distant day; then rush on to snatch the cup their souls thirst after with an impulse not the less savage because there is a dark shadow beside them for evermore.

There is no short cut, no patent tram-road, to wisdom: after all the centuries of invention, the soul's path lies through the thorny wilderness which must be still trodden in solitude, with bleeding feet, with sobs for help, as it was trodden by them of old time.

My mind speculated eagerly on the means by which I should become my brother's successful rival, for I was still too timid, in my ignorance of Bertha's actual feeling, to venture on any step that would urge from her an avowal of it. I thought I should gain confidence even for this, if my vision of Prague proved to have been veracious; and yet, the horror of that certitude! Behind the slim girl Bertha, whose words and looks I watched for, whose touch was bliss, there stood continually that Bertha with the fuller form, the harder eyes, the more rigid mouth—with the barren, selfish soul laid bare; no longer a fascinating secret, but a measured fact, urging itself perpetually on my unwilling sight. Are you unable to give me your sympathy—you who read this? Are you unable to imagine this double consciousness at work within me, flowing on like two parallel streams which never mingle their waters and blend into a common hue? Yet you must have known something of the presentiments that spring from an insight at war with passion; and my visions were only like presentiments intensified to horror. You have known the powerlessness of ideas before the might of impulse; and my visions, when once they had passed into memory, were mere ideas—and pale shadows that beckoned in vain, while my hand was grasped by the living and the loved.

In after-days I thought with bitter regret that if I had foreseen something more or something different—if instead of that hideous vision which poisoned the passion it could not destroy, or if even along with it I could have had a foreshadowing of that moment when I looked on my brother's face for the last time, some softening influence would have been shed over my feeling towards him: pride and hatred would surely have been subdued into pity, and the record of those hidden sins would have been shortened. But this is one of the vain thoughts with which we men flatter ourselves. We try to believe that the egoism within us would have easily been melted, and that it was only the narrowness of our knowledge which hemmed in our generosity, our awe, our human piety, and hindered them from submerging our hard indifference to the sensations and emotions of our fellows. Our tenderness and self-renunciation seem strong when our egoism has had its day—when, after our mean striving for a triumph that is to be another's loss, the triumph comes suddenly, and we shudder at it, because it is held out by the chill hand of death.

Our arrival in Prague happened at night, and I was glad of this, for it seemed like a deferring of a terribly decisive moment, to be in the city for hours without seeing it. As we were not to remain long in Prague, but to go on speedily to Dresden, it was proposed that we should drive out the next morning and take a general view of the place, as well as visit some of its specially interesting spots, before the heat became oppressive —for we were in August, and the season was hot and dry. But it happened that the ladies were rather late at their morning toilet, and to my father's politely-repressed but perceptible annoyance, we were not in the carriage till the morning was far advanced. I thought with a sense of relief, as we entered the Jews' quarter, where we were to visit the old synagogue, that we should be kept in this flat, shut-up part of the city, until we should all be too tired and too warm to go farther, and so we should return without seeing more than the streets through which we had already passed. That would give me another day's suspense—suspense, the only form in which a fearful spirit knows the solace of hope. But, as I stood under the blackened, groined arches of that old synagogue, made dimly visible by the seven thin candles in the sacred lamp, while our Jewish cicerone reached down the Book of the Law, and read to us in its ancient tongue—I felt a shuddering impression that this strange building, with its shrunken lights, this surviving withered remnant of medieval Judaism, was of a piece with my vision. Those darkened dusty Christian saints, with their loftier arches and their larger candles, needed the consolatory scorn with which they might point to a more shrivelled death-in-life than their own.

As I expected, when we left the Jews' quarter the elders of our party wished to return to the hotel. But now, instead of rejoicing in this, as I had done beforehand, I felt a sudden overpowering impulse to go on at once to the bridge, and put an end to the suspense I had been wishing to protract. I declared, with unusual decision, that I would get out of the carriage and walk on alone; they might return without me. My father, thinking this merely a sample of my usual "poetic nonsense," objected that I should only do myself harm by walking in the heat; but when I persisted, he said angrily that I might follow my own absurd devices, but that Schmidt (our courier) must go with me. I assented to this, and set off with Schmidt towards the bridge. I had no sooner passed from under the archway of the grand old gate leading on to the bridge than a trembling seized me, and I turned cold under the midday sun; yet I went on; I was in search of something—a small detail which I remembered with special intensity as part of my vision. There it was—the patch of rainbow light on the pavement transmitted through a lamp in the shape of a star.

CHAPTER II

Before the autumn was at an end, and while the brown leaves still
stood thick on the beeches in our park, my brother and Bertha were engaged to each other, and it was understood that their marriage was to
take place early in the next spring. In spite of the certainty I had felt
from that moment on the bridge at Prague, that Bertha would one day
be my wife, my constitutional timidity and distrust had continued to
benumb me, and the words in which I had sometimes premeditated a
confession of my love, had died away unuttered. The same conflict had
gone on within me as before—the longing for an assurance of love from
Bertha's lips, the dread lest a word of contempt and denial should fall
upon me like a corrosive acid. What was the conviction of a distant necessity to me? I trembled under a present glance, I hungered after a present
joy, I was clogged and chilled by a present fear. And so the days passed
on: I witnessed Bertha's engagement and heard her marriage discussed
as if I were under a conscious nightmare—knowing it was a dream that
would vanish, but feeling stifled under the grasp of hard-clutching fingers.

When I was not in Bertha's presence—and I was with her very often,
for she continued to treat me with a playful patronage that wakened no
jealousy in my brother—I spent my time chiefly in wandering, in strolling,
or taking long rides while the daylight lasted, and then shutting myself
up with my unread books; for books had lost the power of chaining my
attention. My self-consciousness was heightened to that pitch of intensity
in which our own emotions take the form of a drama which urges itself
imperatively on our contemplation, and we begin to weep, less under the
sense of our suffering than at the thought of it. I felt a sort of pitying
anguish over the pathos of my own lot: the lot of a being finely organized
for pain, but with hardly any fibres that responded to pleasure—to whom
the idea of future evil robbed the present of its joy, and for whom the
idea of future good did not still the uneasiness of a present yearning or
a present dread. I went dumbly through that stage of the poet's suffering, in which he feels the delicious pang of utterance, and makes an
image of his sorrows.

I was left entirely without remonstrance concerning this dreamy way-
ward life: I knew my father's thought about me: "That lad will never
be good for anything in life: he may waste his years in an insignificant
way on the income that falls to him: I shall not trouble myself about a
career for him."

One mild morning in the beginning of November, it happened that I was standing outside the portico patting lazy old Caesar, a Newfoundland almost blind with age, the only dog that ever took any notice of me— for the very dogs shunned me, and fawned on the happier people about me—when the groom brought up my brother's horse which was to carry him to the hunt, and my brother himself appeared at the door, florid, broad-chested, and self-complacent, feeling what a good-natured fellow he was not to behave insolently to us all on the strength of his great advantages.

"Latimer, old boy," he said to me in a tone of compassionate cordiality, "what a pity it is you don't have a run with the hounds now and then! The finest thing in the world for low spirits!"

"Low spirits!" I thought bitterly, as he rode away; "that is the sort of phrase with which coarse, narrow natures like yours think to describe experience of which you can know no more than your horse knows. It is to such as you that the good of this world falls: ready dullness, healthy selfishness, good-tempered conceit—these are the keys to happiness."

The quick thought came, that my selfishness was even stronger than his—it was only a suffering selfishness instead of an enjoying one. But then, again, my exasperating insight into Alfred's self-complacent soul, his freedom from all the doubts and fears, the unsatisfied yearnings, the exquisite tortures of sensitiveness, that had made the web of my life, seemed to absolve me from all bonds towards him. This man needed no pity, no love; those fine influences would have been as little felt by him as the delicate white mist is felt by the rock it caresses. There was no evil in store for *him:* if he was not to marry Bertha, it would be because he had found a lot pleasanter to himself.

Mr. Filmore's house lay not more than half a mile beyond our own gates, and whenever I knew my brother was gone in another direction, I went there for the chance of finding Bertha at home. Later on in the day I walked thither. By a rare accident she was alone, and we walked out in the grounds together, for she seldom went on foot beyond the trimly-swept gravel-walks. I remember what a beautiful sylph she looked to me as the low November sun shone on her blond hair, and she tripped along teasing me with her usual light banter, to which I listened half fondly, half moodily; it was all the sign Bertha's mysterious inner self ever made to me. To-day perhaps the moodiness predominated, for I had not yet shaken off the access of jealous hate which my brother had raised in me by his parting patronage. Suddenly I interrupted and startled her by saying, almost fiercely, "Bertha, how can you love Alfred?"

She looked at me with surprise for a moment, but soon her light smile came again, and she answered sarcastically, "Why do you suppose I love him?"

"How can you ask that, Bertha?"

"What! Your wisdom thinks I must love the man I'm going to marry? The most unpleasant thing in the world. I should quarrel with him; I should be jealous of him; our ménage would be conducted in a very ill-bred manner. A little quiet contempt contributes greatly to the elegance of life."

"Bertha, that is not your real feeling. Why do you delight in trying to deceive me by inventing such cynical speeches?"

"I need never take the trouble of invention in order to deceive you, my small Tasso"—that was the mocking name she usually gave me. "The easiest way to deceive a poet is to tell him the truth."

She was testing the validity of her epigram in a daring way, and for a moment the shadow of my vision—the Bertha whose soul was no secret to me—passed between me and the radiant girl, the playful sylph whose feelings were a fascinating mystery. I suppose I must have shuddered, or betrayed in some other way my momentary chill of horror.

"Tasso!" she said, seizing my wrist, and peeping round into my face, "are you really beginning to discern what a heartless girl I am? Why, you are not half the poet I thought you were; you are actually capable of believing the truth about me."

The shadow passed from between us, and was no longer the object nearest to me. The girl whose light fingers grasped me, whose elfish charming face looked into mine—who, I thought, was betraying an interest in my feelings that she would not have directly avowed—this warm breathing presence again possessed my senses and imagination like a returning siren melody which had been overpowered for an instant by the roar of threatening waves. It was a moment as delicious to me as the waking up to a consciousness of youth after a dream of middle age. I forgot everything but my passion, and said with swimming eyes—

"Bertha, shall you love me when we are first married? I wouldn't mind if you really loved me only for a little while."

Her look of astonishment, as she loosed my hand and started away from me, recalled me to a sense of my strange, my criminal indiscretion.

"Forgive me," I said, hurriedly, as soon as I could speak again; "I did not know what I was saying."

"Ah, Tasso's mad fit has come on, I see," she answered quietly, for she had recovered herself sooner than I had. "Let him go home and keep his head cool. I must go in, for the sun is setting."

I left her—full of indignation against myself. I had let slip words which, if she reflected on them, might rouse in her a suspicion of my abnormal mental condition—a suspicion which of all things I dreaded. And besides that, I was ashamed of the apparent baseness I had committed in uttering them to my brother's betrothed wife. I wandered home slowly, entering our park through a private gate instead of by the lodges. As I approached the house, I saw a man dashing off at full speed from the stable-yard across the park. Had any accident happened at home? No; perhaps it was only one of my father's peremptory business errands that required this headlong haste.

Nevertheless I quickened my pace without any distinct motive, and was soon at the house. I will not dwell on the scene I found there. My brother was dead—had been pitched from his horse, and killed on the spot by a concussion of the brain.

I went up to the room where he lay, and where my father was seated beside him with a look of rigid despair. I had shunned my father more than any one since our return home, for the radical antipathy between our natures made my insight into his inner self a constant affliction to me. But now, as I went up to him, and stood beside him in sad silence, I felt the presence of a new element that blended us as we had never been blent before. My father had been one of the most successful men in the money-getting world: he had had no sentimental sufferings, no illness. The heaviest trouble that had befallen him was the death of his first wife. But he married my mother soon after; and I remember he seemed exactly the same, to my keen childish observation, the week after her death as before. But now, at last, a sorrow had come—the sorrow of old age, which suffers the more from the crushing of its pride and its hopes, in proportion as the pride and hope are narrow and prosaic. His son was to have been married soon—would probably have stood for the borough at the next election. That son's existence was the best motive that could be alleged for making new purchases of land every year to round off the estate. It is a dreary thing to live on doing the same things year after year, without knowing why we do them. Perhaps the tragedy of disappointed youth and passion is less piteous than the tragedy of disappointed age and worldliness.

As I saw into the desolation of my father's heart, I felt a movement of deep pity towards him, which was the beginning of a new affection—an affection that grew and strengthened in spite of the strange bitterness with which he regarded me in the first month or two after my brother's death. If it had not been for the softening influence of my compassion for him—the first deep compassion I had ever felt—I should have been stung by the perception that my father transferred the inheritance of an eldest son to me with a mortified sense that fate had compelled him to the unwelcome course of caring for me as an important being. It was only in spite of himself that he began to think of me with anxious regard. There is hardly any neglected child for whom death has made vacant a more favoured place, who will not understand what I mean.

Gradually, however, my new deference to his wishes, the effect of that patience which was born of my pity for him, won upon his affection, and he began to please himself with the endeavour to make me fill my brother's place as fully as my feebler personality would admit. I saw that the prospect which by and by presented itself of my becoming Bertha's husband was welcome to him, and he even contemplated in my case what he had not intended in my brother's—that his son and daughter-in-law should make one household with him. My softened feeling towards my father made this the happiest time I had known since childhood— these last months in which I retained the delicious illusion of loving Bertha, of longing and doubting and hoping that she might love me. She behaved with a certain new consciousness and distance towards me after my brother's death; and I too was under a double constraint—that of delicacy towards my brother's memory, and of anxiety as to the impression my abrupt words had left on her mind. But the additional screen this mutual reserve erected between us only brought me more completely under her power: no matter how empty the adytum, so that the veil be thick enough. So absolute is our soul's need of something hidden and uncertain for the maintenance of that doubt and hope and effort which are the breath of its life, that if the whole future were laid bare to us beyond to-day, the interest of all mankind would be bent on the hours that lie between; we should pant after the uncertainties of our one morning and our one afternoon; we should rush fiercely to the Exchange for our last possibility of speculation, of success, of disappointment: we should have a glut of political prophets foretelling a crisis or a no-crisis within the only twenty-four hours left open to prophecy. Conceive the condition of the human mind if all propositions whatsoever were self-evident except one, which was to become self-evident at the close of a summer's day, but in the meantime might be the subject of question, of hypothesis, of debate.

Art and philosophy, literature and science, would fasten like bees on that one proposition which had the honey of probability in it, and be the more eager because their enjoyment would end with sunset. Our impulses, our spiritual activities, no more adjust themselves to the idea of their future nullity, than the beating of our heart, or the irritability of our muscles.

Bertha, the slim, fair-haired girl, whose present thoughts and emotions were an enigma to me amidst the fatiguing obviousness of the other minds around me, was as absorbing to me as a single unknown to-day— as a single hypothetic proposition to remain problematic till sunset; and all the cramped, hemmed-in belief and disbelief, trust and distrust, of my nature, welled out in this one narrow channel.

And she made me believe that she loved me. Without ever quitting her tone of badinage and playful superiority, she intoxicated me with the sense that I was necessary to her, that she was never at ease unless I was near her, submitting to her playful tyranny. It costs a woman so little effort to besot us in this way! A half-repressed word, a moment's unexpected silence, even an easy fit of petulance on our account, will serve us as hashish for a long while. Out of the subtlest web of scarcely perceptible signs, she set me weaving the fancy that she had always unconsciously loved me better than Alfred, but that, with the ignorant fluttered sensibility of a young girl, she had been imposed on by the charm that lay for her in the distinction of being admired and chosen by a man who made so brilliant a figure in the world as my brother. She satirized herself in a very graceful way for her vanity and ambition. What was it to me that I had the light of my wretched provision on the fact that now it was I who possessed at least all but the personal part of my brother's advantages? Our sweet illusions are half of them conscious illusions, like effects of colour that we know to be made up of tinsel, broken glass, and rags.

We were married eighteen months after Alfred's death, one cold, clear morning in April, when there came hail and sunshine both together; and Bertha, in her white silk and pale-green leaves, and the pale hues of her hair and face, looked like the spirit of the morning. My father was happier than he had thought of being again: my marriage, he felt sure, would complete the desirable modification of my character, and make me practical and worldly enough to take my place in society among sane men. For he delighted in Bertha's tact and acuteness, and felt sure she would be mistress of me, and make me what she chose: I was only twenty-one, and madly in love with her. Poor father! He kept that hope a little while after our first year of marriage, and it was not quite extinct when paralysis came and saved him from utter disappointment.

I shall hurry through the rest of my story, not dwelling so much as I have hitherto done on my inward experience. When people are well known to each other, they talk rather of what befalls them externally, leaving their feelings and sentiments to be inferred.

We lived in a round of visits for some time after our return home, giving splendid dinner-parties, and making a sensation in our neighbourhood by the new lustre of our equipage, for my father had reserved this display of his increased wealth for the period of his son's marriage; and we gave our acquaintances liberal opportunity for remarking that it was a pity I made so poor a figure as an heir and a bridegroom. The nervous fatigue of this existence, the insincerities and platitudes which I had to live through twice over—through my inner and outward sense—would have been maddening to me, if I had not had that sort of intoxicated callousness which came from the delights of a first passion. A bride and bridegroom, surrounded by all the appliances of wealth, hurried through the day by the whirl of society, filling their solitary moments with hastily snatched caresses, are prepared for their future life together as the novice is prepared for the cloister—by experiencing its utmost contrast.

Through all these crowded excited months, Bertha's inward self remained shrouded from me, and I still read her thoughts only through the language of her lips and demeanour: I had still the human interest of wondering whether what I did and said pleased her, of longing to hear a word of affection, of giving a delicious exaggeration of meaning to her smile. But I was conscious of a growing difference in her manner towards me; sometimes strong enough to be called haughty coldness, cutting and chilling me as the hail had done that came across the sunshine on our marriage morning; sometimes only perceptible in the dexterous avoidance of a tête-à-tête walk or dinner to which I had been looking forward. I had been deeply pained by this—had even felt a sort of crushing of the heart, from the sense that my brief day of happiness was near its setting; but still I remained dependent on Bertha, eager for the last rays of a bliss that would soon be gone for ever, hoping and watching for some afterglow more beautiful from the impending night.

I remember—how should I not remember?—the time when that dependence and hope utterly left me, when the sadness I had felt in Bertha's growing estrangement became a joy that I looked back upon with longing as a man might look back on the last pains in a paralysed limb. It was just after the close of my father's last illness, which had necessarily withdrawn us from society and thrown us more upon each other. It was the evening of my father's death. On that evening the veil which had shrouded Bertha's soul from me—had made me find in her alone among my fellow-beings the blessed possibility of mystery, and doubt, and expectation—was first withdrawn. Perhaps it was the first day since the beginning of my passion for her, in which that passion was completely neutralized by the presence of an absorbing feeling of another kind. I had been watching by my father's deathbed: I had been witnessing the last fitful yearning glance his soul had cast back on the spent inheritance of life—the last faint consciousness of love he had gathered from the pressure of my hand. What are all our personal loves when we have been sharing in that supreme agony? In the first moments when we come away from the presence of death, every other relation to the living is merged, to our feeling, in the great relation of a common nature and a common destiny.

In that state of mind I joined Bertha in her private sitting-room. She was seated in a leaning posture on a settee, with her back towards the door; the great rich coils of her pale blond hair surmounting her small neck, visible above the back of the settee. I remember, as I closed the door behind me, a cold tremulousness seizing me, and a vague sense of being hated and lonely—vague and strong, like a presentiment. I know how I looked at that moment, for I saw myself in Bertha's thought as she lifted her cutting grey eyes, and looked at me: a miserable ghost-seer, surrounded by phantoms in the noonday, trembling under a breeze when the leaves were still, without appetite for the common objects of human desires, but pining after the moonbeams. We were front to front with each other, and judged each other. The terrible moment of complete illumination had come to me, and I saw that the darkness had hidden no landscape from me, but only a blank prosaic wall: from that evening forth, through the sickening years which followed, I saw all round the narrow room of this woman's soul—saw petty artifice and mere negation where I had delighted to believe in coy sensibilities and in wit at war with latent feeling—saw the light floating vanities of the girl defining themselves into the systematic coquetry, the scheming selfishness, of the woman—saw repulsion and antipathy harden into cruel hatred, giving pain only for the sake of wreaking itself.

For Bertha too, after her kind, felt the bitterness of disillusion. She had believed that my wild poet's passion for her would make me her slave; and that, being her slave, I should execute her will in all things. With the essential shallowness of a negative, unimaginative nature, she was unable to conceive the fact that sensibilities were anything else than weaknesses. She had thought my weaknesses would put me in her power, and she found them unmanageable forces. Our positions were reversed. Before marriage she had completely mastered my imagination, for she was a secret to me; and I created the unknown thought before which I trembled as if it were hers. But now that her soul was laid open to me, now that I was compelled to share the privacy of her motives, to follow all the petty devices that preceded her words and acts, she found herself powerless with me, except to produce in me the chill shudder of repulsion—powerless, because I could be acted on by no lever within her reach. I was dead to worldly ambitions, to social vanities, to all the incentives within the compass of her narrow imagination, and I lived under influences utterly invisible to her.

She was really pitiable to have such a husband, and so all the world thought. A graceful, brilliant woman, like Bertha, who smiled on morning callers, made a figure in ball-rooms, and was capable of that light repartee which, from such a woman, is accepted as wit, was secure of carrying off all sympathy from a husband who was sickly, abstracted, and, as some suspected, crack-brained. Even the servants in our house gave her the balance of their regard and pity. For there were no audible quarrels between us; our alienation, our repulsion from each other, lay within the silence of our own hearts; and if the mistress went out a great deal, and seemed to dislike the master's society, was it not natural, poor thing? The master was odd. I was kind and just to my dependants, but I excited in them a shrinking, half-contemptuous pity; for this class of men and women are but slightly determined in their estimate of others by general considerations, or even experience, of character. They judge of persons as they judge of coins, and value those who pass current at a high rate.

After a time I interfered so little with Bertha's habits that it might seem wonderful how her hatred towards me could grow so intense and active as it did. But she had begun to suspect, by some involuntary betrayal of mine, that there was an abnormal power of penetration in me—that fitfully, at least, I was strangely cognizant of her thoughts and intentions, and she began to be haunted by a terror of me, which alternated every now and then with defiance. She meditated continually how the incubus could be shaken off her life—how she could be freed from this hateful bond to a being whom she at once despised as an imbecile, and dreaded as an inquisitor. For a long while she lived in the hope that my evident

wretchedness would drive me to the commission of suicide; but suicide
was not in my nature. I was too completely swayed by the sense that I
was in the grasp of unknown forces, to believe in my power of self-
release. Towards my own destiny I had become entirely passive; for my
one ardent desire had spent itself, and impulse no longer predominated
over knowledge. For this reason I never thought of taking any steps
towards a complete separation, which would have made our alienation
evident to the world. Why should I rush for help to a new course, when I
was only suffering from the consequences of a deed which had been the
act of my intensest will? That would have been the logic of one who had
desires to gratify, and I had no desires. But Bertha and I lived more and
more aloof from each other. The rich find it easy to live married and
apart.

That course of our life which I have indicated in a few sentences filled
the space of years. So much misery—so slow and hideous a growth of
hatred and sin, may be compressed into a sentence! And men judge of
each other's lives through this summary medium. They epitomize the experience of their fellow-mortal, and pronounce judgment on him in neat
syntax, and feel themselves wise and virtuous—conquerors over the
temptations they define in well-selected predicates. Seven years of
wretchedness glide glibly over the lips of the man who has never
counted them out in moments of chill disappointment, of head and heart
throbbings, of dread and vain wrestling, of remorse and despair. We learn
words by rote, but not their meaning; *that* must be paid for with our life-
blood, and printed in the subtle fibres of our nerves.

But I will hasten to finish my story. Brevity is justified at once to those
who readily understand, and to those who will never understand.

Some years after my father's death, I was sitting by the dim firelight in
my library one January evening—sitting in the leather chair that used to
be my father's—when Bertha appeared at the door, with a candle in her
hand, and advanced towards me. I knew the ball-dress she had on—the
white ball-dress, with the green jewels, shone upon by the light of the
wax candle which lit up the medallion of the dying Cleopatra on the
mantelpiece. Why did she come to me before going out? I had not seen
her in the library, which was my habitual place for months. Why did she
stand before me with the candle in her hand, with her cruel contemptuous eyes fixed on me, and the glittering serpent, like a familiar demon,
on her breast? For a moment I thought this fulfilment of my vision at
Vienna marked some dreadful crisis in my fate, but I saw nothing in
Bertha's mind, as she stood before me, except scorn for the look of over-

whelming misery with which I sat before her. . . . "Fool, idiot, why don't you kill yourself, then?" that was her thought. But at length her thoughts reverted to her errand, and she spoke aloud. The apparently indifferent nature of the errand seemed to make a ridiculous anticlimax to my prevision and my agitation.

"I have had to hire a new maid. Fletcher is going to be married, and she wants me to ask you to let her husband have the public house and farm at Molton. I wish him to have it. You must give the promise now, because Fletcher is going to-morrow morning—and quickly, because I'm in a hurry."

"Very well; you may promise her," I said, indifferently, and Bertha swept out of the library again.

I always shrank from the sight of a new person, and all the more when it was a person whose mental life was likely to weary my reluctant insight with worldly ignorant trivialities. But I shrank especially from the sight of this new maid, because her advent had been announced to me at a moment to which I could not cease to attach some fatality: I had a vague dread that I should find her mixed up with the dreary drama of my life—that some new sickening vision would reveal her to me as an evil genius. When at last I did unavoidably meet her, the vague dread was changed into definite disgust. She was a tall, wiry, dark-eyed woman, this Mrs. Archer, with a face handsome enough to give her coarse hard nature the odious finish of bold, self-confident coquetry. That was enough to make me avoid her, quite apart from the contemptuous feeling with which she contemplated me. I seldom saw her; but I perceived that she rapidly became a favourite with her mistress, and, after the lapse of eight or nine months, I began to be aware that there had arisen in Bertha's mind towards this woman a mingled feeling of fear and dependence, and that this feeling was associated with ill-defined images of candlelight scenes in her dressing-room, and the locking-up of something in Bertha's cabinet. My interviews with my wife had become so brief and so rarely solitary, that I had no opportunity of perceiving these images in her mind with more definiteness. The recollections of the past become contracted in the rapidity of thought till they sometimes bear hardly a more distinct resemblance to the external reality than the forms of an oriental alphabet to the objects that suggested them.

Besides, for the last year or more a modification had been going forward in my mental condition, and was growing more and more marked. My insight into the minds of those around me was becoming dimmer and more fitful, and the ideas that crowded my double consciousness became less and less dependent on any personal contact. All that was personal in me seemed to be suffering a gradual death, so that I was losing the organ through which the personal agitations and projects of others could affect me. But along with this relief from wearisome insight, there was a new development of what I concluded—as I have since found rightly— to be a prevision of external scenes. It was as if the relation between me and my fellow-men was more and more deadened, and my relation to what we call the inanimate was quickened into new life. The more I lived apart from society, and in proportion as my wretchedness subsided from the violent throb of agonized passion into the dullness of habitual pain, the more frequent and vivid became such visions as that I had had of Prague—of strange cities, of sandy plains, of gigantic ruins, of midnight skies with strange bright constellations, of mountain passes, of grassy nooks flecked with the afternoon sunshine through the boughs: I was in the midst of such scenes, and in all of them one presence seemed to weigh on me in all these mighty shapes—the presence of something unknown and pitiless. For continual suffering had annihilated religious faith within me: to the utterly miserable—the unloving and the unloved —there is no religion possible, no worship but a worship of devils. And beyond all these, and continually recurring, was the vision of my death —the pangs, the suffocation, the last struggle, when life would be grasped at in vain.

Things were in this state near the end of the seventh year. I had become entirely free from insight, from my abnormal cognizance of any other consciousness than my own, and instead of intruding involuntarily into the world of other minds, was living continually in my own solitary future. Bertha was aware that I was greatly changed. To my surprise she had of late seemed to seek opportunities of remaining in my society, and had cultivated that kind of distant yet familiar talk which is customary between a husband and wife who live in polite and irrevocable alienation. I bore this with languid submission, and without feeling enough interest in her motives to be roused into keen observation; yet I could not help perceiving something triumphant and excited in her carriage and the expression of her face—something too subtle to express itself in words or tones, but giving one the idea that she lived in a state of expectation or hopeful suspense. My chief feeling was satisfaction that her inner self was once more shut out from me; and I almost revelled for the moment in the absent melancholy that made me answer her at cross purposes, and betray utter ignorance of what she had been saying. I remember well the look and the smile with which she one day said, after a mistake of this kind on my part: "I used to think you were a clairvoyant, and that was the reason why you were so bitter against other clairvoyants, wanting to keep your monopoly; but I see now you have become rather duller than the rest of the world."

I said nothing in reply. It occurred to me that her recent obtrusion of herself upon me might have been prompted by the wish to test my power of detecting some of her secrets; but I let the thought drop again at once: her motives and her deeds had no interest for me, and whatever pleasures she might be seeking, I had no wish to baulk her. There was still pity in my soul for every living thing, and Bertha was living—was surrounded with possibilities of misery.

Just at this time there occurred an event which roused me somewhat from my inertia, and gave me an interest in the passing moment that I had thought impossible for me. It was a visit from Charles Meunier, who had written me word that he was coming to England for relaxation from too strenuous labour, and would like to see me. Meunier had now a European reputation; but his letter to me expressed that keen remembrance of an early regard, an early debt of sympathy, which is inseparable from nobility of character: and I too felt as if his presence would be to me like a transient resurrection into a happier pre-existence.

He came, and as far as possible, I renewed our old pleasure of making tête-à-tête excursions, though, instead of mountains and glaciers and the wide blue lake, we had to content ourselves with mere slopes and ponds and artificial plantations. The years had changed us both, but with what different result! Meunier was now a brilliant figure in society, to whom elegant women pretended to listen, and whose acquaintance was boasted of by noblemen ambitious of brains. He repressed with the utmost delicacy all betrayal of the shock which I am sure he must have received from our meeting, or of a desire to penetrate into my condition and circumstances, and sought by the utmost exertion of his charming social powers to make our reunion agreeable. Bertha was much struck by the unexpected fascinations of a visitor whom she had expected to find presentable only on the score of his celebrity, and put forth all her coquetries and accomplishments. Apparently she succeeded in attracting his admiration, for his manner towards her was attentive and flattering. The effect of his presence on me was so benignant, especially in those renewals of our old tête-à-tête wanderings, when he poured forth to me wonderful narratives of his professional experience, that more than once, when his talk turned on the psychological relations of disease, the thought crossed my mind that, if his stay with me were long enough, I might possibly

bring myself to tell this man the secrets of my lot. Might there not lie
some remedy for *me*, too, in his science? Might there not at least lie some
comprehension and sympathy ready for me in his large and susceptible
mind? But the thought only flickered feebly now and then, and died out
before it could become a wish. The horror I had of again breaking in on
the privacy of another soul, made me, by an irrational instinct, draw the
shroud of concealment more closely around my own, as we automatically
perform the gesture we feel to be wanting in another.

When Meunier's visit was approaching its conclusion, there happened
an event which caused some excitement in our household, owing to the
surprisingly strong effect it appeared to produce on Bertha—on Bertha,
the self-possessed, who usually seemed inaccessible to feminine agitations, and did even her hate in a self-restrained hygienic manner. This
event was the sudden severe illness of her maid, Mrs. Archer. I have
reserved to this moment the mention of a circumstance which had forced
itself on my notice shortly before Meunier's arrival, namely, that there
had been some quarrel between Bertha and this maid, apparently during
a visit to a distant family, in which she had accompanied her mistress. I
had overheard Archer speaking in a tone of bitter insolence, which I
should have thought an adequate reason for immediate dismissal. No
dismissal followed; on the contrary, Bertha seemed to be silently putting
up with personal inconveniences from the exhibitions of this woman's
temper. I was the more astonished to observe that her illness seemed a
cause of strong solicitude to Bertha; that she was at the bedside night and
day, and would allow no one else to officiate as head-nurse. It happened
that our family doctor was out on a holiday, an accident which made
Meunier's presence in the house doubly welcome, and he apparently
entered into the case with an interest which seemed so much stronger
than the ordinary professional feeling, that one day when he had fallen
into a long fit of silence after visiting her, I said to him—

"Is this a very peculiar case of disease, Meunier?"

"No," he answered, "it is an attack of peritonitis, which will be fatal,
but which does not differ physically from many other cases that have
come under my observation. But I'll tell you what I have on my mind. I
want to make an experiment on this woman, if you will give me permission. It can do her no harm—will give her no pain—for I shall not make
it until life is extinct to all purposes of sensation. I want to try the effect
of transfusing blood into her arteries after the heart has ceased to beat for
some minutes. I have tried the experiment again and again with animals
that have died of this disease, with astounding results, and I want to try it

on a human subject. I have the small tubes necessary, in a case I have with me, and the rest of the apparatus could be prepared readily. I should use my own blood—take it from my own arm. This woman won't live through the night, I'm convinced, and I want you to promise me your assistance in making the experiment. I can't do without another hand, but it would perhaps not be well to call in a medical assistant from among your provincial doctors. A disagreeable foolish version of the thing might get abroad."

"Have you spoken to my wife on the subject?" I said, "because she appears to be peculiarly sensitive about this woman: she has been a favourite maid."

"To tell you the truth," said Meunier, "I don't want her to know about it. There are always insuperable difficulties with women in these matters, and the effect on the supposed dead body may be startling. You and I will sit up together, and be in readiness. When certain symptoms appear I shall take you in, and at the right moment we must manage to get every one else out of the room."

I need not give our farther conversation on the subject. He entered very fully into the details, and overcame my repulsion from them, by exciting in me a mingled awe and curiosity concerning the possible results of his experiment.

We prepared everything, and he instructed me in my part as assistant. He had not told Bertha of his absolute conviction that Archer would not survive through the night, and endeavoured to persuade her to leave the patient and take a night's rest. But she was obstinate, suspecting the fact that death was at hand, and supposing that he wished merely to save her nerves. She refused to leave the sick-room. Meunier and I sat up together in the library, he making frequent visits to the sick-room, and returning with the information that the case was taking precisely the course he expected. Once he said to me, "Can you imagine any cause of ill-feeling this woman has against her mistress, who is so devoted to her?"

"I think there was some misunderstanding between them before her illness. Why do you ask?"

"Because I have observed for the last five or six hours—since, I fancy, she has lost all hope of recovery—there seems a strange prompting in her to say something which pain and failing strength forbid her to utter; and there is a look of hideous meaning in her eyes, which she turns continually towards her mistress. In this disease the mind often remains singularly clear to the last."

"I am not surprised at an indication of malevolent feeling in her," I said. "She is a woman who has always inspired me with distrust and dislike, but she managed to insinuate herself into her mistress's favour." He was silent after this, looking at the fire with an air of absorption, till he went upstairs again. He stayed away longer than usual, and on returning, said to me quietly, "Come now."

I followed him to the chamber where death was hovering. The dark hangings of the large bed made a background that gave a strong relief to Bertha's pale face as I entered. She started forward as she saw me enter, and then looked at Meunier with an expression of angry inquiry; but he lifted up his hand as if to impose silence, while he fixed his glance on the dying woman and felt her pulse. The face was pinched and ghastly, a cold perspiration was on the forehead, and the eyelids were lowered so as to conceal the large dark eyes. After a minute or two, Meunier walked round to the other side of the bed where Bertha stood, and with his usual air of gentle politeness towards her begged her to leave the patient under our care—everything should be done for her—she was no longer in a state to be conscious of an affectionate presence. Bertha was hesitating, apparently almost willing to believe his assurance and to comply. She looked round at the ghastly dying face, as if to read the confirmation of that assurance, when for a moment the lowered eyelids were raised again, and it seemed as if the eyes were looking towards Bertha, but blankly. A shudder passed through Bertha's frame, and she returned to her station near the pillow, tacitly implying that she would not leave the room.

The eyelids were lifted no more. Once I looked at Bertha as she watched the face of the dying one. She wore a rich peignoir, and her blond hair was half covered by a lace cap: in her attire she was, as always, an elegant woman, fit to figure in a picture of modern aristocratic life: but I asked myself how that face of hers could ever have seemed to me the face of a woman born of woman, with memories of childhood, capable of pain, needing to be fondled? The features at that moment seemed so preternaturally sharp, the eyes were so hard and eager—she looked like a cruel immortal, finding her spiritual feast in the agonies of a dying race. For across those hard features there came something like a flash when the last hour had been breathed out, and we all felt that the dark veil had completely fallen. What secret was there between Bertha and this woman? I turned my eyes from her with a horrible dread lest my insight should return, and I should be obliged to see what had been breeding about two unloving women's hearts. I felt that Bertha had been watching for the moment of death as the sealing of her secret: I thanked Heaven it could remain sealed for me.

Meunier said quietly, "She is gone." He then gave his arm to Bertha, and she submitted to be led out of the room.

I suppose it was at her order that two female attendants came into the room, and dismissed the younger one who had been present before. When they entered, Meunier had already opened the artery in the long thin neck that lay rigid on the pillow, and I dismissed them, ordering them to remain at a distance till we rang: the doctor, I said, had an operation to perform—he was not sure about the death. For the next twenty minutes I forgot everything but Meunier and the experiment in which he was so absorbed, that I think his senses would have been closed against all sounds or sights which had no relation to it. It was my task at first to keep up the artificial respiration in the body after the transfusion had been effected, but presently Meunier relieved me, and I could see the wondrous slow return of life; the breast began to heave, the inspirations became stronger, the eyelids quivered, and the soul seemed to have returned beneath them. The artificial respiration was withdrawn: still the breathing continued, and there was a movement of the lips.

Just then I heard the handle of the door moving: I suppose Bertha had heard from the women that they had been dismissed: probably a vague fear had arisen in her mind, for she entered with a look of alarm. She came to the foot of the bed and gave a stifled cry.

The dead woman's eyes were wide open, and met hers in full recognition—the recognition of hate. With a sudden strong effort, the hand that Bertha had thought for ever still was pointed towards her, and the haggard face moved. The gasping eager voice said—

"You mean to poison your husband . . . the poison is in the black cabinet . . . I got it for you . . . you laughed at me, and told lies about me behind my back, to make me disgusting . . . because you were jealous . . . are you sorry . . . now?"

The lips continued to murmur, but the sounds were no longer distinct. Soon there was no sound—only a slight movement: the flame had leaped out, and was being extinguished the faster. The wretched woman's heart-strings had been set to hatred and vengeance; the spirit of life had swept the chords for an instant, and was gone again for ever. Great God! Is this what it is to live again . . . to wake up with our unstilled thirst upon us, with our unuttered curses rising to our lips, with our muscles ready to act out their half-committed sins?

Bertha stood pale at the foot of the bed, quivering and helpless, despairing of devices, like a cunning animal whose hiding-places are surrounded by swift-advancing flame. Even Meunier looked paralysed; life for that moment ceased to be a scientific problem to him. As for me, this scene seemed of one texture with the rest of my existence: horror was my familiar, and this new revelation was only like an old pain recurring with new circumstances.

Since then Bertha and I have lived apart—she in her own neighbourhood, the mistress of half our wealth, I as a wanderer in foreign countries, until I came to this Devonshire nest to die. Bertha lives pitied and admired; for what had I against that charming woman, whom every one but myself could have been happy with? There had been no witness of the scene in the dying room except Meunier, and while Meunier lived his lips were sealed by a promise to me.

Once or twice, weary of wandering, I rested in a favourite spot, and my heart went out towards the men and women and children whose faces were becoming familiar to me; but I was driven away again in terror at the approach of my old insight—driven away to live continually with the one Unknown Presence revealed and yet hidden by the moving curtain of the earth and sky. Till at last disease took hold of me and forced me to rest here—forced me to live in dependence on my servants. And then the curse of insight—of my double consciousness, came again, and has never left me. I know all their narrow thoughts, their feeble regard, their half-wearied pity.

It is the 20th of September, 1850. I know these figures I have just written, as if they were a long familiar inscription. I have seen them on this page in my desk unnumbered times, when the scene of my dying struggle has opened upon me. . . .

Lucius Apuleius

fl. 2nd century A.D.

L et me," he wrote, "briefly introduce myself as Lucius Apuleius, a native of Madaura in North Africa, but of ancient Greek stock." Born early in the second century, he claimed Plutarch as one of his real or imaginary ancestors. On the death of his father, a provincial magistrate, he and his brother between them inherited two million sesterces (nearly $100,000). Lucius went to school at the university in Carthage and later studied Platonic philosophy in Athens. At Corinth he was admitted into the religious cult of Isis. After studying rhetoric in Rome, he practiced at the Roman bar.

On his travels in Egypt and Asia Minor, where he devoted himself to religion and philosophy, he fell sick near Alexandria and was nursed by Sicinius Pontianus, a schoolmate from Athens. Later he married Pontianus' mother. But when she made over her large fortune to him, and Pontianus died soon after, her family charged that he had poisoned his friend and worked magic on his wife. Apuleius' defense before the proconsul Claudius Maximus—it was called *Apologia* or *De Magia* (*Of Magic*)—remains our chief source for his life. He was found not guilty.

His most famous work, *The Metamorphoses of Lucius Apuleius of Madaura,* is also the earliest complete Latin novel that we have. This is the story of how Lucius was turned into an ass, his adventures in that state, and how he was brought back to manhood by the goddess Isis. It is traditionally known as *The Golden Ass,* evidently because Apuleius wrote it in a literary style adapted from the pitchman's lingo of the market-place storytellers. Thus "golden" is carnival talk for "wonderful" or "marvelous."

Robert Graves says that although Apuleius probably knew witchcraft, it was "the 'right-hand' or beneficent magic" pertaining to the goddesses Isis and Demeter. He seems to have been a priest of Isis and Osiris, and of the god of medicine, Aesculapius. He wrote histories and poems now lost.

Cupid and Psyche" is a story from *The Golden Ass,* and one of the great stories of the world. Though Graves writes that the plot "is still widely current as a primitive folk-tale in countries as far apart as Scotland and Hindustan," it is not found among the Greek myths. It has been a favorite in English, redone by William Morris in *The Earthly Paradise,* by Robert Bridges, and by Walter Pater in *Marius the Epicurean.* We read it here in Pater's lordly translation.

A love story? If we call it that we are almost guilty of punning. Its hero is Love himself, Cupid, the god of love, still "fairest among the deathless gods," as Hesiod described him. Psyche's name is a common Greek noun, used as early as Homer to mean "breath" or "life" or "spirit," and later by Plato in the sense of "soul." The story has been called "a neat philosophical allegory of the progress of the rational soul towards intellectual love." No doubt it can be read in that light. Apuleius, as we know, was a student of Plato and probably had some such double meaning in mind.

But we need to ask first what the story is about. Who is Psyche? She is a beautiful young girl in a fix. No storyteller could imagine a better opening than that. Moreover, she is a king's daughter, to whom the best things of this world are promised. Instead, she suffers the cruelest injustice. Because of her beauty, which is not her fault, no one will marry her; and for the same reason she incurs the anger of Venus. She is Cinderella in reverse, she is *too* beautiful; and like Cinderella she has two wicked older sisters who hate her.

What else do we see? Is Venus the cruel stepmother or mother-in-law of the fairy tales? Perhaps. Psyche is told that her lover is a dreadful serpent who will devour her and her child. We recognize that serpent. He comes out of the unconscious: a feminine or Freudian image of the terror of love. He was also, for the Greeks, a death image. Psyche has resolved to kill this monster who loves her, whose child she bears. But she must *see* him first. Her curiosity defies the forbidden, as Pandora and Bluebeard's wives defied it. Psyche does it a second time, in opening Persephone's box. This time she falls into "the sleep of the dead"—or dies, in one version of the story—from which she must be rescued by Cupid.

We notice that the viewpoint shifts between Venus, Psyche, and her sisters. We get no glimpse of the story through male eyes. Its logic, its way of feeling, are purely feminine. Psyche's father, Jupiter, and even Cupid are mere agents. Cupid, undependable male that he is, first ignores his mother's errand and then flies off in a huff when Psyche burns him. For a god of love, he shows little understanding of women. We see finally why all this might be so. "Cupid and Psyche" is a young girl's fantasy, beautifully done, and true in any country or time. This is how she daydreams about the delights and terrors of being beautiful and wronged; of a husband who is rich and a god; of a mother-in-law who is a powerful rival; of marrying, and bearing a child, and finding the immortality of happiness.

"Now read on," said Apuleius, "and enjoy yourself!"

Cupid and Psyche
from *The Golden Ass*

In a certain city lived a king and queen who had three daughters exceeding fair. But the beauty of the elder sisters, though pleasant to behold, yet passed not the measure of human praise, while such was the loveliness of the youngest that men's speech was too poor to commend it worthily and could express it not at all. Many of the citizens and of strangers, whom the fame of this excellent vision had gathered thither, confounded by that matchless beauty, could but kiss the finger-tips of their right hands at sight of her, as in adoration to the goddess Venus herself. And soon a rumour passed through the country that she whom the blue deep had borne, forbearing her divine dignity, was even then moving among men, or that by some fresh germination from the stars, not the sea now, but the earth, had put forth a new Venus, endued with the flower of virginity.

This belief, with the fame of the maiden's loveliness, went daily farther into distant lands, so that many people were drawn together to behold that glorious model of the age. Men sailed no longer to Paphos, to Cnidus or Cythera, to the presence of the goddess Venus: her sacred rites were neglected, her images stood uncrowned, the cold ashes were left to disfigure her forsaken altars. It was to a maiden that men's prayers were offered, to a human countenance they looked, in propitiating so great a godhead: when the girl went forth in the morning they strewed flowers on her way, and the victims proper to that unseen goddess were presented as she passed along. This conveyance of divine worship to a mortal kindled meantime the anger of the true Venus. "Lo! now, the ancient parent of nature," she cried, "the fountain of all elements! Behold me, Venus, benign mother of the world, sharing my honours with a mortal maiden, while my name, built up in heaven, is profaned by the mean things of earth! Shall a perishable woman bear my image about with her?

In vain did the shepherd of Ida prefer me! Yet shall she have little joy, whosoever she be, of her usurped and unlawful loveliness!" Thereupon she called to her that winged, bold boy, of evil ways, who wanders armed by night through men's houses, spoiling their marriages; and stirring yet more by her speech his inborn wantonness, she led him to the city, and showed him Psyche as she walked.

"I pray thee," she said, "give thy mother a full revenge. Let this maid become the slave of an unworthy love." Then, embracing him closely, she departed to the shore and took her throne upon the crest of the wave. And lo! at her unuttered will, her ocean servants are in waiting: the daughters of Nereus are there singing their song, and Portunus, and Salacia, and the tiny charioteer of the dolphin, with a host of Tritons leaping through the billows. And one blows softly through his sounding sea-shell, another spreads a silken web against the sun, a third presents the mirror to the eyes of his mistress, while the others swim side by side below, drawing her chariot. Such was the escort of Venus as she went upon the sea.

Psyche meantime, aware of her loveliness, had no fruit thereof. All people regarded and admired, but none sought her in marriage. It was but as on the finished work of the craftsman that they gazed upon that divine likeness. Her sisters, less fair than she, were happily wedded. She, even as a widow, sitting at home, wept over her desolation, hating in her heart the beauty in which all men were pleased.

And the king, supposing the gods were angry, inquired of the oracle of Apollo, and Apollo answered him thus: "Let the damsel be placed on the top of a certain mountain, adorned as for the bed of marriage and of death. Look not for a son-in-law of mortal birth; but for that evil serpent thing, by reason of whom even the gods tremble and the shadows of Styx are afraid."

So the king returned home and made known the oracle to his wife. For many days she lamented, but at last the fulfilment of the divine precept is urgent upon her, and the company make ready to conduct the maiden to her deadly bridal. And now the nuptial torch gathers dark smoke and ashes; the pleasant sound of the pipe is changed into a cry; the marriage hymn concludes in a sorrowful wailing; below her yellow wedding veil the bride shook away her tears; insomuch that the whole city was afflicted together at the ill luck of the stricken house.

But the mandate of the god impelled the hapless Psyche to her fate, and, these solemnities being ended, the funeral of the living soul goes forth, all the people following. Psyche, bitterly weeping, assists not at her marriage but at her own obsequies, and while the parents hesitate to accomplish a thing so unholy the daughter cries to them: "Wherefore torment your luckless age by long weeping? This was the prize of my extraordinary beauty! When all people celebrated us with divine honours, and in one voice named the New Venus, it was then ye should have wept for me as one dead. Now at last I understand that that one name of Venus has been my ruin. Lead me and set me upon the appointed place. I am in haste to submit to that well-omened marriage, to behold that goodly spouse. Why delay the coming of him who was born for the destruction of the whole world?"

She was silent, and with firm step went on the way. And they proceeded to the appointed place on a steep mountain, and left there the maiden alone, and took their way homewards dejectedly. The wretched parents, in their close-shut house, yielded themselves to perpetual night; while to Psyche, fearful and trembling and weeping sore upon the mountain top, comes the gentle Zephyrus. He lifts her mildly, and, with vesture afloat on either side, bears her by his own soft breathing over the windings of the hills, and sets her lightly among the flowers in the bosom of a valley below.

Psyche, in those delicate grassy places, lying sweetly on her dewy bed, rested from the agitation of her soul and arose in peace. And lo! a grove of mighty trees, with a fount of water, clear as glass, in the midst; and hard by the water, a dwelling-place, built not by human hands but by some divine cunning. One recognized, even at the entering, the delightful hostelry of a god. Golden pillars sustained the roof, arched most curiously in cedar-wood and ivory. The walls were hidden under wrought silver: all tame and woodland creatures leaping forward to the visitor's gaze. Wonderful indeed was the craftsman, divine or half-divine, who by the subtlety of his art had breathed so wild a soul into the silver! The very pavement was distinct with pictures in goodly stones. In the glow of its precious metal the house is its own daylight, having no need of the sun. Well might it seem a place fashioned for the conversation of gods with men!

Psyche, drawn forward by the delight of it, came near, and, her courage growing, stood within the doorway. One by one, she admired the beautiful things she saw; and, most wonderful of all! no lock, no chain, nor living guardian protected that great treasure house. But as she gazed, there came a voice—a voice, as it were unclothed of bodily vesture— "Mistress!" it said, "all these things are thine. Lie down, and relieve thy weariness, and rise again for the bath when thou wilt. We thy servants, whose voice thou hearest, will be beforehand with our service, and a royal feast shall be ready."

And Psyche understood that some divine care was providing, and, refreshed with sleep and the bath, sat down to the feast. Still she saw no one: only she heard words falling here and there, and had voices alone to serve her. And the feast being ended, one entered the chamber and sang to her unseen, while another struck the chords of a harp, invisible with him who played on it. Afterwards the sound of a company singing together came to her, but still so that none was present to sight; yet it appeared that a great multitude of singers was there.

And the hour of evening inviting her, she climbed into the bed; and as the night was far advanced, behold a sound of a certain clemency approaches her. Then, fearing for her maidenhood in so great solitude, she trembled, and more than any evil she knew dreaded that she knew not. And now the husband, that unknown husband, drew near, and ascended the couch, and made her his wife; and lo! before the rise of dawn he had departed hastily. And the attendant voices ministered to the needs of the newly married. And so it happened with her for a long season. And as nature has willed, this new thing, by continual use, became a delight to her: the sound of the voice grew to be her solace in that condition of loneliness and uncertainty.

One night the bridegroom spoke thus to his beloved: "O Psyche, most pleasant bride! Fortune is grown stern with us, and threatens thee with mortal peril. Thy sisters, troubled at the report of thy death and seeking some trace of thee, will come to the mountain's top. But if by chance their cries reach thee, answer not, neither look forth at all, lest thou bring sorrow upon me and destruction upon thyself." Then Psyche promised that she would do according to his will. But the bridegroom was fled away again with the night. And all that day she spent in tears, repeating that she was now dead indeed, shut up in that golden prison, powerless to console her sisters sorrowing after her, or to see their faces; and so went to rest weeping.

And after a while came the bridegroom again, and lay down beside her, and embracing her as she wept, complained: "Was this thy promise, my Psyche? What have I to hope from thee? Even in the arms of thy husband thou ceasest not from pain. Do now as thou wilt. Indulge thine own desire, though it seeks what will ruin thee. Yet wilt thou remember my warning, repentant too late." Then, protesting that she is like to die, she obtains from him that he suffer her to see her sisters, and present to them moreover what gifts she would of golden ornaments; but therewith he oft-times advised her never at any time, yielding to pernicious counsel, to inquire concerning his bodily form, lest she fall, through unholy curiosity, from so great a height of fortune, nor feel ever his embrace again. "I would die a hundred times," she said, cheerful at last, "rather than be deprived of thy most sweet usage. I love thee as my own soul, beyond comparison even with Love himself. Only bid thy servant Zephyrus bring hither my sisters, as he brought me. My honeycomb! My husband! Thy Psyche's breath of life!" So he promised; and after the embraces of the night, ere the light appeared, vanished from the hands of his bride.

And the sisters, coming to the place where Psyche was abandoned, wept loudly among the rocks, and called upon her by name, so that the sound came down to her, and running out of the palace distraught, she cried: "Wherefore afflict your souls with lamentation? I whom you mourn am here." Then, summoning Zephyrus, she reminded him of her husband's bidding; and he bare them down with a gentle blast. "Enter now," she said, "into my house, and relieve your sorrow in the company of Psyche your sister."

And Psyche displayed to them all the treasures of the golden house, and its great family of ministering voices, nursing in them the malice which was already at their hearts. And at last one of them asks curiously who the lord of that celestial array may be, and what manner of man her husband. And Psyche answered dissemblingly: "A young man, handsome and mannerly, with a goodly beard. For the most part he hunts upon the mountains." And lest the secret should slip from her in the way of further speech, loading her sisters with gold and gems, she commanded Zephyrus to bear them away.

And they returned home, on fire with envy. "See now the injustice of fortune!" cried one. "We, the elder children, are given like servants to be the wives of strangers, while the youngest is possessed of so great riches, who scarcely knows how to use them. You saw, sister! what a hoard of wealth lies in the house; what glittering gowns; what splendour of precious gems, besides all that gold trodden under foot. If she indeed hath, as she said, a bridegroom so goodly, then no one in all the world is happier. And it may be that this husband, being of divine nature, will make her too a goddess. Nay! so in truth it is. It was even thus she bore herself. Already she looks aloft and breathes divinity, who, though but a woman, has voices for her handmaidens, and can command the winds." "Think," answered the other, "how arrogantly she dealt with us, grudging us these trifling gifts out of all that store, and when our company became a burden, causing us to be hissed and driven away from her through the air! But I am no woman if she keep her hold on this great fortune; and if the insult done us has touched thee too, take we counsel together. Meanwhile let us hold our peace, and know naught of her, alive or dead. For they are not truly happy of whose happiness other folk are unaware."

And the bridegroom, whom still she knows not, warns her thus a second time, as he talks with her by night: "Seest thou what peril besets thee? Those cunning wolves have made ready for thee their snares, of which the sum is that they persuade thee to search into the fashion of my countenance, the seeing of which, as I have told thee often, will be the seeing of it no more for ever. But do thou neither listen nor make answer to aught regarding thy husband. Besides, we have sown also the seed of our race. Even now this bosom grows with a child to be born to us, a child, if thou but keep our secret, of divine quality; if thou profane it, subject to death." And Psyche was glad at the tidings, rejoicing in that solace of a divine seed, and in the glory of that pledge of love to be, and the dignity of the name of mother. Anxiously she notes the increase of the days, the waning months. And again, as he tarries briefly beside her, the bridegroom repeats his warning: "Even now the sword is drawn with which thy sisters seek thy life. Have pity on thyself, sweet wife, and upon our child, and see not those evil women again." But the sisters make their way into the palace once more, crying to her in wily tones: "O Psyche! and thou too wilt be a mother! How great will be the joy at home! Happy indeed shall we be to have the nursing of the golden child. Truly if he be answerable to the beauty of his parents, it will be a birth of Cupid himself."

So, little by little, they stole upon the heart of their sister. She, meanwhile, bids the lyre to sound for their delight, and the playing is heard: she bids the pipes to move, the choir to sing, and the music and the singing come invisibly, soothing the mind of the listener with sweetest modulation. Yet not even thereby was their malice put to sleep: once more they seek to know what manner of husband she has, and whence that seed. And Psyche, simple overmuch, forgetful of her first story, answers: "My husband comes from a far country, trading for great sums. He is already of middle age, with whitening locks." And therewith she dismisses them again.

And returning home upon the soft breath of Zephyrus, one cried to the other: "What shall be said of so ugly a lie? He who was a young man with goodly beard is now in middle life. It must be that she told a false tale: else is she in very truth ignorant what manner of man he is. Howsoever it be, let us destroy her quickly. For if she indeed knows not, be sure that her bridegroom is one of the gods: it is a god she bears in her womb. And let that be far from us! If she be called mother of a god, then will life be more than I can bear."

So, full of rage against her, they returned to Psyche, and said to her craftily: "Thou livest in an ignorant bliss, all incurious of thy real danger. It is a deadly serpent, as we certainly know, that comes to sleep at thy side. Remember the words of the oracle, which declared thee destined to a cruel beast. There are those who have seen it at nightfall, coming back from its feeding. In no long time, they say, it will end its blandishments. It but waits for the babe to be formed in thee, that it may devour thee by so much the richer. If indeed the solitude of this musical place, or it may be the loathsome commerce of a hidden love, delight thee, we at least in sisterly piety have done our part." And at last the unhappy Psyche, simple and frail of soul, carried away by the terror of their words, losing memory of her husband's precepts and her own promise, brought upon herself a great calamity. Trembling and turning pale, she answers them: "And they who tell those things, it may be, speak the truth. For in very deed never have I seen the face of my husband, nor know I at all what manner of man he is. Always he frights me diligently from the sight of him, threatening some great evil should I too curiously look upon his face. Do ye, if ye can help your sister in her great peril, stand by her now."

Her sisters answered her: "The way of safety we have well considered, and will teach thee. Take a sharp knife, and hide it in that part of the couch where thou art wont to lie; take also a lamp filled with oil, and set it privily behind the curtain. And when he shall have drawn up his coils into the accustomed place, and thou hearest him breathe in sleep, slip then from his side and discover the lamp, and, knife in hand, put forth thy strength, and strike off the serpent's head." And so they departed in haste.

And Psyche left alone (alone but for the furies which beset her) is tossed up and down in her distress, like a wave of the sea; and though her will is firm, yet, in the moment of putting hand to the deed, she falters, and is torn asunder by various apprehensions of the great calamity upon her. She hastens and anon delays, now full of distrust, and now of angry courage: under one bodily form she loathes the monster and loves the bridegroom. But twilight ushers in the night; and at length in haste she makes ready for the terrible deed. Darkness came, and the bridegroom; and he first, after some faint essay of love, falls into a deep sleep.

And she, erewhile of no strength, the hard purpose of destiny assisting her, is confirmed in force. With lamp plucked forth, knife in hand, she put

by her sex; and lo! as the secrets of the bed became manifest, the sweetest
and most gentle of all creatures, Love himself, reclined there, in his own
proper loveliness! At sight of him the very flame of the lamp kindled more
gladly! But Psyche was afraid at the vision, and, faint of soul, trembled
back upon her knees, and would have hidden the steel in her own bosom.
But the knife slipped from her hand; and now, undone, yet ofttimes
looking upon the beauty of that divine countenance, she lives again. She
sees the locks of that golden head, pleasant with the unction of the gods,
shed down in graceful entanglement behind and before, about the ruddy
cheeks and white throat. The pinions of the winged god, yet fresh with
the dew, are spotless upon his shoulders, the delicate plumage wavering
over them as they lie at rest. Smooth he was, and, touched with light,
worthy of Venus his mother. At the foot of the couch lay his bow and
arrows, the instruments of his power, propitious to men.

And Psyche, gazing hungrily thereon, draws an arrow from the quiver,
and trying the point upon her thumb, tremulous still, drove in the barb, so
that a drop of blood came forth. Thus fell she, by her own act, and unaware, into the love of Love. Falling upon the bridegroom, with indrawn
breath, in a hurry of kisses from eager and open lips, she shuddered as
she thought how brief that sleep might be. And it chanced that a drop
of burning oil fell from the lamp upon the god's shoulder. Ah! maladroit
minister of love, thus to wound him from whom all fire comes; though
'twas a lover, I trow, first devised thee, to have the fruit of his desire even
in the darkness! At the touch of the fire the god started up, and beholding
the overthrow of her faith, quietly took flight from her embraces.

And Psyche, as he rose upon the wing, laid hold on him with her two
hands, hanging upon him in his passage through the air, till she sinks to
the earth through weariness. And as she lay there, the divine lover, tarry-
ing still, lighted upon a cypress tree which grew near, and, from the top of
it, spake thus to her, in great emotion: "Foolish one! unmindful of the
command of Venus, my mother, who had devoted thee to one of base
degree, I fled to thee in his stead. Now know I that this was vainly done.
Into mine own flesh pierced mine arrow, and I made thee my wife, only
that I might seem a monster beside thee—that thou shouldst seek to
wound the head wherein lay the eyes so full of love to thee! Again and
again, I thought to put thee on thy guard concerning these things, and
warned thee in lovingkindness. Now I would but punish thee by my flight
hence." And therewith he winged his way into the deep sky.

Psyche, prostrate upon the earth, and following far as sight might reach
the flight of the bridegroom, wept and lamented; and when the breadth

of space had parted him wholly from her, cast herself down from the bank of a river which was nigh. But the stream, turning gentle in honour of the god, put her forth again unhurt upon its margin. And as it happened, Pan, the rustic god, was sitting just then by the waterside, embracing, in the body of a reed, the goddess Canna, teaching her to respond to him in all varieties of slender sound. Hard by, his flock of goats browsed at will. And the shaggy god called her, wounded and outworn, kindly to him and said: "I am but a rustic herdsman, pretty maiden, yet wise, by favour of my great age and long experience; and if I guess truly by those faltering steps, by thy sorrowful eyes and continual sighing, thou labourest with excess of love. Listen then to me, and seek not death again, in the stream or otherwise. Put aside thy woe, and turn thy prayers to Cupid. He is in truth a delicate youth: win him by the delicacy of thy service."

So the shepherd god spoke, and Psyche, answering nothing, but with a reverence to his serviceable deity, went on her way. And while she, in her search after Cupid, wandered through many lands, he was lying in the chamber of his mother, heartsick. And the white bird which floats over the waves plunged in haste into the sea, and approaching Venus, as she bathed, made known to her that her son lies afflicted with some grievous hurt, doubtful of life. And Venus cried angrily: "My son, then, has a mistress! And it is Psyche, who witched away my beauty and was the rival of my godhead, whom he loves!"

Therewith she issued from the sea, and returning to her golden chamber, found there the lad, sick, as she had heard, and cried from the doorway: "Well done, truly! to trample thy mother's precepts under foot, to spare my enemy that cross of an unworthy love; nay, unite her to thyself, child as thou art, that I might have a daughter-in-law who hates me! I will make thee repent of thy sport, and the savour of thy marriage bitter. There is one who shall chasten this body of thine, put out thy torch, and unstring thy bow. Not till she has plucked forth that hair, into which so oft these hands have smoothed the golden light, and sheared away thy wings, shall I feel the injury done me avenged." And with this she hastened in anger from the doors.

And Ceres and Juno met her, and sought to know the meaning of her troubled countenance. "Ye come in season," she cried; "I pray you, find for me Psyche. It must needs be that ye have heard the disgrace of my house." And they, ignorant of what was done, would have soothed her anger, saying: "What fault, Mistress, hath thy son committed, that thou wouldst destroy the girl he loves? Knowest thou not that he is now of age? Because he wears his years so lightly must he seem to thee ever but a child? Wilt thou for ever thus pry into the pastimes of thy son, always accusing his wantonness, and blaming in him those delicate wiles which are all thine own?" Thus, in secret fear of the boy's bow, did they seek to please him with their gracious patronage. But Venus, angry at their light taking of her wrongs, turned her back upon them, and with hasty steps made her way once more to the sea.

Meanwhile Psyche, tost in soul, wandering hither and thither, rested not night or day in the pursuit of her husband, desiring, if she might not soothe his anger by the endearments of a wife, at the least to propitiate him with the prayers of a handmaid. And seeing a certain temple on the top of a high mountain, she said: "Who knows whether yonder place be not the abode of my lord?" Thither, therefore, she turned her steps, hastening now the more because desire and hope pressed her on, weary as she was with the labours of the way, and so, painfully measuring out the highest ridges of the mountain, drew near to the sacred couches. She sees ears of wheat, in heaps or twisted into chaplets; ears of barley also, with sickles and all the instruments of harvest, lying there in disorder, thrown at random from the hands of the labourers in the great heat. These she curiously sets apart, one by one, duly ordering them; for she said within herself: "I may not neglect the shrines, nor the holy service, of any god there be, but must rather win by supplication the kindly mercy of them all."

And Ceres found her bending sadly upon her task, and cried aloud: "Alas, Psyche! Venus, in the furiousness of her anger, tracks thy footsteps through the world, seeking for thee to pay her the utmost penalty; and thou, thinking of anything rather than thine own safety, hast taken on thee the care of what belongs to me!" Then Psyche fell down at her feet, and sweeping the floor with her hair, washing the footsteps of the goddess in her tears, besought her mercy, with many prayers: "By the gladdening rites of harvest, by the lighted lamps and mystic marches of the marriage and mysterious invention of thy daughter Proserpine, and by all beside that the holy place of Attica veils in silence, minister, I pray thee, to the sorrowful heart of Psyche! Suffer me to hide myself but for a few days among the heaps of corn, till time has softened the anger of the goddess, and my strength, outworn in my long travail, is recovered by a little rest."

But Ceres answered her: "Truly thy tears move me, and I would fain help thee; only I dare not incur the ill will of my kinswoman. Depart hence as quickly as may be." And Psyche, repelled against hope, afflicted now with twofold sorrow, making her way back again, beheld among the half-lighted woods of the valley below a sanctuary builded with cunning art. And that she might lose no way of hope, howsoever doubtful, she drew near to the sacred doors. She sees there gifts of price, and garments fixed upon the door-posts and to the branches of the trees, wrought with letters of gold which told the name of the goddess to whom they were dedicated, with thanksgiving for that she had done. So, with bent knee and hands laid about the glowing altar, she prayed, saying: "Sister and spouse of Jupiter! be thou to these my desperate fortunes, Juno the Auspicious! I know that thou dost willingly help those in travail with child; deliver me from the peril that is upon me." And as she prayed thus, Juno in the majesty of her godhead was straightway present, and answered: "Would that I might incline favourably to thee; but against the will of Venus, whom I have ever loved as a daughter, I may not, for very shame, grant thy prayer."

And Psyche, dismayed by this new shipwreck of her hope, communed thus with herself: "Whither, from the midst of the snares that beset me, shall I take my way once more? In what dark solitude shall I hide me from the all-seeing eye of Venus? What if I put on at length a man's courage, and yielding myself unto her as my mistress, soften by a humility not yet too late the fierceness of her purpose? Who knows but that I may find him also whom my soul seeketh after, in the abode of his mother?"

And Venus, renouncing all earthly aid in her search, prepared to return to heaven. She ordered the chariot to be made ready, wrought for her by Vulcan as a marriage gift, with a cunning of hand which had left his work so much the richer by the weight of gold it lost under his tool. From the multitude which housed about the bedchamber of their mistress, white doves came forth, and with joyful motions bent their painted necks beneath the yoke. Behind it, with playful riot, the sparrows sped onward, and other birds sweet of song, making known by their soft notes the approach of the goddess. Eagle and cruel hawk alarmed not the quireful family of Venus. And the clouds broke away, as the uttermost ether opened to receive her, daughter and goddess, with great joy.

And Venus passed straightway to the house of Jupiter to beg from him the service of Mercury, the god of speech. And Jupiter refused not her prayer. And Venus and Mercury descended from heaven together; and as they went, the former said to the latter: "Thou knowest, my brother of Arcady, that never at any time have I done anything without thy help; for how long time, moreover, I have sought a certain maiden in vain. And now naught remains but that, by thy heraldry, I proclaim a reward for whomsoever shall find her. Do thou my bidding quickly." And therewith she conveyed to him a little scrip, in the which was written the name of Psyche, with other things; and so returned home.

And Mercury failed not in his office; but departing into all lands, proclaimed that whosoever delivered up to Venus the fugitive girl, should receive from herself seven kisses—one thereof full of the inmost honey of her throat. With that the doubt of Psyche was ended. And now, as she came near to the doors of Venus, one of the household, whose name was Use-and-Wont, ran out to her, crying: "Hast thou learned, Wicked Maid! now at last! that thou hast a mistress?" and seizing her roughly by the hair, drew her into the presence of Venus. And when Venus saw her, she cried out, saying: "Thou has deigned then to make thy salutations to thy mother-in-law. Now will I in turn treat thee as becometh a dutiful daughter-in-law!"

And she took barley and millet and poppy-seed, every kind of grain and seed, and mixed them together, and laughed, and said to her: "Methinks so plain a maiden can earn lovers only by industrious ministry: now will I also make trial of thy service. Sort me this heap of seed, the one kind from the others, grain by grain; and get thy task done before the evening." And Psyche, stunned by the cruelty of her bidding, was silent, and moved not her hand to the inextricable heap. And there came forth a little ant, which had understanding of the difficulty of her task, and took pity upon the consort of the god of Love; and he ran deftly hither and thither, and called together the whole army of his fellows. "Have pity," he cried, "nimble scholars of the Earth, Mother of all things! —have pity upon the wife of Love, and hasten to help her in her perilous effort." Then, one upon the other, the hosts of the insect people hurried together; and they sorted asunder the whole heap of seed, separating every grain after its kind, and so departed quickly out of sight.

And at nightfall Venus returned, and seeing that task finished with so wonderful diligence, she cried: "The work is not thine, thou naughty maid, but his in whose eyes thou hast found favour." And calling her again in the morning: "See now the grove," she said, "beyond yonder torrent. Certain sheep feed there, whose fleeces shine with gold. Fetch me straightway a lock of that precious stuff, having gotten it as thou mayst."

And Psyche went forth willingly, not to obey the command of Venus, but even to seek a rest from her labour in the depths of the river. But from the river, the green reed, lowly mother of music, spake to her: "O Psyche! pollute not these waters by self-destruction, nor approach that terrible flock; for, as the heat groweth, they wax fierce. Lie down under yon plane-tree, till the quiet of the river's breath has soothed them. There-after thou mayst shake down the fleecy gold from the trees of the grove, for it holdeth by the leaves."

And Psyche, instructed thus by the simple reed, in the humanity of its heart, filled her bosom with the soft golden stuff, and returned to Venus. But the goddess smiled bitterly, and said to her: "Well know I who was the author of this thing also. I will make further trial of thy discretion, and the boldness of thy heart. Seest thou the utmost peak of yonder steep mountain? The dark stream which flows down thence waters the Stygian fields, and swells the flood of Cocytus. Bring me now, in this little urn, a draught from its innermost source." And therewith she put into her hands a vessel of wrought crystal.

And Psyche set forth in haste on her way to the mountain, looking there at last to find the end of her hapless life. But when she came to the region which borders on the cliff that was showed to her, she understood the deadly nature of her task. From a great rock, steep and slippery, a hor-rible river of water poured forth, falling straightway by a channel exceed-ing narrow into the unseen gulf below. And lo! creeping from the rocks on either hand, angry serpents, with their long necks and sleepless eyes. The very waters found a voice and bade her depart, in smothered cries of, "Depart hence!" and "What doest thou here?" "Look around thee!" and "Destruction is upon thee!" And then sense left her, in the immensity of her peril, as one changed to stone.

Yet not even then did the distress of this innocent soul escape the steady eye of a gentle providence. For the bird of Jupiter spread his wings and took flight to her, and asked her: "Didst thou think, simple one, even thou! that thou couldst steal one drop of that relentless stream, the holy river of Styx, terrible even to the gods? But give me thine urn." And the bird took the urn, and filled it at the source, and returned to her quickly from among the teeth of the serpents, bringing with him of the waters, all un-willing—nay! warning him to depart away and not molest them.

And she, receiving the urn with great joy, ran back quickly that she might deliver it to Venus, and yet again satisfied not the angry goddess. "My child!" she said, "in this one thing further must thou serve me. Take now this tiny casket, and get thee down even unto hell, and deliver it to Proserpine. Tell her that Venus would have of her beauty so much at least as may suffice for but one day's use, that beauty she possessed ere-while being foreworn and spoiled, through her tendance upon the sick-bed of her son; and be not slow in returning."

And Psyche perceived there the last ebbing of her fortune—that she

was now thrust openly upon death, who must go down, of her own motion, to Hades and the Shades. And straightway she climbed to the top of
an exceeding high tower, thinking within herself: "I will cast myself down
thence: so shall I descend most quickly into the kingdom of the dead."
And the tower, again, broke forth into speech: "Wretched Maid!
Wretched Maid! Wilt thou destroy thyself? If the breath quit thy body,
then wilt thou indeed go down into Hades, but by no means return hither.
Listen to me. Among the pathless wilds not far from this place lies a certain mountain, and therein one of hell's vent-holes. Through the breach a
rough way lies open, following which thou wilt come, by straight course,
to the castle of Orcus. And thou must not go empty-handed. Take in each
hand a morsel of barley-bread, soaked in hydromel; and in thy mouth two
pieces of money. And when thou shalt be now well onward in the way of
death, then wilt thou overtake a lame ass laden with wood, and a lame
driver, who will pray thee reach him certain cords to fasten the burden
which is falling from the ass: but be thou cautious to pass on in silence.
And soon as thou comest to the river of the dead, Charon, in that crazy
bark he hath, will put thee over upon the farther side. There is greed even
among the dead: and thou shalt deliver to him, for the ferrying, one of
those two pieces of money, in such wise that he take it with his hand
from between thy lips. And as thou passest over the stream, a dead old
man, rising on the water, will put up to thee his mouldering hands, and
pray thee draw him into the ferry-boat. But beware thou yield not to unlawful pity.

"When thou shalt be come over, and art upon the causeway, certain
aged women, spinning, will cry to thee to lend thy hand to their work;
and beware again that thou take no part therein; for this also is the snare
of Venus, whereby she would cause thee to cast away one at least of those
cakes thou bearest in thy hands. And think not that a slight matter; for
the loss of either one of them will be to thee the losing of the light of day.
For a watch-dog exceeding fierce lies ever before the threshold of that
lonely house of Proserpine. Close his mouth with one of thy cakes; so shalt
thou pass by him, and enter straightway into the presence of Proserpine
herself. Then do thou deliver thy message, and taking what she shall give
thee, return back again; offering to the watch-dog the other cake, and to
the ferryman that other piece of money thou hast in thy mouth. After this
manner mayst thou return again beneath the stars. But withal, I charge
thee, think not to look into, nor open, the casket thou bearest, with that
treasure of the beauty of the divine countenance hidden therein."

So spake the stones of the tower; and Psyche delayed not, but proceeding diligently after the manner enjoined, entered into the house of Proserpine, at whose feet she sat down humbly, and would neither the delicate couch nor that divine food the goddess offered her, but did straightway the business of Venus. And Proserpine filled the casket secretly, and shut the lid, and delivered it to Psyche, who fled therewith from Hades with new strength. But coming back into the light of day, even as she hasted now to the ending of her service, she was seized by a rash curiosity. "Lo! now," she said within herself, "my simpleness! who, bearing in my hands the divine loveliness, heed not to touch myself with a particle at least therefrom, that I may please the more, by the favour of it, my fair one, my beloved." Even as she spoke, she lifted the lid; and behold! within, neither beauty, nor anything beside, save sleep only, the sleep of the dead, which took hold upon her, filling all her members with its drowsy vapour, so that she lay down in the way and moved not, as in the slumber of death.

And Cupid being healed of his wound, because he would endure no longer the absence of her he loved, gliding through the narrow window of the chamber wherein he was holden, his pinions being now repaired by a little rest, fled forth swiftly upon them, and coming to the place where Psyche was, shook that sleep away from her, and set himself in his prison again, awaking her with the innocent point of his arrow. "Lo! thine old error again," he said, "which had like once more to have destroyed thee! But do thou now what is lacking of the command of my mother: the rest shall be my care." With these words, the lover rose upon the air; and being consumed inwardly with the greatness of his love, penetrated with vehement wing into the highest place of heaven, to lay his cause before the father of the gods. And the father of gods took his hand in his, and kissed his face, and said to him: "At no time, my son, hast thou regarded me with due honour. Often hast thou vexed my bosom, wherein lies the disposition of the stars, with those busy darts of thine. Nevertheless, because thou hast grown up between these mine hands, I will accomplish thy desire." And straightway he bade Mercury call the gods together; and, the council chamber being filled, sitting upon a high throne, "Ye gods," he said, "all ye whose names are in the white book of the Muses, ye know yonder lad. It seems good to me that his youthful heats should by some means be restrained. And that all occasion may be taken from him, I would even confine him in the bonds of marriage. He has chosen and embraced a mortal maiden. Let him have fruit of his love, and possess her forever."

Thereupon he bade Mercury produce Psyche in heaven; and holding out to her his ambrosial cup, "Take it," he said, "and live forever; nor shall

Cupid ever depart from thee." And the gods sat down together to the marriage feast. On the first couch lay the bridegroom, and Psyche in his bosom. His rustic serving-boy bare the wine to Jupiter; and Bacchus to the rest. The Seasons crimsoned all things with their roses. Apollo sang to the lyre, while a little Pan prattled on his reeds, and Venus danced very sweetly to the soft music. Thus, with due rites, did Psyche pass into the power of Cupid; and from them was born the daughter whom men call Voluptas.

Walter Pater's translation of "Cupid and Psyche" is taken from his
MARIUS THE EPICUREAN.

Ivan Turgenev

1818–1883

Ivan Turgenev was born at Orel, Russia, October 28, 1818 (Old Style). He grew up under a tyrannical mother on the family estate at Spasskoye. He was graduated from the University of St. Petersburg, where he studied under Gogol. In 1843 he took a job in the Ministry of the Interior. That same year he published *Parasha*, a story in verse, and met the Spanish gypsy opera singer Pauline Garcia, wife of Louis Viardot, her manager, and sister of the equally famous Malibran. Turgenev began a lifelong attachment to her.

During the late 1840's, he spent his summers at the Viardots' estate at Courtavenel and wintered in Paris. He wrote *A Month in the Country* and other plays. After his mother's death in 1850 he inherited the Spasskoye estate but bad management largely diminished his income. In 1852 his obituary tribute to Gogol got him imprisoned for a month (visiting friends made it a triumph) and he was later confined to his estate. That same year *A Sportsman's Sketches* was published.

All his life he maintained hot-and-cold friendships with Tolstoy and Dostoevsky. Turgenev's *Rudin* and *A Nest of Gentlefolk* appeared in the late 1850's, followed by *On the Eve* in 1860 and *Fathers and Sons* in 1862. Two years later he was called before a Russian Senatorial committee to answer the charge that he had conspired with Herzen's revolutionary group in London. He was exonerated.

About this time he became a member of the Paris coterie composed of Flaubert, Edmond de Goncourt, Zola, and Daudet. He befriended young Henry James. In 1872 *A Month in the Country* was staged for the first time, in Moscow, and Turgenev published *Spring Freshets*. He and the Viardots built a joint villa at Bougival, near Paris.

Virgin Soil appeared in 1877. By 1882 he was gravely ill, but continued work on *Clara Milich* and *Poems in Prose*. He is regarded as the most Western of the great Russian writers, the most poetic of realists and one of the fathers of the modern objective novel. He died at Bougival on September 3, 1883.

Like Dostoevsky's *White Nights*[1] and Galsworthy's *The Apple-Tree*,[2] *First Love* is a commemoration of that early "happiness verging on imbecility." It was published in March, 1860. In his biography of the author, Avrahm Yarmolinsky mentions that Turgenev said he "drew upon his reminiscences of the family life of his parents. The self-contained, elegantly groomed gentleman of the tale, with his spasmodically affectionate manner toward his family, his excellent horsemanship, and his epicurean tastes, was modeled upon the author's father. . . ." But such reminiscences have been freely transformed into a work of art. The mother of the story, for example, shows little likeness to the author's mother. Even in his old age, Turgenev recalled that when he was young she saw to it that he was "flogged nearly every day."

He spoke of *First Love* as one of his "fairy tales." Why? Partly, perhaps, because the incidents of the story might have happened in any time or place; but partly because it had little to do with the social struggle that nearly all nineteenth-century Russian writers felt themselves obliged to treat. But it is much more than a "fairy tale." It is, quite clearly, a little masterpiece. It is put together with such extraordinary grace that we are hardly conscious of reading a story at all. We simply live it. We take part in young Vladimir's feelings and act them out with him, because they are also ours. They are the feelings of every man who was ever in love in his first youth. And by that sign, in the perfect candor of art, they remind us

---

[1] See Vol. 3, pp. 276–319, in this set.
[2] See Vol. 3, pp. 323–367, in this set.

Notes from the artist: ". . . a fantasy of scenes from Fathers and Sons *surrounds the profile of Turgenev, an interpretation of an amusing, Cyrano-like self-caricature drawn by Turgenev in 1881."*

how much we have forgotten, or sentimentalized, or left out; how much we felt and did not know we felt; how ignorant and violent we were, how callous and how touching.

Even in a writer famous for his portraits of young girls, the Princess Zinaida is a superlative creation. This "tall, slender girl in a striped pink dress"—mischievous, quick-witted, beautiful, tender-cruel, a demanding ringmaster to her little circus of admirers—delights us at first with the freedom of her charm and then touches us with the despairing pathos of the trap in which she feels herself caught. Nor are we likely to forget the peasant grossness of old Princess Zasyekin or the draggletail poverty of her house. It becomes, nevertheless, a magic place for young Vladimir.

We see finally that *First Love* is an astonishing example of Turgenev's psychological perception. This basic drama, father and son in love with the same young woman—does it not reproduce and repeat Freud's Oedipus situation in infancy,[3] in which father and son compete for the mother's love? Moreover, the incidents that convey Vladimir's step-by-step understanding of the love between Zinaida and his father exactly parallel the small boy's gradual discovery of the relation between his parents. And does not Zinaida treat Vladimir "like a child"—that is, as if she were his mother? But we observe one striking difference. Vladimir is at an age to identify himself with his father. So, in their love, it is as if he had both won and lost.

---

[3] See *Great Books of the Western World,* Vol. 54, p. 581 *et seq.*

First Love

The visitors had left long ago. The clock struck half past twelve. Only the host, Sergey Nikolayevich, and Vladimir Petrovich were left in the room.

The host rang and ordered the remains of the supper to be cleared away. "So that's agreed, then," he said, settling himself more deeply in his arm-chair and lighting a cigar. "Each of us is to tell the story of his first love. It's your turn, Sergey Nikolayevich."

Sergey Nikolayevich, a rotund little man with a chubby face and fair hair, glanced first at his host, then raised his eyes to the ceiling. "I had no first love," he said at last. "I started straight with the second."

"How was that?"

"Quite simple. I was eighteen when I first took an interest in a very charming young girl, but I did this as if it were nothing new to me; and it was just like that that I afterwards flirted with others. Strictly speaking, I fell in love for the first and last time with my nurse when I was six years old. But that was a very long time ago. The details of our relationship have been blotted out from my memory, and even if I remembered them, how could they possibly interest anyone?"

"So what are we to do?" began the host. "There's nothing interesting in my first love, either. I did not fall in love with anyone before I met my wife—and everything went swimmingly with us: our parents arranged the match, we very soon fell in love with each other and got married without wasting much time. My tale is soon told. I don't mind admitting, gentlemen, that when I raised the question of first love, I was relying on you—I won't say old, but not such young bachelors, either. Won't you, Valdimir Petrovich, entertain us with some story?"

"My first love certainly cannot be said to be quite ordinary," Vladimir Petrovich, a man of about forty, with greying black hair, replied a little hesitantly.

"Oh," the host and Sergey Nikolayevich cried in one voice, "so much the better! Tell us about it."

"By all means. Or—no! I won't tell it to you; I'm not very good at telling stories. I'm afraid my stories are either too short and dry or too long and unconvincing. If you don't mind, I'd much rather write down all I can remember and read it to you."

At first his friends would not agree, but Vladimir Petrovich insisted on having it his own way. Two weeks later they met again, and Vladimir Petrovich kept his word.

This was what he had written down.

I was sixteen at the time. It happened in the summer of 1833.

I was living in Moscow with my parents. They used to take a country house for the summer near the Kaluga Toll Gate, opposite the Neskoochny Park. I was preparing for the university, but I did very little work and was in no particular hurry.

No one interfered with my freedom. I did what I liked, especially after parting with my last tutor, a Frenchman, who could never get used to the idea that he had dropped like a bomb (*comme une bombe*) into Russia, and he used to lie about in bed for days on end with a resentful expression on his face. My father treated me with good-humoured indifference; my mother scarcely paid any attention to me, although she had no other children: other worries occupied her completely. My father, who was still young and very handsome, had married her for money; she was ten years older than he. My mother's life was far from happy: she was in a state of constant irritation and was always jealous and bad-tempered, though never in my father's presence—she was terrified of him—while his attitude to her was severe, cold, and aloof. I have never seen a man more exquisitely calm, more self-possessed, or more despotic.

I shall never forget the first weeks I spent in the country. The weather was lovely; we left Moscow on the ninth of May, St. Nicholas's Day. I used to go for walks either in the garden of our country house or in the Neskoochny Park or on the other side of the toll gate; I used to take some book with me—Kaydanov's *Primer*, for instance—but I did not open it very often; I preferred much more to recite poetry, and I knew a great many poems by heart; my blood was in a ferment, and my heart ached—so sweetly and so foolishly; I was always expecting something to happen; I was in a state of constant dread of something; and I was full of wonder and seemed always to be seeking something; my imagination fluttered, and the same ideas winged their way swiftly like

martins round a bell tower at dawn; I would fall into a reverie, I would
be sad, and I would even cry; but through the tears and through the
sadness, inspired by some melodious verse or the beauty of the evening,
there always shot up, like the grass in springtime, a joyous feeling of
young, surging life.

I had a horse; I used to saddle it myself and go for long rides into the
country, breaking into a gallop and imagining myself a knight at a tourna-
ment (how gaily the wind whistled in my ears!)—or, turning my face towards the sky, received its shining azure light into my wide-open soul.

I remember that at that time the image of woman, the vision of a
woman's love, hardly ever took any definite shape in my mind; but in
everything I thought, in everything I felt, there was hidden a half-
conscious, shy presentiment of something new, unutterably sweet, feminine.

This presentiment, this expectation, pervaded my whole being: I
breathed it; it ran through my veins with every drop of blood. . . . It
was soon to be fulfilled.

Our country place consisted of a wooden manor house with columns
and two one-storied cottages; in the cottage on the left was a very small
factory for the manufacture of cheap wall-paper; I used to go over there
quite frequently to watch about a dozen thin and dishevelled boys with
pinched faces, in long greasy smocks, who kept jumping onto wooden
levers and pressing them down onto the square blocks of the presses and
in this way, by the weight of their feeble bodies, stamp the brightly
coloured patterns on the wall-paper. The cottage on the right stood
empty and was to let. One day, three weeks after the ninth of May, the
shutters of this cottage were opened and women's faces appeared in the
windows. Some family must have moved in. I remember that that same
day at dinner my mother asked the butler who our new neighbours were,
and hearing the name of Princess Zasyekin first remarked, not without
a certain note of respect, "Oh, a princess," and then added, "A poor one,
I expect."

"They arrived in three cabs, ma'am," observed the butler, handing
her a dish deferentially. "I don't think they have a carriage of their own,
ma'am. Their furniture is of the cheapest kind."

"I see," said my mother. "So much the better."

My father gave her a cold look, and she fell silent.

And indeed Princess Zasyekin could not have been a rich woman; the
cottage she had rented was so dilapidated, so small, and so low that people who were even moderately well off would not have consented to live

in it. However, at the time I paid no attention to it. The princely title had little effect on me; I had just been reading Schiller's *The Robbers*.

I was in the habit of wandering about our garden every evening with a gun, looking for crows. I had for a long time felt a detestation for these wary, predatory, and cunning birds. On the day I am speaking of I also went into the garden, and, having walked through all the avenues without result (the crows knew me and only cawed harshly from afar), I chanced to come near the low fence which separated *our* property from the narrow strip of garden which ran to the right behind the cottage and which belonged to it. I was walking along with my eyes fixed on the ground. Suddenly I heard voices. I looked across the fence and stood rooted to the spot. A curious sight met my eyes.

A few paces from me, in a clearing among the green raspberry bushes, stood a tall, slender girl in a striped pink dress with a white kerchief on her head; she was surrounded by four young men and she was tapping them in turn on the forehead with those small grey flowers whose name I do not know, though they are very well known to children: these flowers form little bags and burst with a pop when struck against anything hard. The young men presented their foreheads so eagerly, and there was in the movements of the young girl (I saw her in profile) something so fascinating, imperious, caressing, mocking, and charming, that I nearly cried out with wonder and delight and would, I believe, have given everything in the world at that moment to have those lovely fingers tap me on the forehead too. My gun slipped to the grass; I forgot everything; my eyes devoured this graceful figure, the slender neck, the beautiful arms, the slightly untidy fair hair under the white kerchief, and the half-closed, intelligent eye, the eyelashes, the delicate cheek beneath them.

"I say, young man," said a voice suddenly near me, "is it proper to stare like that at young ladies you do not know?"

I started, thunderstruck. Near me, on the other side of the fence, stood a man with close-cropped black hair, looking ironically at me. At that very moment the young girl too turned towards me. I saw a pair of enormous grey eyes in a vivacious, lively face, and this face suddenly quivered and laughed; her white teeth flashed and her eyebrows lifted in a rather amusing fashion. I flushed, snatched up my gun from the ground, and, pursued by ringing though not unkind laughter, fled to my room, flung myself on the bed, and covered my face with my hands. My heart leapt inside me; I was very ashamed and happy; I felt tremendously excited.

After a short rest I brushed my hair, tidied myself, and went downstairs to tea. The image of the young girl floated before me; my heart was no longer leaping but seemed to contract delightfully.

"What's the matter with you?" my father asked me suddenly. "Shot a crow?"

I was about to tell him everything, but stopped short and merely smiled to myself. As I was going to bed, without knowing myself why, I spun round three times on one foot, put pomade on my hair, got into bed, and slept soundly all night. Before morning I woke up for a moment, raised my head, looked round me in ecstasy, and—fell asleep again.

"How can I get to know them?" was my first thought when I woke in the morning.

Before breakfast I went for a walk in the garden, but did not go too near the fence and saw no one. After breakfast I walked several times up and down the street before the cottage and peered into the windows from a distance. I thought I could see *her* face behind the curtain, and I walked away quickly in a panic. "Still, I must get to know them," I thought, walking aimlessly about the sandy stretch before the Neskoochny Park. "But how? That is the question." I recalled the minutest details of yesterday's meeting: for some reason I had a most vivid recollection of the way she had laughed at me. But while I worried and made all sorts of plans, fate was already doing her best to gratify my desire.

While I was out, my mother had received from her new neighbour a letter on grey paper, sealed with the sort of brown wax that is used only in official post office notices and on the corks of bottles of cheap wine. In this letter, illiterate and written in a slovenly hand, the princess begged my mother to do her a great favour: my mother, the princess wrote, was on very intimate terms with people in high positions on whom depended the fortunes of herself and her children, for she was engaged in a number of very important lawsuits. "I rite to you," she wrote, "as one noblewoman to another, and becos of that I am pleesed to make use of this oportunity." In conclusion she asked my mother's permission to call on her. I found my mother in a disagreeable mood: my father was not at home, and she had no one to consult. Not to reply to a "noblewoman," and a princess into the bargain, was impossible. But my mother was at a loss as to how to reply. To write a note in French was, she thought, inappropriate, while she was not particularly good at Russian spelling herself. She knew this and did not want to compromise herself. She was therefore glad of my return and at once told me to go round to the princess and explain to her by word of mouth that she was always ready to be of service to Her Highness as far as was in her power and she asked the princess to do her the honour of calling on her at one o'clock. The unexpectedly rapid fulfilment of my secret desires both delighted and frightened me; however, I did not show any sign of the confusion that overcame me and went first to my room to put on my new cravat and frock-coat: at home I still went about in a tunic and a turned-down collar, although I was sick and tired of them.

In the narrow and untidy passage of the cottage, which I entered shaking nervously all over, I was met by a grey-headed old servant with a face the colour of dark copper, surly little pig's eyes and deep furrows on his forehead, and temples such as I had never seen in my life before. He was carrying a plate with a clean-picked herring bone on it, and, shutting the door leading into another room with his foot, said in an abrupt tone of voice, "What do you want?"

"Is Princess Zasyekin at home?" I asked.

"Vonifaty!" a woman's cracked voice screamed from behind the door.

The man-servant turned his back on me without a word, revealing the extremely threadbare back of his livery with a solitary, rusty crested button, and, putting the plate down on the floor, went away.

"Have you been to the police station?" the same woman's voice repeated. The man muttered something in reply. "What? Someone's come?" I heard her say again. "The young gentleman from next door? Well, ask him in."

"Will you step into the drawing room, sir?" said the servant, reappearing before me again and picking up the plate from the floor.

I put myself to rights and went into the "drawing room."

I found myself in a small and not particularly tidy room with rather shoddy furniture which seemed to have been arranged in a hurry. By the window, in an arm-chair with a broken arm, sat a woman of about fifty, bare-headed and rather plain, in an old green dress with a striped worsted kerchief round her neck. She glanced at me with her small black eyes.

I went up to her and bowed.

"Have I the honour to address Princess Zasyekin?"

"I am Princess Zasyekin. Are you the son of Mr. W.?"

"Yes, ma'am, I am. I have come to you with a message from my mother."

"Sit down, please. Vonifaty, where are my keys? You haven't seen them, have you?"

I told Princess Zasyekin my mother's reply to her note. She listened to me, drumming on the window-sill with her thick, red fingers, and when I had finished, she stared at me once more.

"Very good, I shall certainly call," she said at last. "But, gracious me, how young you are! How old are you, may I ask?"

"S-sixteen," I replied with an involuntary stammer.

The princess pulled out of her pocket some greasy papers covered with writing, raised them to her nose, and began looking through them. "An excellent age," she said suddenly, turning to me and fidgeting in her chair. "Please make yourself at home. We're ordinary people here."

"A bit too ordinary," I thought to myself, glancing with a feeling of involuntary disgust at her unprepossessing person.

At that moment another door was flung open and in the doorway there appeared the girl I had seen in the garden the previous evening. She raised her hand, and a mocking smile appeared for a moment on her face.

"And here's my daughter," said the princess, pointing to her with her elbow. "Zeena, darling, this is the son of our neighbour, Mr. W. What's your name, may I ask?"

"V-Vladimir," I replied, getting up and stuttering in my excitement.

"And your patronymic?"

"Petrovich."

"I see. I used to know a police commissioner once. He was also called Vladimir Petrovich. Vonifaty, don't look for the keys—they are in my pocket."

The young girl continued to look at me with the same mocking smile, screwing up her eyes slightly and putting her head a little on one side.

"I've already met M'sieu Woldemar," she began. (The silvery sound of her voice ran through me with a kind of delightful shiver.) "You don't mind me calling you that, do you?"

"Why, of course not," I murmured.

"Where was that?" asked the princess.

The young princess did not answer. "You haven't got anything special to do now, have you?" she asked, without taking her eyes off me.

"Why, no, ma'am."

"Would you like to help me wind some wool? Follow me, please. This way—to my room." She nodded to me and left the drawing room. I followed her.

In the room we entered, the furniture was a little better and arranged with more taste. At that moment, though, I was quite unable to notice anything: I moved as though in a dream and was overwhelmed by an intense feeling of happiness verging on imbecility.

The young princess sat down, took a skein of red wool, and, motioning me to a chair opposite, carefully untied the skein and put it across my hands. All this she did in silence with a kind of amused deliberation and with the same bright, sly smile on her slightly parted lips. She began to wind the wool round a bent card and then suddenly dazzled me with so swift and radiant a glance that I could not help dropping my eyes. When her eyes, mostly half-closed, opened wide, her face was completely transformed, as though flooded with light.

"What did you think of me yesterday, M'sieu Woldemar?" she asked, after a short pause. "I expect you must have thought me dreadful."

"Why, I—er—Princess—I—I—didn't think anything—how—could—I?" I replied in confusion.

"Listen," she said. "You don't know me yet. I'm an awfully strange person. I want people to tell me the truth always. You are sixteen, I hear, and I am twenty-one. You see, I'm very much older than you, and that is why you must always tell me the truth—and," she added, "do what I tell you. Look at me! Why don't you look at me?"

I was more confused than ever, but I did raise my eyes and look at her. She smiled, not as before, but approvingly.

"Look at me," she said, dropping her voice caressingly. "I do not mind it at all. I like your face. I have a feeling we shall be friends. And do you like me?" she added slyly.

"Princess—" I began.

"First of all, you must call me Zinaida Alexandrovna, and, second, what a strange habit children"—she quickly corrected herself—"young men have of not saying frankly what they feel. That's all very well for grown ups. You do like me, don't you?"

Though I was very pleased that she should be talking so frankly to me, I was a little hurt. I wanted to show her that she was not dealing with a mere boy, and, assuming as serious and nonchalant an air as I could, I said, "Of course I like you very much, Zinaida Alexandrovna. I have no wish to conceal it."

She shook her head slowly. "Have you a tutor?" she asked suddenly.

"No, I haven't had one for ages." I was telling a lie: it was not a month since I had parted with my Frenchman.

"Oh, I see, you're quite grown up." She rapped me lightly over the fingers. "Hold your hands straight!"

And she busily began winding the ball of wool. I took advantage of the fact that she did not raise her eyes to examine her at first stealthily and then more and more boldly. I thought her face was even more lovely than on the previous day: everything in it was so delicate, intelligent, and charming. She was sitting with her back to the window, which was covered with a white blind: the sunshine streaming through the blind shed a soft light on her fine, golden hair, her virginal throat, her sloping shoulders, and her calm, tender bosom. I gazed at her—and how dear and near she was already to me! I couldn't help feeling that I had known her a long, long time and that before her I had known nothing and had not lived. She was wearing a dark, rather old and worn dress with an apron; I would gladly have caressed every fold of that dress and that apron. The tips of her shoes peeped from under her skirt: I could have knelt in adoration to those shoes! "And here I am, sitting in front of her," I thought. "I have made her acquaintance. God! What happiness!" I almost leapt from my chair in ecstasy, but, in fact, all I did was to swing my legs a little, like a child eating a sweet.

I was as happy as a fish in water. I could have stayed in that room forever. I could have never left it.

Her eyelids were slowly raised and once more her bright eyes shone caressingly upon me, and again she smiled. "How you do look at me!" she said slowly, and she shook a finger at me.

I blushed. "She understands everything; she sees everything," flashed across my mind. "And how could she fail to understand it all and see it all?"

Suddenly there was a clatter in the next room—a sabre clanked.

"Zeena," the old princess cried from the drawing room, "Belovzorov has brought you a kitten!"

"A kitten!" cried Zinaida, and, rising impetuously from her chair, she threw the ball of wool into my lap and ran out of the room.

I too got up and, leaving the skein and the ball of wool on the windowsill, went out into the drawing room and stopped dead in amazement: a tabby kitten was lying in the middle of the room with its paws in the air; Zinaida was on her knees before it, cautiously lifting up its tiny head. Near the old princess, almost filling the entire space between the two windows, I saw a fair-haired and curly-headed, stalwart, young hussar officer, with a pink face and protruding eyes.

"What a funny little thing!" Zinaida was saying. "And its eyes aren't grey—they're green—and what enormous ears he's got! Thank you, Victor! How sweet of you."

The hussar, whom I recognized as one of the young men I had seen the previous evening, smiled and bowed, clicking his spurs and clinking the chain of his sabre.

"You were pleased to say yesterday that you'd like to have a tabby kitten with large ears, so I—I got one. Your word is law." And he bowed again.

The kitten miaowed feebly and began to sniff the floor.

"It's hungry!" cried Zinaida. "Vonifaty, Sonia, bring some milk."

The maid, in an old yellow dress and with a faded kerchief round her neck, came in with a saucer of milk in her hands and set it before the kitten. The kitten gave a start, screwed up its eyes, and began to lap.

"What a pink little tongue it's got!" observed Zinaida, bending her head almost to the floor and looking at the kitten sideways under its very nose.

The kitten drank its fill and began purring and moving its paws up and down finickingly. Zinaida got up and, turning to the maid, said in an indifferent voice, "Take it away."

"Allow me to kiss your hand in return for the kitten," said the hussar, flashing his teeth and flexing his whole powerful frame, tightly encased in a new uniform.

"Both of them," replied Zinaida, and she held out her hands to him. While he kissed them, she looked at me over his shoulder.

I stood stock still and did not know whether to laugh, to say something, or to remain silent. Suddenly I caught sight of our footman, Fyodor, through the open passage door. He was making signs to me. Mechanically I went out to him.

"What are you doing here?" I asked.

"Your mother has sent for you," he said in a whisper. "She is angry because you haven't come back with the answer."

"Why, have I been here long?"

"Over an hour, sir."

"Over an hour!" I repeated involuntarily and, returning to the drawing room, I began to take my leave, bowing and scraping my feet.

"Where are you off to?" asked the young princess, glancing at me from behind the hussar.

"I'm afraid I have to go home. . . . So I am to say," I added, turning to the old woman, "that you will call on us about two o'clock?"

"Yes, do say that, dear boy." The old princess hurriedly reached for a snuff-box and took the snuff so noisily that it almost made me jump. "Yes, do say that," she repeated, blinking tearfully and groaning.

I bowed once more, turned, and walked out of the room with that uncomfortable sensation in my back which a very young man feels when he knows he is being watched from behind.

"Mind you come and see us again, M'sieu Woldemar!" cried Zinaida, and laughed again.

"Why is she always laughing?" I thought as I was returning home, accompanied by Fyodor, who said nothing to me, but walked behind me with a disapproving air. My mother scolded me and wondered what I could have been doing so long at the princess's. I made no answer and went off to my room. Suddenly I felt very sad. I tried hard not to cry. I was jealous of the hussar.

The old princess paid a visit to my mother as she had promised. My mother did not like her. I was not present at their interview, but at dinner my mother told my father that this Princess Zasyekin struck her as *une femme très vulgaire*, that she had wearied her out with her requests to intercede on her behalf with Prince Sergey, that she seemed to be involved in some lawsuits and shady business deals—*des vilaines affaires d'argent*—and that she must be a thoroughly unpleasant woman. My mother, however, added that she had asked her and her daughter to dinner the next day (hearing the words "and her daughter," I buried my nose in my plate), because she was, after all, a neighbour and a titled woman. Upon which my father informed my mother that he now remembered who this lady was; that when he was a young man he had known the late Prince Zasyekin, a highly cultured but frivolous and ridiculous man; that in society he was known as "*le Parisien*" because he had lived in Paris for a long time; that he had been very rich but had gambled away his entire fortune, and for some unknown reason, probably for money—"though he could have made a much better choice," my father added with a cold smile—married the daughter of some departmental clerk and after his marriage had begun speculating and completely ruined himself.

"I do hope she's not going to ask for a loan," observed my mother.

"I should not be in the least surprised," my father said calmly. "Does she speak French?"

"Very badly."

"I see. However, that doesn't matter. I think you said you'd also asked her daughter? Someone was telling me that she was a very charming and well-educated girl."

"Oh? Then she can't take after her mother."

"No, nor after her father," said my father. "He was cultured too, but a fool."

My mother sighed and sank into thought. My father was silent. I felt very uncomfortable during this conversation.

After dinner I went into the garden, but without my gun. I vowed not to go near the "Zasyekin garden," but an irresistible force drew me there, and I was not disappointed. For I had hardly reached the fence when I caught sight of Zinaida. This time she was alone. She had a book in her hand and was walking slowly along the path. She did not notice me.

I nearly let her pass by, but suddenly recollected myself and coughed. She turned round but did not stop. With her hand she pushed back the broad blue ribbon of her round straw hat, looked at me, smiled gently, and again dropped her eyes to the book.

I took off my cap and, after hesitating a little, walked away with a heavy heart. "*Que suis je pour elle* [What am I to her]?" I thought (goodness only knows why!) in French.

Familiar footsteps sounded behind me: I looked round—my father was coming towards me with his light, quick step. "Is that the young princess?" he asked me.

"Yes."

"Do you know her?"

"I saw her this morning at the old princess's."

My father stopped and, turning sharply on his heels, went back. Drawing level with Zinaida, he bowed to her courteously. She too bowed to him—not without some surprise, though—and lowered her book. I saw how she followed him with her eyes. My father always dressed very exquisitely and simply and in a style all his own; but never before had his figure struck me as more elegant, and never before had his grey hat sat more handsomely on his barely perceptibly thinning hair.

I walked towards Zinaida, but she did not even glance at me. She raised her book again and walked away.

I spent the whole of that evening and the following morning in a state of stunned misery. I remember I tried to work and opened Kaydanov, but the clearly printed lines and pages of the celebrated text-book flashed before my eyes in vain. A dozen times over I read the words: "Julius Caesar was distinguished for martial valour," but did not understand a word and threw the book down. Before dinner I pomaded my hair again and again put on my new coat and cravat.

"What's this for?" asked my mother. "You're not a university student yet, and heaven knows whether you'll ever pass your examinations. Besides, how long is it since I bought you your tunic? You're not going to throw it away, are you?"

"We're going to have visitors," I whispered almost in despair.

"What nonsense! Visitors indeed!"

I had to give in. I changed the coat for my tunic, but I did not take off the cravat.

The princess and her daughter arrived half an hour before dinner. The old woman had thrown a yellow shawl over the green dress in which I had seen her before and put on an old-fashioned bonnet with flame-coloured ribbons. She began talking at once about her bills of exchange, sighing and complaining about her poverty, and went on and on about it without apparently feeling in the least humiliated: she took snuff as noisily as before and fidgeted and turned about on her chair as freely as ever. It never seemed to occur to her that she was a princess. Zinaida, on the other hand, carried herself very gravely, even haughtily, like a true princess. An expression of cold immobility and dignity appeared on her face, and she seemed quite a different person to me; I could discover no trace of the glances, the smiles I knew so well, though in this new guise, too, she seemed beautiful to me. She wore a light *barège* dress with a pale blue pattern; her hair fell in long curls down her cheeks, in the English fashion. This way of doing her hair went well with the cold expression on her face. My father sat beside her during dinner and entertained his neighbour with his usual exquisite and calm courtesy. From time to time he glanced at her, and she too looked at him now and again, but so strangely, almost with hostility. Their conversation was carried on in French; I remember I was surprised by the purity of Zinaida's pronunciation. The old princess was, as before, not in the least put out at dinner, eating a lot and praising the dishes. My mother was obviously bored by her and answered her with a sort of melancholy disdain. Now and then my father frowned a little.

My mother did not like Zinaida either. "Very proud, isn't she?" she said the next day. "And what has she to be so proud about, I wonder—*avec sa mine de grisette* [with her grisette expression]?"

"You've evidently never seen any grisettes," observed my father.

"No, I haven't, thank God!"

"Yes indeed, thank God—only how on earth can you form an opinion of them?"

Zinaida had paid no attention whatsoever to me. Soon after dinner the old princess began to take her leave.

"I shall count on your good offices, madam, and on yours too, sir," she said in a sing-song voice to my mother and father. "I'm afraid there's nothing we can do about it. We've had our good times, but they're gone, so here I am, a Highness," she added with an unpleasant laugh, "but what's the use of a title if you're starving?"

My father bowed to her respectfully and saw her off to the front door. There I stood, in my short tunic, staring at the floor as though under sentence of death. Zinaida's treatment of me had crushed me completely. Imagine my surprise when, as she passed by me, she said in a rapid whisper and with the former affectionate look in her eyes, "Come and see us at eight o'clock. Do you hear? Without fail!"

I did not know what to make of it, but she was already gone, throwing a white scarf over her head.

Punctually at eight o'clock, in my tail-coat, with a raised quiff of hair, I entered the passage of the cottage where the princess lived. The old servant scowled at me and got up unwillingly from the bench. I could hear gay voices in the drawing room. I opened the door and stepped back in astonishment. In the middle of the room, on a chair, stood the young princess, holding a man's hat in front of her; about half a dozen men crowded round the chair. They were trying to put their hands into the hat, while she kept raising it and shaking it violently.

On seeing me she cried, "Wait, wait, another visitor! I must give him a ticket too," and, jumping lightly off the chair, she took me by the cuff of my coat. "Come along," she said. "What are you standing there for? Gentlemen, let me introduce you: this is M'sieu Woldemar, our neighbour's son. And these," she added, turning to me and pointing to each one of her guests in turn, "are Count Malevsky, Dr. Lushin, the poet Maydanov, retired Captain Nirmatsky, and Belovzorov, the hussar, whom you have met already. I hope you will all be good friends."

I was so overcome with confusion that I did not even bow to anyone; in Dr. Lushin I recognized the same dark man who had put me to shame so mercilessly in the garden; the others I did not know.

"Count," Zinaida went on, "write out a ticket for M'sieu Woldemar."

"That's not fair," the count replied with a slight Polish accent. "He did not play forfeits with us."

The count was a very handsome and fashionably dressed, dark-haired young man with expressive brown eyes, a small, narrow white nose, and a thin moustache above a tiny mouth.

"It's not fair," repeated Belovzorov and the gentleman who had been introduced as a retired captain, a man in his forties, hideously pock-marked, with frizzy hair like a Negro's, bandy-legged, and dressed in a military coat without epaulettes, which he wore unbuttoned.

"Write out the ticket, I tell you," repeated the princess. "What is this? A mutiny? M'sieu Woldemar is here for the first time, and today the rules do not apply to him. Don't grumble, and write it out! That is my wish."

The count shrugged his shoulders, but, bowing his head obediently, picked up a pen in his white, beringed fingers, tore off a scrap of paper, and began writing on it.

"Let me at least explain to M'sieu Woldemar what this is all about," began Lushin in a sarcastic voice, "or else he'll be completely at a loss. You see, young man, we are playing a game of forfeits. The princess has to pay a forfeit, and he who draws the lucky ticket will have the right to kiss her hand. Do you understand what I have told you?"

I just glanced at him and continued to stand like one in a trance, while the young princess again jumped on a chair and once more began shaking the hat. They all moved up to her, and I with the rest.

"Maydanov," said the princess to the tall young man with a thin face, short-sighted little eyes, and extremely long black hair, "you, as a poet, ought to be magnanimous and give up your ticket to M'sieu Woldemar so that he may have two chances instead of one."

But Maydanov shook his head and tossed back his hair. I put my hand into the hat after all the others and unfolded my ticket. Good Lord, what did I feel when I saw on it the word *kiss!*

"Kiss!" I cried involuntarily.

"Bravo, he won!" the young princess cried. "I am so glad!" She got off the chair, looked into my eyes, and gave me such a bright and sweet look that my heart turned over within me. "Are you glad?" she asked me.

"Me?" I murmured.

"Sell me your ticket," Belovzorov suddenly blurted out in my ear. "I'll give you a hundred roubles."

I answered the hussar with so indignant a look that Zinaida clapped her hands, while Lushin cried, "Stout fellow! But," he added, "as master of ceremonies, I am obliged to see that all the rules are kept. M'sieu Woldemar, go down on one knee! That's our rule."

Zinaida stood in front of me with her head a little on one side, as though she wished to get a better look at me, and held out her hand to

me with an air of great solemnity. Everything went black before my
eyes; I was about to go down on one knee, but sank on both and touched
Zinaida's fingers so awkwardly with my lips that I scratched the tip of
my nose on her nail.

"Splendid!" cried Lushin, and helped me to get up.

The game of forfeits went on. Zinaida made me sit down beside her.
The forfeits she thought of! She had, among other things, to represent a
statue, and she chose the hideous Nirmatsky as her pedestal, told him to
lie down on the floor and to lower his head to his chest. The laughter
never ceased for a moment. All this noise and uproar, all this uncere-
monious, almost riotous gaiety, all this strange relationship with unknown
persons, simply went to my head, for I had been brought up soberly, in
the seclusion of a staid country house. I was intoxicated, as though with
wine. I began laughing at the top of my voice and talking a lot of nonsense more loudly than the others, so that even the old princess, who was
sitting in the next room with some pettifogging lawyer's clerk from the
Iversky Gate, who had been invited for a consultation, came out to have
a look at me. But I felt so intensely happy that I did not care for anyone's
sarcastic remarks or anyone's disapproving looks.

Zinaida continued to show a preference for me, and would not let me
leave her side. For one forfeit I had to sit beside her, both of us covered
with the same silk kerchief: I had to tell her *my secret*. I remember how
both our heads were suddenly plunged in a close, semi-transparent,
fragrant darkness and how near and how softly her eyes shone in this
darkness, and I remember the burning breath of her parted lips and the
glint of her teeth and how her hair tickled and scorched me. I was silent.
She smiled mysteriously and slyly and at last whispered to me, "Well,
what is it?" but I only blushed and laughed and turned away, hardly able
to breathe. We got tired of forfeits and began playing a game with string.
Heavens, how delighted I was when, in a moment of absentmindedness,
I received a sharp and painful blow on my fingers and how I afterwards
purposely tried to pretend that I was not paying attention and she teased
me and refused to touch the hands that I held out to her!

The things we did that evening! We played the piano, we sang and
danced, and we acted a gipsy encampment. Nirmatsky was dressed up as
a bear and made to drink salt water. Count Malevsky showed us all sorts
of card tricks and finished up by shuffling the cards and dealing himself
all the trumps at whist, upon which Lushin "had the honour" to congratulate him. Maydanov recited passages from his poem "The Murderer"
(all this took place at a time when the romantic movement was at its

height), which he intended to publish in a black cover with the title printed in blood-red letters; we stole the lawyer's clerk's cap off his knee and made him dance a Cossack dance by way of ransom; we dressed up old Vonifaty in a bonnet, and the young princess put on a man's hat . . . It is impossible to enumerate everything we did that evening. Belovzorov alone skulked in a corner, looking cross and frowning. Sometimes his eyes would become bloodshot, he flushed all over, and it seemed as though he would at any moment hurl himself upon us all and scatter us in all directions; but the young princess would glance at him, shake her finger, and he would once more slink back to his corner.

We were quite worn out at last. Even the old princess, who, as she expressed it, could "put up with anything"—no amount of noise seemed to trouble her—felt tired and declared that she would like to have a little rest. At midnight, supper was served. It consisted of a piece of stale, dry cheese and some cold ham patties which seemed more delicious to me than any pies; there was only one bottle of wine, and that too was a rather strange one: a dark-coloured bottle with a blown-out neck, and the wine in it smelt of pink paint: however, no one drank it. Tired and exhausted with happiness, I left the cottage: at parting, Zinaida pressed my hand warmly and again smiled enigmatically.

The night air was heavy and damp against my burning face. A storm seemed to be gathering. Black clouds grew and crept across the sky, changing their smoky outlines even while one looked at them. The breeze quivered restlessly in the dark trees, and somewhere far beyond the horizon thunder was growing angrily and hollowly, as though to itself.

I made my way to my room by the back door. The old man-servant who looked after me was asleep on the floor, and I had to step over him; he woke up, saw me, and told me that my mother had again been angry with me and had again wanted to send for me, but that my father would not let her. (I never went to bed without saying good night to my mother and asking her blessing.) However, there was nothing to be done about it now!

I told my man-servant that I would undress and get myself to bed, and put out the candle. But I did not undress and I did not go to bed.

I sat down on a chair and sat there a long time, like one enchanted. What I felt was so new and so sweet. I sat still, hardly looking around and without moving, breathing slowly, and only at times laughing silently at something I remembered or turning cold inwardly at the thought that I was in love and that that was *it*, that was love. Zinaida's face floated slowly before me in the darkness—floated, but did not float away; her lips still wore the same enigmatic smile; her eyes still looked at me a little sideways, questioningly, dreamily, tenderly, as at the moment when I had parted from her. At last I got up, tiptoed to my bed, and without undressing, carefully laid my head on the pillow, as though afraid to disturb by an abrupt movement that which filled my whole being.

I lay down but did not even close my eyes. Soon I noticed faint glimmers of light continually lighting up my room. I sat up and looked at the window. The window bars showed up against the mysteriously and dimly lit panes. "A thunderstorm," I thought, and I was right. It was a storm, but it was very far away, so that the thunder could not be heard; only the faint, long, branching-out forks of lightning flashed uninterruptedly across the sky: they did not flash so much as quiver and twitch, like the wing of a dying bird. I got up, went to the window, and stood there till morning. The lightning did not cease for a moment; it was what is known among the peasants as a "sparrow night," or a night of uninterrupted storm with thunder and lightning. I looked at the silent stretch of sand and the dark mass of the Neskoochny Park, at the yellowish façades of distant buildings, which also seemed to quiver with each faint flash. I looked and could not tear myself away: this silent lightning, these restrained gleams of light, seemed to respond to the mute and secret fires which kept blazing up in me too. Morning began to break; the dawn came up in crimson patches. As the sun rose higher in the sky, the flashes of lightning grew fainter and less frequent: they quivered more and more seldom and at last vanished, drowned in the tempering and clear light of the rising day.

And the lightning within me vanished too. I felt a great weariness and silence. But Zinaida's image continued to hover triumphant over my soul. Only this image too seemed more at peace; like a swan rising from the reeds of a marsh into the air, it detached itself from the unseemly figures which surrounded it, and as I fell asleep I clung to it for a last time in a parting and trusting adoration.

Oh, gentle feelings, soft sounds, the goodness and the growing calm of a heart that is deeply moved, the melting gladness of the first tender raptures of love—where are you? Where are you?

Next morning when I came down to breakfast my mother scolded me—not as much as I had expected, however—and made me tell her how I had spent the previous evening. I answered her in a few words, leaving out many details and trying to make everything appear most innocent.

"All the same, they're not *comme il faut* [socially proper]," observed my mother, "and you have no business to be hanging about there instead of working for your examinations."

Knowing that my mother's concern for my studies would be confined to these few words, I did not consider it necessary to take exception to what she had said; but after breakfast my father put his arm through mine, and, going into the garden with me, made me give him a full account of all I had seen at the Zasyekins'.

My father had a strange influence on me—and strange indeed were our relations towards one another. He took practically no part in my education, but he never hurt my feelings; he respected my freedom; he even was, if I may put it this way, polite to me; but he never let me come near him. I loved him and I admired him. He seemed to me to be a paragon of a man—and, dear me, how passionately attached to him I should have grown if only I had not constantly felt his restraining hand! Yet he could, whenever he wanted to, arouse in me an absolute trust in him almost instantaneously, by one single movement, as it were. My heart opened up to him and I chatted to him as I would to an intelligent friend or an indulgent teacher; then he would desert me with the same suddenness, and his hand would push me away again—gently and tenderly, but push me away it did for all that.

Occasionally a gay mood would come upon him, and then he would be ready to play with me as though he were a little boy himself (he was fond of all strong physical exertions); once—only once!—he caressed me with such tenderness that I nearly burst into tears. But his gaiety and tenderness vanished without a trace, and what had passed between us gave me no hope for the future; it was as though it had all been happening in a dream. Sometimes as I gazed at his handsome, clever, bright face my heart would leap up and all my being would rush towards him. . . . He seemed to feel what was going on inside me, and he would give me a casual pat on the cheek and go away and do something, or he would suddenly turn cold as only he knew how to turn cold, and I would shrink back within myself at once and go cold too. His rare fits of friendliness towards me were never caused by my mute but unmistakable entreaties: they always came quite unexpectedly. Reflecting on my father's character afterwards, I came to the conclusion that he could not be bothered with me—or with his family; it was other things he cared for, and he derived full satisfaction from them. "Grab all you can, but never allow yourself to be caught; to belong to yourself alone is the whole trick of living," he said to me once. Another time, like the young democrat I was, I began discussing freedom in his presence (that day he was, as I called it, "good," and it was possible to talk to him about everything).

"Freedom," he repeated, "but do you know what can give a man freedom?"

"What?"

"His will, his own will: that will give him power, which is better than freedom. Know how to want something, and you will be free and you will be able to command."

My father wanted to live above everything else and more than everything else, and he *did* live: perhaps he had a premonition that he was not going to enjoy the trick of living long: he died at forty-two.

I gave my father a detailed account of my visit to the Zasyekins'. He listened to me half-attentively and half-absently, sitting on a bench and drawing in the sand with the end of his riding crop. From time to time he would chuckle, look at me in a sort of bright and amused way, and he egged me on with short questions and rejoinders. At first I could not pluck up sufficient courage even to utter Zinaida's name, but I could not contain myself and began extolling her to the skies. My father continued to smile; then he sank into thought, stretched himself, and got up.

I remembered that as he was going out of the house he ordered his horse to be saddled. He was an excellent horseman and he could break in the wildest horse long before Rarey.[1]

"May I come with you, Father?" I asked him.

"No," he replied, and his face assumed its usual half-indifferent, half-affectionate expression. "Go alone, if you like, and tell the groom that I shall not be going."

He turned his back on me and walked rapidly away. I followed him with my eyes—and he disappeared behind the gates. I saw his hat moving along above the fence: he went into the Zasyekins' cottage. He did not stay there more than an hour and then left at once for the town and did not return home till evening.

After dinner I myself called on the Zasyekins. In the drawing room I found only the old princess. On seeing me, she scratched her head under her bonnet with the end of a knitting needle and suddenly asked me whether I would copy out a petition for her.

"With pleasure," I replied, sitting down on the edge of a chair.

---

1. John S. Rarey (1828–1866) was an American horse trainer who introduced a system of throwing down vicious or unruly horses, so as to train them.—Translator.

"Only, mind, make your letters as big as you can," said the old princess, handing me a sheet of paper scribbled over with her writing. "You couldn't do it today, could you, my boy?"

"Yes, ma'am, I'll copy it out today."

The door to the adjoining room was slightly open, and Zinaida's face appeared in the opening—pale, pensive, with her hair carelessly tossed back: she looked at me with big, cold eyes and softly closed the door.

"Zeena! I say, Zeena!" said the old woman.

Zinaida made no answer. I carried away the old woman's petition and sat the whole evening over it.

My passion began from that day. What I felt at that time, I remember, was something similar to what a man must feel on entering government service: I had ceased to be simply a young boy: I was someone in love. I have said that my passion began from that day; I might have added that my suffering began on that day too. Away from Zinaida, I languished: I could not think of anything, I had not the heart to do anything, and for days on end all my thoughts revolved round her. I languished . . . but in her presence I did not feel any happier. I was jealous; I realized my own insignificance; I sulked stupidly and cringed stupidly; and yet an irresistible force drew me towards her, and every time I stepped over the threshold of her room I was seized by an uncontrollable tremor of happiness. Zinaida guessed at once that I had fallen in love with her, and indeed I never thought of concealing it; she amused herself with my passion; she made a fool of me, petted me, and tormented me. It is sweet to be the only source, the despotic and arbitrary cause, of the greatest joys, the greatest sorrows, in another human being, and I was like soft wax in Zinaida's hands.

However, I was not the only one to have fallen in love with her: all the men who visited the house were madly in love with her, and she kept them all on leading strings—at her feet. It amused her to arouse their hopes one moment and their fears another, to twist them round her little finger (she used to call it "knocking people's heads together"); and they never dreamt of offering any resistance and were only too glad to submit to her. Her whole being, so beautiful and so full of vitality, was a curiously fascinating mixture of cunning and carelessness, artificiality and simplicity, calmness and vivacity; there was a subtle, delicate charm about everything she did or said, about every movement of hers; in everything a peculiar, sparklingly vivacious force was at work. Her face too was vivacious and always changing: it expressed almost at one and the same time irony, pensiveness, and passionateness. The most various emotions, light and swift like shadows of clouds on a windy, sunny day, chased each other continuously over her lips and eyes.

Every one of her admirers was necessary to her. Belovzorov, whom she sometimes called "my wild beast," and sometimes simply "mine," would gladly have flung himself into the fire for her; placing little confidence in his own intellectual abilities and other accomplishments, he kept proposing marriage to her, hinting darkly that the others only talked. Maydanov responded to the poetic chords of her soul: a rather cold man, like nearly all writers, he kept assuring her strenuously, and perhaps himself too, that he adored her; he extolled her in endless verses and read them to her with a kind of affected yet sincere enthusiasm. She sympathized with him and at the same time made fun of him a little; she had no great faith in him, and, after listening to his effusions, made him read Pushkin—in order, as she said, to "clear the air." Lushin, the sarcastic doctor, who was so cynical in speech, knew her better than any of them— and loved her more than any of them, though he scolded her to her face and behind her back. She respected him but paid him back in his own coin, and occasionally used to make him feel with particularly malicious pleasure that he was completely in her power. "I am a flirt, I'm heartless, I am an actress by nature," she said to him once in my presence. "Oh, all right, then! Give me your hand and I will stick a pin in it and you'll be ashamed before this young man. It will hurt you, but all the same you will be good enough to laugh, Mr. Truthful Man." Lushin flushed, turned away, bit his lips, but in the end held out his hand to her. She pricked him, and he did begin to laugh—and she laughed too, driving the pin in quite deep, and kept peering into his eyes, with which he tried in vain not to look at her.

Least of all did I understand the relations which existed between Zinaida and Count Malevsky. He was good-looking, adroit, and intelligent, but even I, at sixteen, felt that there was something equivocal, something false about him, and I was surprised that Zinaida did not notice it. But possibly she did notice this falseness and felt no aversion to it. Her irregular education, strange acquaintances and habits, the constant presence of her mother, poverty and disorder in the house—everything, beginning with the very freedom which the young girl enjoyed, and with the consciousness of her superiority over the people round her, had developed in her a sort of half-disdainful carelessness and a lack of fastidiousness. Whatever happened, whether Vonifaty came in to announce that there was no sugar left, or whether some unsavoury piece of scandal

came to light, or her guests began to quarrel, she would only shake her
curls, say, "Nonsense," and take no notice of it.

On the other hand, my blood used to boil every time Malevsky went
up to her, swaying cunningly like a fox, leaned elegantly against the
back of her chair, and began whispering into her ear with a self-satisfied
and ingratiating little smile, while she would fold her arms over her
bosom, look attentively at him, and smile herself and nod her head.

"What do you want to receive Count Malevsky for?" I asked her one
day.

"Oh, but he has such a lovely little moustache," she replied. "But I'm
afraid that is something you don't understand. . . .

"You don't think I'm in love with him, do you?" she said to me another
time. "Oh, no, I couldn't possibly be in love with people whom I have to
look down on. I want someone who will master me. But, thank goodness, I
shall never come across any man like that! I will never fall into any man's
clutches—never!"

"You'll never be in love, then?"

"And what about you? Don't I love you?" she said and flicked me on the
nose with the tips of her glove.

Yes, Zinaida amused herself a great deal at my expense. For three
weeks I saw her every day, and what didn't she do to me! She visited us
seldom, and I was not sorry for it: in our house she became transformed
into a young lady, a princess, and I was shy of her. I was afraid of betraying myself in front of my mother; she was not at all kindly disposed
towards Zinaida, and watched us with an unfriendly eye. I was not so
much afraid of my father: he did not seem to notice me and spoke very
little to her, but whatever he said to her seemed somehow particularly
brilliant and significant.

I stopped working and reading; I even stopped going for walks in the
neighbourhood and riding. Like a beetle tied by the leg, I circled constantly round my beloved little cottage: I would have stayed there forever if I could. But that was impossible. My mother grumbled at me, and
sometimes Zinaida herself used to drive me away. Then I would shut myself up in my room, or go to the end of the garden, climb onto the very
top of the ruin of a high brick green-house, and, with my legs dangling
from the wall that looked onto the road, sit there for hours, staring and
staring and seeing nothing. White butterflies fluttered lazily on the dusty
nettles near me; a cheeky sparrow settled not far off on a half-broken
red brick, twittering irritably, incessantly turning with its whole body
and preening its little tail; now and then the still mistrustful crows

cawed, sitting very high up on the bare top of a birch; the sun and the wind played gently in its sparse branches; the sound of the bells of the Donskoy monastery came floating across at times, tranquil and melancholy, while I sat there, gazing and listening, filled to overflowing with a kind of nameless sensation which had everything in it: sadness and joy, a premonition of the future, and desire, and fear of life. But just then I understood nothing of it and could not have given a name to anything that was seething within me, or I should have called it all by one name —the name of Zinaida.

And Zinaida continued to play with me like a cat with a mouse. Sometimes she would flirt with me, and I was all agitated and melting with emotion; at other times she would suddenly push me away, and I dared not go near her, dared not look at her.

I remember she was very distant with me for several days. I was completely abashed and, dropping in timidly at the cottage, tried to keep close to the old princess, in spite of her being particularly loud-voiced and abusive just at that time: her financial affairs had been going badly and she had already had to give two statements to the police.

One day as I was walking in the garden past the familiar fence I caught sight of Zinaida: she was sitting on the grass, her head propped up on both her hands, and did not stir. I was about to retreat cautiously, but she suddenly raised her head and signalled to me imperiously to come up to her. I was rooted to the spot: I failed to understand what she meant at first. She signalled to me again. I jumped over the fence at once and rushed joyfully up to her, but she stopped me with a glance and pointed to a path two paces away from her. Overcome with confusion and not knowing what to do, I knelt at the edge of the path. She was so pale, and such bitter grief, such profound weariness were manifest in every feature of her face that my heart contracted and I murmured involuntarily, "What's the matter?"

Zinaida stretched out her hand, tore off a blade of grass, bit it, and flung it from her as far as she could. "Do you love me very much?" she asked at last. "Do you?"

I made no answer, and what need was there for me to answer?

"You do," she said, looking at me as before. "That is so. The same eyes," she added; then sank into thought and buried her face in her hands. "I'm sick and tired of it all," she whispered. "I wish I could go away somewhere, far, far away. I can't bear it; I can't do anything about it. And what sort of future can I hope for? Oh, I am so miserable! God, I am so miserable!"

"Why?" I asked timidly.

Zinaida did not reply, and only shrugged her shoulders. I remained on my knees, looking at her with blank despondency. Every word of hers cut me to the heart. At that moment I would, I believe, gladly have given up my life, if only she would have no more cause to grieve. I gazed at her, and, still not understanding why she was so unhappy, I vividly pictured to myself how, suddenly, in a fit of irrepressible sorrow, she had gone into the garden and collapsed on the ground as though felled by a blow. All round us everything was bright and green; the wind rustled in the leaves of the trees, now and again swinging a long raspberry cane over Zinaida's head. Somewhere doves were cooing and bees were buzzing, flying low over the sparse grass. Overhead the sky was blue and tender —but I felt terribly sad.

"Read me some poetry, please," said Zinaida softly, raising herself on an elbow. "I like the way you read poetry. You speak it in a sing-song way, but that doesn't matter; that is because you are so young. Read me 'On the Hills of Georgia,' only first sit down."

I sat down and recited "On the Hills of Georgia."

"'Which it cannot choose but love,'" Zinaida repeated. "That's why poetry is so good: it speaks to us of what does not exist and which is not only better than what exists but even more like the truth. . . . 'Which it cannot choose but love'—it would like not to, but cannot!"

She fell silent again and suddenly started and got up. "Come along. Maydanov is in the house with Mother. He's brought me his poem, but I left him. His feelings too are hurt now, but it can't be helped. You'll find out someday—only don't be angry with me!" Zinaida pressed my hand hurriedly and ran on ahead.

We went back to the cottage. Maydanov began reading to us his "Murderer," which had just been published, but I did not listen to him. He shouted his four-foot iambics in a sing-song voice; the rhymes alternated, ringing like harness bells, loud and hollow, while I kept looking at Zinaida, trying to grasp the meaning of her last words.

> Or perchance some secret rival
> Hath without warning conquered thee?

Maydanov cried suddenly in a nasal tone—and my eyes and Zinaida's met. She dropped them and blushed slightly. I saw her blush, and froze with terror. I had been jealous of her before, but it was only at that moment that the thought that she was in love flashed through my mind. "Good Lord, she is in love!"

From that moment my real torments began. I racked my brain, thought it over again and again, and kept a relentless, though as far as possible secret, watch on Zinaida. It was quite clear that a change had come over her. She went for walks alone and was away for hours. Sometimes she refused to see her visitors; she sat for hours in her room. This had never happened to her before. I had suddenly become—or imagined that I had become—extremely perspicacious. "It isn't he, or is it?" I asked myself in alarm as I went over her different admirers in my mind. Count Malevsky (though for Zinaida's sake I was ashamed to admit it to myself) I secretly regarded as more dangerous than the others.

My powers of observation did not go farther than the end of my nose, and my secrecy most likely deceived no one; Dr. Lushin, at least, soon saw through me. He too, though, had changed of late. He had grown thinner; he laughed just as often, it is true, but his laughter somehow sounded more hollow, more spiteful, and much shorter, and in place of his former light irony and affected cynicism he now displayed a nervous irritability.

"Why are you always hanging about here, young man?" he said to me one day when we were left alone together in the Zasyekins' drawing room. (The young princess had not yet returned from her walk, and the shrill voice of the old princess could be heard on the first floor: she was having words with her maid.) "You ought to be studying, working, while you're young, and what on earth do you think you're doing?"

"You can't tell whether I work at home or not," I replied, not without haughtiness, though not without some embarrassment, either.

"Working indeed! You've something else on your mind. Well, I won't argue with you about it. At your age it's what one would expect. Except that you've been terribly unlucky in your choice. Don't you see what sort of house this is?"

"I don't know what you're talking about," I said.

"Don't you? So much the worse for you. I consider it my duty to warn you. It's all right for old bachelors like me to go on coming here: nothing much could happen to us, could it? We've been hardened in the battle of life. Nothing can hurt us now. But you've still got a tender skin. The atmosphere here is bad for you. Believe me, you might become infected."

"What do you mean?"

"You know what I mean. Are you well now? Are you in a normal condition? Is what you feel now healthy for you? Is it good for you?"

"Why, what am I feeling?" I said, while in my heart I realized full well that the doctor was right.

"Oh, young man, young man," the doctor went on, looking as though there was something highly insulting to me in those two words, "you can't deceive me! For, thank God, one can still read your face like an open book. However, what's the use of talking? I wouldn't be coming here myself if"—the doctor gritted his teeth—"if I hadn't been as big a fool as you. What I'm really surprised at, though, is how, with your intelligence, you can't see what is going on round you."

"Why, what *is* going on?" I said, all ears.

The doctor looked at me with a sort of mocking pity. "I'm a fine one too," he said, as though to himself. "Why should I be telling him this? In short," he added, raising his voice, "let me tell you again: the atmosphere here is no good for you. You like it here, but what does that matter? It smells sweet in a hot-house too, but you can't live in it, can you? Now you'd better listen to me and go back to Kaydanov again."

The old princess came in and began to complain to the doctor about her toothache. Then Zinaida appeared.

"Please, Doctor," added the old princess, "you'd better tell her off properly. She's been drinking iced water all day long. Is that good for her with her weak chest?"

"Why do you do that?" asked Lushin.

"Why, what effect can it have on me?"

"What effect? You might catch cold and die."

"Could I really? Are you sure? Well, so much the better!"

"I see," muttered the doctor.

The old princess went out.

"I see," repeated Zinaida. "Do you think life is so gay? Just look round you! Well, is it so nice, or do you think that I don't understand it, that I don't feel it? I get pleasure from drinking water with ice, and do you seriously tell me that such a life as mine is not worth risking for a moment's pleasure? I don't speak of happiness."

"Oh, well," observed Lushin, "caprice and independence—those two words sum you up: your whole nature is contained in those two words."

Zinaida laughed nervously. "You're too late, my dear doctor. You're not a good observer. You're not abreast of the times. Put on your glasses. This is no time for caprices. To make a fool of you, to make a fool of myself—there's not much fun in that any more. And as for independence—M'sieu Woldemar," Zinaida added suddenly, stamping her foot, "don't pull such a melancholy face. I can't stand it when people pity me." She went quickly out of the room.

"This atmosphere is very bad for you, young man, very bad," Lushin said again.

That same evening the usual visitors gathered at the Zasyekins'; I was among them.

The conversation turned on Maydanov's poem; Zinaida expressed genuine admiration for it.

"But," she said to him, "let me tell you this. If I were a poet, I would choose different subjects. Perhaps it's all nonsense, but all sorts of strange thoughts sometimes come into my head, especially when I can't sleep, at daybreak when the sky begins to turn pink and grey. I would, for instance— You won't laugh at me, will you?"

"No! No!" we all cried in one voice.

"I would describe," she went on, crossing her arms and looking away, "a whole company of young girls in a large boat on a quiet river at night. The moon is shining and they are all in white, with garlands of white flowers, and they are singing, you know, something like a hymn."

"I understand, I understand, go on," Maydanov said dreamily and meaningfully.

"All of a sudden there's an uproar—loud laughter, torches, tambourines on the bank. . . . It's a troupe of bacchantes running, with songs and cries. It's your business, Mr. Poet, to paint this picture, only I'd like the torches to be red and smoking a lot and the eyes of the bacchantes to gleam under their wreaths, and the wreaths to be dark. Don't forget the tiger skins and the goblets and the gold, lots and lots of gold."

"Where should the gold be?" asked Maydanov, tossing back his lank hair and dilating his nostrils.

"Where? On their shoulders, arms, legs, everywhere! In ancient times, they say, women wore gold bracelets on their ankles. The bacchantes call to the girls in the boat. The girls have stopped singing their hymn. They cannot continue it, but they do not stir: the river is carrying them to the bank. Suddenly one of them gently rises. . . . This has to be beautifully described—how she gently rises in the moonlight, and how her companions are frightened. She steps over the edge of the boat; the bacchantes surround her; they whirl her off into the night, into the dark. Here you must describe the smoke rising in clouds and everything becoming confused. All one can hear is their shrill cries, and her wreath is left lying on the bank."

Zinaida fell silent. ("Oh, she is in love!" I thought again.)

"And is that all?" asked Maydanov.

"That's all," she replied.

"That can't be the subject of a whole epic poem," he remarked pompously, "but I shall make use of your idea for a lyric poem."

"In the romantic style?" asked Malevsky.

"Of course, in the romantic style. The Byronic."

"Well, in my opinion Hugo is better than Byron," the young count declared nonchalantly. "More interesting."

"Hugo is a first-rate writer," replied Maydanov, "and my friend Tonkosheyev, in his Spanish novel *El Trovador*—"

"Oh," interrupted Zinaida, "is that the book with the question marks upside down?"

"Yes. That is the rule with the Spaniards. What I wanted to say was that Tonkosheyev—"

"Oh, dear, you'll be arguing again about classicism and romanticism," Zinaida interrupted him a second time. "Come, we'd better play a game."

"Forfeits?" Lushin asked.

"No. Forfeits is boring. Let's play comparisons." (Zinaida had invented this game herself. Some object was mentioned, and everyone tried to compare it with something else, and the one who chose the best comparison got the prize.)

She went up to the window. The sun had just set; long red clouds stood high in the sky.

"What are those clouds like?" asked Zinaida, and, without waiting for an answer, said, "I think they are like the purple sails on the golden ship in which Cleopatra sailed to meet Antony. Remember, Maydanov, you were telling me about it not long ago?"

All of us, like Polonius in *Hamlet*, declared that the clouds were exactly like those sails and that not one of us could find a better comparison.

"And how old was Antony then?" asked Zinaida.

"He was certainly a young man," observed Malevsky.

"Yes, a young man," Maydanov affirmed emphatically.

"I'm sorry," cried Lushin, "but he was over forty!"

"Over forty," repeated Zinaida, giving him a quick glance.

I went home soon. "She's in love," my lips whispered involuntarily. "But with whom?"

Days passed. Zinaida became stranger and stranger and more and more incomprehensible. One day I went into her room and saw her sitting on a wicker chair with her head pressed against the sharp edge of the table. She sat up—her face was wet with tears. "Oh, it's you!" she said with a cruel smile. "Come here."

I went up to her. She put her hand on my head and, seizing me by the hair suddenly began to twist it.

"It hurts!" I said at last.

"Oh, it hurts, does it? And do you think it doesn't hurt me? Me?" she repeated. "Oh, dear!" she cried suddenly, seeing she had pulled a little tuft of hair out of my head. "What have I done? Poor M'sieu Woldemar!" She carefully smoothed the hair she had torn out, wrapped it round her finger, and twisted it into a ring. "I'll put your hair in a locket and wear it round my neck," she said, tears still glistening in her eyes. "This will perhaps comfort you a little, and now good-bye."

I returned home to discover a disagreeable state of affairs. My mother was having words with my father, she was reproaching him for something; and he, as was his habit, responded with a polite and frigid silence, and soon left the house. I could not hear what my mother was saying, and, anyway, I had other things on my mind; I remember only that after her talk with my father, she sent for me to the study and told me that she was very displeased with my frequent visits to the old princess, who, in her words, was *"une femme capable de tout."* I kissed her hand (this was what I always did when I wanted to cut short a conversation) and went up to my room. Zinaida's tears had completely bewildered me. I simply did not know what to think and was about to burst into tears myself: I was a child, after all, in spite of my sixteen years.

I was no longer thinking of Malevsky, though Belovzorov was assuming more and more menacing attitudes every day and kept looking at the shifty count like a wolf at a sheep. As for me, I had no longer any thought of anyone or anything. I was lost in all sorts of speculations and was always trying to find some secluded spots. I became particularly fond of the ruins of the hot-house. I used to climb onto the high wall, sit on top of it, and remain sitting there, an unhappy, solitary, and melancholy youth, so that in the end I felt sorry for myself. And how sweet were those mournful sensations! How I revelled in them!

One day I was sitting on the wall, looking into the distance and listening to the ringing of the church bells; suddenly something passed over me —it wasn't a wind, it wasn't a shiver, but something like a hardly perceptible breath, like a sensation of someone's presence. I looked down. Below, on the road, in a light grey dress with a pink parasol on her shoulder, Zinaida was walking rapidly. She saw me, stopped, and turning back the brim of her straw hat, raised her velvety eyes to me.

"What are you doing up there at such a height?" she asked me with a strange sort of smile. "Now," she went on, "you keep telling me that you love me. Jump down into the road to me, if you really love me."

Zinaida had scarcely uttered those words when I was falling headlong towards her just as though someone had pushed me from behind. The wall was about fifteen feet high. I reached the ground on my feet, but the impact was so strong that I could not keep my balance. I fell down and for a moment lost consciousness. When I came to, I felt, without opening my eyes, Zinaida beside me.

"My sweet boy," she was saying, bending over me, and there was a note of alarmed tenderness in her voice, "how could you do it? How could you listen to me—you know I love you. Please get up."

Her bosom rose and fell close to me; her hands were touching my head; and suddenly—oh, what became of me then?—her soft fresh lips began to cover my face with kisses—they touched my lips—but at that moment, Zinaida probably guessed from the expression on my face that I had regained consciousness, though I still did not open my eyes, and, rising quickly, she said, "Well, get up, you naughty boy, you crazy young lunatic. Why are you lying in the dust?"

I got up.

"Give me my parasol," said Zinaida. "See where I have thrown it! And don't stare at me like that! Really! You're not hurt, are you? Stung by the nettles, I expect. I tell you, don't keep staring at me. . . . Why, he doesn't understand a word, he doesn't answer," she added, as though to herself. "Go home, M'sieu Woldemar, and brush yourself, and don't you dare follow me, or I shall be angry and will never again—"

She did not finish the sentence and walked rapidly away, while I sat down by the side of the road. My legs would not support me. My arms throbbed from the stings of the nettles, my back ached, my head swam, but the feeling of bliss I experienced at that moment I never again felt in my life. It spread like a sweet pain through all my limbs and resolved itself at last in rapturous leaps and shouts. Yes, indeed, I was still a child.

I was so gay and proud all that day, I retained so vividly the sensation of Zinaida's kisses on my face, I recalled her every word with such a shudder of delight, I cherished my unexpected happiness so much, that I felt absolutely terrified, and did not even want to see her who was the cause of all these new sensations. It seemed to me that I had no right to demand anything more of fate, that all I had to do now was "go, take a deep breath for the last time, and die." Yet the next day, on my way to the cottage, I felt greatly embarrassed and I tried in vain to conceal my embarrassment by assuming a modestly nonchalant air, such as is proper for a man who wishes to convey that he knows how to keep a secret.

Zinaida received me very simply, without betraying any emotion. She merely shook a finger at me and asked whether I had any bruises on my body. All my modest nonchalance and air of mystery vanished instantly, and with them my embarrassment. Of course I had never expected anything in particular, but Zinaida's composure made me feel as though someone had poured cold water over me: I realized that I was a child in her eyes—and I felt very unhappy! Zinaida walked up and down the room, giving me a quick smile every time she glanced at me; but her thoughts were far away—I saw that clearly enough. "Shall I speak to her about what happened yesterday," I thought, "and ask her where she was going in such a hurry and find out once and for all?" But I just dismissed it all as hopeless and sat down quietly in a corner.

Belovzorov came in; I was glad to see him.

"I couldn't find you a quiet horse," he said in a hard voice. "Freitag says he can answer for one, but I'm not so sure. I am afraid."

"What are you afraid of, may I ask?" asked Zinaida.

"What am I afraid of? Why, you don't know how to ride. Goodness knows what might happen! And what a fantastic idea has come into your head suddenly!"

"Well, that's my affair, my dear wild beast. In that case, I'll ask Peter." (My father's name was Peter, and I was surprised that she mentioned his name in so free and easy a manner, just as though she were sure of his readiness to do her a service.)

"I see," replied Belovzorov, "so it's with him you mean to go out riding."

"With him or someone else—what difference does it make to you? Not with you, at any rate."

"Not with me," repeated Belovzorov. "As you wish. Oh, all right. I'll get you a horse."

"Only mind it isn't some old cow. I warn you, I want to gallop."

"Gallop, by all means. But with whom? You won't go riding with Malevsky, will you?"

"And why not with him, O Great Warrior? Now please calm down and don't glare at me like that. I'll take you too. You know that for me Malevsky is now—ugh!" She tossed her head.

"You say that to console me," growled Belovzorov.

Zinaida narrowed her eyes. "Does that console you? Oh, oh, oh,

Great Warrior!" she said at last, as though unable to find another word. "And you, M'sieu Woldemar, would you come with us?"

"I shouldn't like to—not in—in a crowd," I murmured without raising my eyes.

"You prefer tête-à-tête? Well," she added with a sigh, "freedom to the free; heaven—to the saints! Go along, Belovzorov, and do your best. I must have a horse for tomorrow."

"Yes, but where are you going to get the money?" the old princess put in.

Zinaida wrinkled her brow. "I'm not asking you for it: Belovzorov will trust me."

"Trust you, trust you," growled the old princess and suddenly shouted at the top of her voice, "Dunyashka!"

"Mother, I've given you a bell," the young princess observed.

"Dunyashka!" the old woman shrieked again.

Belovzorov took his leave; I left with him. Zinaida made no attempt to detain me.

Next day I got up early, cut myself a stick, and went out for a walk beyond the toll gate. "I'll go for a walk," I thought to myself, "and get rid of my grief." It was a beautiful day, sunny and not too hot; a gay, fresh wind roamed the earth, playing and murmuring away gently, setting everything astir but disturbing nothing. I wandered a long time, over hills and through woods; I did not feel happy; I had left home with the intention of giving myself up to melancholy thoughts; but youth, the glorious weather, the fresh air, the fun of rapid walking, the delight of lying on thick grass away from everyone, got the better of me: the recollection of those unforgettable words, of those kisses, again invaded my soul. I was glad to think that Zinaida could not but recognize my resolution, my heroism. "Others may please her better than I," I thought, "let them! They will only tell her what they will do, while I have done it. . . . And that is not the only thing I could do for her!" I gave full rein to my imagination. I imagined how I would save her from the hands of enemies; how, covered with blood, I would drag her out of a dark dungeon; how I would die at her feet. I remembered a picture which hung in our drawing room: Malek-Adel carrying off Matilda—and at that very moment became absorbed in the appearance of a large, brightly coloured woodpecker, busily climbing up the slender trunk of a birch tree and peeping nervously from behind it, first to the right and then to the left, just like a double-bass player behind the neck of his instrument.

Then I began singing, "Not white the snows," and finished up with the at-the-time-popular song, "For you I wait when Zephyr wanton," and so on. Then I began reciting aloud Yermak's invocation to the stars from Khomyakov's tragedy, attempted to compose something myself in a senti- mental vein, and even thought of a line with which the whole of my poem was to conclude: "Oh, Zinaida, oh, Zinaida!" but nothing came of it.

Meanwhile it was getting near dinnertime. I went down into the valley; a narrow, sandy path wound its way through it towards the town. I walked along that path. The dull thud of horses' hooves sounded behind me. I looked round, stopped involuntarily, and took off my cap: I saw my father and Zinaida. They were riding side by side. My father was saying something to her, bending right over her and leaning with his hand on the neck of his horse. He was smiling; Zinaida listened to him in silence, her eyes severely cast down and her lips tightly pressed together. At first I saw only them; a few moments later I caught sight of Belovzo- rov round a bend in the valley in his hussar's uniform with a short cloak, on a foaming black horse. The gallant steed tossed its head, snorted, and pranced. The rider was holding him back and at the same time spurring him on. I stepped aside. My father gathered up the reins, moved away from Zinaida; she raised her eyes to him slowly and they galloped off. Belovzorov raced after them, his sabre rattling. "He's as red as a lobster," I thought, "while she . . . why is she so pale? Out riding the whole morning and—pale?"

I redoubled my steps and got home just before dinner. My father was already sitting, washed and fresh and dressed for dinner, beside my mother's chair, and was reading to her in his even and rich voice an arti- cle from *Journal de Débats;* but my mother listened to him without at- tention and when she saw me asked where I had been all day long, add- ing that she didn't like it when people ran about goodness knows where and with whom. "But I have been taking a walk by myself," I was about to reply, but I looked at my father and for some reason said nothing.

During the next five or six days I scarcely saw Zinaida: she appeared to be unwell, which, however, did not prevent the usual visitors of the cot- tage from calling—in order, as they put it, to "keep watch by the patient's bedside"—all except Maydanov, who immediately lost heart and looked bored whenever there was no chance for going into ecstasies. Belovzorov sat dejectedly in a corner, all buttoned up and red in the face; a kind of evil smile constantly hovered over Count Malevsky's refined face. He really had fallen out of favour with Zinaida and was waiting with special zeal on the old princess, drove with her in a hired carriage to call on the

Governor-General; this visit, however, turned out to be a failure, and Malevsky was even involved in some unpleasantness, for he was reminded of an unsavoury incident with some officers of a sapper regiment and in explaining it away he had to plead his inexperience at the time. Lushin used to come twice a day, but he did not stay long; I was a little frightened of him after our last talk, and yet at the same time I felt genuinely attracted to him. One day he went for a walk with me in the Neskoochny Park, was very amiable and friendly, told me the names and the properties of various herbs and flowers, and suddenly, as they say, "out of the blue," cried, striking himself on the forehead, "And I, fool that I am, thought that she was a flirt. It seems some people find it sweet to sacrifice themselves."

"What do you mean by that?" I asked.

"I don't want to say anything to you," Lushin replied brusquely.

Zinaida avoided me: my presence—I could not help noticing it—made an unpleasant impression on her. She turned away from me involuntarily—involuntarily. It was that that was so bitter, so crushing, but I could do nothing about it. I did my best to keep out of her sight and merely watched her from a distance, which I did not always succeed in doing. As before, something I could not understand was happening to her: her face had changed; she was quite a different person.

The change that had taken place in her struck me particularly one warm, quiet evening. I was sitting on a low seat under a spreading elder bush; I was very fond of that place, for from it I could see the window of Zinaida's room. I sat there; in the dark foliage over my head a little bird was busily moving about; a grey cat, its back arched, was creeping stealthily into the garden, and the early beetles were droning heavily in the air which was still clear, though no longer bright. I sat there looking at her window and waiting to see whether it would open: it did open, and Zinaida appeared in it. She was wearing a white dress, and she was pale: her face, shoulders, and arms were pale, almost white. She stayed there a long time without moving and for a long time gazed straight before her from under her knitted brows. I had never seen her look like that. Then she clasped her hands tight, very tight, raised them to her lips, her forehead, and suddenly pulled her fingers apart and thrust her hair back from her ears, tossed it and nodded her head with an air of determination, and slammed the window to.

Three days later she met me in the garden. I was about to turn away, but she stopped me herself. "Give me your hand," she said to me in her old affectionate tone of voice. "It's a long time since I've had a talk with you."

I looked at her: her eyes shone softly and her face was smiling as though through a haze. "Are you still not well?" I asked her.

"No, that's all over now," she replied and picked a small red rose. "I'm a little tired, but that too will pass."

"And you'll be the same as before?" I asked.

Zinaida held the rose up to her face, and it seemed to me as if her cheeks had caught the reflection of its bright petals. "Why, have I changed?" she asked me.

"Yes, you have," I answered in a low voice.

"I've been cold to you, I know," began Zinaida, "but you shouldn't have paid any attention to it. I'm afraid I couldn't help it—but why talk about it?"

"You don't want me to love you, that's what it is!" I exclaimed darkly, in an uncontrollable outburst.

"No, do love me, but not as before."

"How then?"

"Let us be friends—that's how!" Zinaida said, giving me the rose to smell. "Listen," she said, "you know I am much older than you, don't you? I might be your aunt, mightn't I? Well, perhaps not your aunt, but your elder sister. And you—"

"And I am a child so far as you're concerned," I interrupted.

"Well, yes, a child, but a sweet, good, clever child whom I love very much. Do you know what? I'm going to make you my page from today, and please don't forget that pages should never be very far from their ladies. And here's the token of your new dignity," she added, sticking the rose in the buttonhole of my tunic, "a sign of our gracious favour."

"I used to get other favours from you before," I murmured.

"Oh!" Zinaida said, giving me a sidelong look. "What a memory he has. Oh, well, I'm just as ready now." And bending over me, she imprinted a chaste, calm kiss on my forehead.

I just looked at her, but she turned away and saying, "Follow me, my page," went towards the cottage. I followed her, but still in a state of bewilderment. "Can this gentle sensible girl," I could not help thinking, "be the Zinaida I used to know?" I thought that she walked more quietly now and that her whole figure was more stately and more graceful.

And, good Lord, with what fresh force my love flared up in me!

After dinner the visitors gathered again at the cottage—and the young princess came out to them. The entire company was there in full force, as on that first unforgettable evening. Even Nirmatsky dragged himself to the party to see her; this time Maydanov arrived before anyone else and brought a new poem with him. The game of forfeits began again, but this time without the strange pranks, without the horseplay and noise— the gipsy element had gone. Zinaida gave a new tone to our gathering. I sat beside her, as her page. Among other things, she proposed that anyone who had to pay a forfeit should tell his dream; but this was not a success. The dreams were either uninteresting (Belovzorov had dreamt that he fed carp to his mare and that she had a wooden head), or unnatural and made-up. Maydanov regaled us with a long, long story; there were sepulchres in it, angels with lyres, talking flowers, and mysterious sounds coming from afar.

Zinaida did not let him finish. "If we have to have fiction," she said, "then let everyone tell something he has made up."

It was Belovzorov again who had to begin. The young hussar looked embarrassed. "I can't think of anything!" he exclaimed.

"What nonsense!" Zinaida cried. "Well, imagine, for instance, that you are married and tell us how you would spend your time with your wife. Would you lock her up?"

"Yes, I should."

"And would you stay with her yourself?"

"Yes, I should most certainly stay with her myself."

"Excellent. But what if she got tired of it and was unfaithful to you?"

"I'd kill her."

"And if she ran away?"

"I'd catch up with her and kill her all the same."

"I see. Well, and suppose I were your wife, what would you do then?"

Belovzorov was silent for a minute. "I'd kill myself."

Zinaida laughed. "I can see that your tale is quickly told."

The next forfeit was Zinaida's. She lifted her eyes to the ceiling and sank into thought. "Now listen," she began at last, "this is what I have thought of. Imagine a magnificent palace, a summer night, and a wonderful ball. The ball is being given by a young queen. Everywhere is gold, marble, crystal, silk, lights, diamonds, flowers, burning joss-sticks, all the wild extravagances of luxury."

"You like luxury?" Lushin interrupted her.

"Luxury is beautiful," she replied, "and I love everything beautiful."

"More than the beautiful?" he asked.

"That sounds a little too clever," she replied. "I don't understand it. Please don't interrupt. And so, the ball is magnificent. Lots and lots of guests, and all of them are young, handsome, and brave, and all are head over heels in love with the queen."

"Are there no women among the guests?" Malevsky asked.

"No, or wait—there are."

"Are they all unattractive?"

"No, they're lovely. But the men are all in love with the queen. She is tall and graceful, and she has a little gold diadem on her black hair."

I looked at Zinaida, and at that moment she seemed to me so much above us all, there was such bright intelligence and such power about her white forehead and her motionless eyebrows, that I could not help thinking, "You are that queen yourself!"

"They all crowd round her," Zinaida went on, "they all lavish the most flattering speeches upon her."

"Why, does she like flattery?" asked Lushin.

"What an insufferable creature you are! You *will* interrupt. Who doesn't like flattery?"

"Just one last question," Malevsky observed. "Has the queen a husband?"

"I hadn't thought of that. No, why a husband?"

"Naturally," Malevsky put in. "Why should she?"

"*Silence!*" cried Maydanov in French, which he spoke badly.

"*Merci*," Zinaida said to him. "And so," she went on, "the queen listens to these speeches, listens to the music, but does not look at any of the guests. Six windows are open from top to bottom, from floor to ceiling, and beyond them is a dark sky with big stars and a dark garden with big trees. The queen looks out into the garden. There, near the trees, is a fountain: it is white in the darkness, and it is tall, tall like a ghost. The queen hears through the talk and the music the soft plashing of its waters. She looks and thinks, 'You, gentlemen, are all noble, intelligent, rich, you crowd round me, you treasure every word I utter, you are all ready to die at my feet, I have you all in my power. But there, near the fountain, near that plashing water, he whom *I* love and who holds me in his power awaits me. He wears neither costly garments nor precious stones, no one knows him, but he waits for me, certain that I will come—and I will come, and there is no power on earth which can stop me when I want to go to him, stay with him, and lose myself with him there in the darkness of the garden, with the whispering trees and the plashing of the fountain. . . .'"

Zinaida fell silent.

"Is this—fiction?" Malevsky inquired cunningly.

Zinaida did not even look at him.

"And what should we have done, gentlemen," Lushin suddenly said, "if we had been among the guests and had known of the lucky fellow at the fountain?"

"Wait, wait," Zinaida interrupted. "I will myself tell you what each of you would have done. You, Belovzorov, would have challenged him to a duel; you, Maydanov, would have written an epigram on him—though, no, you don't know how to write epigrams: you would have written a long poem on him in iambics, something in the style of Barbier, and would have published it in the *Telegraph*. You, Nirmatsky, would have borrowed—no, you would have loaned him money at high interest. You, Doctor . . ." She stopped. "I'm sorry, but I really don't know what you would have done."

"As her court physician," replied Lushin, "I should have advised the queen not to give balls when she was not in the mood for entertaining guests."

"Perhaps you'd have been right. And you, Count?"

"And I?" Malevsky repeated with his evil smile.

"You would have offered him a poisoned sweet."

Malevsky's face became slightly twisted and for a moment assumed a villainous look, but he burst out laughing immediately.

"As for you, Woldemar . . ." Zinaida went on. "But I suppose that's enough. Let's play another game."

"M'sieu Woldemar, as the queen's page, would have carried her train as she ran into the garden," Malevsky remarked venomously.

I flushed, but Zinaida quickly laid a hand on my shoulder and, getting up, said in a slightly trembling voice, "I never gave your lordship the right to be insolent, and I must ask you to leave." She pointed to the door.

"Good Lord, Princess," murmured Malevsky, turning very pale.

"The princess is right," cried Belovzorov and he too rose.

"Good Lord, I never expected—" Malevsky went on. "I—I believe there was nothing in my words—I had never intended to insult you. . . . Forgive me."

Zinaida looked him up and down very coldly and smiled coldly. "You may stay, if you like," she said, with a careless gesture of the hand. "M'sieu Woldemar and I have no real cause to be angry. You seem to enjoy stinging people—much good may it do you."

"Forgive me," Malevsky repeated.

But I, recalling Zinaida's gesture, could not help reflecting once more that no real queen could have shown an impertinent man the door with greater dignity.

After this little scene the game of forfeits went on for only a short time; everyone felt rather ill at ease, not so much because of the scene itself as because of another vague but oppressive feeling. No one spoke of it, but everyone was conscious of it in himself and in his neighbour. Maydanov read us his poem, and Malevsky praised it with exaggerated warmth.

"How keen he is to show us now what a good fellow he is," Lushin whispered to me.

We soon left. Zinaida suddenly became thoughtful; the old princess sent word that she had a headache; Nirmatsky started complaining of his rheumatism.

I could not sleep for a long time. I was very much struck by Zinaida's story. "Can there have been a hint in it?" I asked myself. "And at whom and at what could she have been hinting? And if there really is something to hint at, what am I going to do about it?

"No, no, it can't be," I whispered, turning from one hot cheek to the other; but I recalled the expression on Zinaida's face as she told her story; I remembered the exclamation that had escaped Lushin in the Neskoochny Park, the sudden changes in her behaviour to me, and I was lost in conjectures. "Who is he?" These three words seemed to stand before my eyes, traced clearly in the darkness; it was as though a low, omnious cloud hung over me and I felt its pressure and was waiting for it to burst at any moment. I had got used to many things during the last few weeks, and I had seen as much as I wanted at the Zasyekins': their disorderly life, the tallow candle-ends, the broken knives and forks, the gloomy Vonifaty, the slatternly maids, the manners of the old princess herself—all this strange mode of life no longer surprised me. But what I seemed to be dimly discerning now in Zinaida I could never become used to. . . . "An adventuress," my mother had once described her. An adventuress—she, my idol, my goddess! That word stung me. I tried to escape from it into my pillow. I was indignant and, at the same time, what would I not have agreed to do, what would I not have given, to be that lucky fellow at the fountain!

My blood was on fire and coursing through my veins. "The garden—the fountain," I thought. "I'll go to the garden." I dressed quickly and slipped out of the house. The night was dark. The trees scarcely whispered; a gentle chill fell from the sky; the scent of fennel came from the kitchen-garden. I walked through all the avenues; the light sound of my own footsteps disturbed and at the same time emboldened me; every now and then I stopped dead, waited, and listened to my heart beating fast and heavily. At last I went up to the fence and leaned against a stake. Suddenly—or did I imagine it?—a woman's figure flashed by a few paces from me. I stared intently into the darkness; I held my breath. . . . What was that? Did I hear steps, or was it again the beating of my heart? "Who is there?" I murmured, almost inaudibly. What was that again? A smothered laugh? Or the rustling of leaves? Or a sigh close to my ear? I felt frightened. "Who is it?" I repeated, still more softly.

A slight breeze came and went in a moment; a streak of fire flashed across the sky—a falling star. "Zinaida?" I was about to ask, but the sound died on my lips. And suddenly everything became profoundly still all round me, as often happens in the middle of the night. Even the cicadas ceased whirring in the trees—only a window was slammed to somewhere. I stood and stood and then went back to my room, to my bed, which had grown quite cold by then. I felt a strange excitement, as though I had gone to a rendezvous and had been left out in the cold, passing by another man's happiness.

The next day I only caught a glimpse of Zinaida: she was driving somewhere with the old princess in a cab. I did see Lushin, though, who barely acknowledged my greeting, and Malevsky. The young count grinned and began talking to me very amiably. Of all the visitors to the cottage, he alone had managed to worm himself into our house. My mother took a liking to him. My father was not particularly friendly with him and treated him with almost offensive politeness.

"Ah, Monsieur le page," began Malevsky. "Very glad to meet you. What is your beautiful queen doing?"

His fresh, handsome face was so detestable to me at that moment and he was looking at me with such a playfully contemptuous expression at that moment that I did not answer him at all. "Are you still angry with me?" he went on. "You shouldn't be, you know. It wasn't I who called you a page. Besides, queens usually have pages. But I hope you won't mind my telling you that you are performing your duties very badly."

"Oh?"

"Pages should never be far away from their mistresses. Pages should know everything their mistresses do; they should even watch them," he added, lowering his voice, "day and night."

"What do you mean by that?"

"What do I mean? I believe I've made myself perfectly clear. Day—and night. In the daytime it doesn't matter very much. It is light by day, and there are lots of people about. But by night—ah, that's when you should expect trouble. I advise you not to sleep at night and watch, watch with all your might. Remember? At night, in the garden, by the fountain—that's where you must keep watch. You'll thank me for it."

Malevsky laughed and turned his back on me. I don't suppose he attached any great importance to what he had said to me. He had the reputation of a man who was very good at mystifying people, and he was famed for his ability to make fools of people at fancy-dress balls, greatly enhanced by his almost unconscious mendacity, which permeated his whole being. . . . He just wanted to tease me, but every word he uttered ran like poison through my veins. The blood rushed to my head. "Oh, so that's what it is," I said to myself. "Very well, it was not for nothing that I felt drawn into the garden! Well, then, it shall not be!" I exclaimed loudly, striking myself on the chest with my fist, though I had no clear idea what exactly it was that was not to be. "Whether it is Malevsky himself who goes into the garden," I thought (he might have let the cat out of the bag; he certainly was impudent enough for that), "or whether it was someone else" (the fence of our garden was very low, and there was no difficulty in climbing over it), "whoever I happen to come across will be sorry for it! I should not advise anyone to cross my path! I'll prove to all the world and to her, the traitress"—I actually called her a traitress —"that I know how to be revenged!"

I went back to my room, took out of the writing desk an English penknife I had recently bought, felt the sharp edge, and knitting my brows, thrust it into my pocket with a look of cold and concentrated determination, just as though I was quite used to such things and had done them many times before. My heart was full of malice and turned to stone; I kept frowning all day and from time to time would walk up and down with compressed lips, my hand in my pocket clutching the knife, grown warm in my grasp, while I was preparing myself beforehand for something terrible. These new and never-before-experienced sensations absorbed me and even delighted me so much that I scarcely thought of Zinaida herself. All the time I imagined I could see Pushkin's Aleko, the young gipsy— "Where are you going, my handsome youth—lie still . . ." And then: "You're all bespattered with blood! Oh, what have you done? . . . Nothing!" With what a cruel smile I kept repeating this "Nothing!"

My father was not at home; but my mother, who had for some time past been in a state of almost continual wild exasperation, noticed my look of desperate determination and said to me at supper, "What are you sulking for, like a bear with a sore head?"

I just smiled condescendingly to her in reply and thought, "If they only knew!" It struck eleven; I went to my room but did not undress; I was waiting for midnight; at last it struck. "Time I went!" I muttered through my teeth, and buttoned my coat up to the top, and even rolled up my sleeves. I went into the garden. I had already selected the spot from which to keep watch: at the end of the garden, where the fence separating our part of the grounds from the Zasyekins' joined the common wall, grew a solitary pine tree. Standing under its low, thick branches, I could see quite well, as far as the darkness of the night permitted, everything that went on round me; nearby ran a path which always seemed full of mystery to me; like a snake, it crept under the fence which, at that spot, bore the marks of climbing feet and led up to a round summer-house of thickly growing acacias. I made my way to the pine tree, leaned against its trunk, and began my watch.

The night was still and quiet, like the night before; but there were fewer clouds in the sky, and the outlines of the bushes and even of tall flowers could be seen more clearly. The first moments of waiting were full of agonizing suspense and almost of terror. I was determined to stop at nothing; all I was uncertain of was what I had to do. Was I to thunder out, "Where are you going? Stop! Confess, or die!" Or should I simply strike? Every sound, every rustle and whisper, seemed extraordinarily significant. . . . I was getting ready. . . . I leaned forward. . . . But half an hour passed, an hour passed: my blood grew calmer, colder; the realization that I was doing it all for no reason, that I was even a little ridiculous, that Malevsky had pulled my leg began to dawn on me. I left my hiding place and walked all round the garden. As though on purpose, not the slightest noise could be heard; everything was at rest; even our dog was asleep, curled up by the gate. I climbed up on the ruins of the hot-house, saw the open countryside stretching far into the distance, recalled my meeting with Zinaida, and sank into a reverie. . . .

I gave a start; I thought I heard the creak of an opening door, then the faint crack of a snapping twig. In two bounds I got down from the ruin and—stood rooted to the spot. I could clearly hear the sound of rapid, light, but cautious footsteps in the garden. They were coming towards me. "Here he is—here he is at last!" raced through my heart. I pulled the knife out of my pocket convulsively, opened it convulsively—red sparks whirled round before my eyes, my hair stood on end from terror and fury.

The footsteps were coming straight towards me. I stooped and crouched forward to meet them. A man came into view— Good heavens, it was my father!

I recognized him at once, although he was all muffled in a dark cloak and his hat was pulled down over his face. He walked past me on tiptoe. He did not notice me, though nothing concealed me, shrunk into myself and huddled up so that I seemed to be almost level with the ground. Jealous Othello, ready for murder, was suddenly transformed into a schoolboy. I became so terrified by my father's unexpected appearance that for the first few moments I did not notice where he had come from or in what direction he had disappeared. It was only when everything was quiet again that I got up from the ground and thought to myself, "Why is my father walking about in the garden at night?" In my panic I dropped my knife in the grass, but I did not even try to look for it: I was so terribly ashamed of myself. I became quite sober all at once. On my way back, however, I went up to my seat under the elder bush and looked up at the window of Zinaida's bedroom. The small, slightly curved window-panes showed dimly blue in the faint light that fell from the night sky. Suddenly their colour began to change. Behind them I saw— saw quite clearly—a whitish blind pulled down cautiously and gently to the window-sill—and it remained like that, absolutely still.

"What does this mean?" I said aloud, almost involuntarily, when I found myself once more in my room. "A dream, a mere coincidence, or—" The suppositions which suddenly came into my head were so new and disturbing that I did not dare even consider them.

I got up in the morning with a headache. The excitement of the previous day had gone. It was replaced by an oppressive feeling of bewilderment and a strange sadness I had never experienced before. It was as though something were dying inside me. "Why are you looking like a rabbit who has had half its brain removed?" said Lushin as he met me. At lunch I kept glancing stealthily first at my father and then at my mother. My father was, as usual, composed; my mother, also as usual, secretly irritated. I waited to see whether my father would say something friendly to me, as he sometimes did, but he showed not even a sign of his ordinary cold affection. "Shall I tell Zinaida everything?" I thought. "It really can't make any difference—it is all over between us, anyway." I went to see her, but not only told her nothing; I did not even succeed in talking to her, much as I wanted to. The old princess's son, a twelve-year-old cadet, had arrived from Petersburg for his holidays and Zinaida at once asked me to take him under my wing.

"Here," she said, "my dear Vladimir (she called me that for the first time), is a companion for you. His name is Vladimir too. Please be friends. He is still very shy, but he has a kind heart. Show him the Neskoochny Park, take him for walks, take him under your protection. You will do so, won't you? You're so kind too!" She laid both her hands affectionately on my shoulders, and I was completely lost. The arrival of this boy turned me into a boy too. I looked in silence at the cadet, who stared silently back at me.

Zinaida burst out laughing and pushed us towards each other. "Come on, children," she said, "embrace."

We embraced.

"Want me to take you round the garden?" I asked the cadet.

"If you like," he replied in a hoarse, regular cadet-like voice.

Zinaida laughed again. I had time to notice that never before had the colour in her face been so lovely. The cadet and I set off for our walk. There was an old swing in our garden. I sat him down on the thin plank and began swinging him. He sat motionless in his small new uniform of thick cloth with wide gold braiding, and held on tightly to the ropes.

"Why don't you unbutton your collar?" I said to him.

"It's all right, I'm used to it," he said, and cleared his throat. He was like his sister. His eyes especially recalled her. I was glad to be of some use to him, and at the same time an aching sadness was gnawing at my heart. "Now," I thought, "I really am a little boy, whereas yesterday . . ." I remembered where I had dropped my knife the night before, and found it. The cadet asked me for it, broke off a thick stalk of wild parsley, cut himself a whistle out of it, and began whistling. Othello whistled a little too.

But, that very evening, how he wept, this same Othello, in Zinaida's arms, when, finding him in a corner of the garden, she asked him why he was so sad? My tears gushed out of my eyes with such force that she was frightened.

"What's the matter? What's wrong with you, Vladimir?" she kept repeating, and seeing that I neither replied to her nor stopped weeping, she bent down to kiss my wet cheek. But I turned away from her and whispered through my sobs, "I know everything. Why did you play with me? What did you want my love for?"

"I'm sorry, dear, dear Vladimir," said Zinaida. "Oh, I am very much to blame," she said, clasping her hands tightly. "There's so much in me that is evil, dark and wicked. . . . But now I am not playing with you. I do love you. I don't think you even suspect why and how much I love you. . . . But—what is it you know?"

What could I tell her? She stood before me and looked at me, and I belonged to her entirely from head to foot the moment she looked at me. . . . A quarter of an hour later I was running races with the cadet and Zinaida: I was no longer crying, I was laughing, though, as I laughed, my swollen eyelids dropped tears; Zinaida's ribbon was tied round my neck instead of a cravat, and I screamed with joy every time I succeeded in catching her by the waist. She did what she liked with me.

I should have found it very difficult if someone had asked me to describe in detail what was going on within me during the week after my unsuccessful midnight expedition. It was a strange, feverish time, a kind of chaos, in which the most conflicting feelings, thoughts, suspicions, hopes, joys, and pains whirled about madly within me. I was afraid of looking into myself, if a boy of sixteen can ever look into himself. I was afraid of giving an account to myself of anything; I simply tried to live through the day as fast as I could, but at night I slept—the lightheartedness of childhood came to my aid. I did not want to know whether I was loved, and I did not want to admit to myself that I was not loved. I avoided my father, but avoid Zinaida I could not. In her presence I burnt as in a fire, but what did I care what kind of fire it was in which I burnt and melted, so long as I felt happy to burn and melt? I gave myself up to all my sensations and tried to cheat myself by turning away from my memories and shutting my eyes to what I felt was going to happen. . . . This state of sweet anguish would probably not have lasted long in any case. A thunderbolt cut it all short at one blow and flung me onto an altogether new path.

One day when I came back to dinner after a rather long walk I learnt with astonishment that I was to dine alone, that my father had gone away and my mother was not well and did not want any dinner and had shut herself up in her bedroom. I could see by the faces of the footmen that something unusual had happened. I did not dare to question them, but I had a friend among them, a young pantry-boy, Phillip by name, who was passionately fond of poetry and an excellent performer on the guitar, and it was to him that I turned. From him I learnt that a terrible scene had taken place between my father and my mother (every word of it had been overheard in the maids' room; much of it had been spoken in French, but Masha, our parlourmaid, had lived for five years with a dress-maker in Paris and understood every word); that my mother had accused my father of infidelity, of being on intimate terms with the young lady next door; that my father had at first tried to justify himself, but afterwards had lost his temper and, in his turn, said something brutal, "something about Madam's age," which had made my mother cry; that my mother too had alluded to some loan given to the old princess, and spoken very unfavourably of her and of the young lady also, and that then my father had threatened her.

"And the whole trouble arose," continued Phillip, "from an anonymous letter, and no one knows who wrote it. Otherwise there's no reason why anything should have come out at all."

"Why, was there anything?" I managed to bring out with difficulty, while my hands and feet went cold, and something began to tremble deep inside me.

Phillip winked significantly. "There was. There's no hiding these things. However careful your father was this time, he had, you see, to hire a carriage. Besides, you can't do nothing without servants' knowing, neither."

I dismissed Phillip and flung myself on my bed. I did not sob; I did not give myself up to despair; I did not ask myself when and how all this had happened; I did not wonder how it was I had not guessed it all before, long ago; I did not even harbour any ill will against my father. What I had learnt was more than I could cope with: this sudden revelation crushed me utterly. All was at an end. All my flowers were torn out by the roots at one fell swoop and they lay about me, strewn all over the place and trampled underfoot.

Next day my mother announced that she was moving back to town. In the morning my father went into her bedroom and remained with her a long time alone. No one heard what he said to her, but my mother cried no more. She grew calm and asked for food but did not show herself, nor did she change her decision. I remember I wandered about all day, but did not go into the garden and did not once glance at the cottage. In the evening I was the witness of a most extraordinary scene: my father led Count Malevsky by the arm through the drawing room into the hall and, in the presence of the footman, said to him coldly, "A few days ago your lordship was shown the door in a certain house. I shall not enter into any kind of explanation with you, but I should like to make it quite clear to you that if you ever do me the honour of calling on me again I shall throw you out of the window. I don't like your handwriting."

The count bowed, gritted his teeth, shrank into himself, and disappeared.

Preparations began for our removal to town, to the Arbat, where we had a house. I expect my father himself did not want to stay in the country any longer, but he had evidently succeeded in persuading my mother not to make any more scenes; everything was done quietly, without haste; my mother even sent her compliments to the old princess and expressed regret that she was not able to see her before she left because of ill health.

I wandered about the place like one distraught and longed for it all to be over as quickly as possible. One thought kept running through my head: How could she, a young girl and a princess, have made up her mind to do such a thing when she knew that my father was not free and when she had the opportunity of marrying Belovzorov, for instance? What did she hope for? How was it that she was not afraid of ruining her whole future? "Yes," I thought, "this is love, this is passion, this is devotion." And I remembered Lushin's words: *Some people find it sweet to sacrifice themselves. . . .* One day I managed to catch sight of something white in one of the windows of the cottage. "Can it be Zinaida's face?" I thought. Indeed, it was her face. I could bear it no longer. I could not part with her without a final good-bye. I took advantage of a favourable moment and went over to the cottage.

In the drawing room the old princess met me with her usual slovenly and careless greeting. "Why are your people so anxious to leave the country so soon, my boy?" she said, stuffing snuff into both her nostrils.

I looked at her, and a load was lifted from my heart. The word *loan* which Phillip had used had been torturing me. But she did not seem to suspect anything, at least I thought so at the time. Zinaida came in from the next room, pale, in a black dress, and her hair hanging loose. She took me by the hand in silence and led me away with her.

"I heard your voice," she began, "and came out at once. And do you find it so easy to leave us, you bad boy?"

"I've come to say good-bye to you, Princess," I said, "probably forever. I expect you must have heard we are going away."

Zinaida looked intently at me. "Yes, I have heard. Thank you for coming. I had thought that I would not see you again. Don't think badly of me. I've tortured you sometimes, but all the same I'm not the sort of person you imagine me to be." She turned away and leaned against the window. "No, I really am not like that. I know that you have a bad opinion of me."

"Me?"

"Yes—you."

"Me?" I repeated mournfully, and my heart trembled as it always did under the influence of her irresistible, inexpressible fascination. "Me? Believe me, Princess, that I would love and adore you to the end of my life, whatever you did and however much you tortured me."

She turned to me quickly and, flinging her arms wide, put them round my head and kissed me warmly and passionately. God knows for whom that long farewell kiss was meant, but I eagerly tasted its sweetness—I knew that it would never be repeated.

"Good-bye, good-bye," I kept repeating.

She tore herself away and went out of the room. I too went away. I am not able to describe the feelings with which I left. I would not wish them ever to be repeated; but I would have considered myself unfortunate had I never experienced them at all.

We moved back to town. It was some time before I could shake off the past and it was some time before I could sit down to work again. My wound healed slowly; but I bore no ill will against my father. On the contrary, he seemed to have risen in my estimation. Let psychologists explain this contradiction as best they can.

One day I was walking along a boulevard and, to my indescribable joy, ran into Lushin. I liked him for his straight-forward and unhypocritical character, and, besides, he was dear to me because of the memories he awoke in me. I rushed up to him.

"Aha," he said, frowning, "so it's you, young man. Come, let's have a look at you. You're still as sallow as ever, but there's no longer any silly nonsense in your eyes. You look like a man and not like a lap-dog. That's good. Well, what are you doing? Working?"

I heaved a sigh. I did not want to tell a lie, but I was ashamed to tell the truth.

"Well, never mind, don't lose heart. The main thing is to lead a normal life and not to give in to every passing fancy. For what's the use of it? Wherever the tide may carry you, it will all be no good. A man must stand on his feet, even if he has to stand on a rock. As you see, I've got a bad cough. . . . And Belovzorov—have you heard?"

"No. What is it?"

"Vanished without a trace. They say he's gone off to the Caucasus. Let it be a lesson to you, young man, and it's all because people don't know how to part in time, how to break out of the net. You seem to have got out of it unscathed. Mind you don't get caught again. Good-bye."

"I shan't be caught," I thought. "I shall never see her again."

But I was destined to see Zinaida once more.

My father used to go riding every day. He had an excellent roan
English mare, with a long slender neck and long legs, an indefatigable
and vicious animal. She was called Electric. No one could ride her except
my father. One day he came into my room in a good humour, something
which had not happened to him for a long time: he was about to go for
his ride and had already put on his spurs. I began to beg him to take me
with him.

"I'd rather have a game of leap-frog with you," my father replied, "for
you'll never keep up with me on your pony."

"I will. I'll wear spurs too."

"Oh, all right."

We set off. I had a black, shaggy pony, sturdy and very spirited; it is
true he had to gallop at full speed when Electric was in full trot, but all
the same I did not lag behind. I have never seen a horseman who could
ride as well as my father; he sat on his horse so beautifully and with such
effortless ease that it seemed that the horse herself felt it and took pride
in him. We rode through all the boulevards, rode across Devichy Square,
took several fences (at first I used to be afraid of the jumps, but my father
despised timid people, and I stopped being afraid), crossed the Moskva
River twice, and I was beginning to think that we were returning home,
particularly as my father himself remarked that my horse was getting
tired, when suddenly he turned away from me at the Crimean Ford and
galloped off along the bank. I rode after him. On reaching a high pile of
stacked-up old timber, he jumped nimbly off Electric, told me to dis-
mount, and, giving me his bridle to hold, asked me to wait for him there at
the stack, while he himself turned into a small back street and disappeared.

I began to walk up and down along the bank of the river, leading the
horses and scolding Electric, who kept tossing her reins, shaking herself,
snorting, and neighing; whenever I stopped, she kept pawing the ground
and biting my pony in the neck, whinnying—in short, she behaved like
the spoilt thoroughbred she was. My father did not come back. An unpleasant dampness came drifting from the river; a fine rain began to fall
softly, covering with tiny dark spots the stupid grey timber logs which I
kept walking past backwards and forwards and which, by that time, I
was heartily sick of. I was beginning to feel depressed, but still my father
did not come. A Finnish policeman, who was also grey all over, with a
huge, old-fashioned shako like a pot on his head and with a halberd

(why on earth a policeman in such an old-fashioned attire should be patrolling the bank of the river Moskva is quite beyond me!) approached me, and turning his face, wrinkled like an old woman's, towards me, said, "What are you doing here with them horses, sir? Come, let me hold them for you."

I made no answer; he asked me for some tobacco. To get rid of him (besides, I was getting very impatient), I took a few steps in the direction in which my father had disappeared, walked down to the end of the lane, turned the corner, and stopped dead. In the street, about forty paces from me, stood my father in front of the open window of a small wooden house; he had his back to me and was leaning with his chest over the window-sill; inside the house, half-hidden by a curtain, sat a woman in a dark dress, talking to my father; the woman was Zinaida.

I was thunderstruck. That, I confess, I had not expected. My first impulse was to run away. "Father will look round," I thought, "and I shall be done for." But a strange feeling, a feeling stronger than curiosity, stronger even than jealousy, stronger than fear, stopped me. I began to watch. I did my best to hear what they were saying. My father seemed to be insisting on something. Zinaida would not agree. I can see her face just as if it were all happening now—sad, serious, beautiful, and with an indescribable imprint of devotion, sadness, love, and a kind of despair—I can find no other word for it. She uttered words of one syllable; she did not raise her eyes but just smiled—submissively and obstinately. It was by this smile alone that I recognized my Zinaida as I used to know her. My father shrugged and set his hat straight on his head, which was always a sign of impatience with him. Then I heard the words: "*Vous devez vous séparer de cette . . .*" Zinaida drew herself up and stretched out her hand. . . . Suddenly something quite unbelievable took place before my very eyes: my father all of a sudden raised his riding crop, with which he had been flicking the dust from the skirts of his coat, and I heard the sound of a sharp blow across her arm, which was bared to the elbow. I just managed to restrain myself from crying out, while Zinaida gave a start, looked at my father without uttering a word, and, raising her arm to her lips, kissed the scar that showed crimson on it. My father flung away the crop and, running up the steps rapidly, rushed into the house. Zinaida turned round, tossed back her head, and, with arms outstretched, also moved away from the window.

Faint with fright, and my heart gripped with a kind of bewildered horror, I rushed back, and running down the lane, nearly letting go of Electric, returned to the bank of the river. I simply did not know what to make of it. I knew that my cold and reserved father was sometimes given to fits of fury, but for all that I could not possibly make any sense of what I had just seen. But at the same time I felt sure that however long I lived, I could never forget Zinaida's gesture, her look, her smile; and that image of her, this new image which had so suddenly arisen before me, was forever imprinted on my memory. I gazed vacantly at the river and did not notice that tears were streaming down my cheeks. "They are beating her," I thought, "beating, beating. . ."

"Hello there, what are you doing? Give me the horse!" I heard my father's voice behind me.

Mechanically I gave him the bridle. He leapt on Electric's back. The horse, chilled with standing, reared on its hind legs and leapt forward about six feet, but my father soon curbed her; he drove the spurs into her sides and hit her on the neck with his fist.

"Damn, no crop," he murmured.

I recalled the swish and the blow from the same crop a short while before, and shuddered.

"Where have you put it?" I asked my father after a short pause.

My father made no answer and galloped on. I overtook him. I simply had to see his face.

"You weren't bored waiting for me, were you?" he muttered through his teeth.

"A little. Where did you drop your crop?" I asked him again.

My father glanced quickly at me. "I did not drop it," he said. "I threw it away."

He sank into thought and lowered his head, and it was then that I saw for the first and almost for the last time how much tenderness and pity his stern features could express.

He galloped on again, and this time I could not overtake him; I arrived home a quarter of an hour after him.

"This is love," I again said to myself, sitting at night at my writing desk on which my books and exercise books had begun to make their appearance. "This is passion. How was it possible not to feel resentment, to suffer a blow from any hand—even the dearest! But it seems one can if one is in love . . . and I—I imagined . . ."

I had grown much older during the last month—and my love, with all its excitements and sufferings, struck me as something very small and childish and trivial beside that other, unknown something which I could scarcely grasp and which frightened me like an unfamiliar, beautiful, but menacing face one tries in vain to make out in the gathering darkness.

That night I had a strange and terrible dream. I dreamt that I went into a low, dark room. My father, whip in hand, was standing there and stamping angrily with his feet; Zinaida was crouching in a corner, and there was a red scar, not on her arm, but on her forehead, and behind them both rose Belovzorov, covered with blood, and he opened his pale lips and shook his fist angrily at my father.

Two months later I entered the university, and six months after that my father died (of a stroke) in Petersburg, where he had just moved with my mother and me. A few days before his death he received a letter from Moscow which upset him greatly. He went to beg some favour from my mother and, I was told, he even wept, he—my father! On the morning of the day he had his stroke, he had begun a letter to me in French. "My son," he wrote, "fear the love of woman, fear that ecstasy, that poison . . ." My mother, after his death, sent a considerable sum of money to Moscow.

Four years passed. I had just left the university and had not quite made up my mind what to do with myself, at what door to knock; for the time being, I just did nothing. One fine evening I met Maydanov at the theatre. By that time he had got married and joined the civil service, but I found him quite unchanged. He still went into raptures for no obvious reason and grew depressed just as suddenly.

"You know," he said to me, "Mrs. Dolsky is here."

"What Mrs. Dolsky?"

"Why, you've not forgotten, have you? The former Princess Zasyekin. The girl we were all in love with—and you, too. Remember, in the country near the Neskoochny Park?"

"Is she married to a Dolsky?"

"Yes."

"And is she here, in the theatre?"

"No, she's in Petersburg. She arrived a few days ago. She's going abroad."

"What sort of man is her husband?"

"Oh, a splendid fellow. A man of property. He's a colleague of mine in Moscow. You understand, after that affair—I expect you must know all about it"—Maydanov smiled significantly—"it was not so easy for her to make a match. There were consequences—but with her brains, nothing is impossible. Go and see her. I am sure that she'll be very pleased to see you. She is prettier than ever."

Maydanov gave me Zinaida's address. She was staying in the Hotel

Demuth. Old memories stirred in me. . . . I made up my mind to call on my former flame. But all sorts of things prevented me from calling on her. A week passed, then another; and when at last I went to the Hotel Demuth and asked for Mrs. Dolsky I was told that she had died four days before, quite suddenly, in childbirth.

I felt a sudden stab in my heart. The thought that I could have seen her and did not, and would never see her again—that bitter thought drove its sting into me with all the force of an irrepressible reproach. "She is dead," I repeated, staring vacantly at the hotel porter, and, going out into the street quietly, I walked on without knowing myself where I was going. All my past suddenly rose up and stood before me. So that was the end of this young, passionate, and brilliant life! That was the goal to which, in its haste and agitation, it aspired. When I thought of this, I conjured up those dear features, those eyes, those curls—in the narrow box, in the dank underground darkness, quite near, not far from me who was still living, and perhaps only a few paces from my father. I thought of all this; I exerted my imagination; and meanwhile—

> From lips indifferent, the tidings
> Of death I heard, and, indifferent
> To it, I listened—

sounded in my heart. Oh, youth, youth! You don't care for anything, you seem to own all the treasures of the world; even sorrow amuses you, even grief becomes you; you are self-confident and insolent; you say, "I alone am alive—look at me!"—even while your days pass away and vanish without trace and without number, and everything in you melts away like wax in the sun, like snow. . . . And perhaps the whole secret of your charm lies not in your ability to do everything, but in your ability to think that you will do everything—lies just in the way you are scattering to the winds the powers which you could never have used for anything else—in the fact that each of us seriously considers himself to have been a spendthrift, seriously believes that he has a right to say, "Oh, what could I not have done if I had not wasted my time!"

So I too—what did I hope for? What did I expect? What rich promise did the future hold out to me when—with scarcely a sigh, with no more than a feeling of bleak despondency—I bade farewell to the phantom of my first love, risen for a fleeting moment?"

And what came of it all—of all I had hoped for? Now, when evening shadows are beginning to fall on my life, what have I left that is fresher, that is dearer to me than the memories of the storm that came and passed over so swiftly one spring morning?

But I am not quite fair to myself. Even then, in those thoughtless days of my youth, I did not remain deaf to the mournful voice which called to me, to the solemn sound which came to me from beyond the grave. I remember how a few days after I had learnt of Zinaida's death, I myself, in response to an irresistible impulse, was present at the death of a poor old woman who lived in the same house with us. Covered with rags, lying on hard boards, with a sack for a pillow under her head, she was dying a hard and painful death. All her life had been spent in a bitter struggle with daily want. She had known no joy; she had not tasted the honey of happiness; and one would have thought that she of all people would have been glad to die, and thus to gain freedom and rest. And yet, so long as her frail body held out, so long as her breast was still rising and falling in agony under the icy hand that weighed upon her, so long as there was still strength left in her body, the old woman kept crossing herself and kept whispering, "Lord, forgive me my sins," and only after the last spark of consciousness had gone did the look of fear and terror of death disappear from her eyes. . . . And I remember that there, by the death-bed of that poor old woman, I felt terrified for Zinaida, and I longed to say a prayer for her, for my father—and for myself.

Translated by David Magarshack.

Fyodor Dostoevsky

1821–1881

Fyodor Dostoevsky was born in Moscow on October 30, 1821 (Old Style). He studied in Moscow and at the School of Military Engineers in St. Petersburg. After three years he resigned a commission in the army and began to write. A first novel, *Poor Folk*, published in 1845, made his name at once. *The Double*, a brilliant Dickensian study of paranoia, was less well liked and caused a quarrel with the liberal writers, including Turgenev.

Dostoevsky allied himself with a group of theoretical socialists, the Petrashevsky circle. In 1849 they were all arrested and ordered deported. A false sentence of death was read to them. At the last moment, with rifles leveled at their breasts, they were ordered away to the penal settlement at Omsk. Five years later, his epilepsy aggravated by these experiences, Dostoevsky was transferred to the army. In 1859 he was allowed to go back to St. Petersburg. *The Friend of the Family*, his first novel after a long silence, was published in that year.

In Siberia he had married Marya Isaeva. *The House of the Dead* and *The Insulted and the Injured* appeared in the early 1860's. Dostoevsky and his brother started a successful review. It was suppressed and never recovered. He traveled abroad with Pauline Suslova, haunted by his compulsion to gamble. *Letters from the*

Notes from the artist: ". . . an atmosphere of fantasy and dreams in a Russian urban scene surrounds the portrait of Dostoevsky in his uniform. The other figure is that of Raskolnikov, the murderer in Crime and Punishment."

Underworld, in 1864, was the first of his important later works. His first wife having died, he married Anna Snitkina and went abroad again to evade his creditors.

Between 1866 and 1871, he produced *Crime and Punishment, The Gambler, The Idiot, The Eternal Husband,* and *The Possessed.* In the latter year he went back to Russia and edited a conservative weekly. Later he conducted a prosperous journal of his own, *An Author's Diary. A Raw Youth* was published in 1875, and in 1880 came the last great work of his maturity, *The Brothers Karamazov.* He died on January 28, 1881.

We can begin *White Nights* with the perfect assurance that we are in the hands of a great storyteller. True, Dostoevsky has many other facets as a writer. Politically, from first to last, he has been called everything from a radical to a reactionary. As a psychologist, normal or more often than not clinical, he ranks among the first in literature. This talent is vivid enough in all his work and amazing in the best of it. He was an important journalist in his time, though much of his occasional writing is all but unreadable now except to students of Russian history. In his early works at least—the later ones were often written in great haste—he showed a decided sense of literary structure. He emerged from prison an intense Christian. Christianity became fused for him with his mystical sense of Russian nationalism. As leader of the nativist school, he could be the most provincial of Russians. At the same time, his vision was broad enough to contain the whole of humanity. He was a "profound Jobean and Promethean questioner." But from beginning to end, in all his fiction, the story—and it is usually a powerful one—comes first.

This is true of *White Nights* (an idiom meaning "sleepless nights"). The scene is St. Petersburg in summer. The story moves across four nights and the morning of the following day. It is—on the face of it, at least—the simplest of love conflicts. The girl Nastenka and two nameless young men make the three points of the triangle. Behind this simplicity we glimpse the moving shadows of human impulse, of needing and giving, of sincerity and delusion, of love and self-love.

When we first meet the narrator, he is, characteristically, alone. He tells us that he has no friends. Instead, his imagination is peopled with the whole outdoor life of his city. Certain faces have become old acquaintances. He knows the route of every inhabitant. Even the houses are personified for him. He shares in their changes of paint and weather. But now he discovers why so many people seem to be missing, why he has felt deserted. St. Petersburg is moving out to the country for the summer.

At this point of extreme loneliness he meets Nastenka. Though he does not know it at first, she too is lonely, she too has come to a crisis in her life. So their mutual need is intense. They tell each other their life stories—and his, at least, seems to us a little too long. But out of it we get the sense of powerful fantasy, of a poet without poems. He and Nastenka laugh and cry. They seem utterly natural. We believe in their wish to be completely sincere with each other.

But are they? Sincerity is no guarantee of self-knowledge. Skeptics that we are, at first we may even refuse to believe Nastenka's story about the other young man. She is a lonely girl. Is it not possible, we think, that she may have invented this story to make the narrator jealous, to make herself more desirable in his eyes? But we see that we have misjudged her. She really tries to be kind. She warns him not to fall in love with her. But it is useless. He loves her and tries generously to help her. She too is generous. They make plans. He will move into her house and take the room and place of her former lover. So we are touched by the sense of bad faith, of guilt, in her letter on the last morning. Do we feel that she is guilty of betraying him? Or is it only that the unknown and unknowable chances of life have been too much for them?

White Nights

A TALE OF LOVE
FROM THE REMINISCENCES
OF A DREAMER

Could he be born from the start,
If only for a fleeting moment,
To be so dear to your heart?
IVAN TURGENEV

THE FIRST NIGHT

It was a marvelous night, the sort of night one only experiences when one is young. The sky was so bright, and there were so many stars that, gazing upward, one couldn't help wondering how so many whimsical, wicked people could live under such a sky. This too is a question that would only occur to the young, to the very young; but may God make *you* wonder like that as often as possible!

Now, mentioning whimsical, angry people makes me think how well I behaved that day. A strange anguish had tormented me since early morning. I suddenly had the impression that I had been left all alone, that everyone was shrinking away from me, avoiding me. You are, of course, right to ask who that "everyone" is, for although I've lived in Petersburg for eight years now, I haven't managed to make a single friend. But what do I need friends or acquaintances for? As it is, I'm acquainted with all of Petersburg. And that's why I had the impression of being abandoned by everyone when the whole city rose and left for the summer. I was afraid to be left alone, and for three days I roamed dejectedly through the city, unable to understand what was happening to me. Whether I went to Nevsky Avenue, to the park, or wandered along the embankments, I never came across the people I was accustomed to meet in certain spots at certain hours all year round. They, of course, didn't know me, but I knew them, all right. I knew them intimately, and having studied their faces, I rejoiced with them when they were cheerful and grieved with them when they were downcast. I almost became friends with a little old man whom I met every day at a certain time on the Fontanka Embankment. His face was so dignified and thoughtful; he carried a knotty walking cane with a gold top in his right hand, swinging his left arm, and was constantly mumbling something inaudible. He even noticed me and took a keen interest in *my* existence. I'm sure he must've been quite upset when I did not appear at a given hour on the embankment. That's why sometimes we almost exchanged greetings, especially when we both happened to be in a good mood. Recently, two days went by without our seeing each other, and on the third day, our hands almost shot up to our hats, but thank God, we came to our senses, dropped our hands, and passed by with mutual sympathy.

I'm acquainted with houses too. As I walk up a street, each house seems to have darted ahead and to be waiting for me, looking at me out of all its windows, almost saying: "Hello! How are you getting on? I'm fine myself. And do you know what? They're going to add another story to me in May!" Or: "How are you? Well, me, I'll have to undergo some repairs tomorrow." Or: "You know, I almost burned down last night. It gave me such a fright!" And other things of that sort. Among houses, I have my favorites. Some are intimate friends. One had decided to undergo a course of treatment with an architect during the summer. I'll make a point of visiting him every day, in case the treatment turns out to be fatal, God forbid! I'll never forget what happened to one very pretty, rosy little house. Although he was rather haughtily distant with his clumsy neighbors, that little stone house used to look at me so nicely that I always felt glad as I passed by. But last week, as I was walking along that street, my friend looked at me dejectedly, and I heard his plaintive cry: "They're painting me yellow!" Ah, the criminals! The barbarians! They spared nothing; neither the columns nor the cornices, and my friend became yellow as a canary. I nearly had an attack of jaundice myself, and I still haven't been able to go back and visit my poor disfigured friend painted in the color of the Celestial Empire.

So you see, that's what I meant by being acquainted with all Petersburg.

As I said, I'd been uneasy for three days and now I'd discovered why. Things didn't feel right in the street—this one was missing, that one was missing, and where on earth was such-and-such? And at home, too, I wasn't quite myself. For two whole evenings I'd tried to determine what I was missing in my corner, why I was so ill at ease there. Puzzled, I kept examining my green walls with their black soot stains, the ceiling covered with cobwebs that Matryona cultivates with such eminent success. I examined every piece of furniture, every single chair, to see whether the trouble wasn't hidden just there. For I know that I can be badly upset if a chair is not in exactly the same place as it was the day before. I also looked at the window. But all in vain. I even decided to call in Matryona and give her a fatherly scolding about the cobwebs and about her sloven-liness in general. But she only looked at me, surprised, and left without answering a word; the cobwebs remained unmolested.

It was only this morning that I realized what was happening. Why, they were deserting me for their summer places. I must apologize for this trivial way of putting it, but I can't be bothered with style just now, because everyone is either leaving Petersburg or has already left it; because every respectable-looking man hailing a cab in the street is thereby, before my very eyes, turning himself into a venerable *pater familias,* who, having taken care of his usual duties, departs, just as he is, to join his family in their country house; because every passer-by in the street has a special look about him that almost audibly announces to the world at large: "I'm only passing through town—in a couple of hours or so, I'll be back in the country." If slender, sugar-white fingers drum on the inside of a window pane, if that window then opens, and a pretty face peeps out to buy some potted plants from a street flower vendor—I immediately imagine that she's just buying them to pass the time and not at all to enjoy spring and flowers in a stuffy city apartment, and that anyway the people in that apartment will leave for the country and take the flowers along. I've become so perspicacious that I can tell with certitude from people's faces what kind of summer houses they live in. Those from the Rocky and Apothecary Isles, or from the places along Peterhof Road, are recognizable by the studied exquisiteness of their manners, the elegance of their summer suits, and the magnificence of the carriages in which they drive into the city. Those from Pargolov and places beyond always impress me with their solidity and their down-to-earth air. A visitor from Krestovsky Island is distinguishable by his imperturbable cheerfulness. Whether I happen to meet a long caravan of movers' wagons loaded with mountains of furniture—tables, chairs, sofas (Turkish or otherwise), and all sorts of household junk, on top of which, moreover, a thin female cook is enthroned, looking after her master's belongings like a nesting bird after her eggs—or watch the boats and barges, heavily loaded with household goods, sliding down the Neva or the Fontanka toward the Black Stream or the Islands—in my eyes, the wagons and barges multiply by tens and hundreds, and I have the impression that everything has risen up and started moving in long files out of the city to the countryside, that Petersburg will soon be a desert. So, in the end, I feel offended, ashamed, and sad. I have absolutely nowhere to go and no reason to go out of town. I long to leave on any wagon, to drive off with any gentleman hailing a cabbie. But no one has invited me. They seem to have completely forgotten me, as if I really were a stranger to them!

I'd been walking for hours and, as usual, I'd lost track of where I was, when I suddenly realized I'd reached the city limits. I immediately felt happy and, without hesitation, passed beyond the barrier and found myself walking between cultivated fields and meadows. I didn't feel tired at all. On the contrary, every joint in me was as relaxed as if a load had been lifted from my shoulders. All who drove by smiled at me engagingly, almost bowing to me. They looked pleased about something and the whole lot of them were smoking cigars. And I too was happier than I'd ever been before. Such was the impact of nature upon me, a semi-invalid city dweller who'd almost suffocated within the city walls, that I felt almost as if I'd found myself in Italy.

There's something inexpressibly moving in our Petersburg countryside when, with the arrival of spring, it suddenly reveals itself in all its might and with all its God-given gifts; when it dresses up, adorns itself with bright, multicolored flowers. . . . It makes me think of a weak, frail, sickly young girl, usually regarded with pity, sometimes with compassionate love, and sometimes not even noticed, who for one moment, as if by accident, suddenly becomes immensely beautiful; and, struck and charmed, you can't help wondering what force could have lighted the flame in those sad, dreamy eyes. What has caused the blood to rush to those pale, sunken cheeks? What has brought this passion to her delicate features? Why does her bosom heave like that? What has so suddenly communicated vigor, life, and beauty to the poor girl's face; given it that radiant smile; produced that glittering, sparkling laughter? You look around, you try to guess. But then it's all gone, and the next day perhaps, you'll meet her usual pensive, abstract gaze again, recognize her pale face and the timid humility of her movements; you'll even detect remorse and signs of some deadening anguish and shame over that momentary exaltation. . . . And you're sorry that the ephemeral beauty has faded so rapidly, so irretrievably, that it flashed so deceptively and pointlessly before your eyes—you're sorry, for you didn't even have time to fall in love with her. . . .

But, even so, the night was better than the day! This is what happened.

It was very late when I got back into the city. As I approached the house I live in, it struck ten. I was walking along the embankment; at that hour there was no one around, for I live in a remote part of town. I sang as I walked, for when I'm happy, I always hum something—as does every happy, friendless man who has no one with whom to share his happiness. Then suddenly the most unexpected thing happened to me.

I saw a woman leaning against the railing along the embankment. She appeared to be gazing attentively at the murky water. She wore a ravishing little yellow hat and an elegant black cape. "She must be young and dark-haired," I decided. I don't think she heard my footsteps, and she didn't even stir when I passed her, holding my breath, my heart beating wildly. "Strange," I thought, "she must be quite lost in thought—" Suddenly I stopped dead. Stifled sobs reached my ears. Yes, that was it—she was crying. Again I heard the girl trying to catch her breath. Ah, God! My heart contracted with pity, and shy though I am with women, I retraced my steps and walked up to her. I'm sure I'd have exclaimed "Madame!" had I not been so acutely aware that this form of address has already been used so often in Russian novels with a high-society background. That was all that stopped me. But while I was searching for an alternative approach, the girl recovered, turned her head, glanced at me, looked away, and darted off along the embankment. I followed her. She must have realized, for she turned her back to the water, crossed the street, and went along the opposite sidewalk. I didn't dare follow her across the street. My heart was quivering like that of a bird held in a man's hand. Then something came to my assistance.

I saw a man walking on the other side of the street, not far from the girl. He wore a frock coat, and seemed to have reached an age of respectability, although there was nothing respectable about his gait. He was staggering and stumbling along, guiding himself by leaning against the walls. Now the girl was moving lightly and apprehensively, as girls do at night when they don't wish strange men to offer to see them home; the staggering gentleman never would have caught up with her if he hadn't changed his tactics (for which I thank my lucky stars).

But suddenly, without uttering a word, the man set off at a gallop. She darted ahead with quickened, fearful steps, but the swaying figure kept gaining on her. He came closer and closer, then he caught up with her. The girl let out a cry, and—I thank my lucky stars again for placing my excellent knobby walking stick in my right hand. In no time, I was on the opposite sidewalk; in no time, the uninvited gentleman made a practical appraisal of the situation, took into consideration the unanswerable argument in my hand, slowed down, and fell back. And only when he felt there was a safe distance between us did he voice his indignation in no uncertain terms. But his words hardly reached us.

"If," I said to the girl, "you will allow me to take your arm, that man won't dare annoy you again."

Silently she allowed me. Her hand was still trembling from fear and her earlier emotions. Ah, what blessings I wished at that moment upon the unwelcome gentleman! I squinted at her discreetly. She was terribly pretty. Her hair was dark, just as I'd guessed. Tears glistened on her black eyelashes, whether from her recent fright or from her sorrow, I didn't know, but a smile was already sparkling on her lips. She glanced at me out of the corner of her eye, blushed, and looked down.

"Now, you see, you shouldn't have spurned me like that. Nothing would've happened if I'd been at your side."

"But I didn't know you; I thought you too . . ."

"Do you feel you know me now?"

"A little. For instance, I know you're trembling. Tell me why."

"Ah, you've guessed right from the start!" I said, delighted that she should turn out to be so clever—never a drawback in a woman, as long as she's pretty. "Yes, you've seen through me straight away. I'm afraid of women, and it's that fear that makes me tremble, just as it made you tremble a few moments ago when that gentleman frightened you. I'm frightened now, all right. It's like a dream, although I've never actually dreamed that I'd be talking like this to a woman."

"Really?"

"Yes. And if you feel my arm tremble, it's because it has never yet been held by a pretty hand like yours. I'm quite unused to being with women. In fact, I've never got used to them. I live all alone. I don't even know how to talk to women. For instance, I don't know if I haven't said something stupid to you. Please, tell me frankly—I promise I won't be offended."

"No, no, on the contrary. And since you want me to be frank, let me tell you that women like your sort of shyness; I'll even tell you that I like

It too, and I won't ask you to leave me until we're at my doorstep."

"If you go on saying things like that," I said, out of breath with enthusiasm, "I'll lose my shyness and, along with it, my advantage. . . ."

"Advantage? Advantage to what end? Ah, now you've said something I don't like."

"I *am* sorry, it just slipped off my tongue. You can't really expect that, at such a moment, I shouldn't wish that . . ."

"What? Wish that I should like you?"

"Yes, that's it. But please, try to understand: I'm twenty-six already and I've never known anyone closely. So how can I be expected to be good at speaking to people? How can I say things well and to the point? Besides, isn't it better for you when everything is out in the open? For I don't know how to be silent when my heart is talking. Well, what's the difference? But believe me, I've never, never spoken to any woman. Never. I've never known one. I've only gone around dreaming that one day I might meet someone. If you only knew how many times I've fallen in love that way. . . ."

"But how's that, who did you fall in love with?"

"Why, no one in particular, just with the ideal woman, the one I'd dreamed of. I can dream up whole novels, you know. Oh, you really have no idea about me! Of course, as you can well imagine, I have come across two or three women in my time. But what sort of women were they? They were such housewives that— But now you'll laugh when I tell you that I planned for a long time to address some aristocratic lady in the street. When she was alone, of course. Talk to her shyly, respectfully, passionately; tell her that I was perishing in my loneliness; beseech her not to send me away; say that it was impossible for me to get to know any other woman; persuade her that it was even the *duty* of a woman not to spurn the timid approach of one so unhappy; convince her that, finally, all I wanted from her was a few understanding, sisterly words, and that she shouldn't just turn her back on me, but should believe what I told her—then she might laugh at me if she wished, so long as she said one or two words of hope, only two words, then, if she wished, we'd never meet again! . . . I see you're laughing. . . . Well, that's why I told you about it, after all."

"Don't be offended. I'm only laughing because you're your own worst enemy. If you'd tried you'd have succeeded, maybe even in the street. The simpler, the easier. . . . No decent woman, unless she was dismally stupid or happened to be very irritated about something at that particular moment, would have refused you the two words for which you begged with such humility. . . . Although, after all, she might very well have taken you for a madman. I was thinking of how I would have reacted, but then I have quite a good idea of what life is all about."

"Oh, thank you, thank you!" I cried. "You have no idea what you're doing for me!"

"All right, all right. But tell me, what made you think I was the type of woman with whom . . . well, who would be worthy of . . . your attention, your friendship? How did you know that I was not just another housewife, as you put it? What made you decide to speak to me?"

"What made me—why, you were alone, and that man was most indiscreet, and it's nighttime. . . . I couldn't have done anything else."

"No, no, before that, on the other sidewalk. Weren't you thinking of speaking to me?"

"On the other sidewalk? I really don't know what to say. I was happy today. I was walking along and singing. I went beyond the city limits. I'd never before experienced such happy moments. And you—please excuse me, I may have imagined it, but I thought you were crying, and I couldn't bear it. . . . My heart shrank. . . . Ah, God, why shouldn't I be entitled to grieve with you? Why is it a sin for me to feel brotherly compassion for your sorrow? . . . Excuse me, I said compassion. . . . Well, I don't see why it should offend you if I couldn't resist my impulse to come over and talk to you."

"Enough, don't talk of it any more." She lowered her head, and her fingers pressed my arm. "It's my fault for bringing it up, and I'm so pleased that it wasn't a mistake. . . . But we're almost at my place. I must turn here, into that street. It's only a few steps from here. Goodby now, and thank you very much!"

"But is it possible that we'll never meet again? Can we leave it like this?"

"But you said you were only after two words," the girl said, laughing, "and now you . . . However, who can tell, perhaps we'll meet again some day."

"I'll be waiting here tomorrow. Forgive me, I seem to be demanding things already."

"Yes, you're quite impatient, and you *are* almost demanding things—"

"Listen, listen to me," I interrupted her, "and forgive me if I say something wrong. You see, I can't help coming here tomorrow. I'm simply a dreamer who has little real life, and moments like this are so rare in my existence that I must repeat them again and again in my thoughts. You'll stay in my thoughts throughout the night—throughout a whole year. I'll be here without fail tomorrow, in this very spot, at this very time —and I'll be happy thinking of what happened today. Already this spot is dear to me. I have two or three spots like this in Petersburg. Once I even cried, like you. . . . Well, how can I know? Perhaps a few minutes ago you too were crying at the thought . . . Ah, forgive me, I'm forgetting myself again. . . . I simply meant, perhaps you were once especially happy here somehow. . . ."

"All right then," the girl said, "I suppose I'll be here tomorrow night too. At ten. I see I can't stop you, and I have to come here anyway. But don't think I've made a date with you. I warn you: I have to be here for my own reasons. So I may as well tell you now: I won't mind if you're here too, because that may save me an unpleasant incident like tonight's. But that's just incidental. To be brief, I'd be very pleased to see you . . . to say a couple of words to you. But I don't want you to think badly of me. You mustn't think that I make dates so easily. I would never have agreed to meet you again had it not been for . . . No, let it remain a secret! Only, from now on, let's reach an agreement."

"An agreement? Just name it! I agree to anything in advance!" I said with ardor. "I assure you, I'll be docile, respectful . . . you know me."

"It's because I know you that I want you to come tomorrow," the girl said, laughing. "And I know you fully. But if you come, it must be on my terms. First—and please do as I ask, for I'm being completely frank about it—don't fall in love with me. You mustn't, believe me. But I'd like us to be friends. Here, let's shake hands on it. But, remember, no falling in love!"

"I swear!" I shouted, taking her hand.

"Stop, don't swear so readily. I know very well that you can burst into flame in a second, like gunpowder—forgive me for saying so. Ah, if you knew . . . I, too—I have had no one with whom I could exchange a word, of whom to ask advice. Where could I look for advisors? Certainly not in the street. But you're an exception. I know you as if we'd been friends for twenty years. Am I right in thinking you won't let me down?"

"You'll see. Only I don't know how I'll keep myself alive, waiting for twenty-four hours."

"Sleep deeply. Good night, and remember I've put my trust in you. But you put it so well yourself: Does one really have to give an account of every feeling, even of brotherly compassion? You know, you put it so well that right away I decided to confide in you."

"For heaven's sake, what is it? What?"

"Tomorrow. Let it remain a secret for the moment. It's better for you that way; at least from a distance all this may resemble a romance. I may tell you tomorrow and I may not. I'll talk to you some more; we'll become better acquainted first."

"Well, I—I'll tell you everything about myself tomorrow! But it's as if a miracle were happening to me. Where am I? Oh, God! Tell me, are you glad you didn't get angry with me and chase me away at first, as another woman would have done? It took you two minutes to make me happy once and for all. Yes, happy. Who knows, perhaps you've made me accept myself, maybe you've resolved my doubts. Perhaps such moods come over me that . . . Well, I'll tell you everything tomorrow, you'll know all. . . ."

"Good, I accept; and you'll begin. . . ."

"Agreed."

"Good night."

"Good night."

We parted. I walked around all night. I couldn't make myself go home. I was so happy. . . . Tomorrow!

THE SECOND NIGHT

"So you survived after all," she said to me, laughing as she pressed my hands.

"I've been waiting for two hours. You can't imagine how I got through the day."

"I know, I know. . . . But let's talk business. Do you know why I really came? Certainly not to talk nonsense as we did last night. You know, from now on, we'll act more intelligently. I thought a lot about it last night."

"In what? More intelligently in what? I agree to whatever you say, but to be absolutely sincere, it seems to me I've never been cleverer than now in my whole life."

"Is that so? Well, in the first place, I'd like you to stop squeezing my hands like that, and in the second, I wish to inform you that today I've given quite a bit of thought to you."

"And what conclusions have you reached?"

"Conclusions? Well, I decided to start all over again because I concluded that I still knew nothing about you, that yesterday I acted like a child, a little girl—and I ended up blaming everything on my over-sensitive heart. In other words, I ended up praising myself—the way we always end when we begin analyzing ourselves. Now, to correct that mistake, I've decided to find out every little thing about you. And since I have no other way of finding out, you'll just have to supply me with all the information. So, what manner of man are you? Quick, start telling me your story!"

"My story!" I said, becoming alarmed. "What makes you think I have a story to tell in the first place? In fact I don't have any—"

She laughed.

"But how could you live and have no story to tell?"

"So far I've lived without any stories at all. I've lived keeping to myself, as they say, which means that I've been completely alone. Alone, all alone—do you understand what that means?"

"What do you mean alone? You never saw anyone?"

"No, I saw people, of course. But still I was all alone."

"What then? You mean you never spoke to anyone?"

"Strictly speaking, I didn't."

"But who are you, anyway? Tell me! No, wait—I think I can guess. I'll bet you have a grandmother, as I do. Mine is blind, and she doesn't let me go anywhere—I almost forget how to talk. A couple of years ago, when I misbehaved, she felt she couldn't control me any longer, so she called me over to her and pinned my dress to hers with a safety pin. Sometimes we sit like that for days at a time, she knitting a sock despite her blindness and me, at her side, sewing or reading something aloud to her. So, I've been pinned to someone for two years, a rather strange situation, don't you think?"

"Ah, that's really awful! But I don't have a grandmother."

"You haven't? Then how can you sit home all the time?"

"Listen, shall I tell you who I am?"

"Yes, of course."

"Shall I tell you exactly?"

"Yes, exactly."

"All right then, I'm a queer fish."

"So, you're a queer fish, are you? What sort of queer fish?" the girl said, exploding with laughter, as if she had been holding it in for a whole year. "Ah, you're really great fun to be with! Let's sit down on that bench over there. Nobody every passes there, so you can tell me your story without being overheard. Go on now, I want to hear it! You can't make me believe you have nothing to tell; you're just being secretive. First of all, what's a queer fish?"

"A queer fish? A queer fish is a ridiculous man, a man unlike others," I said, infected by her childish laughter. "He's a sort of freak. Listen, do you know what a dreamer is, for instance?"

"A dreamer? Well, how could I *not* know what a dreamer is? I suppose I'm one myself. You can't imagine what things go through my head sometimes as I sit next to my grandmother! I plunge into my dreams, and sometimes, when I really get going, I reach a point where I marry a Chinese prince. . . . Why, sometimes it's so nice to dream!" But then she added unsmilingly: "Well, not really! Especially when there are other things to think of."

"Wonderful! Since you've already been married to a Chinese potentate, you'll probably be able to understand me too. So listen . . . But wait, I don't even know your name."

"It's Nastenka."

"Nastenka. Is that all?"

"Is that all! Nothing satisfies you. You seem to be insatiable."

"Ah, no, it satisfies me all right, it thoroughly satisfies me! You're a very nice girl to become Nastenka for me right away!"

"That's better! But go on, tell me about yourself."

"All right, Nastenka, listen to this ridiculous story then."

I installed myself on the bench next to her, assumed a grave, theatrical pose, and began, as if I were reading the script of a monologue.

"There are, my dear Nastenka, in case you don't know, some rather strange corners in Petersburg. It's as if the sun that warms the rest of the city never shines on them, and instead another sun, especially designed for them, supplies them with a different light. In those corners, Nastenka, a life goes on quite unlike the one seething around us, a life that is possible in some faraway dreamland but certainly not here in our overserious time. That life is a mixture of something out of pure fantasy, ardently idealistic, with, alas, something bleak and dull and ordinary, not to say outright vulgar."

"Brrr! . . . What an introduction! What am I to hear next?"

"You'll hear, Nastenka—I think I'll never get tired of calling you Nastenka—that dreamers live in those corners. A dreamer, if you want me to define him, is not a real human being but a sort of intermediary creature. He usually installs himself in some remote corner, shrinking even from the daylight. And once he's installed in that corner of his, he grows into it like a snail or at least like that curious thing which is at the same time an animal and a house—the tortoise. And why do you think he so loves his four bleak walls that are sooty, reek unspeakably of tobacco smoke, and are always daubed over with green paint? Why do you think this ridiculous creature, when some rare acquaintance comes to see him (ultimately he's bound to lose all his acquaintances anyway), looks so embarrassed and taken aback, as if he'd just committed a crime between those very walls, as if he'd been forging money or writing verses to be sent to a magazine with an anonymous letter explaining that the author of the piece is dead and that the sender considers it his sacred duty to see the poem published? Why do you think, Nastenka, that conversation between the two of them is so painful? Why can't the visitor laugh or say something amusing now? In other circumstances he is prone to laugh, say amusing things, and chat about the fair sex and other pleasant matters. Why does that acquaintance, probably a recent one, on his very first visit—for under such circumstances there cannot be more than one visit, as no friend returns for a second time—even assuming that he's exceptionally perceptive, why does he feel so awkward looking at the agonized face of his host, who, after desperate but futile efforts to comfort the hapless man who has blundered into his house on a friendly visit by making the conversation flow, giving it some sparkle, and showing that he too is fully aware of elegant ways and can talk about the fair sex, has become completely lost by then. And why, in the end, does the visitor suddenly remember that he has some terribly urgent matter to attend to, grab his hat and dart off, managing to free his hand from the warm pressure of his host's while the host tries by every means possible to show that he's sorry and is trying to redeem himself? Why does the departing visitor laugh as he closes the door behind him and promise himself never to return to the house of that queer fish, although deep down the queer fish really means well? Why, at the same time, is the visitor unable to refrain from comparing his host's face during his visit to a kitten perfidiously captured, manhandled, and scared by children—which kitten then, completely bewildered, hides under some chair in the darkness, and can't help bristling and spitting while he washes his offended little face with his front paws, and even after that, goes around for a long time looking with apprehension and hostility at the world and even at the tidbits from the master's table saved for him by a compassionate housekeeper?"

"Now look here," Nastenka interrupted me. She had been listening with her eyes and her small mouth wide open. "I have no idea why it all happened nor why you should ask me to answer all those ridiculous questions. I'm sure of one thing only: that all this happened to you exactly as you have told me."

"You're right," I said with a straight face.

"Well, why don't you go on? I'm anxious to find out how it all ends."

"You'd like to find out, Nastenka, why the hero of the story—that is, me—was so perturbed and bewildered by the unexpected visit of a friend? You'd like to know why I became so flustered and turned so red when the door of my room was opened, why I was incapable of receiving my visitor properly, and why I was crushed so ignominiously under the weight of my embarrassment?"

"Well, yes, yes, that's just it! And then—you speak beautifully, but couldn't you please speak less beautifully? You sound as though you were reading aloud from a book."

"Nastenka," I said with ponderous gravity, hardly able to control my laughter, "I know I say things too beautifully; I'm terribly sorry, but I don't know how to say them otherwise. At this moment, Nastenka, I feel like the spirit of King Solomon that has been kept imprisoned for a thousand years in a jar under seven seals—and now all the seals have been removed. Now, Nastenka, that we have come together again after our long separation—for the fact is, I've known you a long time. You see, I've been looking for someone, and that's a sure sign that it must have been you I was looking for and that we were destined to meet. Now, thousands of valves have been opened in my head, and I cannot hold back the torrent of words or I'll burst. So, I must ask you to be a good girl and listen to me without interrupting. Otherwise, I won't tell you any more!"

"No, no, please go on! Keep talking, I won't say another word."

"So, I'll go on, Nastenka. There's a certain hour of the day, my dear, of which I'm particularly fond. It is the hour when practically all business, office hours, and all that sort of thing come to an end and people rush off home to dine, to have a little rest; and on their way, they think up ways to spend the evening ahead, the night, or whatever free time is left to them that day. At that hour, the hero of this story—for I hope you'll allow me, Nastenka, to go on telling it in the third person, it's really too embarrassing to say certain things in the first person—at that hour, my hero walks along among the others. But there's a strange, pleased expression on his pale, somewhat crumpled face. He watches with a certain pleasure as the red sunset slowly fades in the cold Petersburg sky. When I say he watches, I am wrong; he takes it in distractedly, like someone too tired to look or preoccupied with some more absorbing matter, so that he has only a passing awareness of what is going on around him. He's pleased, for he's through until tomorrow with business that bores him. He's like a schoolboy let out of school hurrying to play his favorite games or pull his favorite pranks. Look at him from the side,

Nastenka, and you'll see right away that his happy feeling has already had a beneficial effect on his weak nerves and over-excitable imagination. Now he is plunged deep in thought. . . . Thinking of dinner? Of the approaching evening? What is he looking at like that? Isn't it at that dignified-looking gentleman who has just bowed so gracefully to the lady driving past in a glittering carriage drawn by fleet-footed steeds? Oh, no, Nastenka, he has no time for such trifles now! Now he's rich in his *inner* life. And he has struck it rich suddenly—the last rays of the setting sun restored warmth to his heart and stirred up a whole stream of impressions. Now he hardly notices the street where, before, the tiniest detail would have struck him. The Goddess of Fantasy has already spun a golden web with her divine hand and has started unfolding before his eyes patterns of an imaginary, marvelous life; who knows, perhaps she has picked him up with her divine hand and transported him from the granite sidewalk he is still following to paradise. Just stop him now and ask him which streets he took to get here and where he is now. I'm sure he won't know, so he'll blush and invent some lies just for appearances' sake. That's why he started so violently, almost let out a cry, and looked around apprehensively when a nice old lady stopped him in the middle of the sidewalk and asked him to help her find her way. Now frowning angrily, he resumes his way, hardly aware of the grins on the faces of the people he passes, some of whom even stop to give him a second look; oblivious of the little girl who jumps quickly out of his path, bursts into loud giggles, and gapes indiscreetly at his absent smile and gesticulating arms. And already the same Goddess of Fantasy has managed to catch in flight the old lady who'd lost her way, the curious passers-by, the giggling little girl, the bargemen on their barges tied up along the Fontanka, and everything around the Fontanka Embankment—assuming that our hero happens to be walking there at the time. The goddess then playfully weaves everyone and everything into her canvas like flies in a spider's web. Now the queer fish carries these new acquisitions off to his den. He sits down at his table, and after his dinner is long over, he is still sitting there, reviving only when the dreamy and ever-sad Matryona removes the remains of the meal and brings him his pipe. Then he suddenly realizes that he's already dined, although dinner had completely escaped his attention. The room has grown dark. His heart feels empty and sad. His world of fancy silently and without a crackle collapses around him and evaporates without his being able to remember what he was dreaming about. But some dark feeling presses on his breast, making it heave faster; a new desire tickles and excites his fancy; and, almost without noticing it, he summons an array of new ghosts. The little room is dark. Loneliness and idleness excite the imagination. The gentle flame is lit, and fancies start perking like the water in the coffee pot around which Matryona is fussing in the kitchen. Then fancy becomes like a flame itself, flashing and flaring so that the book picked up at random drops out of the dreamer's hands before he has reached the third page. Now his imagination is again vibrating, and suddenly another world with a different life unrolls its enchanted horizons before his eyes. A new dream—new happiness! A new dose of refined, voluptuous poison! Ah, what's real life to him! To his perverted eye, your life, Nastenka, and mine are unbearably humdrum, slow, and sluggish. He feels we're discontented with our lot and tired of life. And indeed, at first glance, life is bound to appear cold, gloomy, and rather unfriendly. Ah, the poor creatures! the dreamer thinks—and no wonder. Just look at the magical phantoms who so charmingly, subtly, yet somehow casually fall into place in the panoramic, animated picture that shapes itself before him, a picture in which his own exalted person is always in the foreground. Look at all the different adventures he has there—the endless succession of blissful visions! Now perhaps you would like to ask what he's dreaming about. But why ask? He dreams of everything . . . of being a poet, at first unrecognized, later crowned; of friendship with Hoffmann the poet; of St. Bartholemew Night; of playing a heroic part in the storming of Kazan under Ivan the Terrible; of Diana Vernon, Clara Mowbray, Effie Deans, and other heroines of Sir Walter Scott; of Jan Hus facing the tribunal of prelates; of the rising of the dead in *Robert the Devil* (Remember the music? It has a smell of the churchyard about it, don't you think?); of the Battle of Berezina; of a poetry reading at the Countess Vorontsova-Dashkova's; of Danton; of Cleopatra *i suoi amanti;* of Pushkin's *Little House in Kolomna;* of having a little house of his own and being there on a wintry evening with his beloved listening to him with her eyes and mouth wide open, just as you're listening to me now, my dearest angel. . . .

"No, Nastenka, what can this voluptuous idler find in the life so dear to people like you and me? He thinks it a poor life, without realizing that for him too there may come a sad hour when, for a single day of that miserable life, he would give away all his years of fancy. And he would exchange his dreams neither for happiness, nor joy; at that grim hour of regret and unrelieved gloom he won't even care to choose. But until that perilous time comes, the dreamer can have no desires, for he has everything; he is above desire; he is surfeited; he is himself the artist creating his life at every hour, guided only by his own inspiration.

"And how effortlessly, how naturally the dreamer's world of fantasy springs up! It looks so real and not at all like a mirage! In fact, sometimes he almost believes that his dream life is no figment of the imagination, no self-deception, no delusion, but something real, actual, existing.

"Now tell me, Nastenka, why does he so often feel out of breath at those moments? Tell me, by what magic, by what uncanny chance, does his pulse quicken, do tears gush from his eyes and his pale cheeks flush, as his whole being fills with inexpressible delight? Why do sleepless nights flash by in a second, in inexhaustible gaiety and happiness? Then, when the rosy rays of dawn appear in the window and the uncertain light of our Petersburg morning fills the gloomy room, our exhausted dreamer throws himself on his bed and falls asleep with an aching feeling of rapture.

"Yes, Nastenka, he deceives himself and winds up by believing that he is moved by true, live passion, that there is substance—flesh and blood—to his fancies! And it is quite a deception! Just look at him and see for yourself. Can you believe, looking at him, Nastenka, that he doesn't even know the woman he loved so passionately in his sultry flights of fancy? Can you believe that he has only seen her in irresistibly voluptuous mirages and that he simply dreamed that passion? Is it really possible that they have never walked hand in hand during so many years, spurning the rest of the universe, merging their own two worlds and lives? Is it possible that at the late hour when they had to part, she didn't really lay her head, sobbing and miserable, on his chest, not hearing the wind that snatched tears from her black eyelashes? Would you believe it was all nothing but a dream—the wild, neglected garden with its path overgrown with moss, so lonely and desolate, along which they used to walk together so often, hoping, suffering, loving so tenderly and for so long? And that there was no strange, ancestral home where she had lived for so many dull, lonely years with her stern old husband, always silent and irritable, who frightened them, timid children that they were, children sadly and shyly hiding their love from each other? Ah, how afraid they were, how they languished, how pure and innocent was their love, and how wicked—it goes without saying, Nastenka—were the people around them! And did he never meet her later, far away from their native shore, under an alien, southern sky, in a divine, eternal city, at a glamorous ball, to the thunder of music, the whole affair taking place in a *palazzo* (it must be a *palazzo*) drowned in a sea of lights? . . . They are on a terrace wreathed in myrtle and roses . . . she recognizes him, tears off her mask and, whispering, "I am free now!" flings herself into his arms, trembling with rapture. . . . They hold each other tight, and in a moment they've forgotten their unhappiness, their separation, all their sufferings, the forbidding house, the old man, the bleak garden in their remote homeland, the bench where he kissed her for the last time, holding her in his desperate embrace from which she had to tear herself, leaving him with his suffering. . . .

"Ah, Nastenka, you must agree that anyone would feel awkward and embarrassed and would turn red like a boy who has just stuffed into his pocket an apple he's stolen from the next-door garden if some long-legged, healthy joker, an uninvited friend of his, opened his door and announced, as if nothing had happened: 'Hi, chum! What do you know, I've just arrived from Pavlovsk!'

"It's unbearable. In dreamland the old count is dead and an inconceivable happiness is mine, and then this fellow arrives from Pavlovsk!"

My dramatic exclamations over, I fell dramatically silent. I remember that I wanted to force myself to laugh, for I felt that some hostile imp had installed himself inside me and was squeezing my throat, making my chin tremble and my eyes grow damp. I expected Nastenka, who had been listening with her intelligent, wide-open eyes fixed on me, to burst out in uncontrollable, childish laughter at any second, and I was already regretting having gone too far and told her things which had been weighing on my heart for a long time, things about which I could talk as smoothly as a book because I had long ago pronounced judgment on myself and couldn't help reading it out now and confessing without expecting to be understood. But to my great surprise, she remained silent for a while, then, pressing my hand slightly, asked me with a sort of timid understanding:

"Is that really how you've lived all this time?"

"All the time, Nastenka, and it looks as if I'll go on like that to the end."

"No," she said, looking worried, "that won't happen. That would be like me spending my whole life at my grandmother's side. Listen, I tell you it's not right to live like that."

"Ah, don't I know it, Nastenka!" I exclaimed, unable to control my emotions any longer. "At this moment I see more clearly than ever before that I've wasted my best years. And the realization hurts me even more because it was God who sent you to me, my lovely angel, to make me see it. As I sit here next to you, it is already painful to think of the future, because there's nothing in it but a lonely, stale, useless existence. What could I dream of, now that I've been so happy with you in real life? Oh, bless you, my dearest girl, for not spurning me at first sight, for enabling me to say that I've lived at least two evenings in the course of my existence!"

"Ah, no, no!" Nastenka said with emotion, tears sparkling in her eyes. "No, no more of that life! We shan't part like this! What's two evenings?"

"Ah, Nastenka, Nastenka! Do you realize that you have reconciled me with myself for a long time to come? Do you realize that now I'll never think quite as badly of myself as I sometimes have in the past? Do you know that perhaps I won't be unhappy any more over having committed a crime or a sin in my life, because now I realize that my whole life was nothing but a crime and a sin in itself? And don't imagine, please, that I'm exaggerating, Nastenka, for there are moments when I'm overcome by such anguish and despair that . . . In those moments, I feel that I'll never have a true life because I feel sure I've entirely lost touch with reality; because I feel damned; because, in the middle of my fancy-filled nights, I have moments of lucidity that are unbearable! In the meantime, I hear the din of the human crowd around me and see how people who are awake live, and I realize that their lives are not made to measure, that they don't shatter like dreams, like visions, that their lives are perpetually renewed, every hour in them different from the one before, whereas the timid daydream is horribly monotonous, a slave to the shadows, to ideas, to the first cloud that suddenly hides the sun and squeezes in anguish the heart of a true inhabitant of Petersburg who must have his sunshine—for what fancy is there that can do without sunshine? In the end, you feel that your much-vaunted, inexhaustible fantasy is growing tired, debilitated, exhausted, because you're bound to grow out of your old ideals; they're smashed to splinters and turn to dust, and if you have no other life, you have no choice but to keep rebuilding your dreams from the splinters and dust. But the heart longs for something different! And it is vain to dig in the ashes of your old fancies, trying to find even a tiny spark to fan into a new flame that will warm the chilled heart and bring back to life everything that can send the blood rushing wildly through the body, fill the eyes with tears—everything that can delude you so well!

"And shall I tell you, Nastenka, how far I've gone? Would you believe that I have taken to celebrating the anniversaries of my sensations, the anniversary of something that was delightful at one time, of something that actually never occurred. I am reduced to celebrating anniversaries because I no longer have anything with which to replace even those silly, flimsy dreams. For dreams, Nastenka, have to be renewed too. I like revisiting, at certain times, spots where I was once happy; I like to shape the present in the image of the irretrievable past. So I often roam like a sad, gloomy shadow, without need or aim, along Petersburg's streets and alleys. And what memories come to me! I may remember, for instance, that exactly one year ago, at this very hour, in this very street, I was walking along this very sidewalk, just as gloomy and lonely as now. And I may remember that although my dreams were sad and life was painful, somehow it was not as agonizing as it has become now; the black forebodings that have since taken hold of me weren't there yet; nor was there the gnawing, dreary feeling of guilt that now torments me day and night, never leaving me a moment's peace. And so I ask myself: 'Where are your dreams?' And I shake my head and mutter: 'How the years go by!' And I ask myself again: 'What have you done with those years? Where have you buried your best moments? Have you really lived? Look,' I say to myself, 'how cold it is becoming all over the world!' And more years will pass and behind them will creep grim isolation. Tottering senility will come hobbling, leaning on a crutch, and behind these will come unrelieved boredom and despair. The world of fancies will fade, dreams will wilt and die and fall like autumn leaves from the trees. . . . Ah, Nastenka, won't it be sad to be left alone, all, all alone, without even having anything to regret—nothing, but nothing; for everything I've lost is nothing but a stupid, round zero, nothing but a flimsy fancy?"

"Stop it, stop it. . . ." Nastenka brushed away a little tear. "It's all over now. Now there'll be the two of us. Now, whatever happens, we'll never part again. Listen, I'm only an ordinary girl. I've studied very little, although my grandmother did hire a teacher for me. But, believe me, I understand everything you've said because I felt the same way when Grandma pinned me to her dress. Of course, I can't express it as well as you because of my lack of education," she remarked shyly, apparently feeling that she ought to pay tribute to my pathetic monologue and high-flown style. "But I'm very glad that you've told me everything so frankly. Now I know you completely. And now I want to tell you my story, without holding anything back, then perhaps you'll give me your advice. You are so intelligent—I want you to promise to give me advice."

"Ah, Nastenka, I've never been much of an advisor, especially an intelligent advisor, but since we're going to be together, I feel that my advice will be terribly clever and that each of us will have many, many intelligent suggestions to offer the other. Well, then, pretty Nastenka, let's see what advice I can give you. Come, tell me everything—I'm so happy, cheerful, daring, and clever that I'm sure I won't have to search for words."

"No!" Nastenka laughed. "It isn't clever advice I'm after, it's brotherly understanding from someone who, as it were, has loved me all my life."

"That suits me, Nastenka, suits me fine! As to loving, had I loved you for twenty years, I'm sure I couldn't possibly love you more than I do now."

"Give me your hand," Nastenka said.

I gave it to her.

"Here goes," she said.

"You already know half my story. You know I have an old grand-mother—"

"If the other half is as short as the one I know . . ." I interjected, laughing.

"No, just keep quiet and listen. Don't interrupt me; it puts me off. Just listen.

"I have an old grandmother. I've lived with her ever since I was a very little girl, because my parents are dead. Grandma apparently was much better off before, for she keeps remembering better days. It was she who taught me French and later hired a teacher for me. I stopped taking lessons when I was fifteen—I'm seventeen now. When I was fifteen, I did something naughty. I won't go into what I did exactly, except to say that it wasn't much. Still, Grandma called me over to her that morning and said that since she was blind she couldn't very well watch me. Then she took a safety pin and pinned my dress to hers, saying that we were going to stay sitting like that forever, unless, of course, my behavior im-proved. Well, to make it short, at first it was impossible for me to move away from her; I had to work, study, read—everything—sitting by my grandmother's side. Once I tried to trick her by persuading our maid Fyokla to sit in for me. Grandma had fallen asleep in her armchair. Fyokla is deaf, you see, and she took my place while I ran out to the house of a girl, a friend of mine who lived nearby. But it ended badly. Grandma woke up and asked something, assuming that it was me. Fyokla saw Grandma was trying to say something but, of course, she couldn't hear what it was. So, not knowing what else to do, she unfastened the pin and ran away."

This memory made Nastenka laugh so much that she had to interrupt herself. I laughed too, but as soon as she realized I was laughing, she stopped short and said:

"Now look here, you mustn't laugh at Grandma! I laugh because I can't help it—she really is so funny. But then, you see, I'm fond of her at the same time. Anyway, I was in real trouble. She pinned me to her again, and I wasn't even allowed to move.

"Ah, I forgot to tell you that my grandma owns the house we live in. It's just a tiny wooden house with three windows, and almost as old as she is. It also has an attic room, and a new lodger came to live in the attic—"

"Therefore, I assume that there was a lodger before him," I remarked.

"Of course there was—and he could keep quiet much better than you can," Nastenka said. "True, he had difficulty moving his tongue at all, for he was a very, very old man, quite mute, blind, and lame; in the end, living became too much for him and he just died. So a new lodger took his place, for we can't afford not to have a lodger. That and Grandma's pension make up our entire income. Now, the new lodger happened to be a young man. He came from out of town. When Grandma told him what the rent was, he didn't bargain, so she took him and then asked me:

" 'Tell me, Nastenka, the new lodger is a young man, isn't he?'

"I couldn't lie to her, so I said that although he wasn't old, he wasn't so young either.

" 'Is he good-looking?' she asked me then.

"Again I didn't want to lie.

" 'Yes, Grandma, he's quite good-looking.'

" 'Ah, that's really too bad!' Grandma said, 'because I'm asking you all these questions so you won't keep staring at him. Ah, what times we live in,' she added. 'Think of it—just an insignificant lodger and he turns out to be handsome, too. Ah, what're we all coming to? You never saw such things happening in the good old days.'

"According to Grandma, everything was just wonderful in the good old days—she was younger in those days, and the sun shone brighter and was warmer, and milk didn't go bad as it does now! And while she goes on and on like that, I sit in silence and think to myself: 'It looks as if Grandma were trying to give me ideas, asking whether the lodger is handsome or not.' And then I got absorbed in counting the stitches in my knitting, and the lodger completely vanished from my mind.

"Then one morning the lodger came to inquire when they were going to paper his room as he'd been promised. And, Grandma being a great hand at chatting, they got into a conversation in no time, then she says to me: 'Nastenka, run and bring me the abacus from my bedroom.' I don't know why, but that made me turn red. I forgot all about the safety pin and jumped up to scamper into the other room. The movement yanked the pin and Grandma's armchair came rolling along on its casters. I don't know how I could have forgotten about that safety pin and neglected to unfasten it discreetly! And now, realizing that the lodger had found out about it, I stopped dead where I was and burst into tears. I felt so hopelessly ashamed and humiliated at that moment that I thought I'd never be able to face the world again.

" 'What are you waiting for?' Grandma kept shouting at me, but that only made me cry worse. And the lodger, seeing how embarrassed I was, muttered some excuse and rushed off.

"After that day, I felt like dying whenever I heard the slightest noise in the passage. The lodger's coming, I said to myself each time, and I'd quietly unfasten the pin. But it was never him.

"A couple of weeks passed, and the lodger sent us a note by Fyokla saying he had a lot of books, some French ones among them, and perhaps Grandmother would like him to send us some so that I might read to her to pass the time? Grandmother accepted gratefully after first inquiring whether they were decent, proper books. 'Because if they aren't,' she told me, 'I won't allow you to read them, for I don't want you to learn any wicked things from them, Nastenka.'

" 'But what sort of wicked things,' I asked her, 'could I learn from them, Grandma?'

" 'Well,' she said, 'they may describe young men seducing well-brought-up young girls, abducting them from their parents' homes under the pretext of wishing to marry them, then abandoning them to their fate and perdition. I have read many books like that,' Grandma told me, 'and they describe that sort of thing so well and so vividly that sometimes I used to read them on the sly throughout the night and into the morning. So mind, Nastenka,' she added, 'you stay away from books like that. Now what are the books he's sent us called?'

" 'They're all novels, Grandma, novels by Sir Walter Scott.'

" 'Walter Scott, you say? You'd better make sure there's no trick. See that he hasn't tried to slip some note in along with them, some love letter.'

" 'No, Grandma, there's no note . . . nothing.'

" 'Yes, but we'd better watch out!'

"So we started reading Walter Scott, and within a month or so, we were through almost half of it. Later he sent us some more books, including Pushkin; finally, I couldn't imagine how I could live without books, and I stopped dreaming about marrying that Chinese prince. . . .

"That was the situation when one day I bumped into our lodger on the stairs as I was going on some errand for Grandma. He stepped back, and I saw he'd turned red. But he laughed, said hello, inquired after Grandmother's health, and asked me:

" 'Have you read the books?'

" 'I have.'

" 'And which did you like best?'

" '*Ivanhoe*,' I said, 'and, of course, Pushkin.'

"And that was all that happened that time.

"A week later we again met on the stairs. This time Grandma hadn't sent me. I was going somewhere on an errand of my own. It was around two in the afternoon, and that happened to be the time at which the lodger usually came home.

" 'Hello,' he said.

" 'Hello,' I answered.

" 'Tell me,' he said, 'don't you get bored sitting all day with your grandmother like that?'

"Now when he asked that, I don't know why, but I became very embarrassed, and flushed. I felt humiliated because apparently even strangers were beginning to inquire about what was going on. I decided not to answer, just to turn away and leave, but I didn't have the strength.

" 'Please,' he said, 'forgive me for speaking to you like that. I have great respect for you, and believe me, your well-being means more to me even than it does to your grandmother. Don't you know any girls whom you could visit?'

"I explained to him that I had only one friend, called Mashenka, and that she'd moved to Pskov with her family, and I had no one left.

" 'Tell me,' he asked then, 'what would you say if I asked you to come to the theater with me?'

" 'The theater? But what about my grandmother?'

" 'Couldn't you manage it without her finding out?'

" 'No,' I said, 'I don't want to deceive my grandmother. Good-by.'

" 'Good-by then.'

"And that was all he said.

"But, after dinner, he came down to our rooms, sat down, and had a long talk with Grandma. He asked her whether she ever went out and whether she had any friends, then suddenly slipped in, as if in passing:

" 'I have tickets, a loge in fact, for tonight's performance of *The Barber of Seville*. Some friends of mine got them, but couldn't make it tonight, so I have the tickets—'

"'*The Barber of Seville!*' Grandmother exclaimed. 'Why, it must be the same *Barber* they used to put on in the good old days!'

"'Yes, ma'am,' the lodger said, 'the very same!'

"And as he said that he gave a look that made me go crimson and set my heart skipping in expectation.

"'That's one opera that I really know,' Grandmother said. 'In fact, in my younger days, I myself sang Rosina in an amateur dramatic group.'

"'Wouldn't you like to come with me tonight? I think it'd be a shame to waste the tickets.'

"'Well, I don't see why we shouldn't go,' Grandma decided, 'especially as my Nastenka here has never been to the theater.'

"Ah, what a joy it was! We immediately started preparing, got dressed, and drove over to the Opera. Grandma, although she couldn't see a thing, still wanted to listen to the music. And, deep down, she was a kind old thing and very pleased that I should have such fun—we would never have gone anywhere without this opportunity.

"I won't describe my impressions of *The Barber of Seville*, but I'll tell you that all that evening the lodger kept looking at me so nicely and talking to me so eloquently that I realized that, by asking me earlier whether I'd come to the theater with him in secret, he'd only wanted to test me. Ah, it was such joy! So I went to bed incredibly proud and happy, and my heart beat so hard that I worked up a slight fever and raved about *The Barber of Seville* the rest of the night.

"I imagined, after that, that he'd come to see us often. But, on the contrary, he hardly ever came. He might come in once or twice a month, and only to invite us to the theater. In fact, we went twice more with him, I believe. But I was no longer happy on those occasions. I thought he was just sorry for me, leading that sad life with my grandmother, and that there was nothing else to it on his part. And, as time went by, strange moods started coming over me. I was unable to stay quiet, unable to take in what I was reading, unable to concentrate on my work; sometimes I burst out laughing just to irritate grandmother, and sometimes I suddenly dissolved into tears. I grew very thin and was almost seriously ill. The opera season was over, and the lodger stopped coming at all. And when he did meet me—always on the stairs, of course—he bowed so unsmilingly that I felt sure he didn't even wish to talk to me; and after he had already left the house, I would still be standing in the middle of the stairs, red as a cherry, for when I saw him, the blood never failed to rush to my head.

"Now, let me tell the end of my story. Just a year ago, in May, the lodger came to tell my grandmother that his business in Petersburg was over and that he must now move to Moscow. When I heard that, I turned as pale as the tablecloth and went all limp in my chair. Grandma never noticed anything; the lodger just said good night and left.

"What was I to do? I racked my brains in despair, and finally, I decided. The day before he was to leave I decided to take a desperate step in the evening, after Grandma had gone to bed. And I did. I picked out some dresses and the necessary underwear, made a bundle out of them and, carrying it, went, half-alive, half-dead, upstairs to the lodger's room. Walking up that flight of stairs seemed to take a whole hour.

"When I opened his door, he turned his head and, seeing me, let out a cry. He must have taken me for a ghost, for I had turned white, and my legs were hardly able to carry me. He hurried to get me some water. My heart was beating so hard it hurt, and my head ached, and everything inside it went all blurry.

"When I came to, the first thing I did was put my bundle on his bed, sit down next to it myself, and let my tears pour in two rivers. I believe he understood everything right away. He stood there looking at me, and his expression was so wretched that my heart was torn by a terrible anguish.

"'Nastenka,' he said at last, 'I want you to understand. I can do nothing. I'm poor; I haven't a thing to my name. I don't even have a decent job. So what would we live on if I married you?'

"We discussed it for a long time, in the end, I lost all control over myself and declared that I could no longer live with my grandmother, that I'd run away, that I'd had enough of being fastened to her with a safety pin, and that, whatever he might say, I was going to Moscow with him because I couldn't live without him. Shame, love, pride—everything— was seething within me at the same time, and fearing that he might refuse me, I collapsed on the bed almost in convulsions.

"He sat in complete silence for a few moments, then he got up and took my hand.

"'Listen, my nice little Nastenka,' he said, and I saw that there were tears in his eyes, too. 'I swear to you that I'm certain I'd be happy with you if I were ever in a position to marry you. Listen: I have to go to Moscow, and I'll be staying there for exactly a year. I must go there to take care of my business. When I come back, if you still love me, I swear we'll be happy. But now I have no right to promise you anything. I'll say too, however, that if I can't make it in one year, I'll still come and find you later—that is, if you don't prefer someone else by then, because I cannot, I have no right to bind you to me by promises.'

"The next day he was gone. We'd agreed not to say a word to Grandma. He'd insisted upon that. Well, that's about all there is to my story. The year has gone by, and he's come back. Indeed, he's been here for three days already, and—and—"

"And what?" I cried, unable to stand it any longer.

"He hasn't come to see me," Nastenka said, and I felt that she was making a great effort, "he hasn't given a sign of life—"

She cut herself short, remained silent for a few seconds, then covering her face with her hands, burst into sobs that tore at my heart.

I hadn't expected such an ending.

"Nastenka," I ventured imploringly, "please, please don't cry. Maybe he simply hasn't come yet. . . ."

"No, no, he's here, he's here!" Nastenka cried. "I know it! We agreed that evening before he left. . . . After we'd said all the things I've already told you, we came out to take a walk on this embankment. It was ten o'clock. We sat down on the bench; I'd stopped crying. I loved the things he was saying to me. . . . He told me that as soon as he was back in town, if I still wanted him, we'd tell everything to Grandma. And now he's back in town—I know it for sure—but he still hasn't come to see me. . . ."

And she burst into tears again.

"But, my God, is there really nothing I can do for you?" I leaped up from the bench in complete despair. "Tell me, Nastenka, couldn't I go and see him or something?"

"Do you think that's possible?" she said, suddenly raising her head.

"No, of course not," I said, coming back to my senses. "You know what you should do? Write him a letter."

"No, I can't; that's impossible too," she said firmly, but this time she lowered her eyes.

"Why is it impossible? Why?" I insisted. "Do you know what letter you ought to write, Nastenka? There are letters and letters, you know. So please trust my judgment; I won't give you bad advice. Everything will turn out fine, I'm sure. You took the initiative in the first place, so why not now?"

"Impossible, impossible, it would look as if I were throwing myself at him—"

"But no, you're wrong, dear little Nastenka!" I interrupted her without trying to hide my smile. "You have the right to demand. He promised, after all, didn't he? And, from what I understand, he's an honest, con-

siderate man, and I'm sure there's nothing dishonorable in his behavior."
I continued, admiring the logic of my own reasoning and arguments more
and more: "What did he do? He tied himself down by a promise. He
declared that if he married anyone it would be you, while leaving you
completely free to refuse him if your feelings changed. So it is quite
natural that you make the first move. It's your right, your advantage over
him, and you should do it even if, for instance, you decide to release him
from his word."

"Tell me, how would you write to him?"

"What?"

"The letter, of course."

"Well, I'd start like this: 'Dear Sir—' "

"Must I really address him 'dear sir'?"

"Yes, it's indispensable. But after all, I think—"

"Well, go on!"

"I'd write like this:

" 'Dear Sir, Forgive me—' No, no apologies are necessary. The letter
justifies itself. Write simply:

" 'I thought I would write to you first. Please forgive my impatience,
but for a whole year I have lived on hope. Am I to blame, then, if I
cannot stand even one day of doubt? Now that you are back in town,
and may have had a change of heart, let me assure you by this letter that
I have nothing to reproach you for, for I cannot command your love. So I
will consider it simply as my fate.

" 'You are a decent and honorable man, and I am sure you will not laugh
or be angry reading these impatient lines. You will keep in mind that they
are written by a poor, lonely girl who has no one to advise her and
who never could control her own heart. But forgive me for entertaining
even a fleeting suspicion that you could hurt, even in thought, the girl
who has loved you so much and who still loves you.' "

"Yes, yes, that's exactly what I had in mind!"

Nastenka was very enthusiastic and her eyes sparkled with joy.

"Ah, you have resolved my doubts! I think God Himself sent you to
me! Thank you, thank you, thank you!"

"Thank me for what? For being sent by God?"

It was a delight to look at her pretty face, so happy now.

"Yes, thank you for being sent to me to begin with."

"Ah, Nastenka, since we feel grateful sometimes to people just for
living with us, let me thank you for having met you, for making it possible for me to remember you as long as I live."

"Well, that will do for now. Listen, we agreed that when he came back, he'd let me know by leaving a letter for me with some friends of mine, nice, simple people who know nothing about this. Or, if he couldn't leave the letter, he'd come here to this bench, at ten in the evening, on the very day he returned to Petersburg. Now I know he's in town, but he hasn't kept our date or written the letter. I cannot possibly leave my grandmother in the morning, so couldn't you, please, take my letter to those friends I mentioned? They'll see that he gets it. And if there's an answer, bring it to me here tomorrow evening at ten."

"But what about the letter? You have to write it first; at best, you might get a reply the day after tomorrow."

"The letter . . ." Nastenka said, somewhat at a loss, "the letter . . . but . . ."

She didn't finish. She suddenly turned her face away from me, growing red as a red rose, and I felt her slipping a letter into my hand that, it turned out, had already been written and sealed. Something light, graceful, and familiar flashed through my mind.

"R-r-o-si-i-na . . ." I intoned.

"Rosina!" we sang together, and I was so moved and delighted that I felt terribly like putting my arms around her. She was blushing deeply and laughing, and tiny glistening tears hung on her black eyelashes.

"Enough, enough. Good-by now, good night!" she rattled. "You have the letter and the address. Good night, see you tomorrow!"

She pressed both my hands hard, nodded, and darted off. I remained standing there for a long time, following her with my eyes.

"See you tomorrow . . . tomorrow . . ." flashed in my head as she disappeared around a corner.

THE THIRD NIGHT

It had been a sad, drizzly day, without relief—just like my future senility. I am oppressed by strange thoughts and dark sensations; throngs of vague questions obsess me, but I have neither the strength nor the desire to cope with them. No, I cannot cope with it all!

We won't meet tonight. Last night, as we parted, clouds overcast the sky and a mist was rising. "Tomorrow will be a miserable day," I said. She didn't answer. She didn't want to shed doubt on a day that shone before her bright and sunny. She didn't want to cast a single cloud over it.

"If it rains tomorrow," she said, "I won't come."

I didn't think she'd notice that it was raining, but she must have, for she didn't come.

Last night was our third meeting, our third white night. . . .

Yes, joy and happiness do make a person beautiful. His heart overflows with love, and he seems to try to pour that love into the heart of a fellow creature. He wants everything to laugh and to sparkle. And his joy is so contagious! There was so much tenderness, so much friendliness, for me in her heart last night. She was so full of solicitude for me and tried so hard to make me feel happy. Ah, a happy woman is always so full of seductive charm, but I . . . I took it at its face value; I imagined that . . .

But how could I imagine anything of the sort. How could I be so blind, since I knew that all that had already been taken by someone else, that none of it could be for me; that even her niceness, her solicitude, her love —yes, her love for me—was nothing but happiness caused by a forthcoming meeting with another man, a wish on her part to impart a bit of that happiness to me. And when he didn't turn up, when we'd waited in vain, she frowned, lost her composure, looked afraid. Her movements and her words were no longer light or playful or gay. And, strangely, she doubled the attentions she showered on me, as if she wanted instinctively to give me something she was longing for herself, something she feared she wouldn't get. Nastenka had become so timid and fearful that I believe she grasped finally that I was in love with her and took pity on my poor love, for our own unhappiness makes us more sensitive to the unhappiness of others. When someone is unhappy, his sensitivity is not scattered; it becomes tense and concentrated.

I had come to meet her tense with emotion, hardly able to wait for the moment of meeting. I never expected to feel what I felt, nor that it would end the way it did. She was beaming. She expected an answer from him. The answer was to be himself; he would come running in answer to her call. She'd come a whole hour before me. At first, every word made her burst into happy laughter.

"Do you know why I'm so happy tonight?" she said. "Why I'm so pleased to see you? Why I like you so much?"

"Yes?" I said, beginning to shiver.

"I like you so much because you haven't fallen in love with me. Someone else in your position might have started pestering me, become full of self-pity, moaned—but not you, you're so nice!"

She suddenly pressed my hand so hard that I started and almost cried out. She laughed.

"Ah, you're such a wonderful friend," she said a moment later, seriously this time. "Yes, God sent you to me, really, I mean it. I can't imagine what would have become of me without you. You're so selfless, you've been so nice to me! When I'm married, we'll see a lot of each other, we'll be closer than brother and sister. I'll love you almost as much as I love him. . . ."

Somehow I felt awfully sad, yet something resembling laughter stirred somewhere deep down inside me.

"You're overwrought," I said. "You're afraid he won't come."

"Whatever are you talking about? If I weren't so happy, your remarks and your lack of trust in me would make me cry. But it makes me think, after all . . . But I'll think later; in the meantime, I admit you're right. Yes, I'm not myself now, I'm all expectation, I feel a little too light. . . . But let's leave this conversation about feelings—"

At that second we heard steps and we saw a figure moving through the darkness. It was coming toward us. We both began to tremble. She just managed to suppress a cry. I let go of her hand and moved away discreetly. But it wasn't him.

"What are you afraid of? Why did you let go my hand?" She thrust her hand back into mine. "Well, what do you say, shall we meet him together? I want him to see how much we love each other."

"How much we love each other?" I repeated.

"Ah, Nastenka," I thought, "those words mean so many things! That sort of love sometimes freezes a heart and makes life seem unbearable. Your hand is cold—mine is burning. You're blind. There certainly are times when happy people are unbearable—but I could never be angry with you!"

But finally I couldn't stand it.

"Listen, Nastenka," I said tensely, "to how I got through this day."

"What? Tell me! Why haven't you said anything about it till now?"

"First I went to carry out all your errands. I went to see your friends, left your letter there, then . . . then I went back home and turned in."

"And that's all?" she laughed.

"Almost all . . ."

I made a great effort to control the idiotic tears that otherwise would have spurted from my eyes.

"Then I woke up. About an hour before I was to meet you. But I felt

I hadn't slept at all. I didn't know what was happening to me. It was as if time had stopped and one sensation, one feeling would remain in me from then on; as if one minute was going to stretch out into eternity; as if life would stop and stand still for me. I was going to tell you all this as soon as we met. When I woke up, I was under the impression that some sweet melody, heard somewhere long ago and since forgotten, had come back to me now, that for all these years, I'd been searching for it, longing for it, but only now—"

"My God, what's this all about?" Nastenka interrupted me. "I don't understand a thing you're saying."

"I was trying, Nastenka, to make you understand the strange feeling—" I started in a pitiful voice in which there was still a note of hope, even if a very faint one.

"Stop it! That's enough, stop it," she repeated quickly.

It hadn't taken her long to guess, the sly girl! She suddenly became very talkative, gay, and full of jokes. Laughing, she took my arm, trying to make me laugh, too. Every awkward, embarrassed word of mine set off such long peals of silvery laughter that I was on the point of losing my temper. Then she became flirtatious.

"You see," she began, "I'm a bit offended with you for not falling in love with me. People don't always make sense, remember! But still, Mr. Unmovable, you can't avoid complimenting me for being so straightforward. Why, I tell you everything, however inane, that crosses my mind."

"Wait, I believe that's eleven striking," I said. The even booming had started in a distant clock tower. She stopped laughing and counted.

"Yes, eleven," she said in a weak, hesitant voice.

I was sorry that I had alarmed her and had made her count the strokes. I cursed myself for my spitefulness. I felt miserable for her, and didn't know how to make up for my nastiness. I tried to cheer her up, to find good reasons for his failure to turn up, to argue, prove, plead. She was, of course, very easy to convince on that subject, only too delighted to clutch at any excuse for him that I could think up.

"It's really funny," I was saying heatedly, admiring the persuasive power of my own arguments, "your assurance that he'd be here led me to accept it as a fact and even lose my sense of time. Actually, he couldn't possibly have made it. Just think, he's hardly had time to receive the letter. Now suppose he couldn't come tonight and wrote a note to that effect. It couldn't get to your friends' before tomorrow, could it? I'll go and see first thing tomorrow morning and let you know right away. Now there are hundreds of other possibilities; for instance, he may not have been at home when the letter arrived, and maybe he hasn't read it to this very moment. . . . Anything could've happened."

"Yes, of course," Nastenka said, "that hadn't even occurred to me. Of course—anything could have happened."

Her tone was extremely co-operative, but I detected a jarring, discordant note in it, an echo of thoughts of a different kind.

"Here's what we'll do," she said. "You'll go there tomorrow as early as you can, and if there's something, you'll let me know immediately. You know where I live, of course." And she repeated her address.

Then she became breathtakingly tender and at the same time shy. . . . I thought she was attentively following what I was saying, but when I asked her some question, she said nothing, became embarrassed, and turned her head away from me. I looked into her eyes. That was it— she was crying.

"You mustn't, you mustn't! Ah, you're behaving like a child. You're just a baby!"

She tried to smile to control herself, but her chin was trembling and her bosom heaving.

"I've been thinking of you," she said after a moment's silence. "You've been so kind that I'd have to be made of stone not to be touched. And, you know, I compared the two of you and decided that you are the better of the two, although I love him more."

I didn't answer. She seemed to expect me to say something.

"Of course, I may still not understand him or know him perfectly," she said. "Come to think of it, I've always been afraid of him. He's always been so grave, so proud in a way. Of course, I know that it's only the way he looks, that there's more tenderness in his heart than in my own. . . . I remember how he looked at me when—remember?—I came to his room with that bundle. Still, I look up to him with respect, which may mean we aren't equals, don't you think?"

"No, Nastenka, no, it simply means that you love him more than anything in the world, and much more than yourself."

"All right, let's assume you're right," naïve Nastenka replied. "But shall I tell you what has just occurred to me? All right. Only I won't talk about myself now but speak in general, for this thought has recurred to me several times. Tell me, why aren't we all like brothers? Why does even the best person hold back something from another? Why not say directly what we feel if we know that what we entrust won't be scattered to the winds?

As it is, everyone looks much tougher than he really is, as if he felt it'd be an insult to his feelings if he expressed them too readily—"

"Ah, that's it exactly, Nastenka," I interrupted her, doing more violence than ever to my own feelings, "and it's due to many causes—"

"No, no!" she said heatedly. "Take you, for instance—you're not like the rest. I don't quite know how to explain it . . . but I feel . . . yes, even now, you are sacrificing something for my sake." She shyly cast a sidelong glance at me. "Forgive me for speaking to you like this, but I'm a simple girl who hasn't seen much in this world yet, and there are times when I can't talk." Her voice trembled with some hidden emotion and, at the same time, she tried to smile. "All I wanted to tell you was that I'm grateful, that I too—I feel all that— Ah, may God reward you with happiness! But what you told me before about that dreamer of yours, that's untrue. I mean, it has absolutely nothing to do with you. You're recovering now; you're really a completely different person from the one you tried to pass yourself off as. If you ever fall in love, may you be happy with her! And I don't have to wish her anything, for I know she'll be happy with you. I know it, for I'm a woman myself, and you must believe me. . . ."

She fell silent and squeezed my hand. I couldn't utter a word. Several minutes went by.

"Well, it doesn't look as though he's coming tonight," she said at last, lifting her head. "It's getting quite late."

"He'll be here tomorrow," I said in a firm, convincing voice.

"Yes," she said, growing suddenly cheerful, "I can see now that he'll come tomorrow. So good night, see you tomorrow. If it rains, I may not come. But the night after that I'll be here, without fail, whatever happens. You must be here too; I want to see you and tell you everything."

When we were saying good-by, she gave me her hand, looked at me brightly, and said:

"We'll always be together now, won't we?"

Oh, Nastenka, Nastenka! if you had any idea how lonely I feel!

When it struck nine I couldn't stand it in my room. I dressed and went out. I walked over to our spot and sat on our bench. Then I walked along her street, but I felt ashamed and, before I'd quite reached her house, turned back without even glancing at the windows. I returned home in a state of dejection such as I'd never known before. What gloomy, damp, depressing weather! If only it had been fine I'd have walked around her neighborhood all night.

But she'll tell me everything tomorrow.

Of course, there wasn't any letter today, but then, that's quite natural. They're together already.

THE FOURTH NIGHT

My God, what a way for it all to finish! Ah, what an ending!

I got there by nine. She was already there, waiting. I caught sight of her when I was still at a distance. She was standing as she was the first time, leaning on the guardrail of the embankment, and didn't hear me approach.

"Nastenka!" I called out to her, managing to overcome my anguish.

"Come here," she said. "Hurry!"

I looked at her without understanding.

"Well, let me have the letter! You have it, haven't you?" She clenched the railing with her hand.

"No, I have no letter," I said finally, "but haven't you seen him yet?" She went terribly pale and stared at me. I had shattered her last hope.

"Well, good luck to him," she said in a gasping tone. "Good luck to him, if that's the way he feels about me."

She lowered her eyes, then tried to look up at me, but couldn't. For several moments more, she tried to get hold of herself, but she couldn't. She turned her head away, leaned on the rail, and dissolved into tears.

"Stop, stop . . ." was all I said. Looking at her, I hadn't the strength to say more—and anyway, what else was there to say?

"Don't try to make me feel better," she said, crying. "Don't mention him, don't tell me he'll come, don't persuade me he hasn't thrown me over so cruelly, so callously as he has. What did I do wrong? Could it be something I wrote in that ill-fated letter?"

At this point, sobs overwhelmed her. I couldn't bear to see her this way.

"Ah, how cruel and callous!" she said again. "And he never even bothered to write me a single line! If only he had answered that he didn't need me, that he rejected me. But no, he hasn't written a word during these three days! How easy it is for him to hurt and humiliate a poor girl whose only sin is to love him! Ah, how much I've been through in these three days! Ah, my God! My God! When I think that it was I who came to him in the first place, that I humbled myself before him, cried, begged him for a crumb of his love. . . . And after all that! . . . Listen," she said, turning her flashing dark eyes to me, "it can't be—it's not natural—one of us, you or I, has made a mistake! Maybe he never got my letter! Maybe he doesn't know a thing to this minute! How is it possible—please explain to me, for God's sake—for him to be so unspeakably rude to me? Not a single word! People show more pity than that for the lowest of creatures! Maybe he's heard something; maybe someone has told him some slander about me? What do you think?"

She shouted the last question at me.

"I'll go, Nastenka, and see him on your behalf tomorrow."

"Yes?"

"I'll tell him everything and ask him to explain."

"Yes? Yes?"

"Write him a letter. Don't say no. Wait! I'll force him to respect what you did. He'll be told everything, and if—"

"No, my dear, no, that's enough! No more about it; not one line, not one word, enough's enough! I don't know him. I don't love him any more. I'll forget him . . ."

She couldn't complete her sentence.

"Calm yourself, calm yourself, Nastenka! Here, sit down," I said, indicating the bench.

"But I *am* calm! Stop fussing! It's true. My tears will dry. You don't really think that I'd go and drown myself or something, do you?"

My heart was overflowing. I tried to speak but words wouldn't come.

"Tell me!" she said, catching hold of my hand, "you wouldn't have acted that way, would you? You wouldn't have hurled a shameful sneer at a girl who'd come to you herself; you wouldn't have made fun of her weak, tender heart. You'd have spared her. You'd have realized that she was lonely, unable to take care of herself, unable to prevent herself from falling in love with you, that she hadn't done anything wrong . . . that she hadn't done anything . . . Ah, my God, my God!"

"Nastenka!" I cried, completely overcome, "you're torturing me, Nastenka! You're tearing at my heart, you're killing me! I can't remain silent! I must tell you, at last, all that has accumulated inside me."

I got up from the bench as I said that. She took my hand, looking at me surprised.

"What's come over you?" she said.

"Nastenka, everything I'm going to tell you now is absurd, impossible, idiotic! I know that it can never happen, but I can't remain silent. So, in the name of your present suffering, I beg you to forgive me in advance!"

"Well, what is it?" She stopped crying and looked at me closely. There was a strange curiosity in her eyes.

"I know it cannot be, but I love you, Nastenka. That's what it is. Now you know everything." I shrugged hopelessly. "Now see if you can still talk to me the way you did before, if you can listen to what I'm going to say—"

"But what of it?" Nastenka interrupted me. "I've known all along that you loved me, but I thought that you just loved me simply—you know . . . Oh, good gracious!"

"It was simply at first, Nastenka, but now—now—I'm exactly in the position you were in, Nastenka, when you came to him with that bundle of yours. In fact, my plight is even more hopeless than yours was then, for he wasn't in love with anyone, but you are."

"What are you saying? You puzzle me altogether. But listen, why do you . . . I mean, how is that . . . Ah, God, I don't know what I'm saying. But you . . ."

She became completely confused. Her cheeks were on fire; she lowered her eyes.

"Well, what am I to do, Nastenka, what? I'm to blame for having abused . . . but no, no, it's not my fault, really—I know it, I feel it—for my heart tells me I'm right. There's no way I can harm you or offend you! I was your friend before, and I'm your friend now. I haven't betrayed a thing. And now, Nastenka, the tears are running down my cheeks; let 'em run, they aren't hurting anyone. They'll dry, Nastenka. . . ."

"Oh come, sit down, sit down," she said, pulling me down on the bench. "Ah, dear God!"

"No, Nastenka, I won't sit down; I can't stay here. You shouldn't see me any more. I'll tell you all I have in my heart, then leave. I want only to tell you that you'd never have found out I love you. I'd have kept my secret. I wouldn't have inflicted my selfishness upon you at such a moment. No! But I couldn't keep it to myself. It was you who brought it up; it's your fault, it's all your fault. You can't send me away."

"But no, of course not. I don't intend to send you away," Nastenka rattled off quickly, trying, the poor dear, to conceal her embarrassment.

"So you won't send me away? But I was going to run away from you anyway. I'll leave too, but first I must tell you everything because I could hardly bear it when you were talking and crying and so full of despair, because . . . well, because—let me say it, Nastenka—because you have been rejected, because your love has been spurned. I—I felt so much love for you, Nastenka, so much love . . . and I felt terribly bitter because I couldn't do anything for you, despite all that love . . . I felt I was being torn to pieces. I couldn't keep silent, I had to talk. I had to, Nastenka."

"Yes, yes, tell me, talk to me!" Nastenka said with an inexpressible gesture. "It must seem strange to you that I should say that, but go on, speak! I'll explain later; I'll explain everything!"

"You're sorry for me, Nastenka, you're simply sorry for me. Well, the way I look at it—what is lost is lost, what has been done cannot be undone. Isn't that so? Now you know everything, and that's the point of departure. All right then, that's fine, but listen to this: while you were sitting here crying, I thought—oh, please let me tell you what I thought—I thought—of course I'm well aware it cannot be, Nastenka—I thought that somehow or other, without it having anything to do with me . . . you didn't love him any more. . . . In that case, Nastenka—I thought of that yesterday and the day before—I would've behaved in such a way that you'd have come to love me. . . . For you said yourself that you'd almost fallen in love with me, Nastenka, you said so yourself! And what then? Nothing much. That's just about all I had to say! All I have left to describe is what it would have been like had you fallen in love with me. But there's not much I can say about that. So listen, my friend Nastenka, for you're still my friend—I am, of course, a simple man, poor and unimportant, but that's not what matters (I keep straying from the subject out of shyness, Nastenka); only—I'd have loved you so much that even if you'd still gone on loving that man, you'd still never have felt my love as an imposition upon you. You'd only have heard a grateful, warm heart beating by your side and felt its proximity every second. . . . Ah, Nastenka, Nastenka, what have you done to me?"

"Stop, I don't want you to cry!" She got up quickly from the bench. "Come, get up, come with me, and stop crying! Stop it!" She dried my eyes with her handkerchief. "Come, perhaps I'll tell you something. After all, he's abandoned me, forgotten me, even though I still love him, for I don't want to lie to you. . . . But tell me truly: if, for instance, I did come to love you—that is, if I only—oh, my dear, dear friend, when I think how I hurt you, when I laughed at your love, pretending to congratulate you for not falling in love with me— Ah, God, how could I have failed to foresee . . . How stupid I was! But now I've made up my mind—I'll tell you everything."

"You know what, Nastenka, I'll go away! I simply torment you when I'm near you. Now, because of me, you're feeling guilty about making fun of me. But I don't want to add to your sorrow. I am the guilty one, Nastenka, but forgive me and farewell!"

"Wait, listen to me! Can't you wait?"

"Wait? Wait for what?"

"I do love him but I'll get over it. I'm bound to. In fact, I'm already getting over it. I feel it. . . . One can never tell, I might even overcome it today. Because I hate him—he was making fun of me while you and I were crying here together. Because you haven't pushed me away as he has; because you love me, and he never loved me; because, finally I my-self—I love you. . . . Yes—I love you—I love you the way you love me. Remember, I told you that before; you heard me! Because you're a better man than he is; you're more honorable; because he . . ."

Nastenka was so moved that she couldn't finish. She let her head rest on my shoulder; from there it slipped onto my chest as she shed bitter tears. I tried to cheer her up, but she couldn't stop crying. She just kept pressing my hand and repeating between sobs:

"Wait, wait, I'll get over it in a moment. . . . Don't think these tears mean that . . . I just feel weak. . . ."

Finally she stopped crying and wiped away her tears. We resumed our walk. I would have spoken, but she wanted me to wait a bit longer. So we walked in silence. At last she mustered up her courage and spoke.

"You know," she began in a weak, quivering voice that nevertheless had something in it that immediately clutched at my heart, making it throb with a sweet pain, "you mustn't think I'm so fickle and irresponsible, that I'm so quick to forget and to betray. I've loved him for a whole year, and I swear to God that I've never, not once, been unfaithful to him. Not even in thought. But he's scorned that; he's made light of my feelings. Well, good luck to him! But he has also wounded me and slighted my love. No, I don't love him, for I can only love one who is generous, understanding, and kind, because I myself am like that—so he's unworthy of me. All right, I wish him all the best! It's better like this than finding out later that I had deluded myself, than discovering too late what sort of man he is. . . . Anyway, it's over! But come to think of it, my dear, maybe all my love for him was nothing but a delusion; maybe it began as a childish adventure; maybe it was caused by the wish to escape from under my grandmother's thumb; maybe I was destined to love a man other than him, a man who could feel for me, understand me, and . . . But let's leave that!" Nastenka was short of breath in her excitement. "All I want to say is that if, although I love—no, rather *loved*—him—although, you might say . . . If you think your love is great enough to displace my for-mer love . . . If you will take pity on me and not leave me to face my destiny all alone without offering me consolation, support, and hope—if you're willing to love me always as you love me now, then I swear to you that my gratitude—I mean my love—will, in the end, be worthy of your love. . . . Here, will you take my hand now?"

"Nastenka!" I cried, choked with sobs, "Nastenka! Oh, Nastenka!"

"Enough, enough for now, that's definitely enough," she said, getting hold of herself. "Everything has been said now, hasn't it? Right? And you're happy and so am I. Not another word about it. Wait. Spare me. For heaven's sake talk of something else!"

"Right, Nastenka, enough! I'm happy now, I . . . So, Nastenka, let's talk of something else. Quickly. Yes, I'm ready. . . ."

We didn't know what to say. We laughed. We cried. We exchanged thousands of disconnected, meaningless words. We walked along a street, then suddenly turned and retraced our steps. Without any apparent reason, we crossed the street to the opposite sidewalk; we went to the embankment. . . . We were like a couple of children.

"I live all by myself now, Nastenka. But tomorrow . . . Of course, you know, I'm poor. I've only twelve hundred rubles, but it doesn't matter, for—"

"Of course not. And then my grandmother has a pension. So she won't be a liability. She must, of course, come and live with us."

"Certainly, of course she must live with us. The only snag is that Matryona—"

"Ah! And we have our Fyokla!"

"Matryona's kind. The only thing wrong with her is that she has absolutely no imagination. But it doesn't matter!"

"Never mind, they can live together. Anyway you're coming over to live with us tomorrow."

"What did you say? Come to your place? That's fine by me!"

"Yes, you must rent our top-floor room. It's empty now. There was an old woman living there, but she's left, and I know Grandma wants to let it to a young man. I asked her, 'Why a young man?' and she said: 'I'm getting old, see, but don't you get it into your head, Nastenka, that I'm trying to marry you off.' So I guessed that that was the reason."

"Ah, Nastenka!"

We both laughed.

"All right, that's enough now," she said. "And, by the way, where do you live? I've forgotten."

"Over there, by that bridge, in the Barashnikov House."

"The large house?"

"Yes, it's quite large."

"I know it. It's a nice house, but forget it anyway and come and live with us. Quickly."

"I'll come tomorrow, Nastenka, no later than tomorrow. I'm somewhat late with my rent, but that'll be all right. I'll be getting my pay soon."

"You know what? Perhaps I'll give private lessons. First I'll learn something myself, then I'll teach it."

"It's all turned out wonderfully . . . and soon I'm due for a bonus, Nastenka."

"Then, starting tomorrow, you'll be my lodger."

"Yes, and we'll go to see *The Barber of Seville*, for they'll be putting it on again soon."

"Yes, yes, let's," Nastenka said, laughing, "and if not *The Barber*, we'll go and see something else."

"All right, something else then. That would be better, of course. I should have thought of it myself. . . ."

Talking that way, we walked as if in a drunken haze, like walking through clouds, with no idea of what was going on around us. We stopped, chatted without moving from the spot, then set off walking again. God knows where, as we laughed, cried, and laughed again. . . . Nastenka decided to return home, and I didn't dare detain her; I accompanied her to her very door, but a quarter of an hour later, we found ourselves back at our favorite bench. She sighed and a tear glistened in her eye again; I became frightened, turned cold . . . But she immediately pressed my hand and pulled me along behind her, and we again walked and chatted and talked. . . .

"It's time for me to go back home now," Nastenka declared finally. "Enough of this childish stuff!"

"All right, Nastenka, but I—I won't be able to go to sleep tonight, so I don't think I'll go home."

"I don't expect to sleep either. Nevertheless, I want you to see me to my door."

"Most certainly."

"But this time it must be for good."

"Yes, yes, of course."

"Do I have your promise? For I must get home in the end."

"I promise," I said, laughing.

"Then let's go."

"Let's go, Nastenka," I said. "And look at the sky: it will be a wonderful day tomorrow. What a blue sky! What a moon! Look at that yellow cloud about to veil the moon. Look at it! look at it—no, it has just missed the moon. Look at it—look!"

But Nastenka wasn't looking at the cloud. She stood still as a tree. Then, after a while, she pressed herself against me in a strange way. Her hand was trembling in mine. I looked at her. She pressed herself even closer to me.

At that moment, a young man was passing nearby. Suddenly he stopped and gave us a close, scrutinizing look. Then he walked a few more steps. My heart throbbed.

"Nastenka," I said very softly, "who is it, Nastenka?"

"It's him!" she whispered, pressing herself even more closely to me. I could hardly keep my feet.

"Nastenka, Nastenka, is that you?" I heard a voice behind us, and the young man came toward us.

My God, that cry! The shiver that passed through her! She tore herself from my arm and rushed toward him. I stood staring at them. I was dead. But she hardly had time to seize his hand and fling herself into his arms before she turned her head and looked at me. Then, with the speed of lightning, she was by me, her arms were around my neck, and before I knew what had happened, I felt her passionate kiss. Still without uttering a word, she again rushed toward him, caught his hand, and hurried away with him.

For a long time I kept following them with my eyes . . . Finally they vanished from sight.

THE MORNING

My nights were over. It was the morning after. The weather was bad. It was raining. The rain beat a gloomy tattoo on my window. It was dark inside my room and bleak outside the windows. My head ached. Objects swam before my eyes. Fever was sneaking along my limbs.

"There's a letter for you." Matryona's voice hovered somewhere over me. "It has just come."

I jumped up.

"What letter? From whom?"

"How do I know who it's from? Look; maybe it says inside who wrote it."

I opened it. It was from her. It said:

Please, please forgive me! I beg you on my knees. Forgive me! I deceived both you and myself. It was a dream, a mirage. I feel terrible about you now. Forgive me, forgive me!

Don't be too hard on me, for what I feel for you hasn't changed. I told you I loved you—well, I do love you, and it's even more than love. Oh, God, if only it were possible to love both of you at the same time! Ah, if only you could be him!

"Oh, if only he could be you." The thought flashed through my head. I remembered your very words, Nastenka. The letter continued:

God only knows what I wouldn't do for you! I know that you feel sad and depressed. I have hurt you. But, as you know, we won't resent for long a wound inflicted by those we love, and you do love me!

Thank you! Yes, thank you for that love! It lingers now in my memory like a sweet dream that remains long after awakening. I will always remember the moment when you opened your heart to me so fraternally and when you so nobly accepted the gift of my heart—wounded as it was—to love and cherish it, and heal its wounds. . . . If you forgive me, my memory of you will be ennobled by gratitude that will never fade. I shall cherish that memory, be faithful to it always, never betray it, never betray my heart—it is too constant for that. Only yesterday it went back to the one to whom it belongs forever.

We'll meet again. You'll come to see us. You won't abandon us. You'll always be my friend and my brother. And when we meet, you'll give me your hand, won't you? You'll give it to me because you love me as much as ever.

Please love me, and don't abandon me, because I love you so much at this moment, because I'm worthy of your love, because I'll earn it. . . . oh, my dear, dear friend!

I'm marrying him next week. He came back to me full of love. He hadn't forgotten me. . . . You won't be angry with me for writing this about him, will you? I want to come and see you with him. You'll like him, won't you?

So forgive, remember, and go on loving

your Nastenka

I read and reread that letter. I was on the verge of tears. At last it fell from my hands, and I covered my face.

"Here, look at that!" Matryona said.

"What is it, old woman?"

"Why, I've swept all them cobwebs from the ceiling so now you can marry any time and, while you're at it, invite a houseful of guests."

I looked at Matryona. She was still vigorous. She was a very young *old woman*, but I suddenly visualized her all wrinkled and shrunk, an invalid. And I don't know why, but my whole room suddenly aged the way an old woman ages. The walls and the ceilings peeled, everything faded, cobwebs multiplied. . . . And when I looked out of the window, I don't know why, but the house opposite turned dimmer too, the plaster on its columns fell off, the cornices became all grimy and full of cracks, and the walls, which used to be dark yellow, turned grayish.

A ray of sun that for a second had broken through a rain cloud disappeared behind it again, and everything darkened once more. Or was it just my sad and barren future that flashed before me? Did I see myself exactly the way I am now, fifteen years later, having aged in this very room, just as lonely, still living with Matryona, who hasn't grown any more intelligent in all these years.

I remember the hurt inflicted upon me, Nastenka! But I never sent a dark cloud to sail over your clear, serene sky. I never reproached you, never made you sad or gave you a secret guilty feeling. I never trampled any of the tender flowers that you entwined in your black curls when you walked to the altar with him. Oh, never, never! So may the sky lie cloudless over you, and your smile be bright and carefree; be blessed for the moment of bliss and happiness you gave to another heart, a lonely and a grateful one.

My God, a moment of bliss. Why, isn't that enough for a whole lifetime?

Translated by Andrew R. MacAndrew.

John Galsworthy

1867–1933

John Galsworthy was born at Coombe, Surrey, on August 14, 1867. He attended Harrow and New College, Oxford. He was enrolled as a barrister but turned to literature. In 1892–93, he was a passenger aboard the ship *Torrens*, whose ports included London and Adelaide in Australia. Joseph Conrad was her chief mate. They became close friends. Years later, Conrad's second son was born in Galsworthy's house in London.

His first two novels were not much noticed, but *The Man of Property*, published in 1906, established his reputation. It was the first novel in a series to be called *The Forsyte Saga*, his major work. This embraced *The Indian Summer of a Forsyte* in 1918, *In Chancery*, *Awakening*, and the final *To Let* in 1921. *The Forsyte Saga* made Galsworthy the chief historian of manners for the British upper middle class during Victoria's last years and the reign of Edward VII.

Almost from the beginning, he had another string to his bow. He wrote for the stage. His plays became a staple of the English theater in his lifetime. Beginning with *The Silver Box* in 1906, he touched on social problems in such dramas as *Strife* in 1909 and *Justice* in the following year. These were followed by *The Pigeon, The Eldest Son, The Fugitive, The Skin Game,* and in 1922 his best-known later work for the theater, *Loyalties*.

But he did not neglect the novel. In 1924 *The White Monkey*, a famous best seller of that year, became the first work in a new trilogy, *A Modern Comedy*. It was rounded out with *The Silver Spoon* in 1926 and *Swan Song* in 1928. His later works included *On Forsyte 'Change, Maid in Waiting,* and *Flowering Wilderness.* In 1925 his short stories were collected in *Caravan*. He was awarded the Order of Merit in 1929 and the Nobel Prize for literature in 1932. He died on January 31, 1933.

The Apple-Tree is a story of first love, an idyl of the English countryside at that moment in spring when all the orchard trees turn white under the moon. It is the story of a young man hesitating between two girls. Is there an older and simpler story? We can imagine it happening under the first Pharaoh.

Yet *The Apple-Tree* is more than a simple tale of love. It is also the story of a man in a moral dilemma. Frank Ashurst, the central character, and a member of the English upper class, must choose between Stella—a young girl whose background is very similar to his own and with whom he feels very much at ease, and Megan—a simple, passionate country girl with whom, for the moment, he is deeply in love. He has been stirred to the very depths of his soul— as the phrase goes—by his love for Megan, and he knows that she, too, feels an intense passion for him. The choice would appear to be an easy one: Megan. But Ashurst fears—rather, he knows—that his love for Megan cannot last. Eventually he must return to the city, and her charm would be lost there.

Thus he is faced with one of those terrible dilemmas that we have all encountered and will encounter again: he must choose between two evils. If he returns to Megan, he will be encouraging a love which can endure only for a moment; if he does not return to her, he will be abandoning her at the moment when her hopes are highest.

Is Ashurst's dilemma a genuine one? Is he really concerned about Megan, or is he a snob who has suddenly realized that he has come close to marrying a girl beneath his class? If he is a snob, is he consciously so, or is he an unwitting victim of the class system? Each reader of *The Apple-Tree* will probably answer these questions in a different way.

Was an enduring love between Ashurst and Megan really impossible? Freud thought so, but he did not find fault with either of the lovers. He placed the blame on civilization itself. In commenting on the story, he said, "It shows in a very moving and forcible way how there is no longer any place in present-day civilized life for a simple natural love between two human beings." [1]

---

[1] See *Civilization and Its Discontents* in *Great Books of the Western World*, Vol. 54, p. 784, footnote.

Was Freud right? If he was, why does civilization make such love impossible? Perhaps because it endangers civilization. Such love overturns all barriers, it breaks down all walls, it upsets all arrangements. Civilization cannot exist without barriers, walls, and arrangements. And civilization is a valuable thing—more valuable than love.

The Apple-Tree

The Apple-tree, the singing, and the gold.
Murray's *Hippolytus of Euripides.*

On their silver-wedding day Ashurst and his wife were motoring along the outskirts of the moor, intending to crown the festival by stopping the night at Torquay, where they had first met. This was the idea of Stella Ashurst, whose character contained a streak of sentiment. If she had long lost the blue-eyed, flowerlike charm, the cool slim purity of face and form, the apple-blossom colouring, which had so swiftly and so oddly affected Ashurst twenty-six years ago, she was still at forty-three a comely and faithful companion, whose cheeks were faintly mottled, and whose grey-blue eyes had acquired a certain fullness.

It was she who had stopped the car where the common rose steeply to the left, and a narrow strip of larch and beech, with here and there a pine, stretched out towards the valley between the road and the first long high hill of the full moor. She was looking for a place where they might lunch, for Ashurst never looked for anything; and this, between the golden furze and the feathery green larches smelling of lemons in the last sun of April—this, with a view into the deep valley and up to the long moor heights, seemed fitting to the decisive nature of one who sketched in water-colours, and loved romantic spots. Grasping her paint-box, she got out.

"Won't this do, Frank?"

Ashurst, rather like a bearded Schiller, grey in the wings, tall, long-legged, with large remote grey eyes, which sometimes filled with meaning and became almost beautiful, with nose a little to one side, and bearded lips just open—Ashurst, forty-eight, and silent, grasped the luncheon basket, and got out too.

"Oh! Look, Frank! A grave!"

By the side of the road, where the track from the top of the common

323

crossed it at right angles and ran through a gate past the narrow wood, was a thin mound of turf, six feet by one, with a moorstone to the west, and on it some one had thrown a black-thorn spray and a handful of blue bells. Ashurst looked, and the poet in him moved. At cross-roads—a suicide's grave! Poor mortals with their superstitions! Whoever lay there, though, had the best of it, no clammy sepulchre among other hideous graves carved with futilities—just a rough stone, the wide sky, and way-side blessings! And, without comment, for he had learned not to be a philosopher in the bosom of his family, he strode away up on to the common, dropped the luncheon basket under a wall, spread a rug for his wife to sit on—she would turn up from her sketching when she was hungry—and took from his pocket Murray's translation of the "Hippolytus." He had soon finished reading of "The Cyprian" and her revenge, and looked at the sky instead. And watching the white clouds so bright against the intense blue, Ashurst, on his silver-wedding day, longed for—he knew not what. Maladjusted to life—man's organism! One's mode of life might be high and scrupulous, but there was always an undercurrent of greediness, a hankering, and sense of waste. Did women have it too? Who could tell? And yet, men who gave vent to their appetites for novelty, their riotous longings for new adventures, new risks, new pleasures, these suffered, no doubt, from the reverse side of starvation, from surfeit. No getting out of it—a maladjusted animal, civilized man! There could be no garden of his choosing, of "the Apple-tree, the singing, and the gold," in the words of that lovely Greek chorus, no achievable elysium in life, or lasting haven of happiness for any man with a sense of beauty—nothing which could compare with the captured loveliness in a work of art, set down forever, so that to look on it or read was always to have the same precious sense of exaltation and restful inebriety. Life no doubt had moments with that quality of beauty, of unbidden flying rapture, but the trouble was, they lasted no longer than the span of a cloud's flight over the sun; impossible to keep them with you, as Art caught beauty and held it fast. They were fleeting as one of the glimmering or golden visions one had of the soul in nature, glimpses of its remote and brooding spirit. Here, with the sun hot on his face, a cuckoo calling from a thorn-tree, and in the air the honey savour of gorse—here among the little fronds of the young fern, the starry black-thorn, while the bright clouds drifted by high above the hills and dreamy valleys—here and now was such a glimpse. But in a moment it would pass—as the face of Pan, which looks round the corner of a rock, vanishes at your stare. And suddenly he sat up. Surely there was something familiar about this view, this bit of common, that ribbon of road, the old wall behind him. While they were driving he had not been taking notice—never did; thinking of far things or of nothing—but now he saw! Twenty-six years ago, just at this time of year, from the farm-house within half a mile of this very spot he had started for that day in Torquay whence it might be said he had never returned. And a sudden ache beset his heart; he had stumbled on just one of those past moments in his life whose beauty and rapture he had failed to arrest, whose wings had fluttered away into the unknown; he had stumbled on a buried memory, a wild sweet time, swiftly choked and ended. And, turning on his face, he rested his chin on his hands, and stared at the short grass where the little blue milkwort was growing. . . .

And this is what he remembered.

On the first of May, after their last year together at college, Frank Ashurst and his friend Robert Garton were on a tramp. They had walked that day from Brent, intending to make Chagford, but Ashurst's football knee had given out, and according to their map they had still some seven miles to go. They were sitting on a bank beside the road, where a track crossed alongside a wood, resting the knee and talking of the universe, as young men will. Both were over six feet, and thin as rails; Ashurst pale, idealistic, full of absence; Garton queer, round-the-corner, knotted, curly, like some primeval beast. Both had a literary bent; neither wore a hat. Ashurst's hair was smooth, pale, wavy, and had a way of rising on either side of his brow, as if always being flung back; Garton's was a kind of dark unfathomed mop. They had not met a soul for miles.

"My dear fellow," Garton was saying, "pity's only an effect of self-consciousness; it's a disease of the last five thousand years. The world was happier without."

Ashurst, following the clouds with his eyes, answered: "It's the pearl in the oyster, anyway."

"My dear chap, all our modern unhappiness comes from pity. Look at animals, and Red Indians, limited to feeling their own occasional misfortunes; then look at ourselves—never free from feeling the toothaches of others. Let's get back to feeling for nobody, and have a better time."

"You'll never practise that."

Garton pensively stirred the hotchpotch of his hair.

"To attain full growth, one mustn't be squeamish. To starve oneself emotionally's a mistake. All emotion is to the good—enriches life."

"Yes, and when it runs up against chivalry?"

"Ah! That's so English! If you speak of emotion the English always think you want something physical, and are shocked. They're afraid of passion, but not of lust—oh, no!—so long as they can keep it secret."

Ashurst did not answer; he had plucked a blue floweret, and was twiddling it against the sky. A cuckoo began calling from a thorn-tree. The sky, the flowers, the songs of birds! Robert was talking through his hat! And he said:

"Well, let's go on, and find some farm where we can put up." In uttering those words, he was conscious of a girl coming down from the common just above them. She was outlined against the sky, carrying a basket, and you could see that sky through the crook of her arm. And Ashurst, who saw beauty without wondering how it could advantage him, thought: "How pretty!" The wind, blowing her dark frieze skirt against her legs, lifted her battered peacock Tam o' Shanter; her greyish blouse was worn and old, her shoes were split, her little hands rough and red, her neck browned. Her dark hair waved untidy across her broad forehead, her face was short, her upper lip short, showing a glint of teeth, her brows were straight and dark, her lashes long and dark, her nose straight; but her grey eyes were the wonder—dewy as if opened for the first time that day. She looked at Ashurst—perhaps he struck her as strange, limping along without a hat, with his large eyes on her, and his hair flung back. He could not take off what was not on his head, but put up his hand in a salute, and said: "Can you tell us if there's a farm near here where we could stay the night? I've gone lame."

"There's only our farm near, Sir." She spoke without shyness, in a pretty, soft, crisp voice.

"And where is that?"

"Down here, Sir."

"Would you put us up?"

"Oh! I think we would."

"Will you show us the way?"

"Yes, Sir."

He limped on, silent, and Garton took up the catechism.

"Are you a Devonshire girl?"

"No, Sir."

"What then?"

"From Wales."

"Ah! I *thought* you were a Celt; so it's not your farm?"

"My aunt's, Sir."

"And your uncle's?"

"He is dead."

"Who farms it, then?"

"My aunt, and my three cousins."

"But your uncle was a Devonshire man?"

"Yes, Sir."

"Have you lived here long?"

"Seven years."

"And how d'you like it after Wales?"

"I don't know, Sir."

"I suppose you don't remember?"

"Oh, yes! But it is different."

"I believe you!"

Ashurst broke in suddenly: "How old are you?"

"Seventeen, Sir."

"And what's your name?"

"Megan David."

"This is Robert Garton, and I am Frank Ashurst. We wanted to get on to Chagford."

"It is a pity your leg is hurting you."

Ashurst smiled, and when he smiled his face was rather beautiful.

Descending past the narrow wood, they came on the farm suddenly— a long, low, stone-built dwelling with casement windows, in a farm-yard where pigs and fowls and an old mare were straying. A short steep-up grass hill behind was crowned with a few Scotch firs, and in front, an old orchard of apple-trees, just breaking into flower, stretched down to a stream and a long wild meadow. A little boy with oblique dark eyes was shepherding a pig, and by the house door stood a woman, who came towards them. The girl said: "It is Mrs. Narracombe, my aunt."

"Mrs. Narracombe, my aunt," had a quick, dark eye like a mother wild duck's, and something of the same snaky turn about her neck.

"We met your niece on the road," said Ashurst; "she thought you might perhaps put us up for the night."

Mrs. Narracombe, taking them in from head to heel, answered: "Well, I can, if you don't mind one room. Megan, get the spare room ready, and a bowl of cream. You'll be wanting tea, I suppose."

Passing through a sort of porch made by two yew-trees and some flowering-currant bushes, the girl disappeared into the house, her peacock Tam o' Shanter bright athwart that rosy-pink and the dark green of the yews.

"Will you come into the parlour and rest your leg? You'll be from college, perhaps?"

"We were, but we've gone down now."

Mrs. Narracombe nodded sagely.

The parlour, brick-floored, with bare table and shiny chairs and sofa stuffed with horsehair, seemed never to have been used, it was so terribly clean. Ashurst sat down at once on the sofa, holding his lame knee between his hands, and Mrs. Narracombe gazed at him. He was the only son of a late professor of chemistry, but people found a certain lordliness in one who was often so sublimely unconscious of them.

"Is there a stream where we could bathe?"

"There's the strame at the bottom of the orchard, but sittin' down you'll not be covered!"

"How deep?"

"Well, 'tis about a foot and a half, maybe."

"Oh! That'll do fine. Which way?"

"Down the lane, through the second gate on the right, an' the pool's by the big apple-tree that stands by itself. There's trout there, if you can tickle them."

"They're more likely to tickle us!"

Mrs. Narracombe smiled. "There'll be the tea ready when you come back."

The pool, formed by the damming of a rock, had a sandy bottom; and the big apple-tree, lowest in the orchard, grew so close that its boughs almost overhung the water; it was in leaf, and all but in flower—its crimson buds just bursting. There was not room for more than one at a time in that narrow bath, and Ashurst waited his turn, rubbing his knee and gazing at the wild meadow, all rocks and thorn-trees and field-flowers, with a grove of beeches beyond, raised up on a flat mound. Every bough was swinging in the wind, every spring bird calling, and a slanting sunlight dappled the grass. He thought of Theocritus, and the river Cherwell, of the moon, and the maiden with the dewy eyes; of so many things that he seemed to think of nothing; and he felt absurdly happy.

During a late and sumptuous tea with eggs to it, cream and jam, and thin, fresh cakes touched with saffron, Garton descanted on the Celts. It was about the period of the Celtic awakening, and the discovery that there was Celtic blood about this family had excited one who believed that he was a Celt himself. Sprawling on a horsehair chair, with a hand-made cigarette dribbling from the corner of his curly lips, he had been plunging his cold pin-points of eyes into Ashurst's and praising the refinement of the Welsh. To come out of Wales into England was like the change from china to earthenware! Frank, as a d——d Englishman, had not of course perceived the exquisite refinement and emotional capacity of that Welsh girl! And, delicately stirring in the dark mat of his still wet hair, he explained how exactly she illustrated the writings of the Welsh bard Morgan-ap-Something in the twelfth century.

Ashurst, full length on the horsehair sofa, and jutting far beyond its end, smoked a deeply coloured pipe, and did not listen, thinking of the girl's face when she brought in a relay of cakes. It had been exactly like looking at a flower, or some other pretty sight in Nature—till, with a funny little shiver, she had lowered her glance and gone out, quiet as a mouse.

"Let's go to the kitchen," said Garton, "and see some more of her."

The kitchen was a whitewashed room with rafters, to which were attached smoked hams; there were flower-pots on the window-sill, and guns hanging on nails, queer mugs, china and pewter, and portraits of Queen Victoria. A long, narrow table of plain wood was set with bowls and spoons, under a string of high-hung onions; two sheep-dogs and three cats lay here and there. On one side of the recessed fire-place sat two small boys, idle, and good as gold; on the other sat a stout, light-eyed, red-faced youth with hair and lashes the colour of the tow he was running through the barrel of a gun; between them Mrs. Narracombe dreamily stirred some savoury-scented stew in a large pot. Two other youths, oblique-eyed, dark-haired, rather sly-faced, like the two little boys, were talking together and lolling against the wall; and a short, elderly, clean-shaven man in corduroys, seated in the window, was conning a battered journal. The girl Megan seemed the only active creature—drawing cider and passing with the jugs from cask to table. Seeing them thus about to eat, Garton said:

"Ah! If you'll let us, we'll come back when supper's over," and without waiting for an answer they withdrew again to the parlour. But the colour in the kitchen, the warmth, the scents, and all those faces heightened the bleakness of their shiny room, and they resumed their seats moodily.

"Regular gypsy type, those boys. There was only one Saxon—the fellow cleaning the gun. That girl is a very subtle study psychologically."

Ashurst's lips twitched. Garton seemed to him an ass just then. Subtle study! She was a wild flower. A creature it did you good to look at. Study!

Garton went on: "Emotionally she would be wonderful. She wants awakening."

"Are you going to awaken her?"

Garton looked at him and smiled. "How coarse and English you are!" that curly smile seemed saying.

And Ashurst puffed his pipe. Awaken her! This fool had the best opinion of himself! He threw up the window and leaned out. Dusk had gathered thick. The farm buildings and the wheel-house were all dim and bluish, the apple-trees but a blurred wilderness; the air smelled of wood smoke from the kitchen fire. One bird going to bed later than the others was uttering a half-hearted twitter, as though surprised at the darkness. From the stable came the snuffle and stamp of a feeding horse. And away over there was the loom of the moor, and away and away the shy stars which had not as yet full light, pricking white through the deep blue heavens. A quavering owl hooted. Ashurst drew a deep breath. What a night to wander out in! A padding of unshod hoofs came up the lane, and three dim, dark shapes passed—ponies on an evening march. Their heads, black and fuzzy, showed above the gate. At the tap of his pipe, and a shower of little sparks, they shied round and scampered. A bat went fluttering past, uttering its almost inaudible "chip, chip." Ashurst held out his hand; on the upturned palm he could feel the dew. Suddenly from overhead he heard little burring boys' voices, little thumps of boots thrown down, and another voice, crisp and soft—the girl's putting them to bed, no doubt; and nine clear words: "No, Rick, you can't have the cat in bed"; then came a skirmish of giggles and gurgles, a soft slap, a laugh so low and pretty that it made him shiver a little. A blowing sound, and the glim of the candle which was fingering the dusk above went out; silence reigned. Ashurst withdrew into the room and sat down; his knee pained him, and his soul felt gloomy.

"You go to the kitchen," he said; "I'm going to bed."

For Ashurst the wheel of slumber was wont to turn noiseless and slick and swift, but though he seemed sunk in sleep when his companion came up, he was really wide awake; and long after Garton, smothered in the other bed of that low-roofed room, was worshiping darkness with his upturned nose, he heard the owls. Barring the discomfort of his knee, it was not unpleasant—the cares of life did not loom large in night watches for this young man. In fact he had none; just enrolled a barrister, with literary aspirations, the world before him, no father or mother, and four hundred a year of his own. Did it matter where he went, what he did, or when he did it? His bed, too, was hard, and this preserved him from fever. He lay, sniffing the scent of the night which drifted into the low room through the open casement close to his head. Except for a definite irritation with his friend, natural when you have tramped with a man for three days, Ashurst's memories and visions that sleepless night were kindly and wistful and exciting. One vision, specially clear and unreasonable, for he had not even been conscious of noting it, was the face of the youth cleaning the gun; its intent, stolid, yet startled uplook at the kitchen doorway quickly shifted to the girl carrying the cider jug. This red, blue-eyed, light-lashed, tow-haired face stuck as firmly in his memory as the girl's own face, so dewy and simple. But at last, in the square of darkness through the uncurtained casement, he saw day coming, and heard one hoarse and sleepy caw. Then followed silence, dead as ever, till the song of a blackbird, not properly awake, adventured into the hush. And, from staring at the framed brightening light, Ashurst fell asleep.

Next day his knee was badly swollen; the walking tour was obviously over. Garton, due back in London on the morrow, departed at midday with an ironical smile which left a scar of irritation—healed the moment his loping figure vanished round the corner of the steep lane. All day Ashurst rested his knee, in a green-painted wooden chair on the patch of grass by the yew-tree porch, where the sunlight distilled the scent of stocks and gillyflowers, and a ghost of scent from the flowering-currant bushes. Beatifically he smoked, dreamed, watched.

A farm in spring is all birth—young things coming out of bud and shell, and human beings watching over the process with faint excitement feeding and tending what has been born. So still the young man sat that a mother goose, with stately cross-footed waddle, brought her six yellow-necked grey-backed goslings to strop their little beaks against the grass blades at his feet. Now and again Mrs. Narracombe or the girl Megan would come and ask if he wanted anything, and he would smile and say: "Nothing, thanks. It's splendid here." Towards tea-time they came out together, bearing a long poultice of some dark stuff in a bowl, and after a long and solemn scrutiny of his swollen knee, bound it on. When they were gone, he thought of the girl's soft "Oh!"—of her pitying eyes, and the little wrinkle in her brow. And again he felt that unreasoning irritation against his departed friend, who had talked such rot about her. When she brought out his tea, he said: "How did you like my friend, Megan?"

She forced down her upper lip, as if afraid that to smile was not polite. "He was a funny gentleman; he made us laugh. I think he is very clever."

"What did he say to make you laugh?"

"He said I was a daughter of the bards. What are they?"

"Welsh poets, who lived hundreds of years ago."

"Why am I their daughter, please?"

"He meant that you were the sort of girl they sang about."

She wrinkled her brows. "I think he likes to joke. Am I?"

"Would you believe me, if I told you?"

"Oh, yes."

"Well, I think he was right."

She smiled.

And Ashurst thought: "You *are* a pretty thing!"

"He said, too, that Joe was a Saxon type. What would that be?"

"Which is Joe? With the blue eyes and red face?"

"Yes. My uncle's nephew."

"Not your cousin, then?"

"No."

"Well, he meant that Joe was like the men who came over to England about fourteen hundred years ago, and conquered it."

"Oh! I know about them; but is he?"

"Garton's crazy about that sort of thing; but I must say Joe does look a bit Early Saxon."

"Yes."

That "yes" tickled Ashurst. It was so crisp and graceful, so conclusive, and politely acquiescent in what was evidently Greek to her.

"He said that all the other boys were regular gypsies. He should not have said that. My aunt laughed, but she didn't like it, of course, and my cousins were angry. Uncle was a farmer—farmers are not gypsies. It is wrong to hurt people."

Ashurst wanted to take her hand and give it a squeeze, but he only answered: "Quite right, Megan. By the way, I heard you putting the little ones to bed last night."

She flushed a little. "Please to drink your tea—it is getting cold. Shall I get you some fresh?"

"Do you ever have time to do anything for yourself?"

"Oh, yes."

"I've been watching, but I haven't seen it yet."

She wrinkled her brows in a puzzled frown, and her colour deepened.

When she was gone, Ashurst thought: "Did she think I was chaffing her? I wouldn't for the world!" He was at that age when to some men "Beauty's a flower," as the poet says, and inspires in them the thoughts of chivalry. Never very conscious of his surroundings, it was some time before he was aware that the youth whom Garton had called "a Saxon type" was standing outside the stable door; and a fine bit of colour he made in his soiled brown velvet cords, muddy gaiters, and blue shirt; red-armed, red-faced, the sun turning his hair from tow to flax; immovably stolid, persistent, unsmiling he stood. Then, seeing Ashurst looking at him, he crossed the yard at that gait of the young countryman always ashamed not to be slow and heavy-dwelling on each leg, and disappeared round the end of the house towards the kitchen entrance. A chill came over Ashurst's mood. Clods! With all the good will in the world, how impossible to get on terms with them! And yet—see that girl! Her shoes were split, her hands rough; but—what was it? Was it really her Celtic blood, as Garton had said?—she was a lady born, a jewel, though probably she could do no more than just read and write!

The elderly, clean-shaven man he had seen last night in the kitchen had come into the yard with a dog, driving the cows to their milking. Ashurst saw that he was lame.

"You've got some good ones there!"

The lame man's face brightened. He had the upward look in his eyes which prolonged suffering often brings.

"Yeas; they'm praaper buties; gude milkers tu."

"I bet they are."

"'Ope as yure leg's better, zurr."

"Thank you, it's getting on."

The lame man touched his own: "I know what 'tes, meself; 'tes a main worritin' thing, the knee. I've a 'ad mine bad this ten year."

Ashurst made the sound of sympathy which comes so readily from those who have an independent income, and the lame man smiled again.

"Mustn't complain, though—they mighty near 'ad it off."

"Ho!"

"Yeas; an' compared with what 'twas, 'tis almost so gude as nu."

"They've put a bandage of splendid stuff on mine."

"The maid she picks et. She'm a gude maid wi' the flowers. There's folks zeem to know the healin' in things. My mother was a rare one for that. 'Ope as yu'll zune be better, zurr. Goo ahn, therr!"

Ashurst smiled. "Wi' the flowers!" A flower herself.

That evening, after his supper of cold duck, junket, and cider, the girl came in.

"Please, Auntie says—will you try a piece of our May-day cake?"

"If I may come to the kitchen for it."

"Oh, yes! You'll be missing your friend."

"Not I. But are you sure no one minds?"

"Who would mind? We shall be very pleased."

Ashurst rose too suddenly for his stiff knee, staggered and subsided. The girl gave a little gasp, and held out her hands. Ashurst took them, small, rough, brown; checked his impulse to put them to his lips, and let her pull him up. She came close beside him, offering her shoulder. And leaning on her he walked across the room. That shoulder seemed quite the pleasantest thing he had ever touched. But he had presence of mind enough to catch his stick out of the rack, and withdraw his hand before arriving at the kitchen.

That night he slept like a top, and woke with his knee of almost normal size. He again spent the morning in his chair on the grass patch, scribbling down verses; but in the afternoon he wandered about with the two little boys Nick and Rick. It was Saturday, so they were early home from school; quick, shy, dark little rascals of seven and six, soon talkative, for Ashurst had a way with children. By four o'clock they had shown him all their methods of destroying life, except the tickling of trout; and with breeches tucked up, lay on their stomachs over the trout stream, pretending they had this accomplishment also. They tickled nothing, of course, for their giggling and shouting scared every spotted thing away. Ashurst, on a rock at the edge of the beech clump, watched them, and listened to the cuckoos, till Nick, the elder and less persevering, came up and stood beside him.

"The gypsy bogle zets on that stone," he said.

"What gypsy bogle?"

"Dunno; never zeen 'e. Megan zays 'e zets there; an' old Jim zeed 'e once. 'E was zettin' there naight afore our pony kicked-in father's 'ead. 'E plays the viddle."

"What tune does he play?"

"Dunno."

"What's he like?"

"'E's black. Old Jim zays 'e's all over 'air. 'E's a praaper bogle. 'E don' come only at naight." The little boy's oblique dark eyes slid round. "D'yu think 'e might want to take me away? Megan's feared of 'e."

"Has she seen him?"

"No. She's not afeared o' yu."

"I should think not. Why should she be?"

"She zays a prayer for yu."

"How do you know that, you little rascal?"

"When I was asleep, she said: 'God bless us all, an Mr. Ashes. I eard 'er whisperin'."

"You're a little ruffian to tell what you hear when you're not meant to hear it!"

The little boy was silent. Then he said aggressively: "I can skin rabbits. Megan, she can't bear skinnin' 'em. I like blood."

"Oh! you do; you little monster!"

"What's that?"

"A creature that likes hurting others."

The little boy scowled. "They'm only dead rabbits, what us eats."

"Quite right, Nick. I beg your pardon."

"I can skin frogs, tu."

But Ashurst had become absent. "God bless us all, and Mr. Ashes!" And puzzled by that sudden inaccessibility, Nick ran back to the stream where the giggling and shouts again uprose at once.

When Megan brought his tea, he said: "What's the gypsy bogle, Megan?"

She looked up, startled.

"He brings bad things."

"Surely you don't believe in ghosts?"

"I hope I will never see him."

"Of course you won't. There aren't such things. What old Jim saw was a pony."

"No! There are bogles in the rocks; they are the men who lived long ago."

"They aren't gypsies, anyway; those old men were dead long before gypsies came."

She said simply: "They are all bad."

"Why? If there are any, they're only wild, like the rabbits. The flowers aren't bad for being wild; the thorn-trees were never planted—and you don't mind them. I shall go down at night and look for your bogle, and have a talk with him."

"Oh, no! Oh, no!"

"Oh, yes! I shall go and sit on his rock."

She clasped her hands together: "Oh, please!"

"Why! What does it matter if anything happens to me?"

She did not answer; and in a sort of pet he added: "Well, I daresay I shan't see him, because I suppose I must be off soon."

"Soon?"

"Your aunt won't want to keep me here."

"Oh, yes! We always let lodgings in summer."

Fixing his eyes on her face, he asked: "Would you like me to stay?"

"Yes."

"I'm going to say a prayer for *you* to-night!"

She flushed crimson, frowned, and went out of the room. He sat cursing himself, till his tea was stewed. It was as if he had hacked with his thick boots at a clump of blue-bells. Why had he said such a silly thing? Was he just a towny college ass like Robert Garton, as far from understanding this girl?

Ashurst spent the next week confirming the restoration of his leg, by exploration of the country within easy reach. Spring was a revelation to him this year. In a kind of intoxication he would watch the pink-white buds of some backward beech-tree sprayed up in the sunlight against the deep blue sky, or the trunks and limbs of the few Scotch firs, tawny in violent light, or again on the moor, the gale-bent larches which had such a look of life when the wind streamed in their young green, above the rusty black under-boughs. Or he would lie on the banks, gazing at the clusters of dog-violets, or up in the dead bracken, fingering the pink, transparent buds of the dew-berry, while the cuckoos called and yaffles laughed, or a lark, from very high, dripped its beads of song. It was certainly different from any spring he had ever known, for spring was within him, not without. In the daytime he hardly saw the family; and when Megan brought in his meals she always seemed too busy in the house or among the young things in the yard to stay talking long. But in the evenings he installed himself in the window seat in the kitchen, smoking and chatting with the lame man Jim, or Mrs. Narracombe, while the girl sewed, or moved about, clearing the supper things away. And sometimes with the sensation a cat must feel when it purrs, he would become conscious that Megan's eyes—those dew-grey eyes—were fixed on him with a sort of lingering soft look which was strangely flattering.

It was on Sunday week in the evening, when he was lying in the orchard listening to a blackbird and composing a love poem, that he heard the gate swing to, and saw the girl come running among the trees, with the red-cheeked, stolid Joe in swift pursuit. About twenty yards away the chase ended, and the two stood fronting each other, not noticing the stranger in the grass—the boy pressing on, the girl fending him off. Ashurst could see her face, angry, disturbed; and the youth's—who would have thought that red-faced yokel could look so distraught! And painfully affected by that sight, he jumped up. They saw him then. Megan dropped her hands, and shrank behind a tree-trunk; the boy gave an angry grunt, rushed at the bank, scrambled over and vanished. Ashurst went slowly up to her. She was standing quite still, biting her lip—very pretty, with her fine, dark hair blown loose about her face, and her eyes cast down.

"I beg your pardon," he said.

She gave him one upward look, from eyes much dilated; then, catching her breath, turned away. Ashurst followed.

"Megan!"

But she went on; and taking hold of her arm, he turned her gently round to him.

"Stop and speak to me."

"Why do you beg my pardon? It is not to me you should do that."

"Well, then, to Joe."

"How dare he come after me?"

"In love with you, I suppose."

She stamped her foot.

Ashurst uttered a short laugh. "Would you like me to punch his head?"

She cried with sudden passion: "You laugh at me—you laugh at us!"

He caught hold of her hands, but she shrank back, till her passionate little face and loose dark hair were caught among the pink clusters of the apple-blossom. Ashurst raised one of her imprisoned hands and put his lips to it. He felt how chivalrous he was, and superior to that clod Joe—just brushing that small, rough hand with his mouth! Her shrinking ceased suddenly; she seemed to tremble towards him. A sweet warmth overtook Ashurst from top to toe. This slim maiden, so simple and fine and pretty, was pleased, then, at the touch of his lips. And, yielding to a swift impulse, he put his arms round her, pressed her to him, and kissed her forehead. Then he was frightened—she went so pale, closing her eyes, so that the long, dark lashes lay on her pale cheeks; her hands, too, lay inert at her sides. The touch of her breast sent a shiver through him. "Megan!" he sighed out, and let her go. In the utter silence a blackbird shouted. Then the girl seized his hand, put it to her cheek, her heart, her lips, kissed it passionately, and fled away among the mossy trunks of the apple-trees, till they hid her from him.

Ashurst sat down on a twisted old tree growing almost along the ground, and, all throbbing and bewildered, gazed vacantly at the blossom which had crowned her hair—those pink buds with one white open apple star. What had he done? How had he let himself be thus stampeded by beauty—or—just the spring! He felt curiously happy, all the same; happy and triumphant, with shivers running through his limbs, and a vague alarm. This was the beginning of—what? The midges bit him, the dancing gnats tried to fly into his mouth, and all the spring around him seemed to grow more lovely and alive; the songs of the cuckoos and the blackbirds, the laughter of the yaffles, the level-slanting sunlight, the apple-blossom which had crowned her head—! He got up from the old trunk and strode out of the orchard, wanting space, an open sky, to get on terms with these new sensations. He made for the moor, and from an ash-tree in the hedge a magpie flew out to herald him.

Of man—at any age from five years on—who can say he has never been in love? Ashurst had loved his partners at his dancing class; loved his nursery governess; girls in school-holidays; perhaps never been quite out of love, cherishing always some more or less remote admiration. But this was different, not remote at all. Quite a new sensation; terribly delightful, bringing a sense of completed manhood. To be holding in his fingers such a wild flower, to be able to put it to his lips, and feel it tremble with delight against them! What intoxication, and—embarrassment! What to do with it—how meet her next time? His first caress had been cool, pitiful; but the next could not be, now that, by her burning little kiss on his hand, by her pressure of it to her heart, he knew that she loved him. Some natures are coarsened by love bestowed on them; others, like Ashurst's, are swayed and drawn, warmed and softened, almost exalted, by what they feel to be a sort of miracle.

And up there among the tors he was racked between the passionate desire to revel in this new sensation of spring fulfilled within him, and a vague but very real uneasiness. At one moment he gave himself up completely to his pride at having captured this pretty, trustful, dewy-eyed thing! At the next he thought with factitious solemnity: "Yes, my boy! But look out what you're doing! You know what comes of it!"

Dusk dropped down without his noticing—dusk on the carved, Assyrian-looking masses of the rocks. And the voice of Nature said: "This is a new world for you!" As when a man gets up at four o'clock and goes out into a summer morning, and beasts, birds, trees stare at him and he feels as if all had been made new.

He stayed up there for hours, till it grew cold, then groped his way down the stones and heather roots to the road, back into the lane, and came again past the wild meadow to the orchard. There he struck a match and looked at his watch. Nearly twelve! It was black and unstirring in there now, very different from the lingering, bird-befriended brightness of six hours ago! And suddenly he saw this idyll of his with the eyes of the outer world—had mental vision of Mrs. Narracombe's snakelike neck turned, her quick dark glance taking it all in, her shrewd face hardening; saw the gypsylike cousins coarsely mocking and distrustful; Joe stolid and furious; only the lame man, Jim, with the suffering eyes, seemed tolerable to his mind. And the village pub!—the gossiping matrons he passed on his walks; and then—his own friends—Robert Garton's smile when he went off that morning ten days ago; so ironical and knowing! Disgusting! For a minute he literally hated this earthly, cynical world to which one belonged, willy-nilly. The gate where he was leaning grew grey, a sort of shimmer passed before him and spread into the bluish darkness. The moon! He could just see it over the bank behind; red, nearly round—a strange moon! And turning away, he went up the lane which smelled of the night and cow-dung and young leaves. In the straw yard he could see the dark shapes of cattle, broken by the pale sickles of their horns, like so many thin moons, fallen ends-up. He unlatched the farm gate stealthily. All was dark in the house. Muffling his footsteps, he gained the porch, and, blotted against one of the yew-trees, looked up at Megan's window. It was open. Was she sleeping, or lying awake perhaps disturbed—unhappy at his absence? An owl hooted while he stood there peering up, and the sound seemed to fill the whole night, so quiet was all else, save for the never-ending murmur of the stream running below the orchard. The cuckoos by day, and now the owls—how wonderful they voiced this troubled ecstasy within him! And suddenly he saw her at her window, looking out. He moved a little from the yew-tree, and whispered: "Megan!" She drew back, vanished, reappeared, leaning far down. He stole forward on the grass patch, hit his shin against the green-painted chair, and held his breath at the sound. The pale blur of her stretched-down arm and face did not stir; he moved the chair, and noiselessly mounted it. By stretching up his arm he could just reach. Her hand held the huge key of the front door, and he clasped that burning hand with the cold key in it. He could just see her face, the glint of teeth between her lips, her tumbled hair. She was still dressed—poor child, sitting up for him, no doubt! "Pretty Megan!" Her hot, roughened fingers clung to his; her face had a strange, lost look. To have been able to reach it—even with his hand! The owl hooted, a scent of sweet-brier crept into his nostrils. Then one of the farm dogs barked; her grasp relaxed, she shrank back.

"Good night, Megan!"

"Good night, Sir!" She was gone! With a sigh he dropped back to earth, and, sitting on that chair, took off his boots. Nothing for it but to creep in and go to bed; yet for a long while he sat unmoving, his feet chilly in the dew, drunk on the memory of her lost, half-smiling face, and the clinging grip of her burning fingers, pressing the cold key into his hand.

He awoke feeling as if he had eaten heavily overnight, instead of having eaten nothing. And far off, unreal, seemed yesterday's romance! Yet it was a golden morning. Full spring had burst at last—in one night the "goldie-cups," as the little boys called them, seemed to have made the field their own, and from his window he could see apple-blossoms covering the orchard as with a rose and white quilt. He went down almost dreading to see Megan; and yet when not she but Mrs. Narracombe brought in his breakfast he felt vexed and disappointed. The woman's quick eye and snaky neck seemed to have a new alacrity this morning. Had she noticed?

"So you an' the moon went walkin' last night, Mr. Ashurst! Did ye have your supper anywheres?"

Ashurst shook his head.

"We kept it for you, but I suppose you was too busy in your brain to think o' such a thing as that?"

Was she mocking him, in that voice of hers, which still kept some Welsh crispness against the invading burr of the West Country? If she knew! And at that moment he thought: "No, no; I'll clear out. I won't put myself in such a beastly false position."

But, after breakfast, the longing to see Megan began and increased with every minute, together with fear lest something should have been said to her which had spoiled everything. Sinister that she had not appeared, not given him even a glimpse of her! And the love poem, whose manufacture had been so important and absorbing yesterday afternoon under the apple-trees, now seemed so paltry that he tore it up and rolled it into pipe spills. What had he known of love till she seized his hand and kissed it! And now—what did he not know? But to write of it seemed mere insipidity! He went up to his bedroom to get a book, and his heart began to beat violently, for she was in there making the bed. He stood in the doorway watching; and suddenly, with turbulent joy, he saw her stoop and kiss his pillow, just at the hollow made by his head last night. How let her know he had seen that pretty act of devotion? And yet if she heard him stealing away, it would be even worse. She took the pillow up, holding it as if reluctant to shake out the impress of his cheek, dropped it, and turned round.

"Megan!"

She put her hands up to her cheeks, but her eyes seemed to look right into him. He had never before realized the depth and purity and touching faithfulness in those dew-bright eyes, and he stammered: "It was sweet of you to wait up for me last night."

She still said nothing, and he stammered on: "I was wandering about on the moor; it was such a jolly night. I—I've just come up for a book."

Then, the kiss he had seen her give the pillow afflicted him with sudden headiness, and he went up to her. Touching her eyes with his lips, he thought with queer excitement: "I've done it! Yesterday all was sudden— anyhow; but now—I've done it!" The girl let her forehead rest against his lips, which moved downwards till they reached hers. That first real lover's kiss—strange, wonderful, still almost innocent—in which heart did it make the most disturbance?

"Come to the big apple-tree to-night, after they've gone to bed. Megan —promise!"

She whispered back: "I promise!"

Then, scared at her white face, scared at everything, he let her go, and went downstairs again. Yes! he had done it now! Accepted her love, declared his own! He went out to the green chair as devoid of a book as ever; and there he sat staring vacantly before him, triumphant and remorseful, while under his nose and behind his back the work of the farm went on. How long he had been sitting in that curious state of vacancy he had no notion when he saw Joe standing a little behind him to the right. The youth had evidently come from hard work in the fields, and stood shifting his feet, breathing loudly, his face coloured like a setting sun, and his arms, below the rolled-up sleeves of his blue shirt, showing the hue and furry sheen of ripe peaches. His red lips were open, his blue eyes with their flaxen lashes stared fixedly at Ashurst, who said ironically:

"Well, Joe, anything I can do for you?"

"Yeas."

"What, then?"

"Yu can goo away from yere. Us don' want yu."

Ashurst's face, never too humble, assumed its most lordly look.

"Very good of you, but, do you know, I prefer the others should speak for themselves."

The youth moved a pace or two nearer, and the scent of his honest heat afflicted Ashurst's nostrils.

"What d'yu stay yere for?"

"Because it pleases me."

" 'Twon't please yu when I've bashed yure head in!"

"Indeed! When would you like to begin that?"

Joe answered only with the loudness of his breathing, but his eyes looked like those of a young and angry bull. Then a sort of spasm seemed to convulse his face.

"Megan don' want yu."

A rush of jealousy, of contempt, and anger with this thick, loud-breathing rustic got the better of Ashurst's self-possession; he jumped up and pushed back his chair.

"You can go to the devil!"

And as he said those simple words, he saw Megan in the doorway with a tiny brown spaniel puppy in her arms. She came up to him quickly: "It's eyes are blue!" she said.

Joe turned away; the back of his neck was literally crimson.

Ashurst put his finger to the mouth of the little brown bull-frog of a creature in her arms. How cozy it looked against her!

"It's fond of you already. Ah! Megan, everything is fond of *you*."

"What was Joe saying to you, please?"

"Telling me to go away, because you didn't want me here."

She stamped her foot; then looked up at Ashurst. At that adoring look he felt his nerves quiver, just as if he had seen a moth scorching its wings.

"To-night!" he said. "Don't forget!"

"No." And smothering her face against the puppy's little fat, brown body, she slipped back into the house.

Ashurst wandered down the lane. At the gate of the wild meadow he came on the lame man and his cows.

"Beautiful day, Jim!"

"Ah! 'Tes brave weather for the grass. The ashes be later than th' oaks this year. 'When th' oak before th' ash—'"

Ashurst said idly: "Where were you standing when you saw the gypsy bogle, Jim?"

"It might be under that big apple-tree, as you might say."

"And you really do think it was there?"

The lame man answered cautiously: "I shouldn't like to say rightly that *'twas* there. 'Twas in my mind as 'twas there."

"What do you make of it?"

The lame man lowered his voice. "They du zay old master, Mist' Narracombe, come o' gypsy stock. But that's tellin'. They'm a wonderful people, yu know, for claimin' their own. Maybe they knu 'e was goin', and sent this feller along for company. That's what I've a-thought about it."

"What was he like?"

"'E 'ad 'air all over 'is face, an' goin' like this, he was, zame as if 'e 'ad a viddle. They zay there's no such thing as bogles, but I've a-zeen the 'air on this dog standin' up of a dark naight, when I couldn' zee nothin', meself."

"Was there a moon?"

"Yeas, very near full, but 'twas on'y just risen, goldlike be'ind them trees."

"And you think a ghost means trouble, do you?"

The lame man pushed his hat up; his aspiring eyes looked at Ashurst more earnestly than ever.

"'Tes not for me to zay that—but 'tes they bein' so unrestin'-like. There's things us don' understand, that's zartin, for zure. There's people that zee things, tu, an' others that don't never zee nothin'. Now, our Joe —yu might putt anything under 'is eyes an' 'e'd never see it; and them other boys, tu, they'm rattlin' fellers. But yu take an' putt our Megan where there's suthin', she'll zee it, an' more tu, or I'm mistaken."

"She's sensitive, that's why."

"What's that?"

"I mean, she feels everything."

"Ah! She'm very lovin'-'earted."

Ashurst, who felt colour coming into his cheeks, held out his tobacco-pouch.

"Have a fill, Jim?"

"Thank 'ee, Sir. She'm one in an 'underd, I think."

"I expect so," said Ashurst shortly, and folding up his pouch, walked on.

"Lovin'-'earted!" Yes! And what was he doing? What were his intentions—as they say—towards this loving-hearted girl? The thought dogged him, wandering through fields bright with buttercups, where the little red calves were feeding, and the swallows flying high. Yes, the oaks were before the ashes, brown-gold already; every tree in different stage and hue. The cuckoos and a thousand birds were singing; the little streams were very bright. The ancients believed in a golden age, in the garden of the Hesperides! . . . A queen wasp settled on his sleeve. Each queen wasp killed meant two thousand fewer wasps to thieve the apples which would grow from that blossom in the orchard; but who, with love in his heart, could kill anything on a day like this? He entered a field where a young red bull was feeding. It seemed to Ashurst that he looked like Joe. But the young bull took no notice of this visitor, a little drunk himself, perhaps, on the singing and the glamour of the golden pasture, under his short legs. Ashurst crossed out unchallenged to the hill-side above the stream. From that slope a tor mounted to its crown of rocks. The ground there was covered with a mist of blue bells, and nearly a score of crab-apple trees were in full bloom. He threw himself down on the grass. The change from the buttercup glory and oak-goldened glamour of the fields to this ethereal beauty under the grey tor filled him with a sort of wonder; nothing the same, save the sound of running water and the songs of the cuckoos. He lay there a long time, watching the sunlight wheel till the crab-trees threw shadows over the blue bells, his only companions a few wild bees. He was not quite sane, thinking of that morning's kiss, and of to-night under the apple-tree. In such a spot as this, fauns and dryads surely lived; nymphs, white as the crab-apple blossom, retired within those trees; fauns, brown as the dead bracken, with pointed ears, lay in wait for them. The cuckoos were still calling when he woke, there was the sound of running water; but the sun had couched behind the tor, the hill-side was cool, and some rabbits had come out. "To-night!" he thought. Just as from the earth everything was pushing up, unfolding under the soft insistent fingers of an unseen hand, so were his heart and senses being pushed, unfolded. He got up and broke off a spray from a crab-apple tree. The buds were like Megan—shell-like, rose-pink, wild, and fresh; and so, too, the opening flowers, white, and wild, and touching. He put the spray into his coat. And all the rush of the spring within him escaped in a triumphant sigh. But the rabbits scurried away.

It was nearly eleven that night when Ashurst put down the pocket "Odyssey" which for half an hour he had held in his hands without reading, and slipped through the yard down to the orchard. The moon had just risen, very golden, over the hill, and like a bright, powerful, watching spirit peered through the bars of an ash-tree's half-naked boughs. In among the apple-trees it was still dark, and he stood making sure of his direction, feeling the rough grass with his feet. A black mass close behind him stirred with a heavy grunting sound, and three large pigs settled down again close to each other, under the wall. He listened. There was no wind, but the stream's burbling whispering chuckle had gained twice its daytime strength. One bird, he could not tell what, cried "Pip—pip," "Pip—pip," with perfect monotony; he could hear a nightjar spinning very far off; an owl hooting. Ashurst moved a step or two, and again halted, aware of a dim living whiteness all round his head. On the dark unstirring trees innumerable flowers and buds all soft and blurred were being bewitched to life by the creeping moonlight. He had the oddest feeling of actual companionship, as if a million white moths or spirits had floated in and settled between dark sky and darker ground, and were opening and shutting their wings on a level with his eyes. In the bewildering, still, scentless beauty of that moment he almost lost memory of why he had come to the orchard. The flying glamour which had clothed the earth all day had not gone now that night had fallen, but only changed into this new form. He moved on through the thicket of stems and boughs covered with that live powdering whiteness, till he reached the big apple-tree. No mistaking that, even in the dark, nearly twice the height and size of any other, and leaning out towards the open meadows and the stream. Under the thick branches he stood still again, to listen. The same sounds exactly, and a faint grunting from the sleepy pigs. He put his hands on the dry, almost warm tree trunk, whose rough mossy surface gave forth a peaty scent at his touch. Would she come—would she? And among these quivering, haunted, moon-witched trees he was seized with doubts of everything! All was unearthly here, fit for no earthly lovers; fit only for god and goddess, faun and nymph—not for him and this little country girl. Would it not be almost a relief if she did not come? But all the time he was listening. And still that unknown bird went "Pip—pip," "Pip—pip," and there rose the busy chatter of the little trout stream, whereon the moon was flinging glances through the bars of her tree-prison. The blossom on a level with his eyes seemed to grow more living every moment, seemed with its mysterious white beauty more and more a part of his suspense. He plucked a fragment and held it close—three blossoms. Sacrilege to pluck fruit-tree blossom—soft, sacred, young blossom —and throw it away! Then suddenly he heard the gate close, the pigs stirring again and grunting; and leaning against the trunk, he pressed his hands to its mossy sides behind him, and held his breath. She might have been a spirit threading the trees, for all the noise she made! Then he saw her quite close—her dark form part of a little tree, her white face part of its blossom; so still, and peering towards him. He whispered: "Megan!" and held out his hands. She ran forward, straight to his breast. When he felt her heart beating against him, Ashurst knew to the full the sensations of chivalry and passion. Because she was not of his world, because she was so simple and young and headlong, adoring and defence-less, how could he be other than her protector in the dark! Because she was all simple Nature and beauty, as much a part of this spring night as was the living blossom, how should he not take all that she would give him—how not fulfill the spring in her heart and his! And torn between these two emotions he clasped her close, and kissed her hair. How long they stood there without speaking he knew not. The stream went on chattering, the owls hooting, the moon kept stealing up and growing whiter; the blossom all round them and above brightened in suspense of living beauty. Their lips had sought each other's, and they did not speak. The moment speech began all would be unreal! Spring has no speech, nothing but rustling and whispering. Spring has so much more than speech in its unfolding flowers and leaves, and the coursing of its streams, and in its sweet restless seeking! And sometimes spring will come alive, and, like a mysterious Presence, stand, encircling lovers with its arms, laying on them the fingers of enchantment, so that, standing lips to lips, they forget everything but just a kiss. While her heart beat against him, and her lips quivered on his, Ashurst felt nothing but simple rapture—Destiny meant her for his arms, Love could not be flouted! But when their lips parted for breath, division began again at once. Only, passion now was so much the stronger, and he sighed: "Oh! Megan! Why did you come?"

She looked up, hurt, amazed.

"Sir, you asked me to."

"Don't call me 'Sir,' my pretty sweet."

"What should I be callin' you."

"Frank."

"I could not. Oh, no!"

"But you love me—don't you?"

"I could not help lovin' you. I want to be with you—that's all."

"All!"

So faint that he hardly heard, she whispered: "I shall die if I can't be with you."

Ashurst took a mighty breath.

"Come and be with me, then!"

"Oh!"

Intoxicated by the awe and rapture in that "Oh!" he went on, whispering: "We'll go to London. I'll show you the world. And I *will* take care of you, I promise, Megan. I'll never be a brute to you!"

"If I can be with you—that is all."

He stroked her hair, and whispered on: "To-morrow I'll go to Torquay and get some money, and get you some clothes that won't be noticed, and then we'll steal away. And when we get to London, soon perhaps, if you love me well enough, we'll be married."

He could feel her hair shiver with the shake of her head.

"Oh, no! I could not. I only want to be with you!"

Drunk on his own chivalry, Ashurst went on murmuring: "It's I who am not good enough for you. Oh! Megan, when did you begin to love me?"

"When I saw you in the road, and you looked at me. The first night I loved you; but I never thought you would want me."

She slipped down suddenly to her knees, trying to kiss his feet.

A shiver of horror went through Ashurst; he lifted her up bodily and held her fast—too upset to speak.

She whispered: "Why won't you let me?"

"It's I who will kiss your feet!"

Her smile brought tears into his eyes. The whiteness of her moonlit face so close to his, the faint pink of her opened lips, had the living, unearthly beauty of the apple-blossom.

And then, suddenly, her eyes widened and stared past him painfully; she writhed out of his arms, and whispered: "Look!"

Ashurst saw nothing but the brightened stream, the furze faintly gilded, the beech-trees glistening, and behind them all the wide loom of the moonlit hill. Behind him came her frozen whisper: "The gypsy bogle!"

"Where?"

"There—by the stone—under the trees!"

Exasperated, he leapt the stream, and strode towards the beech clump. Prank of the moonlight! Nothing! In and out of the boulders and thorn-trees, muttering and cursing, yet with a kind of terror, he rushed and stumbled. Absurd! Silly! Then he went back to the apple-tree. But she was gone; he could hear a rustle, the grunting of the pigs, the sound of a gate closing. Instead of her, only this old apple-tree! He flung his arms round the trunk. What a substitute for her soft body; the rough moss against his face—what a substitute for her soft cheek; only the scent, as of the woods, a little the same! And above him, and around, the blossoms, more living, more moonlit than ever, seemed to glow and breathe.

Descending from the train at Torquay station, Ashurst wandered un-certainly along the front, for he did not know this particular queen of English watering-places. Having little sense of what he had on, he was quite unconscious of being remarkable among its inhabitants, and strode along in his rough Norfolk jacket, dusty boots, and battered hat, without observing that people gazed at him rather blankly. He was seeking a branch of his London bank, and having found one, found also the first obstacle to his mood. Did he know any one in Torquay? No. In that case, if he would wire to his bank in London, they would be happy to oblige him on receipt of the reply. That suspicious breath from the matter-of-fact world somewhat tarnished the brightness of his visions. But he sent the telegram.

Nearly opposite to the post office he saw a shop full of ladies' gar-ments, and examined the window with strange sensations. To have to un-dertake the clothing of his rustic love was more than a little disturbing. He went in. A young woman came forward; she had blue eyes and a faintly puzzled forehead. Ashurst stared at her in silence.

"Yes, Sir?"

"I want a dress for a young lady."

The young woman smiled. Ashurst frowned—the peculiarity of his request struck him with sudden force.

The young woman added hastily: "What style would you like—something modish?"

"No. Simple."

"What figure would the young lady be?"

"I don't know; about two inches shorter than you, I should say."

"Could you give me her waist measurement?"

Megan's waist!

"Oh! anything usual!"

"Quite!"

While she was gone he stood disconsolately eyeing the models in the window, and suddenly it seemed to him incredible that Megan—his Megan—could ever be dressed save in the rough tweed skirt, coarse blouse, and Tam o' Shanter cap he was wont to see her in. The young woman had come back with several dresses in her arms, and Ashurst eyed her laying them against her own modish figure. There was one whose colour he liked, a dove-grey, but to imagine Megan clothed in it was beyond him. The young woman went away, and brought some more. But on Ashurst there had now come a feeling of paralysis. How choose? She would want a hat too, and shoes, and gloves; and, suppose, when he had got them all, they commonized her, as Sunday clothes always commonized village folk! Why should she not travel as she was? Ah? But conspicuousness would matter; this was a serious elopement. And, staring at the young woman, he thought: "I wonder if she guesses, and thinks me a blackguard?"

"Do you mind putting aside that grey one for me?" he said desperately at last. "I can't decide now; I'll come in again this afternoon."

The young woman sighed.

"Oh! certainly. It's a very tasteful costume. I don't think you'll get anything that will suit your purpose better."

"I expect not," Ashurst murmured, and went out.

Freed again from the suspicious matter of factness of the world, he took a long breath, and went back to visions. In fancy he saw the trustful, pretty creature who was going to join her life to his; saw himself and her stealing forth at night, walking over the moor under the moon, he with his arm around her, and carrying her new garments, till, in some far-off wood, when dawn was coming, she would slip off her old things and put on these, and an early train at a distant station would bear them away on their honeymoon journey, till London swallowed them up, and the dreams of love came true.

"Frank Ashurst! Haven't seen you since Rugby, old chap!"

Ashurst's frown dissolved; the face, close to his own, was blue-eyed, suffused with sun—one of those faces where sun from within and without join in a sort of lustre. And he answered: "Phil Halliday, by Jove!"

"What are you doing here?"

"Oh! nothing. Just looking round, and getting some money. I'm staying on the moor."

"Are you lunching anywhere? Come and lunch with us; I'm here with my young sisters. They've had measles."

Hooked in by that friendly arm Ashurst went along, up a hill, down a hill, away out of the town, while the voice of Halliday, redolent of optimism as his face was of sun, explained how "in this mouldy place the only decent things were the bathing and boating," and so on, till presently they came to a crescent of houses a little above and back from the sea, and into the centre one—a hotel—made their way.

"Come up to my room and have a wash. Lunch'll be ready in a jiffy."

Ashurst contemplated his visage in a looking-glass. After his farm-house bedroom, the comb and one spare shirt *régime* of the last forenight, this room littered with clothes and brushes was a sort of Capua; and he thought: "Queer—one doesn't realize—" But what—he did not quite know.

When he followed Halliday into the sitting-room for lunch, three faces, very fair and blue-eyed, were turned suddenly at the words: "This is Frank Ashurst—my young sisters."

Two were indeed young, about eleven and ten. The third was perhaps seventeen, tall and fair-haired too, with pink-and-white cheeks just touched by the sun, and eyebrows, rather darker than the hair, running a little upwards from her nose to their outer points. The voices of all three were like Halliday's, high and cheerful; they stood up straight, shook hands with a quick movement, looked at Ashurst critically, away again at once, and began to talk of what they were going to do in the afternoon. A regular Diana and attendant nymphs! After the farm this crisp, slangy, eager talk, this cool, clean, off-hand refinement, was queer at first, and then so natural that what he had come from became suddenly remote. The names of the two little ones seemed to be Sabina and Freda; of the eldest, Stella.

Presently the one called Sabina turned to him and said: "I say, will you come shrimping with us?—it's awful fun!"

Surprised by this unexpected friendliness, Ashurst murmured: "I'm afraid I've got to get back this afternoon."

"Oh!"

"Can't you put it off?"

Ashurst turned to the new speaker, Stella, shook his head, and smiled. She was very pretty! Sabina said regretfully: "You might!" Then the talk switched off to caves and swimming.

"Can you swim far?"

"About two miles."

"Oh!"

"I say!"

"How jolly!"

The three pairs of blue eyes, fixed on him, made him conscious of his new importance. The sensation was agreeable. Halliday said: "I say, you simply must stop and have a bathe. You'd better stay the night."

"Yes, do!"

But again Ashurst smiled and shook his head. Then suddenly he found himself being catechized about his physical achievements. He had rowed—it seemed—in his college boat, played in his college football team, won his college mile, and he rose from table a sort of hero. The two little girls insisted that he must see "their" cave, and they set forth chattering like magpies, Ashurst between them, Stella and her brother a little behind. In the cave, damp and darkish like any other cave, the great feature was a pool with possibility of creatures which might be caught and put into bottles. Sabina and Freda who wore no stockings on their shapely brown legs, exhorted Ashurst to join them in the middle of it, and help sieve the water. He too was soon bootless and sockless. Time goes fast for one who has a sense of beauty, when there are pretty children in a pool and a young Diana on the edge to receive with wonder anything you can catch! Ashurst never had much sense of time. It was a shock when, pulling out his watch, he saw it was well past three. No cashing his check to-day—the bank would be closed before he could get there. Watching his expression, the little girls cried out at once: "Hurrah! Now you'll have to stay!"

Ashurst did not answer. He was seeing again Megan's face, when at breakfast he had whispered: "I'm going to Torquay, darling, to get everything; I shall be back this evening. If it's fine we can go to-night. Be ready." He was seeing again how she quivered and hung on his words.

What would she think? Then he pulled himself together, conscious suddenly of the calm scrutiny of this other young girl, so tall and fair and
Diana-like, at the edge of the pool, of her wondering blue eyes under
those brows which slanted up a little. If they knew what was in his mind
—if they knew that this very night he had meant—! Well, there would
be a little sound of disgust, and he would be alone in the cave. And with
a curious mixture of anger, chagrin, and shame, he put his watch back
into his pocket and said abruptly: "Yes; I'm dished for to-day."

"Hurrah! Now you can bathe with us."

It was impossible not to succumb a little to the contentment of these
pretty children, to the smile on Stella's lips, to Halliday's "Ripping, old
chap! I can lend you things for the night!" But again a spasm of longing
and remorse throbbed through Ashurst, and he said moodily: "I must send
a wire!"

The attractions of the pool palling, they went back to the hotel. Ashurst
sent his wire, addressing it to Mrs. Narracombe: "Sorry, detained for the
night, back tomorrow." Surely Megan would understand that he had too
much to do; and his heart grew lighter. It was a lovely afternoon, warm,
the sea calm and blue, and swimming his great passion; the favor of these
pretty children flattered him, the pleasure of looking at them, at Stella, at
Halliday's sunny face; the slight unreality, yet extreme naturalness of it
all—as of a last peep at normality before he took this plunge with Megan!
He got his borrowed bathing dress, and they all set forth. Halliday and
he undressed behind one rock, the three girls behind another. He was
first into the sea, and at once swam out with the bravado of justifying his
self-given reputation. When he turned he could see Halliday swimming
along shore, and the girls flopping and dipping, and riding the little
waves, in the way he was accustomed to despise, but now thought pretty
and sensible, since it gave him the distinction of the only deep-water fish.
But drawing near, he wondered if they would like him, a stranger, to
come into their splashing group; he felt shy, approaching that slim
nymph. Then Sabina summoned him to teach her to float, and between
them the little girls kept him so busy that he had no time even to notice whether Stella was accustomed to his presence, till suddenly he heard
a startled sound from her. She was standing submerged to the waist, leaning a little forward, her slim white arms stretched out and pointing, her
wet face puckered by the sun and an expression of fear.

"Look at Phil! Is he all right? Oh, look!"

Ashurst saw at once that Phil was not all right. He was splashing and
struggling out of his depth, perhaps a hundred yards away; suddenly he

gave a cry, threw up his arms, and went down. Ashurst saw the girl launch herself towards him, and crying out: "Go back, Stella! Go back!" he dashed out. He had never swum so fast, and reached Halliday just as he was coming up a second time. It was a case of cramp, but to get him in was not difficult, for he did not struggle. The girl, who had stopped where Ashurst told her to, helped as soon as he was in his depth, and once on the beach they sat down one on each side of him to rub his limbs, while the little ones stood by with scared faces. Halliday was soon smiling. It was—he said—rotten of him, absolutely rotten! If Frank would give him an arm, he could get to his clothes all right now. Ashurst gave him the arm, and as he did so caught sight of Stella's face, wet and flushed and tearful, all broken up out of its calm; and he thought: "I called her Stella! Wonder if she minded?"

While they were dressing, Halliday said quietly: "You saved my life, old chap!"

"Rot!"

Clothed, but not quite in their right minds, they went up all together to the hotel and sat down to tea, except Halliday, who was lying down in his room. After some slices of bread and jam, Sabina said: "I say, you know, you *are* a brick!"

And Freda chimed in: "Rather!"

Ashurst saw Stella looking down; he got up in confusion, and went to the window. From there he heard Sabina mutter: "I say, let's swear blood bond. Where's your knife, Freda?" and out of the corner of his eye he could see each of them solemnly prick herself, squeeze out a drop of blood and dabble on a bit of paper. He turned and made for the door.

"Don't be a stoat! Come back!" His arms were seized; imprisoned between the little girls he was brought back to the table. On it lay a piece of paper with an effigy drawn in blood, and the three names Stella Halliday, Sabina Halliday, Freda Halliday—also in blood, running towards it like the rays of a star. Sabina said: "That's you. We shall have to kiss you, you know."

And Freda echoed: "Oh! Blow—Yes!"

Before Ashurst could escape, some wettish hair dangled against his face, something like a bite descended on his nose, he felt his left arm pinched, and other teeth softly searching his cheek. Then he was released, and Freda said: "Now, Stella."

Ashurst, red and rigid, looked across the table at a red and rigid Stella. Sabina giggled; Freda cried: "Buck up—it spoils everything!"

A queer, ashamed eagerness shot through Ashurst; then he said quietly: "Shut up, you little demons!"

Again Sabina giggled.

"Well, then, she can kiss her hand, and you can put it against your nose. It *is* on one side!"

To his amazement the girl did kiss her hand and stretch it out. Solemnly he took that cool, slim hand and laid it to his cheek. The two little girls broke into clapping, and Freda said: "Now, then, we shall have to save your life at any time; that's settled. Can I have another cup, Stella, not so beastly weak?"

Tea was resumed, and Ashurst, folding up the paper, put it in his pocket. The talk turned on the advantages of measles, tangerine oranges, honey in a spoon, no lessons, and so forth. Ashurst listened, silent, exchanging friendly looks with Stella, whose face was again of its normal sun-touched pink and white. It was soothing to be so taken to the heart of this jolly family, fascinating to watch their faces. And after tea, while the two little girls pressed seaweed, he talked to Stella in the window-seat and looked at her water-colour sketches. The whole thing was like a pleasurable dream; time and incident hung up, importance and reality suspended. To-morrow he would go back to Megan, with nothing of all this left save the paper with the blood of these children, in his pocket. Children! Stella was not quite that—as old as Megan! Her talk—quick, rather hard and shy, yet friendly—seemed to flourish on his silences, and about her there was something cool and virginal—a maiden in a bower. At dinner, to which Halliday, who had swallowed too much sea-water, did not come, Sabina said: "I'm going to call you Frank."

Freda echoed: "Frank, Frank, Franky."

Ashurst grinned and bowed.

"Every time Stella calls you Mr. Ashurst, she's got to pay a forfeit. It's ridiculous."

Ashurst looked at Stella, who grew slowly red. Sabina giggled; Freda cried: "She's 'smoking'—'smoking!'—Yah!"

Ashurst reached out to right and left, and grasped some fair hair in each hand.

"Look here," he said, "you two! Leave Stella alone, or I'll tie you together!"

Freda gurgled: "Ouch! You *are* a beast!"

Sabina murmured cautiously: "*You* call *her* Stella, you see!"

"Why shouldn't I? It's a jolly name!"

"All right; we give you leave to!"

Ashurst released the hair. Stella! What would she call him—after this? But she called him nothing; till at bedtime he said, deliberately: "Good night, Stella!"

"Good night, Mr.—Good night, Frank! It *was* jolly of you, you know!"

"Oh—that! Bosh!"

Her quick, straight handshake tightened suddenly, and as suddenly, became slack.

Ashurst stood motionless in the empty sitting-room. Only last night, under the apple-tree and the living blossoms, he had held Megan to him, kissing her eyes and lips. And he gasped, swept by that rush of remembrance. To-night it should have begun—his life with her who only wanted to be with him! And now, twenty-four hours and more must pass, because —of not looking at his watch! Why had he made friends with this family of innocents just when he was saying good-bye to innocence, and all the rest of it? "But I mean to marry her," he thought; "I told her so!"

He took a candle, lighted it, and went to his bedroom, which was next to Halliday's. His friend's voice called as he was passing: "Is that you, old chap? I say, come in."

He was sitting up in bed, smoking a pipe and reading.

"Sit down a bit."

Ashurst sat down by the open window.

"I've been thinking about this afternoon, you know," said Halliday rather suddenly. "They say you go through all your past. I didn't. I suppose I wasn't far enough gone."

"What did you think of?"

Halliday was silent for a little, then said quietly: "Well, I did think of one thing—rather odd—of a girl at Cambridge that I might have—you know; I was glad I hadn't got her on my mind. Anyhow, old chap, I owe it to you that I'm here; I should have been in the big dark by now. No more bed, or baccy; no more anything. I say, what d'you suppose happens to us?"

Ashurst murmured: "Go out like flames, I expect."

"Phew!"

"We may flicker, and cling about a bit, perhaps."

"H'm! I think that's rather gloomy. I say, I hope my young sisters have been decent to you?"

"Awfully decent."

Halliday put his pipe down, crossed his hands behind his neck, and turned his face towards the window.

"They're not bad kids!" he said.

Watching his friend, lying there, with that smile, and the candlelight on his face, Ashurst shuddered. Quite true! He might have been lying there with no smile, with all that sunny look gone out forever! He might not have been lying there at all, but "sanded" at the bottom of the sea, waiting for resurrection on the—ninth day, was it? And that smile of Halliday's seemed to him suddenly something wonderful, as if in it were all the difference between life and death—the little flame—the all! He got up, and said softly: "Well, you ought to sleep, I expect. Shall I blow out?"

Halliday caught his hand.

"I can't say it, you know; but it must be rotten to be dead. Good night, old boy!"

Stirred and moved, Ashurst squeezed the hand, and went downstairs. The hall-door was still open, and he passed out on to the lawn before the Crescent. The stars were bright in a very dark blue sky, and by their light some lilacs had that mysterious colour of flowers by night which no one can describe. Ashurst pressed his face against a spray; and before his closed eyes Megan started up, with the tiny brown spaniel pup against her breast. "I thought of a girl that I might have—you know. I was glad I hadn't got her on my mind!" He jerked his head away from the lilac, and began pacing up and down over the grass, a grey phantom coming to substance for a moment in the light from the lamp at either end. He was with her again under the living, breathing whiteness of the blossom, the stream chattering by, the moon glinting steel-blue on the bathing-pool; back in the rapture of his kisses on her upturned face of innocence and humble passion, back in the suspense and beauty of that pagan night. He stood still once more in the shadow of the lilacs. Here the sea, not the stream, was Night's voice; the sea with its sigh and rustle; no little bird, no owl, no nightjar called or spun; but a piano tinkled, and the white houses cut the sky with solid curve, and the scent from the lilacs filled the air. A window of the hotel, high up, was lighted; he saw a shadow move across the blind. And most queer sensations stirred within him, a sort of churning, and twining, and turning of a single emotion on itself, as though spring and love, bewildered and confused, seeking the way, were baffled. This girl, who had called him Frank, whose hand had given his that sudden little clutch, this girl so cool and pure—what would *she* think of such wild, unlawful loving? He sank down on the grass, sitting there cross-legged, with his back to the house, motionless as some carved Buddha. Was he really going to break through innocence, and steal? Sniff the scent out of a wild flower, and—perhaps—throw it away? "Of a girl at Cambridge that I might have—you know!" He put his hands to the grass, one on each side, palms downwards, and pressed; it was just warm still—the grass, barely moist, soft and firm and friendly. "What am I going to do?" he thought. Perhaps Megan was at her window, looking out at the blossom, thinking of him! Poor little Megan! "Why not?" he thought. "I love her! But do I—really love her? or do I only want her because she is so pretty, and loves me? What am I going to do?" The piano tinkled on, the stars winked; and Ashurst gazed out before him at the dark sea, as if spellbound. He got up at last, cramped and rather chilly. There was no longer light in any window. And he went in to bed.

Out of a deep and dreamless sleep he was awakened by the sound of thumping on the door. A shrill voice called: "Hi! Breakfast's ready."

He jumped up. Where was he—? Ah!

He found them already eating marmalade, and sat down in the empty place between Stella and Sabina, who, after watching him a little, said: "I say, do buck up; we're going to start at half past nine."

"We're going to Berry Head, old chap; you *must* come!"

Ashurst thought: "Come! Impossible. I shall be getting things and going back." He looked at Stella. She said quickly: "Do come!"

Sabina chimed in: "It'll be no fun without you."

Freda got up and stood behind his chair.

"You've got to come, or else I'll pull your hair!"

Ashurst thought: "Well—one day more—to think it over! One day more!" And he said: "All right! You needn't tweak my mane!"

"Hurrah!"

At the station he wrote a second telegram to the farm and then—tore it up; he could not have explained why. From Brixham they drove in a very little wagonette. There, squeezed between Sabina and Freda, with his knees touching Stella's, they played "Up Jenkins"; and the gloom he was feeling gave way to frolic. In this one day more to think it over, he did not want to think! They ran races, wrestled, paddled—for to-day nobody wanted to bathe—they sang catches, played games, and ate all they had brought. The little girls fell asleep against him on the way back, and his knees still touched Stella's in the wagonette. It seemed incredible that thirty hours ago he had never set eyes on any of those three flaxen heads. In the train he talked to Stella of poetry, discovering her favourites, and telling her his own with a pleasing sense of superiority; till suddenly she said, rather low: "Phil says you don't believe in a future life, Frank. I think that's dreadful."

Disconcerted, Ashurst muttered: "I don't either believe or not believe —I simply don't know."

She said quickly: "I couldn't bear that. What would be the use of living?"

Watching the frown of those pretty oblique brows, Ashurst answered: "I don't believe in believing things because one wants to."

"But why should one *wish* to live again, if one isn't going to?"

And she looked full at him.

He did not want to hurt her, but an itch to dominate pushed him on to say: "While one's alive one naturally wants to go on living forever; that's part of being alive. But it probably isn't anything more."

"Don't you believe in the Bible at all, then?"

Ashurst thought: "Now I shall really hurt her!"

"I believe in the Sermon on the Mount, because it's beautiful and good for all time."

"But don't you believe Christ was divine?"

He shook his head.

She turned her face quickly to the window, and there sprang into his mind Megan's prayer, repeated by little Nick: "God bless us all, and Mr. Ashes!" Who else would ever say a prayer for him, like her who at this moment must be waiting—waiting to see him come down the lane? And he thought suddenly: "What a scoundrel I am!"

All that evening this thought kept coming back; but, as is not unusual, each time with less poignancy, till it seemed almost a matter of course to be a scoundrel. And—strange!—he did not know whether he was a scoundrel if he meant to go back to Megan, or if he did not mean to go back to her.

They played cards till the children were sent off to bed; then Stella went to the piano. From over on the window seat, where it was nearly dark, Ashurst watched her between the candles—that fair head on the long, white neck bending to the movement of her hands. She played fluently, without much expression; but what a picture she made, the faint golden radiance, a sort of angelic atmosphere—hovering about her! Who could have passionate thoughts or wild desires in the presence of that swaying, white-clothed girl with the seraphic head? She played a thing of Schumann's called "*Warum?*" Then Halliday brought out a flute, and the spell was broken. After this they made Ashurst sing, Stella playing him accompaniments from a book of Schumann songs, till, in the middle of "*Ich grolle nicht*," two small figures clad in blue dressing-gowns crept in and tried to conceal themselves beneath the piano. The evening broke up in confusion, and what Sabina called "a splendid rag."

That night Ashurst hardly slept at all. He was thinking, tossing and turning. The intense domestic intimacy of these last two days, the strength of this Halliday atmosphere, seemed to ring him round, and make the farm and Megan—even Megan—seem unreal. Had he really made love to her—really promised to take her away to live with him? He must have been bewitched by the spring, the night, the apple-blossom! The notion that he was going to make her his mistress—that simple child not yet eighteen—now filled him with a sort of horror, even while it still stung and whipped his blood. He muttered to himself: "It's awful, what I've done—awful!" And the sound of Schumann's music throbbed and mingled with his fevered thoughts, and he saw again Stella's cool, white, fair-haired figure and bending neck, the queer, angelic radiance about her. "I must have been—I must be—mad!" he thought. "What came into me? Poor little Megan!" "God bless us all, and Mr. Ashes!" "I want to be with you—only to be with you!" And burying his face in his pillow, he smothered down a fit of sobbing. Not to go back was awful! To go back—more awful still!

Emotion, when you are young, and give real vent to it, loses its power of torture. And he fell asleep, thinking: "What was it—a few kisses—all forgotten in a month!"

Next morning he got his check cashed, but avoided the shop of the dove-grey dress like the plague; and, instead, bought himself some necessaries. He spent the whole day in a queer mood, cherishing a kind of sullenness against himself. Instead of the hankering of the last two days, he felt nothing but a blank—all passionate longing gone, as if quenched in that outburst of tears. After tea Stella put a book down beside him, and said shyly: "Have you read that, Frank?"

It was Farrar's "Life of Christ." Ashurst smiled. Her anxiety about his beliefs seemed to him comic, but touching. Infectious, too, perhaps, for he began to have an itch to justify himself, if not to convert her. And in the evening, when the children and Halliday were mending their shrimping nets, he said: "At the back of orthodox religion, so far as I can see, there's always the idea of reward—what you can get for being good; a kind of begging for favours. I think it all starts in fear."

She was sitting on the sofa making reefer knots with a bit of string. She looked up quickly: "I think it's much deeper than that."

Ashurst felt again that wish to dominate.

"You think so," he said; "but wanting the *quid pro quo* is about the deepest thing in all of us! It's jolly hard to get to the bottom of it!"

She wrinkled her brows in a puzzled frown.

"I don't think I understand."

He went on obstinately: "Well, think, and see if the most religious people aren't those who feel that this life doesn't give them all they want. I believe in being good because to be good is good in itself."

"Then you do believe in being good?"

How pretty she looked now—it was easy to be good with her! And he nodded and said: "I say, show me how to make that knot!"

With her fingers touching his, in manoeuvring the bit of string he felt soothed and happy. And when he went to bed he willfully kept his thoughts on her, wrapping himself in her fair, cool sisterly radiance, as in some garment of protection.

Next day he found they had arranged to go by train to Totness, and picnic at Berry Pomeroy Castle. Still in that resolute oblivion of the past, he took his place with them in the landau beside Halliday, back to the horses. And, then, along the sea-front, nearly at the turning to the railway station, his heart almost leaped into his mouth. Megan—Megan herself!— was walking on the far pathway, in her old skirt and jacket and her Tam o' Shanter, looking up into the faces of the passers-by. Instinctively he threw his hand up for cover, then made a feint of clearing dust out of his eyes; but between his fingers he could see her still, moving, not with her free country step, but wavering, lost-looking, pitiful—like some little dog which has missed its master and does not know whether to run on, to run back—where to run. How had she come like this?—what excuse had she found to get away?—what did she hope for? But with every turn of the wheels bearing him away from her, his heart revolted and cried to him to stop them, to get out, and go to her! When the landau turned the corner to the station he could stand it no more, and opening the carriage door, muttered: "I've forgotten something! Go on—don't wait for me! I'll join you at the castle by the next train!" He jumped, stumbled, spun round, recovered his balance, and walked forward, while the carriage with the astonished Hallidays rolled on.

From the corner he could only just see Megan, a long way ahead now. He ran a few steps, checked himself, and dropped into a walk. With each step nearer to her, further from the Hallidays, he walked more and more slowly. How did it alter anything—this sight of her? How make the going to her, and that which must come of it, less ugly? For there was no hiding it—since he had met the Hallidays he had become gradually sure that he would not marry Megan. It would only be a wild love-time, a troubled, remorseful, difficult time—and then—well, then he would get tired, just because she gave him everything, was so simple, and so trustful, so dewy. And dew—wears off! The little spot of faded colour, her Tam o'

Shanter cap, wavered on far in front of him; she was looking up into every face, and at the house windows. Had any man ever such a cruel moment to go through? Whatever he did, he felt he would be a beast. And he uttered a groan which made a nursemaid turn and stare. He saw Megan stop and lean against the sea-wall, looking at the sea; and he too stopped. Quite likely she had never seen the sea before, and even in her distress could not resist that sight. "Yes—she's seen nothing," he thought; "every-thing's before her. And just for a few weeks' passion, I shall bo cutting her life to ribbons. I'd better go and hang myself rather than do it!" And sud-denly he seemed to see Stella's calm eyes looking into his, the wave of fluffy hair on her forehead stirred by the wind. Ah! it would be madness, would mean giving up all that he respected, and his own self-respect. He turned and walked quickly back towards the station. But memory of that poor, bewildered little figure, those anxious eyes searching the passers-by, smote him too hard again, and once more he turned towards the sea. The cap was no longer visible; that little spot of colour had vanished in the stream of the noon promenaders. And impelled by the passion of long-ing, the dearth which comes on one when life seems to be whiling some-thing out of reach, he hurried forward. She was nowhere to be seen; for half an hour he looked for her; then on the beach flung himself face down-ward in the sand. To find her again he knew he had only to go to the station and wait till she returned from her fruitless quest, to take her train home; or to take train himself and go back to the farm, so that she found him there when she returned. But he lay inert in the sand, among the indifferent groups of children with their spades and buckets. Pity at her little figure wandering, seeking, was well nigh merged in the spring-running of his blood; for it was all wild feeling now—the chivalrous part, what there had been of it, was gone. He wanted her again, wanted her kisses, her soft, little body, her abandonment, all her quick, warm, pagan emotion; wanted the wonderful feeling of that night under the moonlit apple boughs; wanted it all with a horrible intensity, as the faun wants the nymph. The quick chatter of the little bright trout-stream, the daz-zle of the buttercups, the rocks of the old "wild men"; the calling of the cuckoos and yaffles, the hooting of the owls; and the red moon peeping out of the velvet dark at the living whiteness of the blossom; and her face just out of reach at the window, lost in its love-look; and her heart against his, her lips answering his, under the apple-tree—all this besieged him. Yet he lay inert. What was it which struggled against pity and this feverish longing, and kept him there paralyzed in the warm sand? Three flaxen heads—a fair face with friendly blue-grey eyes, a slim hand pressing his, a quick voice speaking his name—"So you do believe in being good?" Yes, and a sort of atmosphere as of some old walled-in English garden, with pinks, and cornflowers, and roses, and scents of lavender and lilac—cool and fair, untouched, almost holy—all that he had been brought up to feel was clean and good. And suddenly he thought: "She might come along the front again and see me!" and he got up and made his way to the rock at the far end of the beach. There, with the spray biting into his face, he could think more coolly. To go back to the farm and love Megan out in the woods, among the rocks, with everything around wild and fitting—that, he knew, was impossible, utterly. To transplant her to a great town, to keep, in some little flat or rooms, one who belonged so wholly to Nature—the poet in him shrank from it. His passion would be a mere sensuous revel, soon gone; in London, her very simplicity, her lack of all intellectual quality, would make her his secret plaything—nothing else. The longer he sat on the rock, with his feet dangling over a greenish pool from which the sea was ebbing, the more clearly he saw this; but it was as if her arms and all of her were slipping slowly, slowly down from him, into the pool, to be carried away out to sea; and her face looking up, her lost face with beseeching eyes, and dark, wet hair—possessed, haunted, tortured him! He got up at last, scaled the low rock-cliff, and made his way down into a sheltered cove. Perhaps in the sea he could get back his control—lose this fever! And stripping off his clothes, he swam out. He wanted to tire himself so that nothing mattered, and swam recklessly, fast and far; then suddenly, for no reason, felt afraid. Suppose he could not reach shore again—suppose the current set him out—or he got cramps, like Halliday! He turned to swim in. The red cliffs looked a long way off. If he were drowned they would find his clothes. The Hallidays would know; but Megan perhaps never—they took no newspaper at the farm. And Phil Halliday's words came back to him again: "A girl at Cambridge I might have— Glad I haven't got her on my mind!" And in that moment of unreasoning fear he vowed he would not have her on his mind. Then his fear left him; he swam in easily enough, dried himself in the sun, and put on his clothes. His heart felt sore, but no longer ached; his body cool and refreshed.

When one is as young as Ashurst, pity is not a violent emotion. And, back in the Hallidays' sitting-room, eating a ravenous tea, he felt much like a man recovered from fever. Everything seemed new and clear; the tea, the buttered toast, and jam tasted absurdly good; tobacco had never smelt so nice. And walking up and down the empty room, he stopped here and there to touch or look. He took up Stella's work-basket, fingered the cotton reels and a gayly coloured plait of sewing silks, smelt at the little bag filled with woodruff she kept among them. He sat down at the piano, playing tunes with one finger, thinking: "To-night she'll play; I shall watch her while she's playing; it does me good to watch her." He took up the book, which still lay where she had placed it beside him, and tried to read. But Megan's little, sad figure began to come back at once, and he got up and leaned in the window, listening to the thrushes in the Crescent gardens, gazing at the sea, dreamy and blue below the trees. A servant came in and cleared the tea away, and he still stood, inhaling the evening air, trying not to think. Then he saw the Hallidays coming through the gate of the Crescent, Stella a little in front of Phil and the children, with their baskets, and instinctively he drew back. His heart, too sore and discomfited, shrank from this encounter, yet wanted its friendly solace—bore a grudge against this influence, yet craved its cool innocence, and the pleasure of watching Stella's face. From against the wall behind the piano he saw her come in and stand looking a little blank as though disappointed; then she saw him and smiled, a swift, brilliant smile which warmed yet irritated Ashurst.

"You never came after us, Frank."

"No; I found I couldn't."

"Look! We picked such lovely late violets!" She held out a bunch. Ashurst put his nose to them, and there stirred within him vague longings, chilled instantly by a vision of Megan's anxious face lifted to the faces of the passers-by.

He said shortly: "How jolly!" and turned away. He went up to his room, and, avoiding the children, who were coming up the stairs, threw himself on his bed, and lay there with his arms crossed over his face. Now that he felt the die really cast, and Megan given up, he hated himself, and almost hated the Hallidays and their atmosphere of healthy, happy English homes. Why should they have chanced here, to drive away first love—to show him that he was going to be no better than a common seducer? What right had Stella, with her fair, shy beauty, to make him know for certain that he would never marry Megan; and, tarnishing it all, bring him such bitterness of regretful longing and such pity? Megan would be back by now, worn out by her miserable seeking—poor little thing!—expecting, perhaps, to find him there when she reached home. Ashurst bit at his sleeve, to stifle a groan of remorseful longing. He went to dinner glum and silent, and his mood threw a dinge even over the children. It was a melancholy, rather ill-tempered evening, for they were all tired; several times he caught Stella looking at him with a hurt, puzzled expression, and this pleased his evil mood. He slept miserably; got up quite early, and wandered out. He went down to the beach. Alone there with the serene, the blue, the sunlit sea, his heart relaxed a little. Conceited fool—to think that Megan would take it so hard! In a week or two she would almost have forgotten! And he—well, he would have the reward of virtue! A good young man! If Stella knew, she would give him her blessing for resisting that devil she believed in; and he uttered a hard laugh. But slowly the peace and beauty of sea and sky, the flight of the lonely sea-gulls, made him feel ashamed. He bathed, and turned homewards.

In the Crescent gardens Stella herself was sitting on a camp-stool, sketching. He stole up close behind. How fair and pretty she was, bent diligently, holding up her brush, measuring, wrinkling her brows.

He said gently: "Sorry I was such a beast last night, Stella."

She turned round, startled, flushed very pink, and said in her quick way: "It's all right. I knew there was something. Between friends it doesn't matter, does it?"

Ashurst answered: "Between friends—and we are, aren't we?"

She looked up at him, nodded vehemently, and her upper teeth gleamed again in that swift, brilliant smile.

Three days later he went back to London, traveling with the Hallidays. He had not written to the farm. What was there he could say?

On the last day of April in the following year he and Stella were married. . . .

Such were Ashurst's memories, sitting against the wall among the gorse, on his silver-wedding day. At this very spot, where he had laid out the lunch, Megan must have stood outlined against the sky when he had first caught sight of her. Of all queer coincidences! And there moved in him a longing to go down and see again the farm and the orchard, and the meadow of the gypsy bogle. It would not take long; Stella would be an hour yet, perhaps.

How well he remembered it all—the little crowning group of pine-trees, the steep-up grass hill behind! He paused at the farm gate. The low stone house, the yew-tree porch, the flowering currants—not changed a bit; even the old green chair was out there on the grass under the window, where he had reached up to her that night to take the key. Then he turned down the lane, and stood leaning on the orchard gate—grey skeleton of a gate, as then. A black pig even was wandering in there among the trees. Was it true that twenty-six years had passed, or had he dreamed and awakened to find Megan waiting for him by the big apple-tree? Unconsciously he put up his hand to his grizzled beard and brought himself back to reality. Opening the gate, he made his way down through the docks and nettles till he came to the edge, and the old apple-tree itself. Unchanged! A little more of the grey-green lichen, a dead branch or two, and for the rest it might have been only last night that he had embraced that mossy trunk after Megan's flight and inhaled its woody savour, while above his head the moonlit blossom had seemed to breathe and live. In that early spring a few buds were showing already; the blackbirds shouting their songs, a cuckoo calling, the sunlight bright and warm. Incredibly the same—the chattering trout-stream, the narrow pool he had lain in every morning, splashing the water over his flanks and chest; and out there in the wild meadow the beech clump and the stone where the gypsy bogle was supposed to sit. And an ache for lost youth, a hankering, a sense of wasted love and sweetness, gripped Ashurst by the throat. Surely, on this earth of such wild beauty, one was meant to hold rapture to one's heart, as this earth and sky held it! And yet, one could not!

He went to the edge of the stream, and, looking down at the little pool, thought: "Youth and spring! What has become of them all, I won-der?" And then, in sudden fear of having this memory jarred by human encounter, he went back to the lane, and pensively retraced his steps to the cross-roads.

Beside the car an old, grey-bearded labourer was leaning on a stick, talking to the chauffeur. He broke off at once, as though guilty of disre-spect, and, touching his hat, prepared to limp on down the lane.

Ashurst pointed to the narrow green mound. "Can you tell me what this is?"

The old fellow stopped; on his face had come a look as though he were thinking: "You've come to the right shop, Mister!"

" 'Tes a grave," he said.

"But why out here?"

The old man smiled. "That's a tale, as yu may say. An' not the first time as I've a-told et—there's plenty folks asks 'bout that bit o' turf. 'Maid's Grave' us calls et, 'ereabouts."

Ashurst held out his pouch. "Have a fill?"

The old man touched his hat again, and slowly filled an old clay pipe. His eyes, looking upward out of a mass of wrinkles and hair, were still quite bright.

"If yu don' mind, zurr, I'll zet down—my leg's 'urtin' a bit to-day." And he sat down on the mound of turf.

"There's always a vlower on this grave. An' 'tain't so very lonesome, neither; brave lot o' folks goes by now, in they new motor cars an' things —not as 'twas in th' old days. She've a-got company up 'ere. 'Twas a poor soul killed 'erself."

"I see!" said Ashurst. "Cross-roads burial. I didn't know that custom was kept up."

"Ah! but 'twas a main long time ago. Us 'ad a parson as was very God-fearin' then. Let me see, I've 'ad my pension six year come Michaelmas, an' I were just on fifty when 't 'appened. There's none livin' knows more about et than what I du. She belonged close 'ere; same farm as where I used to work along o' Mrs. Narracombe—'tes Nick Narracombe's now; I dus a bit for 'im still, odd times."

Ashurst, who was leaning against the gate, lighting his pipe, left his curved hands before his face for long after the flame of the match had gone out.

"Yes?" he said, and to himself his voice sounded hoarse and queer.

"She was one in an 'underd, poor maid! I putts a vlower 'ere every time I passes. Pretty maid an' gude maid she was, though they wouldn't burry 'er up tu th' church, nor where she wanted to be burried neither." The old labourer paused, and put his hairy, twisted hand flat down on the turf beside the blue bells.

"Yes?" said Ashurst.

"In a manner of speakin'," the old man went on, "I think as 'twas a love-story—though there's no one never knu for zartin. Yu can't tell what's in a maid's 'ead—but that's wot I think about it." He drew his hand along the turf. "I was fond o' that maid—don' know as there was any one as wasn' fond of 'er. But she was tu lovin'-'earted—that's where 'twas, I think." He looked up. And Ashurst, whose lips were trembling in the cover of his beard, murmured again: "Yes?"

" 'Twas in the spring, 'bout now as't might be, or a little later—blossom time—an' we 'ad one o' they young college gentlemen stayin' at the farm —nice feller tu, with 'is 'ead in the air. I liked 'e very well, an' I never see nothin' between 'em, but to my thinkin' 'e turned the maid's fancy." The old man took the pipe out of his mouth, spat, and went on:

"Yu see, 'e went away sudden one day, an' never come back. They got 'is knapsack and bits o' things down there still. That's what stuck in my mind—'is never sendin' for 'em. 'Is name was Ashes, or somethin' like that."

"Yes?" said Ashurst once more.

The old man licked his lips.

" 'Er never said nothin', but from that day 'er went kind of dazed lukin';

didn' seem rightly therr at all. I never knu a 'uman creature so changed in me life—never. There was another young feller at the farm—Joe Bid-daford 'is name wer'—that was praaperly sweet on 'er, tu; I guess 'e used to plague 'er wi' 'is attentions. She got to luke quite wild. I'd zee her sometimes of an avenin' when I was bringin' up the calves; ther' she'd stand in th' orchard, under the big apple-tree, lukin' straight before 'er. 'Well,' I used t' think, 'I dunno what 'tes that's the matter wi' yu, but yu'm lukin' pittiful, that yu be!' "

The old man relit his pipe, and sucked at it reflectively.

"Yes?" said Ashurst.

"I remembers one day I said to 'er: 'What's the matter, Megan?'—'er name was Megan David, she come from Wales same as 'er aunt, ol' Missis Narracombe. 'Yu'm frettin' about something,' I says. 'No, Jim,' she says, 'I'm not frettin'.' 'Yes, yu be!' I says. 'No,' she says, and tu tears cam' rollin' out. 'Yu'm cryin'—what's that, then?' I says. She putts 'er 'and over 'er 'eart: 'It 'urts me,' she says; 'but 'twill sune be better,' she says. 'But if anything shude 'appen to me, Jim, I wants to be buried under this 'ere apple-tree.' I laughed. 'What's goin' to 'appen to yu?' I says: 'don't 'ee be fulish.' 'No,' she says, 'I won't be fulish.' Well, I know what maids are, an' I never thought no more about et, till tu days arter that, 'bout six in the avenin' I was comin' up wi' the calves, when I see somethin' dark lyin' in the strame, close to that big apple-tree. I says to meself: 'Is that a pig—funny place for a pig to get to!' an' I goes up to et, an' I see what 'twas."

The old man stopped: his eyes, turned upward, had a bright, suffering look.

" 'Twas the maid, in a little narrer pool ther' that's made by the stoppin' of a rock—where I see the young gentleman bathin' once or twice. 'Er was lyin' on 'er face in the watter. There was a plant o' goldie-cups growin' out o' the stone just above 'er 'ead. An' when I come to luke at 'er face, 'twas luvly, butiful, so calm's a baby's—wonderful butiful et was. When the doctor saw 'er, 'e said: ' 'Er culdn' never a-done it in that lit-tle bit o' watter if 'er 'adn't a-been in an extarsy.' Ah! an' judgin' from 'er face, that was just 'ow she was. Et made me cry praaper—butiful et was! 'Twas June then, but she'd a-found a little bit of apple-blossom left over somewheres, and stuck et in 'er 'air. That's why I thinks 'er must a-been in an extarsy, to go to et gay, like that. Why! there wasn't more than a fute and 'arf o' watter. But I tell 'ee one thing—that meadder's 'arnted; I knu et, an' she knu et; an' no one'll persuade me as 'tesn't. I told 'em what she said to me 'bout bein' burried under th' apple-tree. But I think that turned 'em—made et luke tu much 's ef she'd 'ad it in 'er mind deliberate; an' so they burried 'er up 'ere. Parson we 'ad then was very particular, 'e was."

Again the old man drew his hand over the turf.

" 'Tes wonderful, et seems," he added slowly, "what maids 'll du for love. She 'ad a lovin' 'eart; I guess 'twas broken. But us never *knu* nothin'!"

He looked up as if for approval of his story, but Ashurst had walked past him as if he were not there.

Up on the top of the hill, beyond where he had spread the lunch, over, out of sight, he lay down on his face. So had his virtue been rewarded, and "the Cyprian," goddess of love, taken her revenge! And before his eyes, dim with tears, came Megan's face with the sprig of apple-blossoms in her dark, wet hair. "What did I do that was wrong?" he thought. "What did I do?" But he could not answer. Spring, with its rush of passion, its flowers and song—the spring in his heart and Megan's! Was it just Love seeking a victim! The Greek was right, then—the words of the "Hippolytus" as true to-day!

> For mad is the heart of Love,
> And gold the gleam of his wing;
> And all to the spell thereof
> Bend when he makes his spring.
> All life that is wild and young
> In mountain and wave and stream,
> All that of earth is sprung,
> Or breathes in the red sunbeam;
> Yea, and Mankind. O'er all a royal throne
> Cyprian, Cyprian, is thine alone!

The Greek was right! Megan! Poor little Megan—coming over the hill! Megan under the old apple-tree waiting and looking! Megan dead, with beauty printed on her! . . .

A voice said: "Oh, there you are! Look."

Ashurst rose, took his wife's sketch, and stared at it in silence.

"Is the foreground right, Frank?"

"Yes."

"But there's something wanting, isn't there?"

Ashurst nodded. Wanting? The apple-tree, the singing, and the gold!

Gustave Flaubert

1821–1880

Gustave Flaubert was born in Rouen, France, on December 12, 1821. He grew up in the city hospital, where his father was chief surgeon. In 1837, while he was still in school, his work was first published in a review, *Le Colibri*. He visited the Pyrénées, Marseilles, and Corsica with the anatomist Jules Cloquet and studied law at the University of Paris. Nervous troubles and lack of interest caused him to drop out. After the death of his father and sister in 1846, he retired with his mother to the family estate at Croisset on the Seine, where he would spend most of his life.

In the summer of that year he met the poet Louise Colet and began a nine-year association with her. A walking tour in Brittany with the writer Maxime du Camp produced *By Fields and by Strands*, published after his death. During this period he was engaged on manuscripts that would later be reworked into his famous books. In 1849–51 he and du Camp traveled in Egypt, Palestine, Syria, Turkey, Greece, and Italy.

Five years of steady labor created *Madame Bovary*, perhaps the first modern novel. In 1856 it was brought out in the *Revue de Paris* and appeared as a book the next year. At once the French government indicted Flaubert on charges of immorality. He was acquitted. Six months later the same court convicted the poet Baudelaire for certain poems in *Les Fleurs du mal*.

Flaubert traveled in North Africa and devoured whole libraries to produce *Salammbô*, a novel about Hamilcar's daughter and the war between Carthaginians and mercenaries. The book, published in 1862 (dated 1863), was given a triumphant welcome. Like Henry James, Flaubert wrote plays and had little luck with them. The novel *Sentimental Education*, his great picture of Paris in mid-century, went largely unnoticed in the excitement that preceded the War of 1870.

Then there were Prussians in Flaubert's garden at Croisset. After the war, his niece's husband was threatened with bankruptcy. Flaubert signed over his fortune to them. *The Temptation of Saint Anthony* appeared in 1874. *Three Tales*, which included *A Simple Heart, The Legend of St. Julian the Hospitaller* (see below), and *Hérodias*, was published three years later. At his death, he had all but finished *Bouvard and Pécuchet*. He was the prime inventor of the modern novel, the first writer to treat the novel as an art and make it one. He died at Croisset on May 8, 1880.

I n 1846 Flaubert had seen and remembered a small statue of St. Julian at Caudebec. A stained-glass window in Rouen Cathedral, familiar to him since childhood, depicted episodes from St. Julian's life. Out of such hints he began to weave the superb tapestry of *The Legend of St. Julian the Hospitaller*. Aside from his extreme Christian charity, Flaubert's Julian bears little likeness to the saint. The canonized Julian was said to be an Egyptian who lived with his wife, Basilissa, "in perpetual chastity" and kept "a kind of hospital." It is reported that his skull was brought into France and presented to Queen Brunehault in the time of St. Gregory the Great.

Flaubert made a fresh beginning and created a medieval legend of great richness and power. Though it is written in sharp and compact modern French, it catches the tone and bare movement of the true medieval romance. It is graver and more realistic than such *romans d'aventure* as *Aucassin and Nicolette*.[1] Its magic and supernatural touches remind us of the Breton romances. But when we have said these things, we cannot help but acknowledge the quite "modern" starkness of Julian's mad hunting, the "modern" rightness of choice in each detail. Nor should we forget that Oedipus and Orestes too were condemned to the same fate as Julian, or what self-punishment they too found for themselves.

Out of his sense of guilt, his need for self-punishment—to do penance, in the religious phrase—comes Julian's humble and practical service to others. He does not call it love. But it is unlimited, as perfect love may be. He has risked his life many times,

---

[1] See Vol. 2, pp. 523–551, in this set.

boldly, in hunting and war. Now he is willing to risk it again to save a loathsome fellow creature from freezing to death. So the Leper and Julian are both transformed. A miracle happens—the kind of miracle we encounter in the literature of every compassionate religion, because the need to help others, even at the risk of our lives, is a basic human trait of feeling. We are not surprised that Turgenev translated his friend's tale into Russian. Readers of Dostoevsky and the later Tolstoy would understand it very well.

But unlike Tolstoy, Flaubert allows no moralizing shadow to fall on his page. "Devotion to art was a law of his nature," says the biographer Philip Spencer. From first to last the tale must be held to its own true shape and feeling. And what a triumph of selection and placement it is! What a living stir and color it has! *St. Julian* contains enough movement for a dozen historical novels, yet it remains perfectly in scale. We follow it as eagerly as if it were some trivial adventure story, convinced that even its phantoms and speaking animals are "true," happy or grieved or horrified at Julian's progress through a world of coarse sense and spirit. Does it tell us something about the mixture of masculine and feminine in our nature? Is it a parable of moral death and redemption? Or of perfect mystical union with Christ? Or do we find in Julian a symbol of man at war, who can be brought to love again only by overwhelming guilt and grief?

The Legend of St. Julian
the Hospitaller

Julian's father and mother lived in a castle with a forest round it, on the slope of a hill.

The four towers at its corners had pointed roofs covered with scales of lead, and the walls were planted upon shafts of rock which fell steeply to the bottom of the moat. The pavement of the court-yard was as clean as the flag-stones of a church. Long gutter spouts in the form of leaning dragons spat the rain-water down into the cistern; and on the window-ledges of each story, in pots of painted earthenware, a heliotrope or basil flowered.

A second enclosure made with stakes held a fruit-orchard to begin with, and then a flower garden patterned into figures; then a trellis with arbours where you took the air, and an alley for the pages to play mall. On the other side were the kennels, the stables, the bake-house, the presses, and the barns. A green and turfy pasture spread all round this, enclosed in turn by a stout thorn-hedge.

They had lived at peace so long that the portcullis was never lowered now. The moats were full of grass; swallows nested in the cracks of the battlements; and when the sun blazed too strongly the archer who paced all day long the rampart took refuge in his turret and slept like a monk.

Inside there was a sheen of ironwork everywhere; the rooms were hung with tapestries against the cold; the cupboards overflowed with linen; casks of wine were piled up in the cellars, and the oaken coffers creaked with the weight of bags of money. In the armoury, between standards and wild beasts' heads, could be seen weapons of every age and every nation, from the slings of the Amalekites and the javelins of the Garamantes to the short swords of the Saracens and Norman coats of mail. The chief spit in the kitchen could roast an ox; the chapel was as splendid as a king's oratory. There was even, in a secluded corner, a Roman vapour-bath; but the good lord abstained from using it, considering it a practice of the heathen.

Wrapped always in a mantle of fox skins, he walked about his castle, administering justice to his vassals and setting the disputes of his neighbours at rest. In winter he watched the snowflakes falling or had stories read to him. With the first fine days he rode out on his mule along the by-ways, beside the greening corn, and chatted with the peasants, to whom he gave advice. After many adventures he had taken a lady of high lineage as his wife.

Very white of skin she was, a little proud and serious. The horns of her coif brushed against the door lintel, and the train of her dress trailed three paces behind her. Her household was ordered like the inside of a monastery; every morning she gave out the tasks to the servants, inspected the preserves and unguents, span at her distaff or embroidered altar-cloths. By dint of prayer to God a son was born to her.

Then there were great rejoicings and a banquet which lasted three days and four nights, with the illumination of torches, the sound of harps, and strewing of green branches. They ate of the rarest spices, and fowls as large as sheep; a dwarf came out of a pasty, to amuse the guests; and as the throng was always increasing and the bowls would go round no longer, they were obliged to drink out of horns and helmets.

The lady who had just been made a mother was not present at this cheer. She stayed quietly in her bed. Waking one evening, she saw as it were a shadow moving under a ray of the moon which came through the window. It was an old man in a frieze gown, with a chaplet at his side, a wallet on his shoulder, and all the semblance of a hermit. He came towards her pillow and said to her, without opening his lips: "Rejoice, O mother, thy son shall be a saint!"

She was just going to cry out, but he glided over the streak of moonlight, rose gently into the air and vanished. The songs of the banqueters broke out louder. She heard angels' voices; and her head fell back on the pillow, over which, framed with garnets, hung a martyr's bone.

Next morning all the servants were questioned and said they had seen no hermit. Whether it were a dream or reality, it must have been a communication from Heaven; but she was careful not to speak of it, fearing she might be taxed with pride.

The guests went off at morning twilight, and Julian's father was outside the postern gate, to which he had just escorted the last to go, when suddenly a beggar rose before him in the mist. He was a gipsy, with a plaited beard and silver rings on his arms, and fiery eyes. With an air of inspiration he stammered these disjointed words:

"Ah, ah! thy son! Blood in plenty! . . . Fame in plenty! . . . Blest always—the family of an emperor!"

And stooping to pick up his alms he was lost in the grass and disappeared.

The good castellan looked right and left, and called with all his might. No one! The wind blew shrill; the mists of morning flew away.

He put down this vision to a weary head, from having slept too little. "If I speak of it they will make a jest of me," he said to himself. Yet the glories destined to his son dazzled him, although the promise was not clear and he doubted even whether he had heard it.

The husband and wife each kept their secret. But they cherished their child, both of them, with an equal love; and, reverencing him as marked out by God, had an infinite care for his person. His cot was stuffed with the finest down; a lamp shaped like a dove burned continually above it, three nurses rocked him; and well swaddled in his clothes, with his rosy looks and blue eyes, a brocade cloak and a cap set with pearls, he looked a little Jesus. He teethed without crying at any time.

When he was seven his mother taught him to sing. To make him brave his father lifted him on to a big horse. The child smiled with pleasure and before long knew all about chargers.

A learned old monk taught him Holy Writ, the Arabic way of counting, the Latin letters, and how to make dainty pictures on vellum. They worked together high up in a turret away from all noise. The lesson over, they came down into the garden and studied the flowers, pausing at every step.

Sometimes a string of laden beasts was seen passing below in the valley, led by a man on foot dressed in the Eastern way. The castellan, recognizing him for a merchant, would send a servant out to him, and the stranger, taking heart, would turn out of his road. He would be brought into the parlour, where he drew out of his coffers strips of velvet and silk, jewels, perfumes, and curious things of unknown use; after which the worthy man went off, having taken a great profit and suffered no violence. At other times a band of pilgrims would come knocking at the gate. Their draggled garments steamed before the fire; and when they had been well fed they told the story of their travels: wanderings on shipboard over foamy seas, journeyings afoot in burning sands, the furious rage of paynims, the caves of Syria, the Manger and the Sepulchre. Then they would give the young lord scallop-shells from their cloaks.

Often the castellan feasted his old companions-at-arms. While they drank they called to mind their wars and the storming of fortresses, with the crash of warlike engines and the prodigious wounds. Julian listened to them and uttered cries; and his father had no doubt, then, that he would be a conqueror one day. Yet at evening, coming from the Angelus, as he passed between the bending rows of poor, he dipped in his purse with such modesty and so noble a mien that his mother thought surely to see him an archbishop in his time.

His place in chapel was by the side of his parents, and however long the offices might be he stayed kneeling at his stool, with his cap on the floor and his hands clasped in prayer.

One day, while mass was being said, he raised his head and saw a little white mouse coming out of a hole in the wall. It trotted along the first pace of the altar, and after making two or three turns to right and left fled by the way it had come. Next Sunday he was troubled by the thought that he might see it again. It did come back; and then every Sunday he watched for it, was troubled, seized with hatred for it, and determined to get rid of the mouse.

So, having shut the door and sprinkled some cake crumbs along the altar steps, he took post in front of the hole with a little stick in his hand.

After a very long time a small pink nose appeared, and then the entire mouse. He struck a light blow, and stood lost in amazement at this tiny body which did not stir again. A drop of blood spotted the pavement. Julian wiped it off rapidly with his sleeve, threw the mouse away, and did not say a word to anyone.

There were all kinds of little birds which pecked at the seeds in the garden. Julian had the thought of putting peas into a hollow reed. When he heard the sound of chirruping in a tree he came up softly, lifted his pipe, and blew out his cheeks; and the little creatures rained down in such abundance on his shoulders that he could not help laughing in delight at his trick.

One morning, as he was going back along the curtain wall, he saw a fat pigeon on the top of the rampart, preening itself in the sun. Julian stopped to look at it, and as there was a breach in this part of the wall a fragment of stone lay ready to his hand. He swung his arm, and the stone brought down the bird, which fell like a lump into the moat.

He dashed down after it, tearing himself in the briars and scouring everywhere, nimbler than a young dog. The pigeon, its wings broken, hung quivering in the boughs of a privet. The obstinate life in it annoyed the child. He began to throttle it, and the bird's convulsions made his heart beat, filled him with a savage, passionate delight. When it stiffened for the last time he felt that he would swoon.

At supper in the evening his father declared that it was time for him to learn the art of venery, and he went to look for an old manuscript which contained, in questions and answers, the whole pastime of the chase. A master explained in it to his pupil the craft of breaking in dogs, taming falcons, and setting snares; how to know the stag by his droppings, the fox by his foot-marks, the wolf by his scratchings of the ground; the right way to discern their tracks, the manner of starting them, the usual places of their lairs, the most favourable winds, and a list of all the calls and the rules for the quarry.

When Julian could repeat all this by heart his father gathered a pack of hounds for him.

The first to catch the eye were twenty-four greyhounds from Barbary, swifter than gazelles, but prone to get out of hand; and then seventeen couples of Breton hounds, with red coats and white spots, unshakeable in control, deep-chested, loud to bay. To face the wild boar and its dangerous redoublings there were forty boar-hounds, as shaggy as bears. Mastiffs from Tartary nearly as tall as asses and flame-coloured, with broad backs and straight legs, were assigned to hunt the aurochs. The black coats of the spaniels shone like satin, and the yapping of the talbots matched the chanting of the beagles. In a yard by themselves, tossing their chains and rolling their eyes, growled eight Alain dogs, fearsome animals that fly at the belly of a horseman and have no dread of lions.

All of them ate wheaten bread, drank out of stone troughs, and bore sonorous names.

The falconry, maybe, was choicer even than the pack; for by dint of money the good lord had secured tercelets of the Caucasus, sakers from Babylonia, gerfalcons of Germany, and peregrines taken on the cliffs at the edge of cold seas in far quarters of the world. They were housed in a big shed roofed with thatch, and fastened to the perching bar in a row according to their size, with a strip of turf before them where they were placed from time to time to unstiffen their limbs.

Purse-nets, hooks, wolf-traps, and engines of every kind were artfully made.

Often they took out setters into the country, who quickly came to a point. Then huntsmen, advancing step by step, cautiously spread a huge net over their motionless bodies. At a word of command they barked; quails took wing; and the ladies of the neighbourhood who had been bidden with their husbands, the children, the handmaids, the whole company darted on the birds and easily caught them. At other times they would beat drums to start the hares; foxes fell into pits, or a trap would spring and take hold of a wolf's paw.

But Julian spurned these handy devices. He preferred to hunt far away from the rest with his horse and his falcon. It was almost always a great Scythian tartaret, white as snow. Its leathern hood was topped with a plume, bells of gold quivered on its blue feet; and it stood firmly in its master's arm while the horse galloped and the plains unrolled below. Julian, freeing the jesses, would suddenly let it go; the daring bird rose straight as an arrow into the sky; and you saw two specks, one larger and one smaller, circle, meet, and then vanish in the high blue spaces. The falcon soon came down, tearing a quarry, and returned to perch on the gauntlet with its wings a-quiver.

In that way Julian flew his falcons at the heron, the kite, the crow, and the vulture.

He loved to blow his horn and follow his hounds as they coursed along the sloping hills, jumped the streams, and climbed to the woods again; and when the stag began groaning under their bites he felled it cleverly, and was delighted by the fury of the mastiffs as they devoured it, hewn in pieces on its reeking hide.

On misty days he went down into a marsh to ambush the geese, otters, and wild duck.

Three squires waited for him from dawn at the foot of the steps, and though the old monk might lean out of his window and make signs to call him back Julian would not turn. He went out in the heat of the sun, under the rain, and amidst storms, drinking water from the springs out of his hand, munching wild apples as he trotted along, and resting under an oak if he were tired; and he came in at midnight covered in blood and mire, with thorns in his hair and the odour of the wild beasts hanging round him. He became as one of them. When his mother kissed him he took her embrace coldly, and seemed to be dreaming of deep things.

He slew bears with strokes of his knife, bulls with the axe, and wild boars with the pike; and once, even, defended himself with nothing but a stick against wolves that were gnawing corpses at the foot of a gibbet.

One winter morning he started in full trim before dawn, with a crossbow on his shoulder and a quiver of arrows at his saddle-bow.

His Danish jennet [horse], followed by two bassets, made the earth ring under its even tread. Drops of rime stuck to his cloak, and a fierce breeze blew. The sky lightened at one side, and in the pale twilight he saw rabbits hopping at the edge of their burrows. The two bassets dashed for them at once, jumping hither and thither as they broke their backs.

Soon after he entered a wood. At the end of a branch a grouse, numbed by the cold, slept with its head under its wing. With a back-stroke of his sword Julian cut off its two feet, and without stopping to pick it up went on his way.

Three hours later he found himself on the top of a mountain, which was so high that the sky seemed almost black. A rock like a long wall sloped away in front of him, cresting a precipice; and at the farther end of it two wild goats were looking down into the chasm. Not having his arrows at hand—he had left his horse behind—he thought he would go right down upon the goats; and stooping double, barefoot, he reached the first of them at last and plunged his dagger under its ribs. The other was seized with panic and jumped into the abyss. Julian leaped to strike it, and, his right foot slipping, fell across the body of the first, with his face hanging over the gulf and arms flung wide.

He came down into the plain again and followed a line of willows bordering a river. Cranes, flying very low, passed overhead from time to time. Julian brought them down with his whip, not missing one.

Meanwhile the air had grown warmer and melted the rime; there were broad wreaths of vapour floating, and the sun appeared. Far off he saw a still lake glistening like a sheet of lead. In the middle of it was an animal which Julian did not know, a black-headed beaver. In spite of the distance he killed it with an arrow, and was vexed not to be able to carry off its skin.

Then he went on down an avenue of great trees, whose tops made a kind of triumphal arch at the entrance of a forest. A roebuck bounded out of a thicket, a fallow deer showed itself at a crossing, a badger came out of a hole, a peacock spread its tail on the grass; and when he had slain them all more roebuck, deer, badgers, peacocks and blackbirds, jays, polecats, foxes, hedgehogs, lynxes—an endless company of beasts—appeared and grew more numerous at every step. Tremblingly they circled round him, with gentle supplicating looks. But Julian did not tire of killing, by turns bending his cross-bow, unsheathing his long sword, and thrusting with his short, thinking of nothing, with no memory of anything at all. Only the fact of his existence told him that for an indefinite time he had been hunting in some vague country, where all happened with the ease of dreams. An extraordinary sight brought him to a halt. A valley shaped like an arena was filled with stags, who crowded close together warming each other with their breath, which could be seen steaming in the mist.

The prospect of a slaughter like this for a minute or two took Julian's breath away for pleasure. Then he dismounted, rolled up his sleeves, and began to shoot.

At the whistle of the first arrow all the stags turned their heads at once. Hollows opened in the mass, plaintive cries rose, and a great stir shook the herd.

The brim of the valley was too high to climb. They leaped about in this enclosure, trying to escape. Julian aimed and shot, and the arrows fell like rain shafts in a thunder-storm. The maddened stags fought, reared, and climbed on each other's backs; and the bodies and entangled antlers made a broad mound which crumbled and changed.

At last they died, stretched on the sand, their nostrils frothing, entrails bursting, and bellies slowly ceasing to heave. Then all was motionless. Night was close at hand; and behind the woods, in the interspaces of the boughs, the sky was red as a sheet of blood.

Julian leant back against a tree, and gazed with staring eyes at the enormous massacre; he could not think how it had been done.

Then across the valley, at the edge of the forest, he saw a stag with its hind and its fawn.

The stag was black and hugely tall; it carried sixteen points and a white beard. The hind, pale yellow like a dead leaf, was grazing; and the spotted fawn, without hindering her movements, pulled at her dugs.

Once more the cross-bow sang. The fawn was killed on the spot. Then its mother, looking skyward, bellowed with a deep, heart-breaking, human cry. In exasperation Julian stretched her on the ground with a shot full in the breast.

The great stag had seen it, and made a bound. Julian shot his last arrow at him. It hit the stag in the forehead and stuck fast there.

The great stag did not seem to feel it; striding over the dead bodies, he came on and on, in act to charge and disembowel him; and Julian retreated in unspeakable terror. The monstrous creature stopped, and with flaming eyes, as solemn as a patriarch or judge, said three times, while a bell tinkled in the distance:

"Accurst! accurst! accurst! one day, ferocious heart, thou shalt murder thy father and thy mother!"

The stag's knees bent, his eyes closed gently, and he died.

Julian was thunderstruck, and then suddenly felt crushed with fatigue;

disgust and boundless sadness came over him. He buried his face in his hands and wept for a long time.

His horse was lost, his dogs had left him; the solitude which folded round him seemed looming with vague dangers. Seized with alarm, he struck across country, and choosing a path at random found himself almost immediately at the castle-gate.

He could not sleep at night. By the flickering of the hanging lamps he always saw the great black stag. The creature's prophecy besieged him, and he fought against it. "No! no! no! it cannot be that I should kill them!" And then he mused: "Yet if I should wish to kill?" and he was afraid that the Devil might inspire him with the wish.

For three months his mother prayed in anguish by his pillow, and his father walked to and fro along the corridors with groans. He sent for the most famous master physicians, who prescribed quantities of drugs. Julian's malady, they said, was caused by a noxious wind, or by a love-desire. But the young man, in answer to all questions, shook his head.

His strength came back to him, and they took him out to walk in the court-yard, the old monk and the good lord each propping him with an arm.

When he had recovered altogether he obstinately refused to hunt. His father, hoping to cheer him, made him a present of a great Saracen sword. It was in a stand of arms, at the top of a pillar, and a ladder was needed to reach it. Julian went up. The sword was too heavy and slipped from his fingers, and in the fall grazed the worthy lord so close as to cut his mantle; Julian thought he had killed his father, and fainted away.

From that moment he dreaded weapons. The sight of a bare blade made him turn pale. This weakness was a sorrow to his family, and at last the old monk, in the name of God, of honour, and his ancestors, bade him take up the exercises of his gentle birth again.

The squires amused themselves daily at practising with the javelin. Julian very quickly excelled in this; he could throw his javelin into the neck of a bottle, break the teeth of a weather-vane, and hit the nails on a door a hundred paces off.

One summer evening, at the hour when things grow indistinct in the dusk, he was under the trellis in the garden and saw right at the end of it two white wings fluttering by the top of its supports. He made sure it was a stork, and threw his javelin. A piercing cry rang out.

It was his mother, whose bonnet with long flaps stayed pinned to the wall.

Julian fled from the castle and was seen there no more.

He took service with a passing troop of adventurers and knew hunger and thirst, fevers and vermin. He grew accustomed to the din of mellays and the sight of dying men. The wind tanned his skin. His limbs hardened under the clasp of armour; and as he was very strong, valiant, temperate, and wary he won the command of a company with ease.

When a battle opened he swept on his soldiers with a great flourish of his sword. He scaled the walls of citadels with a knotted rope at night, swinging in the blasts, while sparks of Greek fire stuck to his cuirass and boiling resin and molten lead hissed from the battlements. Often a stone crashed and shivered his buckler. Bridges overladen with men gave way under him. Swinging his battle-ax to and fro, he got rid of fourteen horsemen. In the lists he overcame all challengers. More than a score of times he was left for dead.

Thanks to the favour of Heaven he always came out safely, for he protected clerks, orphans, widows, and, most of all, old men. When he saw one of them walking in front of him he called out to see his face, as though he were afraid of killing him by mistake.

Runaway slaves, peasants in revolt, fortuneless bastards, and venturous men of all sorts flocked under his banner, and he made an army of his own.

It grew, and he became famous. The world sought him out. He succoured in turn the Dauphin of France and the King of England, the Templars of Jerusalem, the Surena of the Parthians, the Negus of Abyssinia, and the Emperor of Calicut. He fought against Scandinavians covered with fish-scales, Negroes with bucklers of hippopotamus hide, mounted on red asses, and gold-coloured Indians flourishing broadswords brighter than mirrors above their diadems. He subdued the Troglodytes and the Anthropophages. He went through such burning regions that the hair on the head caught fire of itself, like torches, in the sun's heat; through others so freezing that the arms snapped from the body and fell to the ground; and countries where there was so much mist that you walked surrounded by phantoms.

Republics in distress consulted him, and in colloquies with ambassadors he gained unhoped-for terms. If a monarch behaved too badly Julian was quickly on the spot and took him to task. He set free peoples and delivered queens immured in towers. He it was, no other, who slew the viper of Milan and the dragon of Oberbirbach.

Now the Emperor of Occitania, having triumphed over the Spanish

Moslems, had taken the sister of the Caliph of Cordova as his concubine, and by her he had a daughter whom he had brought up to be a Christian. But the Caliph, feigning a wish to be converted, came to return his visit with a numerous escort, put all his garrison to the sword, and threw him into an underground dungeon, where he used him cruelly to extort his treasure.

Julian hastened to his aid, destroyed the army of the infidels, besieged the town, killed the Caliph, cut off his head, and threw it over the ramparts like a ball. Then he drew the Emperor out of prison and set him on his throne again, in the presence of all his court.

To requite this great service the Emperor presented him with basketfuls of money; Julian would have none of it. Thinking that he wanted more, he offered him three-quarters of his wealth, and was refused again; then the half of his kingdom; Julian thanked him and declined. The Emperor was in tears of distress, seeing no way to show his gratitude, when he tapped his forehead and whispered in a courtier's ear; the curtains of a tapestry lifted and a maiden appeared.

Her large dark eyes gleamed like two gentle lamps; her lips were parted in a winning smile. The ringlets of her hair caught in the jewels of a half-opened robe, and under the transparent tunic the young lines of her body could be guessed. She was slim of figure, all daintiness and softness.

Julian was dazzled with love, the more because he had lived in great chastity till then.

So he took the Emperor's daughter in marriage, with a castle that she held from her mother; and when the wedding was over he and his host parted, after a long exchange of courtesies.

It was a palace of white marble, in the Moorish fashion, built on a promontory in a grove of orange-trees. Terraces of flowers sloped to the edge of a bay, where there were pink shells that crackled under foot. Behind the castle stretched a forest in the shape of a fan. The sky was blue unceasingly, and the trees waved by turns under the sea breeze and the wind from the mountains, which closed the horizon far away.

The rooms were full of shadow, but drew light from their incrusted walls. High columns, slender as reeds, supported their domed vaults, which were embossed in relief to imitate the stalactites in caves. There were fountains in the greater rooms, mosaics in the courts, festooned partitions, delicacies of architecture beyond number, and everywhere so deep a silence that one heard the rustle of a scarf or the echo of a sigh.

Julian made war no longer. He rested with a quiet people round him, and every day a crowd passed before him, making obeisances and kissing hands in the Eastern style.

In his purple dress he would stay leaning in the embrasure of a window, recalling his hunts of former days; and he would have liked to scour the desert after gazelles and ostriches, hide among the bamboos to wait for leopards, traverse forests full of rhinoceroses, climb the most inaccessible mountain tops to take better aim at eagles, and fight with white bears on icebergs in the sea.

Sometimes, in dreams, he saw himself like our father Adam in the midst of Paradise, among all the beasts. He stretched out his arm against them, and they died; or else, again, they defiled before him, two by two according to their size, from the elephants and lions to the ermines and the ducks, as on the day when they entered Noah's ark. From the shadow of a cave he rained darts on them which never missed; other animals appeared; there was no end to them, and he woke with his eyes rolling wildly.

Among his friends there were princes who invited him to hunt. He always refused, thinking that by a penance of this kind he would turn aside his curse, for it seemed to him that the slaughter of animals would decide the fate of his father and mother. But it was a grief to him not to see his parents, and his other secret desire became impossible to bear.

His wife sent for jugglers and dancers to amuse him. She went out with him into the country in an open litter; and at other times they would lie in a boat and watch, over the side, the fish roaming in water as clear as the sky. Often she threw flowers in his face, or crouching at his feet drew music from a three-stringed mandolin; and then, laying her clasped hands on his shoulder, said timidly, "What ails thee then, dear Lord?"

He did not answer, or break into sobs. At last, one day, he confessed his horrible thought.

She fought against it, arguing very well. His father and mother, most likely, were already dead; but if he ever saw them again what chance or purpose could lead him to this abominable deed? His fear was causeless, then, and he should return to the hunt.

Julian smiled as he listened to her, but could not make up his mind to fulfil his desire.

One August evening they were in their chamber, she being just in bed and he kneeling down to pray, when he heard a fox barking, and then some light footfalls under the window. He caught a glimpse, in the dusk, of what seemed to be the shapes of animals. The temptation was too strong, and he took down his quiver.

She showed surprise.

"I do it to obey you," he said; "I shall be back at sunrise." Still, she was afraid of a disastrous venture.

He reassured her and went out, surprised at her inconsistent mood.

Soon afterwards a page came in to say that two strangers, as they could not see the absent lord, were asking instantly to see his lady.

And soon there entered the room an old man and an old woman, bowed and dusty, dressed in rough linen, each leaning on a staff.

Taking courage, they said that they were bringing Julian news of his parents. She leaned out of bed to listen.

But, having first exchanged a look, they asked her if he was still fond of them, and if he spoke of them at times.

"Ah, yes!" she said.

"Well, we are they!" they cried, and, being very weary and spent with fatigue, sat down.

The young wife felt no assurance that her husband was their son, but they proved it by describing some particular marks on his skin.

Then she leaped out of bed, called the page, and a repast was served to them.

They could scarcely eat, though they were very hungry; she observed, aside, how their bony hands trembled as they grasped the cups. They asked countless questions about Julian, and she answered all, but took care not to speak of the ghastly fancy in which they were concerned.

After waiting in vain for his return they had left their castle, and they had been travelling for several years after vague clues, without losing hope. So much money had been swallowed up by river tolls and inns, the dues of princes and demands of thieves that their purse was emptied to the bottom, and now they begged their way. But what of that, when they would soon embrace their son? They extolled his happiness to have so fair a wife, and could not have enough of watching her and kissing her.

They were much astonished by the richness of the room, and the old man, after examing its walls, asked why the Emperor of Occitania's coat of arms was there.

"He is my father," she replied.

At that he started, remembering the gipsy's prophecy, while the old woman thought of the hermit's words. Doubtless their son's glory was but the dawn of an eternal splendour; and they both sat open-mouthed under the light of the great candlestick upon the table.

They must have been very handsome in their youth. The mother had

kept all her hair, and its fine plaits hung to the bottom of her cheeks like
drifts of snow. The father, with his height and his great beard, was like a
statue in a church.

Julian's wife persuaded them not to wait for him. With her own hands
she placed them in her bed, then shut the window, and they went to
sleep. Daybreak was near, and little birds were beginning to sing outside.

Julian had crossed the park and walked through the forest with a
springing step, enjoying the soft turf and mild night air. Shadows fell
from the trees across the moss. From time to time the moonlight made
white patches in the drives and he hesitated to go forward, thinking he
saw a pool; or, again, the surface of the still ponds would itself be lost in
the colour of the grass. There was a deep silence everywhere, and he
found no trace of the animals which a few minutes earlier had been straying round his castle.

The wood thickened and grew profoundly dark. Puffs of warm air went
by him, with relaxing scents. His feet sank among dead leaves, and he
leaned against an oak to breathe a little.

Suddenly, from behind his back, a darker mass leaped out. It was a wild
boar. Julian had no time to snatch his bow, and was as vexed as though it
was a disaster.

Then, when he had left the wood, he saw a wolf stealing along a
hedge. Julian sent an arrow after it. The wolf paused, turned round to
look at him, and went on again. It trotted on, always at the same distance,
stopping from time to time, and taking flight again as soon as Julian
aimed.

In this way Julian went over an endless plain and a tract of sand-hills,
and came out upon high ground which looked over a great breadth of
country. Flat stones lay scattered on it from ruined vaults all round. His
feet stumbled on dead bones, and in places there were worm-eaten
crosses leaning mournfully askew. But forms stirred in the dim shadow
of the tombs; and hyenas rose out of them, scared and panting. Their
hoofs clattered on the pave-stones as they came up to Julian, sniffing
at him and showing their gums with a yawn. When he drew his sword
they went off at once in all directions, with a headlong, limping gallop
which lasted till they vanished in the distance under a cloud of dust.

An hour later he met a savage bull in a ravine, lowering its horns and
ploughing the sand up with its foot. Julian thrust with his lance at it under the dewlap. The lance was shivered, as though the animal were
made of bronze; he closed his eyes, expecting to be killed. When he reopened them the bull had disappeared.

Then his heart sank for shame. A higher power was bringing his strength to nought, and he went back into the forest to regain his home.

The forest was tangled with creepers; and as he was cutting them with his sword a marten slipped sharply between his legs, a panther made a bound over his shoulder, and a snake wound its way up an ash tree. A huge jackdaw looked down at Julian out of its leaves, and on every side among the branches appeared a multitude of great sparks, as though the firmament had showered all its stars into the forest. They were eyes of animals—wild cats, squirrels, owls, parrots, monkeys.

Julian darted his arrows at them; the feathered shafts settled on the leaves like white butterflies. He threw stones at them, and the stones fell back without touching anything. He cursed, wanted to fight, shouted imprecations, and choked with rage.

And all the animals which he had been hunting appeared again and made a narrow circle round him. Some sat upon their haunches, others stood erect. He was rooted in the middle, frozen with terror, and impotent to move at all. With a supreme effort of will he took a step; the creatures on the branches spread their wings, those on the ground stretched their limbs, and all went on with him.

The hyenas walked in front, the wolf and the boar behind. The bull was on his right, swaying its head, while on his left the serpent wound through the grass and the panther arched its back and advanced with long, velvet-footed strides. He walked as slowly as he could to avoid irritating them; and as he went he saw porcupines, foxes, vipers, jackals, and bears come out of the dense undergrowth.

Julian began to run; they ran too. The serpent hissed, and the stinking creatures slavered. The wild boar's tusks prodded his heels, and the wolf rubbed the palms of his hands with his hairy muzzle. The monkeys pinched him and made faces, and the marten rolled over his feet. A bear swung its paw back and knocked his hat off, and the panther, which had been carrying an arrow in its mouth, let it fall in disdain.

Their sly movements gave peeps of irony. As they watched him out of the corner of their eyes they seemed to be meditating a plan of revenge; while he, deafened by the buzzing insects, lashed by the birds' tails, and smothered by the breath of the animals, walked with arms outstretched and eyes shut like a blind man, without even having strength to cry for mercy.

A cock-crow rang in the air, and others answered. It was day, and he recognized his palace roof beyond the orange-trees.

Then at the edge of a field he saw, three paces off him, some red partridges fluttering in the stubble. He unfastened his cloak and threw

it over them as a net. When he uncovered them he found but one, long
dead and rotten.

This deception infuriated him more than all the others. His thirst to
kill swept over him again, and for want of beasts he would gladly have
slain men.

He climbed the three terraces and burst open the door with a blow
of his fist; but when he reached the staircase his heart unbent at the
thought of his dear wife She was asleep, doubtless, and he would take
her by surprise.

He drew off his sandals, turned the lock gently, and went in.

The pale dawn came dimly through the leaded window-panes. Julian's
feet caught in clothes lying on the floor; a little farther, and he knocked
against a buffet still laden with plate. "Her supper, doubtless," he said
to himself, and went on towards the bed, which he could not see in the
darkness at the end of the room. He came close, and to kiss his wife
bent down over the pillow where the two heads were lying side by side
Then he felt the touch of a beard against his mouth.

He drew back, thinking he was going mad, but came near the bed
again, and as he felt about with his fingers they encountered long tresses
of hair. To convince himself that he was wrong he passed his hand
again slowly over the pillow. It was really a beard this time, and a man—
a man lying with his wife!

In a fit of boundless fury he leaped on them, striking with his dagger,
he stamped and foamed, roaring like a wild beast. Then he stopped.
The dead folk, pierced to the heart, had not so much as stirred. He listened closely to their dying groans, which almost kept time together;
and as they grew feebler another, in the far distance, took them up.
Vague at first, this plaintive, long-drawn voice came nearer, swelled, rang
cruelly; and he recognized in terror the belling of the great black stag.

And as he turned round he thought he saw his wife's ghost framed in
the doorway, with a light in her hand.

The noise of the murder had drawn her there. In one wide glance she
grasped it all, and fled in horror, dropping her torch. He picked it up.

His father and mother lay before him, stretched on their backs, with
breasts pierced through; and their faces, in a gentle majesty, looked as
though they were keeping a secret for ever. Splashes and pools of blood
showed on their white skin, over the bed-clothes and the floor, and trick-
led down an ivory crucifix in the alcove. The scarlet reflection from the
window, which the sun was striking, lit up these red patches and cast
others, more numerous still, all round the room. Julian walked towards

the two dead figures, saying to himself, and struggling to believe, that this thing could not be and that he was deceived by an error—by one of those resemblances which nothing can explain. Finally he bent down a little to look close at the old man, and saw between the unshut eyelids a glazed eye which scorched him like fire. Then he went to the other side of the couch where the other body lay, its white hair hiding part of the face. Julian passed his fingers under the plaits and lifted the head; and holding it at arm's length with one hand, while in the other he held up the torch, he looked at it. Drops of blood were oozing from the mattress and falling one by one upon the floor.

At the end of the day he came into his wife's presence; and in a voice not his own bade her first of all not to answer him, come near him, or even look at him. Under pain of damnation she must follow all his orders, which would not be gainsaid.

The funerals must be carried out according to injunctions which he had left in writing, on a *prie-dieu* in the chamber of the dead. He ceded to her his palace. his vassals. and all his possessions, not excepting even his clothes or his sandals, which would be found at the head of the stairs.

She had obeyed God's will in making the occasion of his crime, and she must pray for his soul, since from that day he ceased to exist.

The dead were sumptuously buried in an abbey church at three days' journey from the castle. A monk in shrouded hood followed the procession at a distance from the others, and no one dared to speak to him. He remained while the mass lasted, lying flat in the middle of the porch, with his arms making the form of a cross and his forehead in the dust.

After the burial he was seen to take the road leading to the mountains He turned to look round several times, and finally disappeared.

He went onwards, begging his way throughout the world.

He held out his hand to the riders on the high roads and bent his knee when he approached the reapers. Or he would stand motionless before the gates of court-yards. and his face was so sad that he was never refused alms.

In a spirit of humbleness he would tell his story; and then all fled from him, making the sign of the cross. In the villages which he had passed through before, the people, as soon as they recognized him, shut their doors, shouted abuse at him, threw stones at him. The most charitable of them placed a bowl on their window-sills and then closed the shutters so as not to see him.

Being repulsed everywhere, he shunned mankind. and fed on roots, plants, wayside fruit, and shell-fish which he gathered along the beaches.

Sometimes, at the turn of a hill-side, he saw a jumble of crowded roofs under his eyes, with stone spires, bridges, towers, and a network of dark streets, from which a ceaseless hum rose up to him. A need to mingle with the life of others would draw him down into the town. But the brutal look in their faces, their noisy crafts and callous words made his heart freeze. On festal days, when the great cathedral bells tuned the whole populace to joy from daybreak, he watched the folk issuing from their houses, and the dancing in public spaces, the beer fountains at the cross-ways, the damask hung before the lodgings of princes; and then at evening, through the lower windows, the long family tables where grand-parents dandled little children on their knees. Sobs choked him, and he turned away towards the country.

He had thrills of love as he gazed at young horses in the meadows, birds in their nests, and insects on the flowers; all, at his approach, ran farther off, hid in terror, or flew swiftly away.

He sought deserted places. But the wind grated on his ear like the rattle of a death-agony; the dewdrops falling to the ground brought other, heavier drops to mind. Every evening the sun tinged the clouds blood-red, and each night the murder of his parents began again in dreams.

He made himself a hair shirt with iron spikes, and climbed on his knees up every hill which had a chapel at the top. But his pitiless thought dimmed the radiance of the shrines, and stung him even in his acts of mortification. He did not rebel against God for having brought the deed upon him, and yet the idea that he could have done it made him despair.

His own person filled him with such horror that in the hope of release he risked it among dangers. He saved the paralysed from fires and children from the bottom of chasms. The abyss cast him up; the flames spared him.

Time brought no relief to his suffering. It became intolerable, and he resolved to die.

And one day when he was by a spring, leaning over it to judge the water's depth, he saw opposite him on a sudden an emaciated old man, with a white beard and a look so dolorous that Julian could not keep back his tears. The other wept also. Without recognizing him exactly, Julian had a confused memory of a face like his. He uttered a cry; it was his father; and he thought no more of killing himself.

So with the burden of his recollections he travelled many lands, and came one day to a river, which, owing to its violence and a great stretch of slime along its banks, was dangerous to cross. No one for a long time had dared to make the passage.

An old boat, whose stern had been embedded, lifted its prow among the reeds. Julian examined it and found a pair of oars; and the thought came to him that he might use his life in the service of others.

He began by making a sort of roadway on the bank to lead down to the channel of the river; and he broke his nails in moving enormous stones, propped them against his waist to carry them, slipped in the mud and sank there, and nearly perished several times. Then he repaired the boat with pieces of wreckage, and made a hut for himself out of clay and tree-trunks.

The ferry came to be heard of and travellers appeared. They waved flags and hailed him from the other side, and Julian at once jumped into his boat. It was very heavy, and they overweighted it with baggage and loads of all kinds, without counting the beasts of burden, who made the crowding worse by kicking in alarm. He asked nothing for his labour; some of the passengers gave him remnants of food out of their wallets or worn-out clothes which they had no more use for. The brutal ones shouted blasphemies. Julian reproved them gently, and they retorted with abuse. He was content to bless them.

A little table, a stool, a bed of dry leaves, and three clay cups—that was the whole of his furniture. Two holes in the wall served for windows. On one side barren plains stretched away out of view, dotted with pale meres here and there; and in front of him the great river rolled its greenish waters. In spring the damp soil breathed an odour of decay. Then came a riotous wind that lifted the dust and whirled it. It found its way in everywhere, muddying the water and grating in the mouth. A little later there were clouds of mosquitoes, which pinged and pricked without ceasing day and night. And then came on appalling frosts which turned everything to the hardness of stone and roused a wild craving to eat meat.

Months glided by when Julian did not see a soul. Often he closed his eyes and tried to revive his youth in memory. The court-yard of a castle would rise before him, with greyhounds on a flight of steps, grooms in the armoury, and a fair-haired boy under a vine trellis between an old man dressed in furs and a lady wearing a great coif. Suddenly, the two corpses were there. He threw himself face downwards on his bed and kept murmuring with tears: "Ah, poor father! Poor mother, poor mother!" —and fell into a drowsiness through which the mournful visions still went on.

When he was asleep one night he thought he heard someone calling him. He strained his ears and made out nothing except the roar of the water.

But the same voice cried again: "Julian!"

It came from the other bank, which amazed him, considering the breadth of the river.

A third time he was hailed: "Julian!"

And the loud voice had the tone of a church bell.

Julian lit his lantern and went out of the hovel. A wild hurricane was sweeping through the night. There was an intense darkness, pierced now and then by the whiteness of the leaping waves.

After a moment's hesitation Julian unfastened his moorings. The water instantly became calm, and the boat glided over it to the other bank, where a man stood waiting.

He was wrapped in a tattered cloth and his face was like a plaster mask, with eyes redder than coals. Holding the lantern to him, Julian saw that he was covered with a hideous leprosy; yet there was something of a royal majesty in his posture.

As soon as he entered the boat it sank prodigiously, overwhelmed by his weight. It rose again with a shake, and Julian began to row.

At every stroke the surf tossed the boat up by its bows. The water, blacker than ink, ran furiously against the planks on both sides. It hollowed into gulfs and rose into mountains, which the boat leaped over, only to fall back into the depths, where it spun round at the mercy of the wind.

Julian bent low, stretched his arms out, and propping himself against his feet swung back with a twist to get more power. The hail lashed his hands, the rain streamed down his back, he could not breathe in the fierce wind, and stopped. Then the boat drifted and was carried away. But feeling that there was a great matter at stake, an order which might not be disobeyed, he took up the oars again, and the clacking of the thole-pins cut through the stormy clamour.

The little lantern burned in front of him. Birds hid it from time to time as they fluttered by. But he always saw the eyes of the Leper, who stood, motionless as a pillar, at the stern.

It went on long, very long.

When at last they had entered the hovel Julian shut the door; and he saw the Leper sitting on the stool. The kind of shroud which covered him had fallen to his hips; and his shoulders, chest, and wizened arms were hardly to be seen for the scaly pustules which coated them. Immense wrinkles furrowed his brow. He had a hole in place of a nose, like a skeleton, and his bluish lips exhaled a breath as thick as fog, and nauseous.

"I am hungry!" he said.

Julian gave him what he had, an old piece of bacon and the crust of a black loaf. When he had devoured them, the table, the dish, and the handle of the knife bore the same spots that could be seen on his body.

Next he said, "I am thirsty!"

Julian went to get his pitcher, and it gave out an aroma, as he took it, which enlarged his heart and nostrils. It was wine—what happiness! But the Leper put out his arm and emptied the whole pitcher at a draught.

Then he said, "I am cold!"

And Julian, with his candle, set light to a pile of bracken in the middle of the hut.

The Leper came to warm himself, and as he crouched on his heels he trembled in every limb and weakened. His eyes ceased to gleam, his sores ran, and in an almost lifeless voice he murmured:

"Thy bed!"

Julian helped him gently to drag himself there, and even spread the canvas of his boat over him as a covering.

The Leper groaned. His teeth showed at the corners of his mouth, a faster rattle shook his chest, and as each breath was taken his body hollowed to the backbone.

Then he shut his eyes.

"It is like ice in my bones! Come close to me!"

And Julian, lifting the cloth, lay down on the dead leaves side by side with him.

The Leper turned his head. "Take off thy clothes, that I may have thy body's warmth!"

Julian took off his clothes and lay down on the bed again, naked as when he was born; and he felt the Leper's skin against his thigh, colder than a serpent and rough as a file.

He tried to hearten him, and the other answered in gasps: "Ah, I am dying! Come closer, warm me! Not with the hands; no, with thy whole body!"

Julian stretched himself completely over him, mouth to mouth and chest on chest.

Then the Leper clasped him, and his eyes suddenly became as bright as stars; his hair drew out like sunbeams; the breath of his nostrils was as sweet as roses; a cloud of incense rose from the hearth, and the waves began to sing. Meanwhile an abundance of delight, a superhuman joy flooded into Julian's soul as he lay swooning; and he who still clasped him in his arms grew taller, ever taller, until his head and feet touched the two walls of the hut. The roof flew off, the firmament unrolled—and Julian rose towards the blue spaces, face to face with Our Lord Jesus, who carried him to heaven.

And that is the story of St. Julian the Hospitaller, more or less as you will find it on a church-window in the region where I live.

---

*The foregoing story is
from Flaubert's* THREE TALES,
translated by Arthur McDowall.

F. Scott Fitzgerald

1896–1940

Francis Scott Key Fitzgerald was born in St. Paul, Minnesota, on September 24, 1896. He attended the Newman School and entered Princeton University in the class of 1917. In 1917–19 he served as a lieutenant in the army but did not get to France. He wrote advertising copy in New York and went back to St. Paul to rewrite his first novel, *This Side of Paradise*, published in 1920. At one stroke it made him the prophet and golden boy of the beginning Jazz Age.

In April of the same year he married Zelda Sayre of Montgomery, Alabama. They lived in New York City and Westport, Connecticut, made a first foray to Europe, and returned to St. Paul. There Fitzgerald finished a second novel, *The Beautiful and the Damned.* This appeared in 1922, between two collections of stories: *Flappers and Philosophers* and *Tales of the Jazz Age.* During this period he was also working on a satiric play, *The Vegetable.* It was tried out on the road but never reached Broadway.

In 1922 he rented a house at Great Neck, Long Island. It became a weekend resort for New York party goers. Between November and April, Fitzgerald wrote himself out of debt with eleven short stories. In Great Neck and in St. Raphaël, France, he took up the short novel he had begun a year or two before. This was *The Great Gatsby*, finished in late 1924 and published in April of the next year.

A third book of stories, *All the Sad Young Men*, came out in 1926. While the 1920's moved to their disastrous close, Fitzgerald traveled back and forth between Paris, Hollywood, Wilmington, and Cap d'Antibes, France. In 1934, after several false starts, he produced his second important novel, *Tender Is the Night.* The stories in *Taps at Reveille* appeared the following year. He suffered from a drinking habit traceable, in part at least, to a condition diagnosed as hyperInsulinism. He died in Hollywood on December 21, 1940. After Fitzgerald's death, his friend Edmund Wilson edited two supplements to his work: *The Last Tycoon,* an unfinished novel, and a miscellany called *The Crack-Up.*

The *Diamond as Big as the Ritz* belongs to Fitzgerald's first period. The setting appears to derive from a 1915 vacation visit to the opulent ranch of his friend Charles W. ("Sap") Donahoe at White Sulphur Springs, Montana. But the story of a secret and impossibly rich never-never land in the mountains is an old western American legend; and the detail of diamonds picked up from the ground recalls the Great Diamond Hoax that amused San Francisco in the late nineteenth century. Fitzgerald wrote the story in a downtown office in St. Paul. It came out in *Smart Set* magazine for June, 1922, and was reprinted that same year in *Tales of the Jazz Age.*

It is, first of all, a good story, told with verve and a kind of gleeful ingenuity. Beyond that, it suggests many things, and one thing in particular. What do we notice first? We say to ourselves that this is the burlesque satire of the 1920's, a satire based on wild exaggeration of the typical and familiar. H. L. Mencken set the tone in his magazines. We catch it in *Elmer Gantry,* and even in some of the dialogues in Hemingway's *The Sun Also Rises.*

What does Fitzgerald do with it? We observe that the name of John T. Unger's home town is Hades. (Every American small town was by definition "Hades" in the 1920's.) There are vaudeville jokes about it. A "Rolls-Pierce" automobile is mentioned (Rolls-Royce and the now extinct Pierce-Arrow). The word "Ritz" occurs in the title. (The Ritz-Carlton Hotel in New York, classic symbol of luxury in the 1920's, has long since fallen under the wrecker's ball.) But it does not escape us that "St. Midas' School" or its equivalent still exists, and that middle western boys are still sent to it; that the Ritz has been replaced by vaster and chillier luxury hotels, whose good

Notes from the artist: ". . . characters of the 'Newport set'
of the 1920's and a drawing technique
popular in those years were used in the portrait of Fitzgerald. The author
as a boy of eight is at the lower right."

taste is far more in doubt; or that the suburban Hades has inherited most of the faults and few of the virtues of the small-town one.

So we move in toward the center of Fitzgerald's story. What does he mean by that symbol of his, that tyrannical utopia lost in the American mountains? What are we to make of this Arabian Nights domain where every luxury is blown up into something monstrously absurd, where the slaves have never been freed, where a young girl collects rhinestones because diamonds bore her?

And who is Braddock Washington? Is he only the last of the nineteenth-century robber barons, living beyond his time? Or is he a kind of Hitler before his time, preparing his own Götterdämmerung? For Fitzgerald, we may suspect, he was neither. Washington is the barbarous extreme of a figure that he would come back to time after time, in the Tom Buchanan of *The Great Gatsby*, in the Warren family of *Tender Is the Night*, and in a dozen other stories. He is the man of great wealth whose wealth may be turned into a kind of social privilege that makes possible the fullest kind of good life or the most arrogantly inhuman evil. In Washington it creates a monster who claims the right to murder his guests and bribe God.

The Diamond
as Big as the Ritz

J ohn T. Unger came from a family that had been well known in
Hades—a small town on the Mississippi River—for several generations. John's father had held the amateur golf championship through
many a heated contest; Mrs. Unger was known "from hot-box to hot-bed,"
as the local phrase went, for her political addresses; and young John T.
Unger, who had just turned sixteen, had danced all the latest dances from
New York before he put on long trousers. And now, for a certain time, he
was to be away from home. That respect for a New England education
which is the bane of all provincial places, which drains them yearly of
their most promising young men, had seized upon his parents. Nothing
would suit them but that he should go to St. Midas' School near Boston—
Hades was too small to hold their darling and gifted son.

Now in Hades—as you know if you ever have been there—the names
of the more fashionable preparatory schools and colleges mean very little.
The inhabitants have been so long out of the world that, though they
make a show of keeping up to date in dress and manners and literature,
they depend to a great extent on hearsay, and a function that in Hades
would be considered elaborate would doubtless be hailed by a Chicago
beef princess as "perhaps a little tacky."

John T. Unger was on the eve of departure. Mrs. Unger, with maternal
fatuity, packed his trunks full of linen suits and electric fans, and Mr.
Unger presented his son with an asbestos pocketbook stuffed with money.

"Remember, you are always welcome here," he said. "You can be sure,
boy, that we'll keep the home fires burning."

"I know," answered John huskily.

"Don't forget who you are and where you come from," continued his father proudly, "and you can do nothing to harm you. You are an Unger —from Hades."

So the old man and the young shook hands and John walked away with tears streaming from his eyes. Ten minutes later he had passed outside the city limits, and he stopped to glance back for the last time. Over the gates the old-fashioned Victorian motto seemed strangely attractive to him. His father had tried time and time again to have it changed to something with a little more push and verve about it, such as "Hades—Your Opportunity," or else a plain "Welcome" sign set over a hearty handshake pricked out in electric lights. The old motto was a little depressing, Mr. Unger had thought—but now. . . .

So John took his look and then set his face resolutely toward his destination. And, as he turned away, the lights of Hades against the sky seemed full of a warm and passionate beauty.

St. Midas' School is half an hour from Boston in a Rolls-Pierce motorcar. The actual distance will never be known, for no one, except John T Unger, had ever arrived there save in a Rolls-Pierce and probably no one ever will again. St. Midas' is the most expensive and the most exclusive boys' preparatory school in the world.

John's first two years there passed pleasantly. The fathers of all the boys were money-kings and John spent his summers visiting at fashionable resorts. While he was very fond of all the boys he visited, their fathers struck him as being much of a piece, and in his boyish way he often wondered at their exceeding sameness. When he told them where his home was they would ask jovially, "Pretty hot down there?" and John would muster a faint smile and answer, "It certainly is." His response would have been heartier had they not all made this joke—at best varying it with, "Is it hot enough for you down there?" which he hated just as much.

In the middle of his second year at school. a quiet handsome boy named Percy Washington had been put in John's form. The newcomer was pleasant in his manner and exceedingly well dressed even for St. Midas', but for some reason he kept aloof from the other boys. The only person with whom he was intimate was John T. Unger, but even to John he was entirely uncommunicative concerning his home or his family. That he was wealthy went without saying, but beyond a few such deductions John knew little of his friend, so it promised rich confectionery for his curiosity when Percy invited him to spend the summer at his home "in the West." He accepted, without hesitation.

It was only when they were in the train that Percy became, for the first time, rather communicative. One day while they were eating lunch in the dining car and discussing the imperfect characters of several of the boys at school, Percy suddenly changed his tone and made an abrupt remark.

"My father," he said, "is by far the richest man in the world."

"Oh," said John, politely. He could think of no answer to make to this confidence. He considered "That's very nice," but it sounded hollow and was on the point of saying, "Really?" but refrained since it would seem to question Percy's statement. And such an astounding statement could scarcely be questioned.

"By far the richest," repeated Percy.

"I was reading in the *World Almanac*," began John, "that there was one man in America with an income of over five million a year and four men with incomes of over three million a year, and—"

"Oh, they're nothing," Percy's mouth was a half-moon of scorn. "Catchpenny capitalists, financial small fry, petty merchants and moneylenders. My father could buy them out and not know he'd done it."

"But how does he—"

"Why haven't they put down *his* income tax? Because he doesn't pay any At least he pays a little one—but he doesn't pay any on his *real* income."

"He must be very rich," said John simply. "I'm glad. I like very rich people.

"The richer a fella is, the better I like him." There was a look of passionate frankness upon his dark face. "I visited the Schnlitzer-Murphys last Easter. Vivian Schnlitzer-Murphy had rubies as big as hen's eggs, and sapphires that were like globes with lights inside them—"

"I love jewels," agreed Percy enthusiastically. "Of course I wouldn't want anyone at school to know about it, but I've got quite a collection myself. I used to collect them instead of stamps."

"And diamonds," continued John eagerly. "The Schnlitzer-Murphys had diamonds as big as walnuts—"

"That's nothing." Percy had leaned forward and dropped his voice to a low whisper. "That's nothing at all. My father has a diamond bigger than the Ritz-Carlton Hotel."

The Montana sunset lay between two mountains like a gigantic bruise from which dark arteries spread themselves over a poisoned sky. An immense distance under the sky crouched the village of Fish, minute, dismal, and forgotten There were twelve men, so it was said, in the village of Fish, twelve sombre and inexplicable souls who sucked a lean milk from the almost literally bare rock upon which a mysterious populatory force had begotten them. They had become a race apart, these twelve men of Fish, like some species developed by an early whim of nature, which on second thought had abandoned them to struggle and extermination.

Out of the blue-black bruise in the distance crept a long line of moving lights upon the desolation of the land, and the twelve men of Fish gathered like ghosts at the shanty depot to watch the passing of the seven o'clock train, the Transcontinental Express from Chicago. Six times or so a year the Transcontinental Express, through some inconceivable jurisdiction, stopped at the village of Fish, and when this occurred a figure or so would disembark, mount into a buggy that always appeared from out of the dusk, and drive off toward the bruised sunset. The observation of this pointless and preposterous phenomenon had become a sort of cult among the men of Fish. To observe, that was all; there remained in them none of the vital quality of illusion which would make them wonder or speculate, else a religion might have grown up around these mysterious visitations. But the men of Fish were beyond all religion—the barest and most savage tenets of even Christianity could gain no foothold on that barren rock—so there was no altar, no priest, no sacrifice; only each night at seven the silent concourse by the shanty depot, a congregation who lifted up a prayer of dim, anaemic wonder.

On this June night, the Great Brakeman, whom, had they deified anyone, they might well have chosen as their celestial protagonist, had ordained that the seven o'clock train should leave its human (or inhuman) deposit at Fish. At two minutes after seven Percy Washington and John T. Unger disembarked, hurried past the spellbound, the agape, the fearsome eyes of the twelve men of Fish, mounted into a buggy which had obviously appeared from nowhere, and drove away.

After half an hour, when the twilight had coagulated into dark, the silent Negro who was driving the buggy hailed an opaque body somewhere ahead of them in the gloom. In response to his cry, it turned upon them a luminous disk which regarded them like a malignant eye out of the unfathomable night. As they came closer, John saw that it was the taillight of an immense automobile, larger and more magnificent than any he had ever seen. Its body was of gleaming metal richer than nickel and lighter than silver, and the hubs of the wheels were studded with iridescent geometric figures of green and yellow—John did not dare to guess whether they were glass or jewel.

Two Negroes, dressed in glittering livery such as one sees in pictures of royal processions in London, were standing at attention beside the car and as the two young men dismounted from the buggy they were greeted in some language which the guest could not understand, but which seemed to be an extreme form of the Southern Negro's dialect.

"Get in," said Percy to his friend, as their trunks were tossed to the ebony roof of the limousine. "Sorry we had to bring you this far in that buggy, but of course it wouldn't do for the people on the train or those Godforsaken fellas in Fish to see this automobile."

"Gosh! What a car!" This ejaculation was provoked by its interior. John saw that the upholstery consisted of a thousand minute and exquisite tapestries of silk, woven with jewels and embroideries, and set upon a background of cloth of gold. The two armchair seats in which the boys luxuriated were covered with stuff that resembled duvetyn, but seemed woven in numberless colors of the ends of ostrich feathers.

"What a car!" cried John again, in amazement.

"This thing?" Percy laughed. "Why, it's just an old junk we use for a station wagon."

By this time they were gliding along through the darkness toward the break between the two mountains.

"We'll be there in an hour and a half," said Percy, looking at the clock. "I may as well tell you it's not going to be like anything you ever saw before."

If the car was any indication of what John would see, he was prepared to be astonished indeed. The simple piety prevalent in Hades has the earnest worship of and respect for riches as the first article of its creed—had John felt otherwise than radiantly humble before them, his parents would have turned away in horror at the blasphemy.

They had now reached and were entering the break between the two mountains and almost immediately the way became much rougher.

"If the moon shone down here, you'd see that we're in a big gulch," said Percy, trying to peer out of the window. He spoke a few words into the mouthpiece and immediately the footman turned on a searchlight and swept the hillsides with an immense beam.

"Rocky, you see. An ordinary car would be knocked to pieces in half an hour. In fact, it'd take a tank to navigate it unless you knew the way. You notice we're going uphill now."

They were obviously ascending, and within a few minutes the car was crossing a high rise, where they caught a glimpse of a pale moon newly risen in the distance. The car stopped suddenly and several figures took shape out of the dark beside it—these were Negroes also. Again the two

young men were saluted in the same dimly recognizable dialect; then
the Negroes set to work and four immense cables dangling from overhead were attached with hooks to the hubs of the great jeweled wheels.
At a resounding "Hey-yah!" John felt the car being lifted slowly from the
ground—up and up—clear of the tallest rocks on both sides—then higher,
until he could see a wavy, moonlit valley stretched out before him in
sharp contrast to the quagmire of rocks that they had just left. Only on
one side was there still rock—and then suddenly there was no rock beside them or anywhere around.

It was apparent that they had surmounted some immense knife-
blade of stone, projecting perpendicularly into the air. In a moment they
were going down again, and finally with a soft bump they were landed
upon the smooth earth.

"The worst is over," said Percy, squinting out the window. "It's only
five miles from here, and our own road—tapestry brick—all the way. This
belongs to us. This is where the United States ends, father says."

"Are we in Canada?"

"We are not. We're in the middle of the Montana Rockies. But you are
now on the only five square miles of land in the country that's never been
surveyed."

"Why hasn't it? Did they forget it?"

"No," said Percy, grinning, "they tried to do it three times. The first
time my grandfather corrupted a whole department of the State survey;
the second time he had the official maps of the United States tinkered
with—that held them for fifteen years. The last time was harder. My father fixed it so that their compasses were in the strongest magnetic field
ever artificially set up. He had a whole set of surveying instruments made
with a slight defection that would allow for this territory not to appear,
and he substituted them for the ones that were to be used. Then he had
a river deflected and he had what looked like a village built upon its
banks—so that they'd see it, and think it was a town ten miles farther up
the valley. There's only one thing my father's afraid of," he concluded,
"only one thing in the world that could be used to find us out."

"What's that?"

Percy sank his voice to a whisper.

"Airplanes," he breathed. "We've got half a dozen antiaircraft guns
and we've arranged it so far—but there've been a few deaths and a great
many prisoners. Not that we mind *that*, you know, father and I, but it
upsets mother and the girls, and there's always the chance that some time
we won't be able to arrange it."

Shreds and tatters of chinchilla, courtesy clouds in the green moon's heaven, were passing the green moon like precious Eastern stuffs paraded for the inspection of some Tartar Khan. It seemed to John that it was day, and that he was looking at some lads sailing above him in the air, showering down tracts and patent medicine circulars, with their messages of hope for despairing, rockbound hamlets. It seemed to him that he could see them look down out of the clouds and stare—and stare at whatever there was to stare at in this place whither he was bound— What then? Were they induced to land by some insidious device there to be immured far from patent medicines and from tracts until the judgment day—or, should they fail to fall into the trap, did a quick puff of smoke and the sharp round of a splitting shell bring them dropping to earth—and "upset" Percy's mother and sisters? John shook his head and the wraith of a hollow laugh issued silently from his parted lips. What desperate transaction lay hidden here? What a moral expedient of a bizarre Croesus? What terrible and golden mystery? . . .

The chinchilla clouds had drifted past now and outside the Montana night was bright as day. The tapestry brick of the road was smooth to the tread of the great tires as they rounded a still, moonlit lake; they passed into darkness for a moment, a pine grove, pungent and cool, then they came out into a broad avenue of lawn and John's exclamation of pleasure was simultaneous with Percy's taciturn "We're home."

Full in the light of the stars, an exquisite château rose from the borders of the lake, climbed in marble radiance half the height of an adjoining mountain, then melted in grace, in perfect symmetry, in translucent feminine languor, into the massed darkness of a forest of pine. The many towers, the slender tracery of the sloping parapets, the chiseled wonder of a thousand yellow windows with their oblongs and hectagons and triangles of golden light, the shattered softness of the intersecting planes of starshine and blue shade, all trembled on John's spirit like a chord of music. On one of the towers, the tallest, the blackest at its base, an arrangement of exterior lights at the top made a sort of floating fairyland —and as John gazed up in warm enchantment the faint *acciaccatura* sound of violins drifted down in a rococo harmony that was like nothing he had ever heard before. Then in a moment the car stopped before wide, high marble steps around which the night air was fragrant with a host of flowers. At the top of the steps two great doors swung silently open and amber light flooded out upon the darkness, silhouetting the figure of an exquisite lady with black, high-piled hair, who held out her arms toward them.

"Mother," Percy was saying, "this is my friend, John Unger, from Hades."

Afterward John remembered that first night as a daze of many colors, of quick sensory impressions, of music soft as a voice in love, and of the beauty of things, lights and shadows, and motions and faces. There was a white-haired man who stood drinking a many-hued cordial from a crystal thimble set on a golden stem. There was a girl with a flowery face, dressed like Titania with braided sapphires in her hair. There was a room where the solid, soft gold of the walls yielded to the pressure of his hand, and a room that was like a platonic conception of the ultimate prison—ceiling, floor, and all, it was lined with an unbroken mass of diamonds, diamonds of every size and shape, until, lit with tall violet lamps in the corners, it dazzled the eyes with a whiteness that could be compared only with itself, beyond human wish or dream.

Through a maze of these rooms the two boys wandered. Sometimes the floor under their feet would flame in brilliant patterns from lighting below, patterns of barbaric clashing colors, of pastel delicacy, of sheer whiteness, or of subtle and intricate mosaic, surely from some mosque on the Adriatic Sea. Sometimes beneath layers of thick crystal he would see blue or green water swirling, inhabited by vivid fish and growths of rainbow foliage. Then they would be treading on furs of every texture and color or along corridors of palest ivory, unbroken as though carved complete from the gigantic tusks of dinosaurs extinct before the age of man. . . .

Then a hazily remembered transition, and they were at dinner—where each plate was of two almost imperceptible layers of solid diamond between which was curiously worked a filigree of emerald design, a shaving sliced from green air. Music, plangent and unobtrusive, drifted down through far corridors—his chair, feathered and curved insidiously to his back, seemed to engulf and overpower him as he drank his first glass of port. He tried drowsily to answer a question that had been asked him, but the honeyed luxury that clasped his body added to the illusion of sleep—jewels, fabrics, wines, and metals blurred before his eyes into a sweet mist. . . .

"Yes," he replied with a polite effort, "it certainly is hot enough for me down there."

He managed to add a ghostly laugh; then, without movement, without resistance, he seemed to float off and away, leaving an iced dessert that was pink as a dream. . . . He fell asleep.

When he awoke he knew that several hours had passed. He was in a great quiet room with ebony walls and a dull illumination that was too faint, too subtle, to be called a light. His young host was standing over him.

"You fell asleep at dinner," Percy was saying. "I nearly did, too—it was such a treat to be comfortable again after this year of school. Servants undressed and bathed you while you were sleeping."

"Is this a bed or a cloud?" sighed John. "Percy, Percy—before you go, I want to apologize."

"For what?"

"For doubting you when you said you had a diamond as big as the Ritz-Carlton Hotel."

Percy smiled.

"I thought you didn't believe me. It's that mountain, you know."

"What mountain?"

"The mountain the château rests on. It's not very big for a mountain. But except about fifty feet of sod and gravel on top it's solid diamond. One diamond, one cubic mile without a flaw. Aren't you listening? Say—"

But John T. Unger had again fallen asleep.

Morning. As he awoke he perceived drowsily that the room had at the same moment become dense with sunlight. The ebony panels of one wall had slid aside on a sort of track, leaving his chamber half open to the day. A large Negro in a white uniform stood beside his bed.

"Good-evening," muttered John, summoning his brains from the wild places.

"Good-morning, sir. Are you ready for your bath, sir? Oh, don't get up —I'll put you in, if you'll just unbutton your pajamas—there. Thank you, sir."

John lay quietly as his pajamas were removed—he was amused and delighted; he expected to be lifted like a child by this black Gargantua who was tending him, but nothing of the sort happened; instead he felt the bed tilt up slowly on its side—he began to roll, startled at first, in the direction of the wall, but when he reached the wall its drapery gave way, and sliding two yards farther down a fleecy incline he plumped gently into water the same temperature as his body.

He looked about him. The runway or rollway on which he had arrived had folded gently back into place. He had been projected into another chamber and was sitting in a sunken bath with his head just above the level of the floor. All about him, lining the walls of the room and the sides and bottom of the bath itself, was a blue aquarium, and gazing through the crystal surface on which he sat, he could see fish swimming among amber lights and even gliding without curiosity past his outstretched toes, which were separated from them only by the thickness of the crystal. From overhead, sunlight came down through sea-green glass.

"I suppose, sir, that you'd like hot rose water and soapsuds this morning, sir—and perhaps cold salt water to finish."

The Negro was standing beside him.

"Yes," agreed John, smiling inanely, "as you please." Any idea of ordering this bath according to his own meagre standards of living would have been priggish and not a little wicked.

The Negro pressed a button and a warm rain began to fall, apparently from overhead, but really, so John discovered after a moment, from a fountain arrangement near by. The water turned to a pale rose color and jets of liquid soap spurted into it from four miniature walrus heads at the corners of the bath. In a moment a dozen little paddle wheels, fixed to the sides, had churned the mixture into a radiant rainbow of pink foam which enveloped him softly with its delicious lightness, and burst in shining, rosy bubbles here and there about him.

"Shall I turn on the moving-picture machine, sir?" suggested the Negro deferentially. "There's a good one-reel comedy in this machine today, or I can put in a serious piece in a moment, if you prefer it."

"No, thanks," answered John, politely but firmly. He was enjoying his bath too much to desire any distraction. But distraction came. In a moment he was listening intently to the sound of flutes from just outside, flutes dripping a melody that was like a waterfall, cool and green as the room itself, accompanying a frothy piccolo, in play more fragile than the lace of suds that covered and charmed him.

After a cold salt-water bracer and a cold fresh finish, he stepped out into a fleecy robe, and upon a couch covered with the same material he was rubbed with oil, alcohol, and spice. Later he sat in a voluptuous chair while he was shaved and his hair was trimmed.

"Mr. Percy is waiting in your sitting-room," said the Negro, when these operations were finished. "My name is Gygsum, Mr. Unger, sir. I am to see to Mr. Unger every morning."

John walked out into the brisk sunshine of his living room, where he found breakfast waiting for him and Percy, gorgeous in white kid knickerbockers, smoking in an easy chair.

This is a story of the Washington family as Percy sketched it for John during breakfast.

The father of the present Mr. Washington had been a Virginian, a direct descendant of George Washington, and Lord Baltimore. At the close of the Civil War he was a twenty-five-year-old Colonel with a played-out plantation and about a thousand dollars in gold.

Fitz-Norman Culpepper Washington, for that was the young Colonel's name, decided to present the Virginia estate to his younger brother and go West. He selected two dozen of the most faithful blacks, who, of course, worshipped him, and bought twenty-five tickets to the West, where he intended to take out land in their names and start a sheep and cattle ranch.

When he had been in Montana for less than a month and things were going very poorly indeed, he stumbled on his great discovery. He had lost his way when riding in the hills, and after a day without food he began to grow hungry. As he was without his rifle, he was forced to pursue a squirrel, and in the course of the pursuit he noticed that it was carrying something shiny in its mouth. Just before it vanished into its hole—for Providence did not intend that this squirrel should alleviate his hunger—it dropped its burden. Sitting down to consider the situation Fitz-Norman's eye was caught by a gleam in the grass beside him. In ten seconds he had completely lost his appetite and gained one hundred thousand dollars. The squirrel, which had refused with annoying persistence to become food, had made him a present of a large and perfect diamond.

Late that night he found his way to camp and twelve hours later all the males among his darkies were back by the squirrel hole digging furiously at the side of the mountain. He told them he had discovered a rhinestone mine, and, as only one or two of them had ever seen even a small diamond before, they believed him, without question. When the magnitude of his discovery became apparent to him, he found himself in a quandary. The mountain was a diamond—it was literally nothing else but solid diamond. He filled four saddle bags full of glittering samples and started on horseback for St. Paul. There he managed to dispose of half a dozen small stones—when he tried a larger one a storekeeper fainted and Fitz-Norman was arrested as a public disturber. He escaped from jail and caught the train for New York, where he sold a few medium-sized diamonds and received in exchange about two hundred thousand dollars in gold. But he did not dare to produce any exceptional gems—in fact, he left New York just in time. Tremendous excitement had been created in jewelry circles, not so much by the size of his diamonds as by their appearance in the city from mysterious sources. Wild rumors became current that a diamond mine had been discovered in the Catskills, on the Jersey coast, on Long Island, beneath Washington Square. Excursion trains packed with men carrying picks and shovels began to leave New York hourly, bound for various neighboring El Dorados. But by that time young Fitz-Norman was on his way back to Montana.

By the end of a fortnight he had estimated that the diamond in the mountain was approximately equal in quantity to all the rest of the diamonds known to exist in the world. There was no valuing it by any regular computation, however, for it was *one solid diamond*—and if it were offered for sale not only would the bottom fall out of the market, but also, if the value should vary with its size in the usual arithmetical progression, there would not be enough gold in the world to buy a tenth part of it. And what could any one do with a diamond that size?

It was an amazing predicament. He was, in one sense, the richest man that ever lived—and yet was he worth anything at all? If his secret should transpire there was no telling to what measures the government might resort in order to prevent a panic, in gold as well as in jewels. They might take over the claim immediately and institute a monopoly.

There was no alternative—he must market his mountain in secret. He sent South for his younger brother and put him in charge of his colored following—darkies who had never realized that slavery was abolished. To make sure of this, he read them a proclamation that he had composed, which announced that General Forrest had reorganized the shattered Southern armies and defeated the North in one pitched battle. The Negroes believed him implicitly. They passed a vote declaring it a good thing and held revival services immediately.

Fitz-Norman himself set out for foreign parts with one hundred thousand dollars and two trunks filled with rough diamonds of all sizes. He sailed for Russia in a Chinese junk and six months after his departure from Montana he was in St. Petersburg. He took obscure lodgings and called immediately upon the court jeweler, announcing that he had a diamond for the Czar. He remained in St. Petersburg for two weeks, in constant danger of being murdered, living from lodging to lodging, and afraid to visit his trunks more than three or four times during the whole fortnight.

On his promise to return in a year with larger and finer stones, he was allowed to leave for India. Before he left, however, the Court Treasurers had deposited to his credit, in American banks, the sum of fifteen million dollars—under four different aliases.

He returned to America in 1868, having been gone a little over two years. He had visited the capitals of twenty-two countries and talked with five emperors, eleven kings, three princes, a shah, a khan, and a sultan. At that time Fitz-Norman estimated his own wealth at one billion dollars. One fact worked consistently against the disclosure of his secret. No one of his larger diamonds remained in the public eye for a week before being invested with a history of enough fatalities, amours, revolutions, and wars to have occupied it from the days of the first Babylonian Empire.

From 1870 until his death in 1900, the history of Fitz-Norman Washington was a long epic in gold. There were side issues, of course—he evaded the surveys, he married a Virginia lady, by whom he had a single son, and he was compelled, due to a series of unfortunate complications, to murder his brother, whose unfortunate habit of drinking himself into an indiscreet stupor had several times endangered their safety. But very few other murders stained these happy years of progress and expansion.

Just before he died he changed his policy, and with all but a few million dollars of his outside wealth bought up rare minerals in bulk, which he deposited in the safety vaults of banks all over the world, marked as bric-a-brac. His son, Braddock Tarleton Washington, followed this policy on an even more extensive scale. The minerals were converted into the rarest of all elements—radium—so that the equivalent of a billion dollars in gold could be placed in a receptacle no bigger than a cigar box.

When Fitz-Norman had been dead three years his son, Braddock, decided that the business had gone far enough. The amount of wealth that he and his father had taken out of the mountain was beyond all exact computation. He kept a notebook in cipher in which he set down the approximate quantity of radium in each of the thousand banks he patronized, and recorded the alias under which it was held. Then he did a very simple thing—he sealed up the mine.

He sealed up the mine. What had been taken out of it would support all the Washingtons yet to be born in unparalleled luxury for generations. His one care must be the protection of his secret, lest in the possible panic attendant on its discovery he should be reduced with all the property-holders in the world to utter poverty.

This was the family among whom John T. Unger was staying. This was the story he heard in his silver-walled living room the morning after his arrival.

After breakfast, John found his way out the great marble entrance, and looked curiously at the scene before him. The whole valley, from the diamond mountain to the steep granite cliff five miles away, still gave off a breath of golden haze which hovered idly above the fine sweep of lawns

and lakes and gardens. Here and there clusters of elms made delicate
groves of shade, contrasting strangely with the tough masses of pine
forest that held the hills in a grip of dark-blue green. Even as John looked
he saw three fawns in single file patter out from one clump about a half
mile away and disappear with awkward gayety into the black-ribbed
half-light of another. John would not have been surprised to see a goat
foot piping his way among the trees or to catch a glimpse of pink nymph
skin and flying yellow hair between the greenest of the green leaves.

In some such cool hope he descended the marble steps, disturbing
faintly the sleep of two silky Russian wolfhounds at the bottom, and set
off along a walk of white and blue brick that seemed to lead in no particular direction.

He was enjoying himself as much as he was able. It is youth's felicity
as well as its insufficiency that it can never live in the present, but must
always be measuring up the day against its own radiantly imagined future—flowers and gold, girls and stars, they are only prefigurations and
prophecies of that incomparable, unattainable young dream.

John rounded a soft corner where the massed rosebushes filled the air
with heavy scent, and struck off across a park toward a patch of moss
under some trees. He had never lain upon moss, and he wanted to see
whether it was really soft enough to justify the use of its name as an ad-
jective. Then he saw a girl coming toward him over the grass. She was
the most beautiful person he had ever seen.

She was dressed in a white little gown that came just below her knees,
and a wreath of mignonettes clasped with blue slices of sapphire bound
up her hair. Her pink bare feet scattered the dew before them as she
came. She was younger than John—not more than sixteen.

"Hello," she cried softly, "I'm Kismine."

She was much more than that to John already. He advanced toward
her, scarcely moving as he drew near lest he should tread on her bare
toes.

"You haven't met me," said her soft voice. Her blue eyes added, "Oh,
but you've missed a great deal!". . . "You met my sister, Jasmine, last
night, I was sick with lettuce poisoning," went on her soft voice, and her
eyes continued, "and when I'm sick I'm sweet—and when I'm well."

"You have made an enormous impression on me," said John's eyes,
"and I'm not so slow myself"—"How do you do?" said his voice. "I hope
you're better this morning."—"You darling," added his eyes tremulously.

John observed that they had been walking along the path. On her suggestion they sat down together upon the moss, the softness of which he failed to determine.

He was critical about women. A single defect—a thick ankle, a hoarse voice, a glass eye—was enough to make him utterly indifferent. And here for the first time in his life he was beside a girl who seemed to him the incarnation of physical perfection.

"Are you from the East?" asked Kismine with charming interest.

"No," answered John simply. "I'm from Hades."

Either she had never heard of Hades, or she could think of no pleasant comment to make upon it, for she did not discuss it further.

"I'm going East to school this fall," she said. "D'you think I'll make it? I'm going to New York to Miss Bulge's. It's very strict, but you see over the weekends I'm going to live at home with the family in our New York house, because father heard that the girls had to go walking two by two."

"Your father wants you to be proud," observed John.

"We are," she answered, her eyes shining with dignity. "None of us has ever been punished. Father said we never should be. Once when my sister Jasmine was a little girl she pushed him down-stairs and he just got up and limped away.

"Mother was—well, a little startled," continued Kismine, "when she heard that you were from—from where you *are* from, you know. She said that when she was a young girl—but then, you see, she's a Spaniard and old-fashioned."

"Do you spend much time out here?" asked John, to conceal the fact that he was somewhat hurt by this remark. It seemed an unkind allusion to his provincialism.

"Percy and Jasmine and I are here every summer, but next summer Jasmine is going to Newport. She's coming out in London a year from this fall. She'll be presented at court."

"Do you know," began John hesitantly, "you're much more sophisticated than I thought you were when I first saw you?"

"Oh, no, I'm not," she exclaimed hurriedly. "Oh, I wouldn't think of being. I think that sophisticated young people are *terribly* common, don't you? I'm not at all, really. If you say I am, I'm going to cry."

She was so distressed that her lip was trembling. John was impelled to protest.

"I didn't mean that, I only said it to tease you."

"Because I wouldn't mind if I *were*," she persisted, "but I'm *not*. I'm very innocent and girlish. I never smoke, or drink, or read anything except poetry. I know scarcely any mathematics or chemistry. I dress *very* simply—in fact, I scarcely dress at all. I think sophisticated is the last thing you can say about me. I believe that girls ought to enjoy their youths in a wholesome way."

"I do too," said John heartily.

Kismine was cheerful again. She smiled at him, and a stillborn tear dripped from the corner of one blue eye.

"I like you," she whispered, intimately. "Are you going to spend all your time with Percy while you're here, or will you be nice to me? Just think—I'm absolutely fresh ground. I've never had a boy in love with me in all my life. I've never been allowed even to *see* boys alone—except Percy. I came all the way out here into this grove hoping to run into you, where the family wouldn't be around."

Deeply flattered, John bowed from the hips as he had been taught at dancing school in Hades.

"We'd better go now," said Kismine sweetly. "I have to be with mother at eleven. You haven't asked me to kiss you once. I thought boys always did that nowadays."

John drew himself up proudly.

"Some of them do," he answered, "but not me. Girls don't do that sort of thing—in Hades."

Side by side they walked back toward the house.

John stood facing Mr. Braddock Washington in the full sunlight. The elder man was about forty with a proud, vacuous face, intelligent eyes, and a robust figure. In the mornings he smelt of horses—the best horses. He carried a plain walking stick of gray birch with a single large opal for a grip. He and Percy were showing John around.

"The slaves' quarters are there." His walking stick indicated a cloister of marble on their left that ran in graceful Gothic along the side of the mountain. "In my youth I was distracted for a while from the business of life by a period of absurd idealism. During that time they lived in luxury. For instance, I equipped every one of their rooms with a tile bath."

"I suppose," ventured John, with an ingratiating laugh, "that they used the bathtubs to keep coal in. Mr. Schnlitzer-Murphy told me that once he—"

"The opinions of Mr. Schnlitzer-Murphy are of little importance, I should imagine," interrupted Braddock Washington, coldly. "My slaves did not keep coal in their bathtubs. They had orders to bathe every day, and they did. If they hadn't I might have ordered a sulphuric acid shampoo. I discontinued the baths for quite another reason. Several of them caught cold and died. Water is not good for certain races—except as a beverage."

John laughed, and then decided to nod his head in sober agreement. Braddock Washington made him uncomfortable.

"All these Negroes are descendants of the ones my father brought North with him. There are about two hundred and fifty now. You notice that they've lived so long apart from the world that their original dialect has become an almost indistinguishable patois. We bring a few of them up to speak English—my secretary and two or three of the house servants.

"This is the golf course," he continued, as they strolled along the velvet winter grass. "It's all a green, you see—no fairway, no rough, no hazards."

He smiled pleasantly at John.

"Many men in the cage, father?" asked Percy suddenly.

Braddock Washington stumbled, and let forth an involuntary curse.

"One less than there should be," he ejaculated darkly—and then added after a moment, "We've had difficulties."

"Mother was telling me," exclaimed Percy, "that Italian teacher—"

"A ghastly error," said Braddock Washington angrily. "But of course there's a good chance that we may have got him. Perhaps he fell somewhere in the woods or stumbled over a cliff. And then there's always the probability that if he did get away his story wouldn't be believed. Nevertheless, I've had two dozen men looking for him in different towns around here."

"And no luck?"

"Some. Fourteen of them reported to my agent that they'd each killed a man answering to that description, but of course it was probably only the reward they were after—"

He broke off. They had come to a large cavity in the earth about the circumference of a merry-go-round and covered by a strong iron grating. Braddock Washington beckoned to John, and pointed his cane down through the grating. John stepped to the edge and gazed. Immediately his ears were assailed by a wild clamor from below.

"Come on down to Hell!"

"Hello, kiddo, how's the air up there?"

"Hey! Throw us a rope!"

"Got an old doughnut, Buddy, or a couple of secondhand sandwiches?"

"Say, fella, if you'll push down that guy you're with, we'll show you a quick disappearance scene."

"Paste him one for me, will you?"

It was too dark to see clearly into the pit below, but John could tell from the coarse optimism and rugged vitality of the remarks and voices that they proceeded from middle-class Americans of the more spirited type. Then Mr. Washington put out his cane and touched a button in the grass, and the scene below sprang into light.

"These are some adventurous mariners who had the misfortune to discover El Dorado," he remarked.

Below them there had appeared a large hollow in the earth shaped like the interior of a bowl. The sides were steep and apparently of polished glass, and on its slightly concave surface stood about two dozen men clad in the half costume, half uniform, of aviators. Their upturned faces, lit with wrath, with malice, with despair, with cynical humor, were covered by long growths of beard, but with the exception of a few who had pined perceptibly away, they seemed to be a well-fed, healthy lot.

Braddock Washington drew a garden chair to the edge of the pit and sat down.

"Well, how are you, boys?" he inquired genially.

A chorus of execration, in which all joined except a few too dispirited to cry out, rose up into the sunny air, but Braddock Washington heard it with unruffled composure. When its last echo had died away he spoke again.

"Have you thought up a way out of your difficulty?"

From here and there among them a remark floated up.

"We decided to stay here for love!"

"Bring us up there and we'll find us a way!"

Braddock Washington waited until they were again quiet. Then he said: "I've told you the situation. I don't want you here. I wish to heaven I'd never seen you. Your own curiosity got you here, and any time that you can think of a way out which protects me and my interests I'll be glad to consider it. But so long as you confine your efforts to digging tunnels—yes, I know about the new one you've started—you won't get very far. This isn't as hard on you as you make it out, with all your howling for the loved ones at home. If you were the type who worried much about the loved ones at home, you'd never have taken up aviation."

A tall man moved apart from the others, and held up his hand to call his captor's attention to what he was about to say.

"Let me ask you a few questions!" he cried. "You pretend to be a fair-minded man."

"How absurd. How could a man of *my* position be fair minded toward *you?* You might as well speak of a Spaniard being fair minded toward a piece of steak."

At this harsh observation the faces of the two dozen steaks fell, but the tall man continued:

"All right!" he cried. "We've argued this out before. You're not a humanitarian and you're not fair minded, but you're human—at least you say you are—and you ought to be able to put yourself in our place for long enough to think how—how—how—"

"How what?" demanded Washington, coldly.

"—how unnecessary—"

"Not to me."

"Well—how cruel—"

"We've covered that. Cruelty doesn't exist where self-preservation is involved. You've been soldiers: you know that. Try another."

"Well, then, how stupid."

"There," admitted Washington, "I grant you that. But try to think of an alternative. I've offered to have all or any of you painlessly executed if you wish. I've offered to have your wives, sweethearts, children, and mothers kidnapped and brought out here. I'll enlarge your place down there and feed and clothe you the rest of your lives. If there was some method of producing permanent amnesia I'd have all of you operated on and released immediately, somewhere outside of my preserves. But that's as far as my ideas go."

"How about trusting us not to peach on you?" cried someone.

"You don't proffer that suggestion seriously," said Washington, with an expression of scorn. "I did take out one man to teach my daughter Italian. Last week he got away."

A wild yell of jubilation went up suddenly from two dozen throats and a pandemonium of joy ensued. The prisoners clog danced and cheered and yodled and wrestled with one another in a sudden uprush of animal spirits. They even ran up the glass sides of the bowl as far as they could, and slid back to the bottom upon the natural cushions of their bodies. The tall man started a song in which they all joined—

> Oh, we'll hang the kaiser
> On a sour apple tree—

Braddock Washington sat in inscrutable silence until the song was over.

"You see," he remarked, when he could gain a modicum of attention, "I bear you no ill will. I like to see you enjoying yourselves. That's why I didn't tell you the whole story at once. The man—what was his name? Critchtichiello?—was shot by some of my agents in fourteen different places."

Not guessing that the places referred to were cities, the tumult of rejoicing subsided immediately.

"Nevertheless," cried Washington with a touch of anger, "he tried to run away. Do you expect me to take chances with any of you after an experience like that?"

Again a series of ejaculations went up.

"Sure!"

"Would your daughter like to learn Chinese?"

"Hey, I can speak Italian! My mother was a wop."

"Maybe she'd like t'learna speak N'Yawk!"

"If she's the little one with the big blue eyes I can teach her a lot of things better than Italian."

"I know some Irish songs—and I could hammer brass once't."

Mr. Washington reached forward suddenly with his cane and pushed the button in the grass so that the picture below went out instantly, and there remained only that great dark mouth covered dismally with the black teeth of the grating.

"Hey!" called a single voice from below, "you ain't goin' away without givin' us your blessing?"

But Mr. Washington, followed by the two boys, was already strolling on toward the ninth hole of the golf course, as though the pit and its contents were no more than a hazard over which his facile iron had triumphed with ease.

July under the lee of the diamond mountain was a month of blanket nights and of warm, glowing days. John and Kismine were in love. He did not know that the little gold football (inscribed with the legend *Pro deo et patria et St. Mida*) which he had given her rested on a platinum chain next to her bosom. But it did. And she for her part was not aware that a large sapphire which had dropped one day from her simple coiffure was stowed away tenderly in John's jewel box.

Late one afternoon when the ruby and ermine music room was quiet, they spent an hour there together. He held her hand and she gave him such a look that he whispered her name aloud. She bent toward him— then hesitated.

"Did you say 'Kismine'?" she asked softly, "or—"

She had wanted to be sure. She thought she might have misunderstood.

Neither of them had ever kissed before, but in the course of an hour it seemed to make little difference.

The afternoon drifted away. That night when a last breath of music drifted down from the highest tower, they each lay awake, happily dreaming over the separate minutes of the day. They had decided to be married as soon as possible.

Every day Mr. Washington and the two young men went hunting or fishing in the deep forests or played golf around the somnolent course— games which John diplomatically allowed his host to win—or swam in the mountain coolness of the lake. John found Mr. Washington a somewhat exacting personality—utterly uninterested in any ideas or opinions except his own. Mrs. Washington was aloof and reserved at all times. She was apparently indifferent to her two daughters, and entirely absorbed in her son Percy, with whom she held interminable conversations in rapid Spanish at dinner.

Jasmine, the elder daughter, resembled Kismine in appearance—except that she was somewhat bow-legged, and terminated in large hands and feet—but was utterly unlike her in temperament. Her favorite books had to do with poor girls who kept house for widowed fathers. John learned from Kismine that Jasmine had never recovered from the shock and disappointment caused her by the termination of the World War, just as she was about to start for Europe as a canteen expert. She had even pined away for a time, and Braddock Washington had taken steps to promote a new war in the Balkans—but she had seen a photograph of some wounded Serbian soldiers and lost interest in the whole proceedings. But Percy and Kismine seemed to have inherited the arrogant attitude in all its harsh magnificence from their father. A chaste and consistent selfishness ran like a pattern through their every idea.

John was enchanted by the wonders of the château and the valley. Braddock Washington, so Percy told him, had caused to be kidnapped a landscape gardener, an architect, a designer of stage settings, and a French decadent poet left over from the last century. He had put his entire force of Negroes at their disposal, guaranteed to supply them with any materials that the world could offer, and left them to work out some ideas of their own. But one by one they had shown their uselessness. The decadent poet had at once begun bewailing his separation from the boulevards in spring—he made some vague remarks about spices, apes, and ivories, but said nothing that was of any practical value. The stage designer on his part wanted to make the whole valley a series of tricks and sensational effects—a state of things that the Washingtons would soon have grown tired of. And as for the architect and the landscape gardener, they thought only in terms of convention. They must make this like this and that like that.

But they had, at least, solved the problem of what was to be done with them—they all went mad early one morning after spending the night in a single room trying to agree upon the location of a fountain, and were now confined comfortably in an insane asylum at Westport, Connecticut.

"But," inquired John curiously, "who did plan all your wonderful reception rooms and halls, and approaches and bathrooms—?"

"Well," answered Percy, "I blush to tell you, but it was a moving-picture fella. He was the only man we found who was used to playing with an unlimited amount of money, though he did tuck his napkin in his collar and couldn't read or write."

As August drew to a close John began to regret that he must soon go back to school. He and Kismine had decided to elope the following June.

"It would be nicer to be married here," Kismine confessed, "but of course I could never get father's permission to marry you at all. Next to that I'd rather elope. It's terrible for wealthy people to be married in America at present—they always have to send out bulletins to the press saying that they're going to be married in remnants, when what they mean is just a peck of old secondhand pearls and some used lace worn once by the Empress Eugénie."

"I know," agreed John fervently. "When I was visiting the Schnlitzer-Murphys, the eldest daughter, Gwendolyn, married a man whose father owns half of West Virginia. She wrote home saying what a tough struggle she was carrying on on his salary as a bank clerk—and then she ended up by saying that 'Thank God, I have four good maids anyhow, and that helps a little.'"

"It's absurd," commented Kismine. "Think of the millions and millions of people in the world, laborers and all, who get along with only two maids."

One afternoon late in August a chance remark of Kismine's changed the face of the entire situation, and threw John into a state of terror.

They were in their favorite grove, and between kisses John was indulging in some romantic forebodings which he fancied added poignancy to their relations.

"Sometimes I think we'll never marry," he said sadly. "You're too wealthy, too magnificent. No one as rich as you are can be like other girls. I should marry the daughter of some well-to-do wholesale hardware man from Omaha or Sioux City, and be content with her half million."

"I knew the daughter of a wholesale hardware man once," remarked Kismine. "I don't think you'd have been contented with her. She was a friend of my sister's. She visited here."

"Oh, then you've had other guests?" exclaimed John in surprise.

Kismine seemed to regret her words.

"Oh, yes," she said hurriedly, "we've had a few."

"But aren't you—wasn't your father afraid they'd talk outside?"

"Oh, to some extent, to some extent," she answered. "Let's talk about something pleasanter."

But John's curiosity was aroused.

"Something pleasanter!" he demanded. "What's unpleasant about that? Weren't they nice girls?"

To his great surprise Kismine began to weep.

"Yes—th—that's the—the whole t-trouble. I grew qu-quite attached to some of them. So did Jasmine, but she kept inv-viting them anyway. I couldn't under*stand* it."

A dark suspicion was born in John's heart.

"Do you mean that they *told*, and your father had them—removed?"

"Worse than that," she muttered brokenly. "Father took no chances—and Jasmine kept writing them to come, and they had *such* a good time!"

She was overcome by a paroxysm of grief.

Stunned with the horror of this revelation, John sat there open-mouthed, feeling the nerves of his body twitter like so many sparrows perched upon his spinal column.

"Now, I've told you, and I shouldn't have," she said, calming suddenly and drying her dark blue eyes.

"Do you mean to say that your father had them *murdered* before they left?"

She nodded.

"In August usually—or early in September. It's only natural for us to get all the pleasure out of them that we can first."

"How abominable! How—why, I must be going crazy! Did you really admit that—"

"I did," interrupted Kismine, shrugging her shoulders. "We can't very well imprison them like those aviators, where they'd be a continual reproach to us every day. And it's always been made easier for Jasmine and me, because father had it done sooner than we expected. In that way we avoided any farewell scene—"

"So you murdered them! Uh!" cried John.

"It was done very nicely. They were drugged while they were asleep—and their families were always told that they died of scarlet fever in Butte."

"But—I fail to understand why you kept on inviting them!"

"I didn't," burst out Kismine. "I never invited one. Jasmine did. And they always had a very good time. She'd give them the nicest presents toward the last. I shall probably have visitors too—I'll harden up to it. We can't let such an inevitable thing as death stand in the way of enjoying life while we have it. Think how lonesome it'd be out here if we never had *any* one. Why, father and mother have sacrificed some of their best friends just as we have."

"And so," cried John accusingly, "and so you were letting me make love to you and pretending to return it, and talking about marriage, all the time knowing perfectly well that I'd never get out of here alive—"

"No," she protested passionately. "Not any more. I did at first. You were here. I couldn't help that, and I thought your last days might as well be pleasant for both of us. But then I fell in love with you, and—and I'm honestly sorry you're going to—going to be put away—though I'd rather you'd be put away than ever kiss another girl."

"Oh, you would, would you?" cried John ferociously.

"Much rather. Besides, I've always heard that a girl can have more fun with a man whom she knows she can never marry. Oh, why did I tell you? I've probably spoiled your whole good time now, and we were really enjoying things when you didn't know it. I knew it would make things sort of depressing for you."

"Oh, you did, did you?" John's voice trembled with anger. "I've heard about enough of this. If you haven't any more pride and decency than to have an affair with a fellow that you know isn't much better than a corpse, I don't want to have any more to do with you."

"You're not a corpse!" she protested in horror. "You're not a corpse! I won't have you saying that I kissed a corpse!"

"I said nothing of the sort!"

"You did! You said I kissed a corpse!"

"I didn't!"

Their voices had risen, but upon a sudden interruption they both subsided into immediate silence. Footsteps were coming along the path in their direction, and a moment later the rose bushes were parted displaying Braddock Washington, whose intelligent eyes set in his good-looking vacuous face were peering in at them.

"Who kissed a corpse?" he demanded in obvious disapproval.

"Nobody," answered Kismine quickly. "We were just joking."

"What are you two doing here, anyhow?" he demanded gruffly. "Kismine, you ought to be—to be reading or playing golf with your sister. Go read! Go play golf! Don't let me find you here when I come back!"

Then he bowed at John and went up the path.

"See?" said Kismine crossly, when he was out of hearing. "You've spoiled it all. We can never meet any more. He won't let me meet you. He'd have you poisoned if he thought we were in love."

"We're not, any more!" cried John fiercely, "so he can set his mind at rest upon that. Moreover, don't fool yourself that I'm going to stay around here. Inside of six hours I'll be over those mountains, if I have to gnaw a passage through them, and on my way East."

They had both got to their feet, and at this remark Kismine came close and put her arm through his.

"I'm going, too."

"You must be crazy—"

"Of course I'm going," she interrupted impatiently.

"You most certainly are not. You—"

"Very well," she said quietly, "we'll catch up with father now and talk it over with him."

Defeated, John mustered a sickly smile.

"Very well, dearest," he agreed, with pale and unconvincing affection, "we'll go together."

His love for her returned and settled placidly on his heart. She was his —she would go with him to share his dangers. He put his arms about her and kissed her fervently. After all she loved him; she had saved him, in fact.

Discussing the matter they walked slowly back toward the château. They decided that since Braddock Washington had seen them together they had best depart the next night. Nevertheless, John's lips were unusually dry at dinner, and he nervously emptied a great spoonful of peacock soup into his left lung. He had to be carried into the tourquoise and sable cardroom and pounded on the back by one of the underbutlers, which Percy considered a great joke.

Long after midnight John's body gave a nervous jerk, and he sat suddenly upright, staring into the veils of somnolence that draped the room.

Through the squares of blue darkness that were his open windows, he had heard a faint faraway sound that died upon a bed of wind before identifying itself on his memory, clouded with uneasy dreams. But the sharp noise that had succeeded it was nearer, was just outside the room —the click of a turned knob, a footstep, a whisper, he could not tell; a hard lump gathered in the pit of his stomach, and his whole body ached in the moment that he strained agonizingly to hear. Then one of the veils seemed to dissolve, and he saw a vague figure standing by the door, a figure only faintly limned and blocked in upon the darkness, mingled so with the folds of the drapery as to seem distorted, like a reflection seen in a dirty pane of glass.

With a sudden movement of fright or resolution John pressed the button by his bedside, and the next moment he was sitting in the green sunken bath of the adjoining room, waked into alertness by the shock of the cold water which half filled it.

He sprang out, and, his wet pajamas scattering a heavy trickle of water behind him, ran for the aquamarine door which he knew led out onto the ivory landing of the second floor. The door opened noiselessly. A single crimson lamp burning in a great dome above lit the magnificent sweep of the carved stairways with a poignant beauty. For a moment John hesitated, appalled by the silent splendor massed about him, seeming to envelop in its gigantic folds and contours the solitary drenched little figure shivering upon the ivory landing. Then simultaneously two things happened. The door of his own sitting room swung open, precipitating three naked Negroes into the hall—and, as John swayed in wild terror toward the stairway, another door slid back in the wall on the other side of the corridor, and John saw Braddock Washington standing in the lighted lift, wearing a fur coat and a pair of riding boots which reached to his knees and displayed, above, the glow of his rose-colored pajamas.

On the instant the three Negroes—John had never seen any of them before, and it flashed through his mind that they must be the professional executioners—paused in their movement toward John, and turned expectantly to the man in the lift, who burst out with an imperious command:

"Get in here! All three of you! Quick as hell!"

Then, within the instant, the three Negroes darted into the cage, the oblong of light was blotted out as the lift door slid shut, and John was again alone in the hall. He slumped weakly down against an ivory stair.

It was apparent that something portentous had occurred, something which, for the moment at least, had postponed his own petty disaster. What was it? Had the Negroes risen in revolt? Had the aviators forced aside the iron bars of the grating? Or had the men of Fish stumbled blindly through the hills and gazed with bleak, joyless eyes upon the gaudy valley? John did not know. He heard a faint whir of air as the lift whizzed up again, and then, a moment later, as it descended. It was probable that Percy was hurrying to his father's assistance, and it occurred to John that this was his opportunity to join Kismine and plan an immediate escape. He waited until the lift had been silent for several minutes; shivering a little with the night cool that whipped in through his wet pajamas, he returned to his room and dressed himself quickly. Then he mounted a long flight of stairs and turned down the corridor carpeted with Russian sable which led to Kismine's suite.

The door of her sitting room was open and the lamps were lighted. Kismine, in an angora kimono, stood near the window of the room in a listening attitude, and as John entered noiselessly, she turned toward him.

"Oh, it's you!" she whispered, crossing the room to him. "Did you hear them?"

"I heard your father's slaves in my—"

"No," she interrupted excitedly. "Airplanes!"

"Airplanes? Perhaps that was the sound that woke me."

"There're at least a dozen. I saw one a few moments ago dead against the moon. The guard back by the cliff fired his rifle and that's what roused father. We're going to open on them right away."

"Are they here on purpose?"

"Yes, it's that Italian who got away—"

Simultaneously with her last word, a succession of sharp cracks tumbled in through the open window. Kismine uttered a little cry, took a penny with fumbling fingers from a box on her dresser, and ran to one of the electric lights. In an instant the entire château was in darkness—she had blown out the fuse.

"Come on!" she cried to him. "We'll go up to the roof garden, and watch it from there!"

Drawing a cape about her, she took his hand, and they found their way out the door. It was only a step to the tower lift, and as she pressed the button that shot them upward he put his arms around her in the darkness and kissed her mouth. Romance had come to John Unger at last. A minute later they had stepped out upon the star-white platform. Above, under the misty moon, sliding in and out of the patches of cloud that eddied below it, floated a dozen dark-winged bodies in a constant circling course. From here and there in the valley flashes of fire leaped toward them, followed by sharp detonations. Kismine clapped her hands with pleasure, which a moment later turned to dismay as the airplanes at some prearranged signal began to release their bombs and the whole of the valley became a panorama of deep reverberate sound and lurid light.

Before long the aim of the attackers became concentrated upon the points where the antiaircraft guns were situated, and one of them was almost immediately reduced to a giant cinder to lie smouldering in a park of rose bushes.

"Kismine," begged John, "you'll be glad when I tell you that this attack came on the eve of my murder. If I hadn't heard that guard shoot off his gun back by the pass I should now be stone dead—"

"I can't hear you!" cried Kismine, intent on the scene before her. "You'll have to talk louder!"

"I simply said," shouted John, "that we'd better get out before they begin to shell the château!"

Suddenly the whole portico of the Negro quarters cracked asunder, a geyser of flame shot up from under the colonnades, and great fragments of jagged marble were hurled as far as the borders of the lake.

"There go fifty thousand dollars' worth of slaves," cried Kismine, "at prewar prices. So few Americans have any respect for property."

John renewed his efforts to compel her to leave. The aim of the airplanes was becoming more precise minute by minute, and only two of the antiaircraft guns were still retaliating. It was obvious that the garrison, encircled with fire, could not hold out much longer.

"Come on!" cried John, pulling Kismine's arm, "we've got to go. Do you realize that those aviators will kill you without question if they find you?"

She consented reluctantly.

"We'll have to wake Jasmine!" she said, as they hurried toward the lift. Then she added in a sort of childish delight: "We'll be poor, won't we? Like people in books. And I'll be an orphan and utterly free. Free and poor! What fun!" She stopped and raised her lips to him in a delighted kiss.

"It's impossible to be both together," said John grimly. "People have found that out. And I should choose to be free as preferable of the two. As an extra caution you'd better dump the contents of your jewel box into your pockets."

Ten minutes later the two girls met John in the dark corridor and they descended to the main floor of the château. Passing for the last time through the magnificence of the splendid halls, they stood for a moment out on the terrace, watching the burning Negro quarters and the flaming embers of two planes which had fallen on the other side of the lake. A solitary gun was still keeping up a sturdy popping, and the attackers seemed timorous about descending lower, but sent their thunderous fire-works in a circle around it, until any chance shot might annihilate its Ethiopian crew.

John and the two sisters passed down the marble steps, turned sharply to the left, and began to ascend a narrow path that wound like a garter about the diamond mountain. Kismine knew a heavily wooded spot half-way up where they could lie concealed and yet be able to observe the wild night in the valley—finally to make an escape, when it should be necessary, along a secret path laid in a rocky gully.

It was three o'clock when they attained their destination. The obliging and phlegmatic Jasmine fell off to sleep immediately, leaning against the trunk of a large tree, while John and Kismine sat, his arm around her, and watched the desperate ebb and flow of the dying battle among the ruins of a vista that had been a garden spot that morning. Shortly after four o'clock the last remaining gun gave out a clanging sound and went out of action in a swift tongue of red smoke. Though the moon was down, they saw that the flying bodies were circling closer to the earth. When the planes had made certain that the beleaguered possessed no further resources, they would land and the dark and glittering reign of the Wash-ingtons would be over.

With the cessation of the firing the valley grew quiet. The embers of the two airplanes glowed like the eyes of some monster crouching in the grass. The château stood dark and silent, beautiful without light as it had been beautiful in the sun, while the woody rattles of Nemesis filled the air above with a growing and receding complaint. Then John per-ceived that Kismine, like her sister, had fallen sound asleep.

It was long after four when he became aware of footsteps along the path they had lately followed, and he waited in breathless silence until the persons to whom they belonged had passed the vantage point he oc-cupied. There was a faint stir in the air now that was not of human origin, and the dew was cold; he knew that the dawn would break soon. John waited until the steps had gone a safe distance up the mountain and were inaudible. Then he followed. About half-way to the steep summit the trees fell away and a hard saddle of rock spread itself over the diamond beneath. Just before he reached this point he slowed down his pace, warned by an animal sense that there was life just ahead of him. Coming to a high boulder, he lifted his head gradually above its edge. His curiosity was rewarded; this is what he saw:

Braddock Washington was standing there motionless, silhouetted against the gray sky without sound or sign of life. As the dawn came up out of the east, lending a cold green color to the earth, it brought the solitary figure into insignificant contrast with the new day.

While John watched, his host remained for a few moments absorbed in some inscrutable contemplation; then he signaled to the two Negroes who crouched at his feet to lift the burden which lay between them. As they struggled upright, the first yellow beam of the sun struck through the innumerable prisms of an immense and exquisitely chiseled diamond —and a white radiance was kindled that glowed upon the air like a fragment of the morning star. The bearers staggered beneath its weight for a moment—then their rippling muscles caught and hardened under the wet shine of the skins and the three figures were again motionless in their defiant impotency before the heavens.

After a while the white man lifted his head and slowly raised his arms in a gesture of attention, as one who would call a great crowd to hear— but there was no crowd, only the vast silence of the mountain and the sky, broken by faint bird voices down among the trees. The figure on the saddle of rock began to speak ponderously and with an inextinguishable pride.

"You out there—" he cried in a trembling voice. "You—there—!" He paused, his arms still uplifted, his head held attentively as though he were expecting an answer. John strained his eyes to see whether there might be men coming down the mountain, but the mountain was bare of human life. There was only sky and a mocking flute of wind along the treetops. Could Washington be praying? For a moment John wondered. Then the illusion passed—there was something in the man's whole attitude antithetical to prayer.

"Oh, you above there!"

The voice was become strong and confident. This was no forlorn supplication. If anything, there was in it a quality of monstrous condescension.

"You there—"

Words, too quickly uttered to be understood, flowing one into the other. . . . John listened breathlessly, catching a phrase here and there, while the voice broke off, resumed, broke off again—now strong and argumentative, now colored with a slow, puzzled impatience. Then a conviction commenced to dawn on the single listener, and as realization crept over him a spray of quick blood rushed through his arteries. Braddock Washington was offering a bribe to God!

That was it—there was no doubt. The diamond in the arms of his slaves was some advance sample, a promise of more to follow.

That, John perceived after a time, was the thread running through his sentences. Prometheus Enriched was calling to witness forgotten sacrifices, forgotten rituals, prayers obsolete before the birth of Christ. For a while his discourse took the form of reminding God of this gift or that which Divinity had deigned to accept from men—great churches if he would rescue cities from the plague, gifts of myrrh and gold, of human lives and beautiful women and captive armies, of children and queens, of beasts of the forest and field, sheep and goats, harvests and cities, whole conquered lands that had been offered up in lust or blood for His appeasal, buying a meed's worth of alleviation from the Divine wrath—and now he, Braddock Washington, Emperor of Diamonds, king and priest of the age of gold, arbiter of splendor and luxury, would offer up a treasure such as princes before him had never dreamed of, offer it up not in suppliance, but in pride.

He would give to God, he continued, getting down to specifications, the greatest diamond in the world. This diamond would be cut with many more thousand facets than there were leaves on a tree, and yet the whole diamond would be shaped with the perfection of a stone no bigger than a fly. Many men would work upon it for many years. It would be set in a great dome of beaten gold, wonderfully carved and equipped with gates of opal and crusted sapphire. In the middle would be hollowed out a chapel presided over by an altar of iridescent, decomposing, ever-changing radium which would burn out the eyes of any worshipper who lifted up his head from prayer—and on this altar there would be slain for the amusement of the Divine Benefactor any victim He should choose, even though it should be the greatest and most powerful man alive.

In return he asked only a simple thing, a thing that for God would be absurdly easy—only that matters should be as they were yesterday at this hour and that they should so remain. So very simple! Let but the heavens open, swallowing these men and their airplanes—and then close again. Let him have his slaves once more, restored to life and well.

There was no one else with whom he had ever needed to treat or bargain.

He doubted only whether he had made his bribe big enough. God had His price, of course. God was made in man's image, so it had been said: He must have His price. And the price would be rare—no cathedral whose building consumed many years, no pyramid constructed by ten thousand workmen, would be like this cathedral, this pyramid.

He paused here. That was his proposition. Everything would be up to specifications and there was nothing vulgar in his assertion that it would be cheap at the price. He implied that Providence could take it or leave it.

As he approached the end his sentences became broken, became short and uncertain, and his body seemed tense, seemed strained to catch the slightest pressure or whisper of life in the spaces around him. His hair had turned gradually white as he talked, and now he lifted his head high to the heavens like a prophet of old—magnificently mad.

Then, as John stared in giddy fascination, it seemed to him that a curious phenomenon took place somewhere around him. It was as though the sky had darkened for an instant, as though there had been a sudden murmur in a gust of wind, a sound of faraway trumpets, a sighing like the rustle of a great silken robe—for a time the whole of nature round about partook of this darkness: the birds' song ceased; the trees were still and far over the mountain there was a mutter of dull, menacing thunder.

That was all. The wind died along the tall grasses of the valley. The dawn and the day resumed their place in a time, and the risen sun sent hot waves of yellow mist that made its path bright before it. The leaves laughed in the sun, and their laughter shook the trees until each bough was like a girl's school in fairyland. God had refused to accept the bribe.

For another moment John watched the triumph of the day. Then, turning, he saw a flutter of brown down by the lake, then another flutter, then another, like the dance of golden angels alighting from the clouds. The airplanes had come to earth.

John slid off the boulder and ran down the side of the mountain to the clump of trees, where the two girls were awake and waiting for him. Kismine sprang to her feet, the jewels in her pockets jingling, a question on her parted lips, but instinct told John that there was no time for words. They must get off the mountain without losing a moment. He seized a hand of each, and in silence they threaded the tree trunks, washed with light now and with the rising mist. Behind them from the valley came no sound at all, except the complaint of the peacocks far away and the pleasant undertone of morning.

When they had gone about half a mile, they avoided the park land and entered a narrow path that led over the next rise of ground. At the high-

est point of this they paused and turned around. Their eyes rested upon
the mountainside they had just left—oppressed by some dark sense of
tragic impendency.

Clear against the sky a broken, white-haired man was slowly descending the steep slope, followed by two gigantic and emotionless Negroes,
who carried a burden between them which still flashed and glittered in
the sun. Half-way down two other figures joined them—John could see
that they were Mrs. Washington and her son, upon whose arm she
leaned. The aviators had clambered from their machines to the sweeping
lawn in front of the château, and with rifles in hand were starting up the
diamond mountain in skirmishing formation.

But the little group of five which had formed farther up and was en-
grossing all the watchers' attention had stopped upon a ledge of rock.
The Negroes stooped and pulled up what appeared to be a trap door in
the side of the mountain. Into this they all disappeared, the white-haired
man first, then his wife and son, finally the two Negroes, the glittering tips
of whose jeweled headdress caught the sun for a moment before the
trap door descended and engulfed them all.

Kismine clutched John's arm.

"Oh," she cried wildly, "where are they going? What are they going to
do?"

"It must be some underground way of escape—"

A little scream from the two girls interrupted his sentence.

"Don't you see?" sobbed Kismine hysterically. "The mountain is
wired!"

Even as she spoke John put up his hands to shield his sight. Before
their eyes the whole surface of the mountain had changed suddenly to a
dazzling burning yellow, which showed up through the jacket of turf as
light shows through a human hand. For a moment the intolerable glow
continued, and then like an extinguished filament it disappeared, revealing a black waste from which blue smoke arose slowly, carrying off with
it what remained of vegetation and of human flesh. Of the aviators there
was left neither blood nor bone—they were consumed as completely as
the five souls who had gone inside.

Simultaneously, and with an immense concussion, the château literally
threw itself into the air, bursting into flaming fragments as it rose, and
then tumbling back upon itself in a smoking pile that lay projecting half
into the water of the lake. There was no fire—what smoke there was
drifted off mingling with the sunshine, and for a few minutes longer a
powdery dust of marble drifted from the great featureless pile that had

once been the house of jewels. There was no more sound and the three people were alone in the valley.

At sunset John and his two companions reached the high cliff which had marked the boundaries of the Washingtons' dominion, and looking back found the valley tranquil and lovely in the dusk. They sat down to finish the food which Jasmine had brought with her in a basket.

"There!" she said, as she spread the tablecloth and put the sandwiches in a neat pile upon it. "Don't they look tempting? I always think that food tastes better outdoors."

"With that remark," remarked Kismine, "Jasmine enters the middle class."

"Now," said John eagerly, "turn out your pocket and let's see what jewels you brought along. If you made a good selection we three ought to live comfortably all the rest of our lives."

Obediently Kismine put her hand in her pocket and tossed two handfuls of glittering stones before him.

"Not so bad," cried John, enthusiastically. "They aren't very big, but— Hello!" His expression changed as he held one of them up to the declining sun "Why, these aren't diamonds! There's something the matter!"

"By golly!" exclaimed Kismine, with a startled look. "What an idiot I am!"

"Why, these are rhinestones!" cried John.

"I know." She broke into a laugh. "I opened the wrong drawer. They belonged on the dress of a girl who visited Jasmine. I got her to give them to me in exchange for diamonds. I'd never seen anything but precious stones before."

"And this is what you brought?"

"I'm afraid so." She fingered the brilliants wistfully "I think I like these better. I'm a little tired of diamonds."

"Very well," said John gloomily. "We'll have to live in Hades. And you will grow old telling incredulous women that you got the wrong drawer. Unfortunately your father's bankbooks were consumed with him."

"Well, what's the matter with Hades?"

"If I come home with a wife at my age my father is just as liable as not to cut me off with a hot coal, as they say down there."

Jasmine spoke up.

"I love washing," she said quietly. "I have always washed my own handkerchiefs. I'll take in laundry and support you both."

"Do they have washwomen in Hades?" asked Kismine innocently.

"Of course," answered John. "It's just like anywhere else."

"I thought—perhaps it was too hot to wear any clothes."

John laughed.

"Just try it!" he suggested. "They'll run you out before you're half started."

"Will father be there?" she asked.

John turned to her in astonishment.

"Your father is dead," he replied somberly. "Why should he go to Hades? You have it confused with another place that was abolished long ago."

After supper they folded up the tablecloth and spread their blankets for the night.

"What a dream it was," Kismine sighed, gazing up at the stars. "How strange it seems to be here with one dress and a penniless fiancé!

"Under the stars," she repeated. "I never noticed the stars before. I always thought of them as great big diamonds that belonged to someone. Now they frighten me. They make me feel that it was all a dream, all my youth."

"It *was* a dream," said John quietly. "Everybody's youth is a dream, a form of chemical madness."

"How pleasant then to be insane!"

"So I'm told," said John gloomily. "I don't know any longer. At any rate, let us love for a while, for a year or so, you and me. That's a form of divine drunkenness that we can all try. There are only diamonds in the whole world, diamonds and perhaps the shabby gift of disillusion. Well, I have that last and I will make the usual nothing of it." He shivered. "Turn up your coat collar, little girl, the night's full of chill and you'll get pneumonia. His was a great sin who first invented consciousness. Let us lose it for a few hours."

So wrapping himself in his blanket he fell off to sleep.

Honoré de Balzac

1799–1850

Honoré Balzac (he adopted the aristocratic *de* about 1831) was born in Tours, France, on May 20, 1799. He studied law at the University of Paris. In 1819 his family gave him a starvation allowance to try literature. He wrote a verse tragedy, *Cromwell*. For five or six years he worked as a journalist, fathered stillborn magazines, and turned out romantic thrillers by the yard. A speculation in publishing, printing, and type founding crashed in 1828, leaving him heavily in debt to his mother and his friend Madame de Berny.

A first novel under his own name, *The Last Chouan* (later *The Chouans*), was published in 1829. *The Physiology of Marriage*, in the following year, made him a celebrity. About this time his plan for *The Human Comedy*, a great structure of fiction that would embody the social life of his period, began to take shape. *The Shagreen Skin* in 1831 was followed, during the period of 1832 to 1836, by more than twenty works, including *Louis Lambert, The Country Doctor, Eugénie Grandet,* and *Père Goriot*—the latter two among his masterpieces.

An affair with the Marquise de Castries gave him access to the upper levels of French society. For the rest of the 1830's and into the 1840's, his tremendous production rolled on in such works as *Lost Illusions, César Birotteau, The Village Curé, Béatrix, Droll Stories,*

Notes from the artist: ". . . the sectioning of Balzac's head into pie-shaped pieces was suggested by the author's own intention to build up a complete conspectus of human society (La Comédie humaine), with each of his works contributing one piece of the whole."

and *Modeste Mignon*. He traveled in Italy and cultivated the society of the Countess Guidoboni-Visconti, an Englishwoman. As president of the Society of Men of Letters, he was active in promoting the rights of authors.

In 1833 he had first met the Polish Countess Éveline Hanska. He courted her for nearly twenty years. *Splendors and Miseries of the Courtesans, Cousin Bette,* and *Cousin Pons* belong among his later works. He wrote about a hundred books. It is estimated that what he had finished of *The Human Comedy* includes about three thousand characters. His health was declining, but he made several trips to Poland. He married Madame Hanska at Berdichev in March, 1850. They returned to Paris, where Balzac died on August 18th of the same year.

A *Passion in the Desert* was published in 1837, in the same year as *César Birotteau* and the first part of *Lost Illusions*. We observe first that it is a story within a story. Why did the author choose this form? One reason, we may guess, is that in the first scene at M. Martin's menagerie Balzac wishes to remind us that what are called "the big cats" in the circus can be gentled and trained. Thus the soldier's adventure in the desert will appear less unlikely. Another reason, and perhaps the chief one, is that Balzac evidently preferred not to limit himself to the old soldier's matter-of-fact expression. So he gives us a worldly narrator who is capable of suggesting all the emotional and "philosophic" niceties of the situation. Moreover, since this is a story about love, the narrator's woman friend becomes his expert and skeptical audience.

Like other stories of Balzac's, this one seems now and then to be poised on the margin between reality and fable. We feel this, for example, in the incident in which the leopard ("panther" is a more general term) drags the soldier out of the quicksand. It reminds us of Pliny the Elder's term for leopards—"spotted ladies"—and his remark that only the lion "shows mercy to suppliants." Clearly we are in the region of fable. But how often do we feel this in Balzac's story? Hardly at all. This is his first triumph: that he makes us believe the events in the story *could* happen.

He begins by giving us an example of the soldier's cool resolution in his escape from the Arab camp. The soldier will need all of it that first night in the cave when he wakes up in the dark and hears "a respiration whose savage energy could not belong to a human creature." Already this Napoleonic soldier, this trooper (he wears spurs) from Provence, has endured the excitement of escape, the despair of finding himself alone in the desert, and the joy of discovering date palms loaded with fruit. Now he faces raw terror as the moon gradually reveals a panther sleeping in the mouth of his cave.

It is unlikely, again. She would have scented him, we think. Perhaps she would have waked him as she prowled back and forth in front of the cave. But again, we are willing to believe it. The trooper has a loaded rifle, a scimitar, a dagger. But he does not try to kill her. We believe in his prudence and his forbearance—so French, so intrepid in the Napoleonic style. He is cool enough to observe that she has blood on her muzzle. She will not be hungry again for a while.

So begins what is perhaps the strangest love story in all fiction. He is charmed by her feminine power, her suppleness and grace. He woos her. She responds with the languorous affection of a great house cat. He is reminded of his first sweetheart, Virginie, and of how he was always a little afraid of the knife she threatened him with. He too keeps his dagger in hand. But gradually, though he does not give up hope of rescue, he feels in himself a great change of heart. The desert becomes a magic dwelling place. He discovers "in the rising and setting of the sun sights unknown to the world." For a moment—but only for a moment—the Peaceable Kingdom is at hand.

A Passion
in the Desert

The whole show is dreadful," she cried, coming out of the menagerie of M. Martin. She had just been looking at that daring speculator "working with his hyena"—to speak in the style of the program.

"By what means," she continued, "can he have tamed these animals to such a point as to be certain of their affection for—."

"What seems to you a problem," said I, interrupting, "is really quite natural."

"Oh!" she cried, letting an incredulous smile wander over her lips.

"You think that beasts are wholly without passions?" I asked her. "Quite the reverse; we can communicate to them all the vices arising in our own state of civilization."

She looked at me with an air of astonishment.

"Nevertheless," I continued, "the first time I saw M. Martin, I admit, like you, I did give vent to an exclamation of surprise. I found myself next to an old soldier with the right leg amputated, who had come in with me. His face had struck me. He had one of those intrepid heads, stamped with the seal of warfare, and on which the battles of Napoleon are written. Besides, he had that frank good-humored expression which always impresses me favorably. He was without doubt one of those troopers who are surprised at nothing, who find matter for laughter in the contortions of a dying comrade, who bury or plunder him quite lightheartedly, who stand intrepidly in the way of bullets; in fact, one of those men who waste no time in deliberation, and would not hesitate to make friends with the devil himself. After looking very attentively at the proprietor of the menagerie getting out of his box, my companion pursed up his lips with an air of mockery and contempt, with that peculiar and expressive twist which superior people assume to show they are not taken in. Then when I was expatiating on the courage of M. Martin, he smiled, shook his head knowingly, and said, 'Well known.'

"How 'well known'?" I said. "If you would only explain to me the mystery I should be vastly obliged."

"After a few minutes, during which we made acquaintance, we went to dine at the first *restaurateur's* whose shop caught our eye. At dessert a bottle of champagne completely refreshed and brightened up the memories of this odd old soldier. He told me his story, and I said he had every reason to exclaim, 'Well known.'"

When she got home, she teased me to that extent and made so many promises that I consented to communicate to her the old soldier's confidences. Next day she received the following episode of an epic which one might call "The Frenchman in Egypt."

During the expedition in Upper Egypt under General Desaix, a Provençal soldier fell into the hands of the Mangrabins, and was taken by these Arabs into the deserts beyond the falls of the Nile.

In order to place a sufficient distance between themselves and the French Army, the Mangrabins made forced marches, and only rested during the night. They camped round a well overshadowed by palm trees under which they had previously concealed a store of provisions. Not surmising that the notion of flight would occur to their prisoner, they contented themselves with binding his hands, and after eating a few dates, and giving provender to their horses, went to sleep.

When the brave Provençal saw that his enemies were no longer watching him, he made use of his teeth to steal a scimitar, fixed the blade between his knees, and cut the cords which prevented using his hands; in a moment he was free. He at once seized a rifle and dagger, then taking the precaution to provide himself with a sack of dried dates, oats, and powder and shot, and to fasten a scimitar to his waist, he leaped onto a horse, and spurred on vigorously in the direction where he thought to find the French Army. So impatient was he to see a bivouac again that he pressed on the already tired courser at such speed that its flanks were lacerated with his spurs, and at last the poor animal died, leaving the Frenchman alone in the desert. After walking some time in the sand with all the courage of an escaped convict, the soldier was obliged to stop, as the day had already ended. In spite of the beauty of an oriental sky at night, he felt he had not strength enough to go on. Fortunately he had been able to find a small hill, on the summit of which a few palm trees shot up into the air; it was their verdure seen from afar which had brought hope and consolation to his heart. His fatigue was so great that he lay down upon a rock of granite, capriciously cut out like a camp bed; there he fell asleep without taking any precaution to defend himself while he slept. He had made the sacrifice of his life. His last thought was one of regret. He repented having left the Mangrabins, whose nomad life seemed to smile on him now that he was afar from them and without help. He was awakened by the sun, whose pitiless rays fell with all their force on the granite and produced an intolerable heat—for he had had the stupidity to place himself inversely to the shadow thrown by the verdant majestic heads of the palm trees. He looked at the solitary trees and shuddered—they reminded him of the graceful shafts crowned with foliage which characterize the Saracen columns in the cathedral of Aries.

But when, after counting the palm trees, he cast his eye around him, the most horrible despair was infused into his soul. Before him stretched an ocean without limit. The dark sand of the desert spread farther than sight could reach in every direction, and glittered like steel struck with a bright light. It might have been a sea of looking glass, or lakes melted together in a mirror. A fiery vapor carried up in streaks made a perpetual whirlwind over the quivering land. The sky was lit with an oriental splendor of insupportable purity, leaving naught for the imagination to desire. Heaven and earth were on fire.

The silence was awful in its wild and terrible majesty. Infinity, immensity, closed in upon the soul from every side. Not a cloud in the sky, not a breath in the air, not a flaw on the bosom of the sand, ever moving in diminutive waves; the horizon ended as at sea on a clear day, with one line of light, definite as the cut of a sword.

The Provençal threw his arms around the trunk of one of the palm trees, as though it were the body of a friend, and then in the shelter of the thin straight shadow that the palm cast upon the granite, he wept. Then sitting down he remained as he was, contemplating with profound sadness the implacable scene, which was all he had to look upon. He cried aloud, to measure the solitude. His voice, lost in the hollows of the hill, sounded faintly, and aroused no echo—the echo was in his own heart. The Provençal was twenty-two years old;—he loaded his carbine.

"There'll be time enough," he said to himself, laying on the ground the weapon which alone could bring him deliverance.

Looking by turns at the black expanse and the blue expanse, the soldier dreamed of France—he smelt with delight the gutters of Paris—he remembered the towns through which he had passed, the faces of his fellow soldiers, the most minute details of his life. His southern fancy soon

showed him the stones of his beloved Provence, in the play of the heat
which waved over the spread sheet of the desert. Fearing the danger of
this cruel mirage, he went down the opposite side of the hill to that by
which he had come up the day before. The remains of a rug showed that
this place of refuge had at one time been inhabited; at a short distance
he saw some palm trees full of dates. Then the instinct which binds us to
life awoke again in his heart. He hoped to live long enough to await the
passing of some Arabs, or perhaps he might hear the sound of cannon;
for at this time Bonaparte was traversing Egypt.

This thought gave him new life. The palm tree seemed to bend with
the weight of the ripe fruit. He shook some of it down. When he tasted
this unhoped-for manna, he felt sure that the palms had been cultivated
by a former inhabitant—the savory, fresh meat of the dates was proof
of the care of his predecessor. He passed suddenly from dark despair to
an almost insane joy. He went up again to the top of the hill, and spent
the rest of the day in cutting down one of the sterile palm trees, which
the night before had served him for shelter. A vague memory made him
think of the animals of the desert; and in case they might come to drink at
the spring, visible from the base of the rocks but lost farther down, he
resolved to guard himself from their visits by placing a barrier at the
entrance of his hermitage.

In spite of his diligence, and the strength which the fear of being
devoured asleep gave him, he was unable to cut the palm in pieces,
though he succeeded in cutting it down. At eventide the king of the
desert fell; the sound of its fall resounded far and wide, like a sigh in the
solitude; the soldier shuddered as though he had heard some voice pre-
dicting woe.

But like an heir who does not long bewail a deceased parent, he tore
off from this beautiful tree the tall broad green leaves which are its
poetic adornment, and used them to mend the mat on which he was to
sleep.

Fatigued by the heat and his work, he fell asleep under the red
curtains of his wet cave.

In the middle of the night his sleep was troubled by an extraordinary
noise; he sat up, and the deep silence around him allowed him to distinguish the alternative accents of a respiration whose savage energy
could not belong to a human creature.

A profound terror, increased still further by the darkness, the silence,
and his waking images, froze his heart within him. He almost felt his
hair stand on end, when by straining his eyes to their utmost he perceived

through the shadows two faint yellow lights. At first he attributed these lights to the reflection of his own pupils, but soon the vivid brilliance of the night aided him gradually to distinguish the objects around him in the cave, and he beheld a huge animal lying but two steps from him. Was it a lion, a tiger, or a crocodile?

The Provençal was not educated enough to know under what species his enemy ought to be classed; but his fright was all the greater, as his ignorance led him to imagine all terrors at once; he endured a cruel torture, noting every variation of the breathing close to him without daring to make the slightest movement. An odor, pungent like that of a fox, but more penetrating, profounder—so to speak—filled the cave, and when the Provençal became sensible of this, his terror reached its height, for he could not longer doubt the proximity of a terrible companion, whose royal dwelling served him for shelter.

Presently the reflection of the moon, descending on the horizon, lit up the den, rendering gradually visible and resplendent the spotted skin of a panther.

The lion of Egypt slept, curled up like a big dog, the peaceful possessor of a sumptuous niche at the gate of a hotel; its eyes opened for a moment and closed again; its face was turned toward the man. A thousand confused thoughts passed through the Frenchman's mind; first he thought of killing it with a bullet from his gun, but he saw there was not enough distance between them for him to take proper aim—the shot would miss the mark. And if it were to wake!—the thought made his limbs rigid. He listened to his own heart beating in the midst of the silence, and cursed the too violent pulsations which the flow of blood brought on, fearing to disturb that sleep which allowed him time to think of some means of escape.

Twice he placed his hand on his scimitar, intending to cut off the head of his enemy; but the difficulty of cutting the stiff, short hair compelled him to abandon this daring project. To miss would be to die for *certain*, he thought; he preferred the chances of fair fight, and made up his mind to wait till morning; the morning did not leave him long to wait.

He could now examine the panther at ease; its muzzle was smeared with blood.

"She's had a good dinner," he thought, without troubling himself as to whether her feast might have been on human flesh. "She won't be hungry when she gets up."

It was a female. The fur on her belly and flanks was glistening white; many small marks like velvet formed beautiful bracelets round her feet;

her sinuous tail was also white, ending with black rings; the overpart of her dress, yellow like unburnished gold, very lissome and soft, had the characteristic blotches in the form of rosettes, which distinguish the panther from every other feline species.

This tranquil and formidable hostess snored in an attitude as graceful as that of a cat lying on a cushion. Her bloodstained paws, nervous and well armed, were stretched out before her face, which rested upon them, and from which radiated her straight, slender whiskers, like threads of silver.

If she had been like that in a cage, the Provençal would doubtless have admired the grace of the animal, and the vigorous contrasts of vivid color which gave her robe an imperial splendor; but just then his sight was troubled by her sinister appearance.

The presence of the panther, even asleep, could not fail to produce the effect which the magnetic eyes of the serpent are said to have on the nightingale.

For a moment the courage of the soldier began to fail before this danger, though no doubt it would have risen at the mouth of a cannon charged with shell. Nevertheless, a bold thought brought daylight to his soul and sealed up the source of the cold sweat which sprang forth on his brow. Like men driven to bay who defy death and offer their body to the smiter, so he, seeing in this merely a tragic episode, resolved to play his part with honor to the last.

"The day before yesterday the Arabs would have killed me perhaps," he said; so considering himself as good as dead already, he waited bravely, with excited curiosity, his enemy's awakening.

When the sun appeared, the panther suddenly opened her eyes; then she put out her paws with energy, as if to stretch them and get rid of cramp. At last she yawned, showing the formidable apparatus of her teeth and pointed tongue, rough as a file.

"A regular *petite maîtresse*," thought the Frenchman, seeing her roll herself about so softly and coquettishly. She licked off the blood which stained her paws and muzzle, and scratched her head with reiterated gestures full of prettiness. "All right, make a little toilet," the Frenchman said to himself, beginning to recover his gaiety with his courage; "we'll say good morning to each other presently," and he seized the small, short dagger which he had taken from the Mangrabins. At this moment the panther turned her head toward the man and looked at him fixedly without moving.

The rigidity of her metallic eyes and their insupportable luster made him shudder, especially when the animal walked toward him. But he looked at her caressingly, staring into her eyes in order to magnetize her, and let her come quite close to him; then with a movement both gentle and amorous, as though he were caressing the most beautiful of women, he passed his hand over her whole body, from the head to the tail, scratching the flexible vertebrae which divided the panther's yellow back. The animal waved her tail voluptuously, and her eyes grew gentle; and when for the third time the Frenchman accomplished this interesting flattery, she gave forth one of those purrings by which our cats express their pleasure; but this murmur issued from a throat so powerful and so deep, that it resounded through the cave like the last vibrations of an organ in a church. The man, understanding the importance of his caresses, redoubled them in such a way as to surprise and stupefy his imperious courtesan. When he felt sure of having extinguished the ferocity of his capricious companion, whose hunger had so fortunately been satisfied the day before, he got up to go out of the cave; the panther let him go out, but when he had reached the summit of the hill she sprang with the lightness of a sparrow hopping from twig to twig, and rubbed herself against his legs, putting up her back after the manner of all the race of cats. Then regarding her guest with eyes whose glare had softened a little, she gave vent to that wild cry which naturalists compare to the grating of a saw.

"She is exacting," said the Frenchman, smilingly.

He was bold enough to play with her ears; he caressed her belly and scratched her head as hard as he could.

When he saw that he was successful, he tickled her skull with the point of his dagger, watching for the right moment to kill her, but the hardness of her bones made him tremble for his success.

The sultana of the desert showed herself gracious to her slave; she lifted her head, stretched out her neck, and manifested her delight by the tranquillity of her attitude. It suddenly occurred to the soldier that to kill this savage princess with one blow he must poniard her in the throat.

He raised the blade, when the panther, satisfied no doubt, laid herself gracefully at his feet, and cast up at him glances in which, in spite of their natural fierceness, was mingled confusedly a kind of good will. The poor Provençal ate his dates, leaning against one of the palm trees, and casting his eyes alternately on the desert in quest of some liberator and on his terrible companion to watch her uncertain clemency.

The panther looked at the place where the date stones fell, and every time that he threw one down her eyes expressed an incredible mistrust.

She examined the man with an almost commercial prudence. However, this examination was favorable to him, for when he had finished his meager meal she licked his boots with her powerful rough tongue, brushing off with marvelous skill the dust gathered in the creases.

"Ah, but when she's really hungry!" thought the Frenchman. In spite of the shudder this thought caused him, the soldier began to measure curiously the proportions of the panther, certainly one of the most splendid specimens of its race. She was three feet high and four feet long without counting her tail; this powerful weapon, rounded like a cudgel, was nearly three feet long. The head, large as that of a lioness, was distinguished by a rare expression of refinement. The cold cruelty of a tiger was dominant, it was true, but there was also a vague resemblance to the face of a sensual woman. Indeed, the face of this solitary queen had something of the gaiety of a drunken Nero: she had satiated herself with blood, and she wanted to play.

The soldier tried if he might walk up and down, and the panther left him free, contenting herself with following him with her eyes, less like a faithful dog than a big Angora cat, observing everything, and every movement of her master.

When he looked around, he saw, by the spring, the remains of his horse; the panther had dragged the carcass all that way; about two-thirds of it had been devoured already. The sight reassured him.

It was easy to explain the panther's absence, and the respect she had had for him while he slept. The first piece of good luck emboldened him to tempt the future, and he conceived the wild hope of continuing on good terms with the panther during the entire day, neglecting no means of taming her, and remaining in her good graces.

He returned to her, and had the unspeakable joy of seeing her wag her tail with an almost imperceptible movement at his approach. He sat down then, without fear, by her side, and they began to play together; he took her paws and muzzle, pulled her ears, rolled her over on her back, stroked her warm, delicate flanks. She let him do whatever he liked, and when he began to stroke the hair on her feet she drew her claws in carefully.

The man, keeping the dagger in one hand, thought to plunge it into the belly of the too-confiding panther, but he was afraid that he would be immediately strangled in her last convulsive struggle; besides, he felt in his heart a sort of remorse which bid him respect a creature that had done him no harm. He seemed to have found a friend, in a boundless desert; half unconsciously he thought of his first sweetheart, whom he had nicknamed "Mignonne" by way of contrast, because she was so atrociously jealous that all the time of their love he was in fear of the knife with which she had always threatened him.

This memory of his early days suggested to him the idea of making the young panther answer to this name, now that he began to admire with less terror her swiftness, suppleness, and softness. Toward the end of the day he had familiarized himself with his perilous position; he now almost liked the painfulness of it. At last his companion had got into the habit of looking up at him whenever he cried in a falsetto voice, "Mignonne."

At the setting of the sun Mignonne gave, several times running, a profound melancholy cry. "She's been well brought up," said the light-hearted soldier; "she says her prayers." But this mental joke only occurred to him when he noticed what a pacific attitude his companion remained in. "Come, *ma petite blonde,* I'll let you go to bed first," he said to her, counting on the activity of his own legs to run away as quickly as possible, directly she was asleep, and seek another shelter for the night.

The soldier waited with impatience the hour of his flight, and when it had arrived he walked vigorously in the direction of the Nile; but hardly had he made a quarter of a league in the sand when he heard the panther bounding after him, crying with that sawlike cry more dreadful even than the sound of her leaping.

"Ah!" he said, "then she's taken a fancy to me; she has never met any one before, and it is really quite flattering to have her first love." That instant the man fell into one of those movable quicksands so terrible to travelers and from which it is impossible to save oneself. Feeling himself caught, he gave a shriek of alarm; the panther seized him with her teeth by the collar, and, springing vigorously backward, drew him as if by magic out of the whirling sand.

"Ah, Mignonne!" cried the soldier, caressing her enthusiastically; "we're bound together for life and death—but no jokes, mind!" and he retraced his steps.

From that time the desert seemed inhabited. It contained a being to whom the man could talk, and whose ferocity was rendered gentle by him, though he could not explain to himself the reason for their strange friendship. Great as was the soldier's desire to stay upon guard, he slept.

On awakening he could not find Mignonne; he mounted the hill, and in the distance saw her springing toward him after the habit of these animals, who cannot run on account of the extreme flexibility of the vertebral column. Mignonne arrived, her jaws covered with blood; she received the wonted caress of her companion, showing with much purring how happy it made her. Her eyes, full of languor, turned still more gently than the day before toward the Provençal, who talked to her as one would to a tame animal.

"Ah! Mademoiselle, you are a nice girl, aren't you? Just look at that! So we like to be made much of, don't we? Aren't you ashamed of yourself? So you have been eating some Arab or other, have you? That doesn't matter. They're animals just the same as you are; but don't you take to eating Frenchmen, or I shan't like you any longer."

She played like a dog with its master, letting herself be rolled over, knocked about, and stroked, alternately; sometimes she herself would provoke the soldier, putting up her paw with a soliciting gesture.

Some days passed in this manner. This companionship permitted the Provençal to appreciate the sublime beauty of the desert; now that he had a living thing to think about, alternations of fear and quiet, and plenty to eat, his mind became filled with contrast and his life began to be diversified.

Solitude revealed to him all her secrets, and enveloped him in her delights. He discovered in the rising and setting of the sun sights unknown to the world. He knew what it was to tremble when he heard over his head the hiss of a bird's wing, so rarely did they pass, or when he saw the clouds, changing and many-colored travelers, melt one into another. He studied in the nighttime the effect of the moon upon the ocean of sand, where the simoom made waves swift of movement and rapid in their change. He lived the life of the Eastern day, marveling at its wonderful pomp; then, after having reveled in the sight of a hurricane over the plain where the whirling sands made red, dry mists and death-bearing clouds, he would welcome the night with joy, for then fell the healthful freshness of the stars, and he listened to imaginary music in the skies. Then solitude taught him to unroll the treasures of dreams. He passed whole hours in remembering mere nothings, and comparing his present life with his past.

At last he grew passionately fond of the panther; for some sort of affection was a necessity.

Whether it was that his will powerfully projected had modified the character of his companion, or whether, because she found abundant food in her predatory excursions in the desert, she respected the man's life, he began to fear for it no longer, seeing her so well tamed.

He devoted the greater part of his time to sleep, but he was obliged to watch like a spider in its web that the moment of his deliverance might not escape him, if anyone should pass the line marked by the horizon. He had sacrificed his shirt to make a flag, which he hung at the top of a palm tree, whose foliage he had torn off. Taught by necessity, he found the means of keeping it spread out, by fastening it with little sticks; for the wind might not be blowing at the moment when the passing traveler was looking through the desert.

It was during the long hours, when he had abandoned hope, that he amused himself with the panther. He had come to learn the different inflections of her voice, the expressions of her eyes; he had studied the capricious patterns of all the rosettes which marked the gold of her robe. Mignonne was not even angry when he took hold of the tuft at the end of her tail to count her rings, those graceful ornaments which glittered in the sun like jewelry. It gave him pleasure to contemplate the supple, fine outlines of her form, the whiteness of her belly, the graceful pose of her head. But it was especially when she was playing that he felt most pleasure in looking at her; the agility and youthful lightness of her movements were a continual surprise to him; he wondered at the supple way in which she jumped and climbed, washed herself and arranged her fur, crouched down and prepared to spring. However rapid her spring might be, however slippery the stone she was on, she would always stop short at the word "Mignonne."

One day, in a bright midday sun, an enormous bird coursed through the air. The man left his panther to look at this new guest; but after waiting a moment the deserted sultana growled deeply.

"My goodness! I do believe she's jealous," he cried, seeing her eyes become hard again; "the soul of Virginie has passed into her body; that's certain."

The eagle disappeared into the air, while the soldier admired the curved contour of the panther.

But there were such youth and grace in her form! She was beautiful as a woman! The blond fur of her robe mingled well with the delicate tints of faint white which marked her flanks.

The profuse light cast down by the sun made this living gold, these russet markings, to burn in a way to give them an indefinable attraction.

The man and the panther looked at one another with a look full of meaning; the coquette quivered when she felt her friend stroke her head; her eyes flashed like lightning—then she shut them tightly.

"She has a soul," he said, looking at the stillness of this queen of the sands, golden like them, white like them, solitary and burning like them.

"Well," she said, "I have read your plea in favor of beasts; but how did two so well adapted to understand each other end?"

"Ah, well! you see, they ended as all great passions do end—by a misunderstanding. For some reason *one* suspects the other of treason; they don't come to an explanation through pride, and quarrel and part from sheer obstinacy."

"Yet sometimes at the best moments a single word or a look is enough—but anyhow go on with your story."

"It's horribly difficult, but you will understand, after what the old villain told me over his champagne.

"He said, 'I don't know if I hurt her, but she turned round, as if enraged, and with her sharp teeth caught hold of my leg—gently, I daresay; but I, thinking she would devour me, plunged my dagger into her throat. She rolled over, giving a cry that froze my heart; and I saw her dying, still looking at me without anger. I would have given all the world— my cross even, which I had not got then—to have brought her to life again. It was as though I had murdered a real person; and the soldiers who had seen my flag, and had come to my assistance, found me in tears.

"'Well sir,' he said, after a moment of silence, 'since then I have been in war in Germany, in Spain, in Russia, in France; I've certainly carried my carcass about a good deal, but never have I seen anything like the desert. Ah! yes, it is very beautiful!'

"'What did you feel there?' I asked him.

"'Oh! that can't be described, young man. Besides, I am not always regretting my palm trees and my panther. I should have to be very melancholy for that. In the desert, you see, there is everything, and nothing.'

"'Yes, but explain—'

"'Well,' he said, with an impatient gesture, 'it is God without mankind.'"

Anton Chekhov

1860–1904

Anton Chekhov was born in Taganrog, Russia, on January 17 (Old Style), 1860. His grandfather, a serf, saved 3,500 rubles and bought his family's freedom. Anton took a medical degree at the University of Moscow. During this period he helped support his family by writing for the Moscow comic papers. His first book went unnoticed, but a second, *Motley Stories*, published in 1886, became broadly popular. In the following year his first play, *Ivanov*, pleased audiences in Moscow and St. Petersburg. He was awarded the Pushkin Prize.

In 1890–91 he traveled across the great breadth of Russia to investigate the penal colony on Sakhalin Island, north of Japan. His exposé of conditions there helped to bring about prison reforms. He bought a small estate outside Moscow and lived there during most of the 1890's. He did medical work among the peasants, especially during the cholera epidemic of 1892–93, and served as a hospital administrator. These and other experiences gave him material for the short stories he continued to produce all his life.

In 1896 his second play, *The Seagull,* was a failure in the St. Petersburg production but a decided success in the Moscow Art Theater version two years later. The onset of tuberculosis forced him to spend most of his time in the Crimea or abroad. From the

Notes from the artist: ". . . the portrait of Chekhov was done in a contemporary interpretation of early Russian iconography. In the author's hand is a sprig of cherry leaves, symbolizing his famous play The Cherry Orchard."

А·П·ЧЕХОВ

late 1890's most of his work was done for the theater—not, as he said, because he preferred it, but because it gave him a better income. The Moscow Art Theater under Stanislavsky produced *Uncle Vanya* (a rewriting of *The Wood Demon*) in 1899, *The Three Sisters* in 1901, and *The Cherry Orchard* in 1904.

Chekhov married the actress Olga Knipper in 1901. Some of his best stories—*The Darling* (see below), *The Bishop, My Life,* and *In the Ravine*—were written during this final period. He died at Badenweiler in the Black Forest on July 2 (O. S.), 1904.

The work of Chekhov, says the critic Arnold Hauser, gives the effect of "something overheard by chance, intimated by chance, something that has occurred by chance." Is this true? Insofar as it is, we note how it goes against what was perhaps the chief tendency in late-nineteenth-century literature. This was determinism, the idea that social conditions operate as a kind of fate predictable in advance. Taine became its literary prophet. It was worked out in fiction by such writers as Zola, the Goncourts, and even Maupassant. But in the free-will stories of Chekhov, chance itself often plays the part of a kind of sad fatality.

This is truer, we feel, of the early stories than of such a late one as *The Darling*, published in 1898. But what is chance? Tolstoy considered it a kind of ignorance or partial knowledge, "a certain stage of understanding of phenomena." Mathematicians have tried to frame it in formulas of probability. But we need to remember that here we are dealing, not with chance in the open, but with the *effect* of chance as the artist creates it.

The Romans had their goddess Fortuna. The Greek goddess of chance was Tyche, mistress of "whatever may happen," who was "stronger than the rule of Zeus." Chekhov's heroine, too, is a kind of goddess—Olenka Plemyannikova, "the darling," daughter of a retired assessor in a provincial Russian town. She is altogether a woman, and more than that. She is the goddess Woman—Woman who accomplishes her immemorial purposes in spite of every misfortune.

Olenka is, in fact, more Aphrodite, goddess of erotic love, than Tyche. She is philanthropic in the basic sense. She loves people, and—with the usual reaction—they love her. She has a gift—a sometimes embarrassing gift—for total intimacy. She identifies herself with anyone she loves. She is infinitely suggestible. Her life becomes almost a demonstration of the myth that man and woman are orphan halves of each other.[1]

But Olenka's gift as Tyche, goddess of fortune, is displayed in the misfortunes she survives and the dangers she avoids. Her temperament might easily have made her a victim—exploited by other people, starved by her inability to find love, or unable to get along with it when it came to her. The human chances are endless. Even so, we cannot help but believe in the pattern the author lays down for us. The power and warmth of her instinct carry her triumphantly over every misfortune.

A more imaginative, even a more restless, woman might have made more demands on life. Olenka plays according to the easy human rules. In each case, she finds it possible to love the most convenient object—her father, her teacher, the theater manager Kukin, the merchant Pustovalov, Smirnin the veterinary. And even when she has "aged and grown homely," straining against the lack of a child, luck does not abandon her. The veterinary's boy Sasha becomes the recipient of her final absorption in love.

---

[1] See Plato's *Symposium, Great Books of the Western World,* Vol. 7, pp. 149–173.

The Darling

Olenka Plemyannikova, the daughter of a retired collegiate assessor, was sitting on her porch, which gave on the courtyard, deep in thought. It was hot, the flies were persistent and annoying, and it was pleasant to think that it would soon be evening. Dark rainclouds were gathering in the east and there was a breath of moisture in the wind that occasionally blew from that direction.

Kukin, a theater manager who ran a summer garden known as The Tivoli and lodged in the wing of the house, was standing in the middle of the courtyard, staring at the sky.

"Again!" he was saying in despair. "It's going to rain again! Rain every day, every day, as if to spite me! It will be the death of me! It's ruin! Such a frightful loss every day!"

He struck his hands together and continued, turning to Olenka:

"There, Olga Semyonovna, that's our life. It's enough to make you weep! You work, you try your utmost, you wear yourself out, you lie awake nights, you rack your brains trying to make a better thing of it, and what's the upshot? In the first place, the public is ignorant, barbarous. I give them the very best operetta, an elaborate spectacle, first-rate vaudeville artists. But do you think they want that? It's all above their heads. All they want is slapstick! Give them trash! And then look at the weather! Rain almost every evening. It started raining on the tenth of May, and it has kept it up all May and June. It's simply terrible! The public doesn't come, but don't I have to pay the rent? Don't I have to pay the artists?"

The next day toward evening the sky would again be overcast and Kukin would say, laughing hysterically:

"Well, go on, rain! Flood the garden, drown me! Bad luck to me in this world and the next! Let the artists sue me! Let them send me to prison—to Siberia—to the scaffold! Ha, ha, ha!"

The next day it was the same thing all over again.

Olenka listened to Kukin silently, gravely, and sometimes tears would come to her eyes. In the end his misfortunes moved her and she fell in love with him. He was a short, thin man with a sallow face, and wore his hair combed down over his temples. He had a thin tenor voice and when he spoke, his mouth twisted, and his face perpetually wore an expression of despair. Nevertheless he aroused a genuine, deep feeling in her. She was always enamored of someone and could not live otherwise. At first it had been her papa, who was now ill and sat in an armchair in a darkened room, breathing with difficulty. Then she had devoted her affections to her aunt, who used to come from Bryansk every other year. Still earlier, when she went to school, she had been in love with her French teacher. She was a quiet, kind, softhearted girl, with meek, gentle eyes, and she enjoyed very good health. At the sight of her full pink cheeks, her soft white neck with a dark birthmark on it, and the kind artless smile that came into her face when she listened to anything pleasant, men said to themselves, "Yes, not half bad," and smiled too, while the ladies present could not refrain from suddenly seizing her hand in the middle of the conversation and exclaiming delightedly, "You darling!"

The house in which she lived all her life, and which was to be hers by her father's will, was situated on the outskirts of the city on what was known as Gypsy Road, not far from The Tivoli. In the evening and at night she could hear the band play and the skyrockets go off, and it seemed to her that it was Kukin fighting his fate and assaulting his chief enemy, the apathetic public. Her heart contracted sweetly, she had no desire to sleep, and when he returned home at dawn, she would tap softly at her bedroom window and, showing him only her face and one shoulder through the curtain, give him a friendly smile.

He proposed to her, and they were married. And when he had a good look at her neck and her plump firm shoulders, he struck his hands together, and exclaimed, "Darling!"

He was happy, but as it rained on their wedding day and the night that followed, the expression of despair did not leave his face.

As a married couple, they got on well together. She presided over the box office, looked after things in the summer garden, kept accounts and paid salaries; and her rosy cheeks, the radiance of her sweet artless smile showed now in the box-office window, now in the wings of the theater, now at the buffet. And she was already telling her friends that the theater was the most remarkable, the most important, and the most essential thing in the world, and that it was only the theater that could give true pleasure and make you a cultivated and humane person.

"But do you suppose the public understands that?" she would ask. "What it wants is slapstick! Yesterday we gave 'Faust Inside Out,' and almost all the boxes were empty, and if Vanichka and I had put on something vulgar, I assure you the theater would have been packed. Tomorrow Vanichka and I are giving 'Orpheus in Hell.' Do come."

And what Kukin said about artists and the theater she would repeat. Like him she despised the public for its ignorance and indifference to art; she took a hand in the rehearsals, correcting the actors, kept an eye on the musicians, and when there was an unfavorable notice in the local paper, she wept and went to see the editor about it.

The actors were fond of her and called her "the darling," and "Vanichka-and-I." She was sorry for them and would lend them small sums, and if they cheated her, she cried in private but did not complain to her husband.

The pair got on just as well together when winter came. They leased the municipal theater for the season and sublet it for short periods to a Ukrainian troupe, a magician, or a local dramatic club. Olenka was gaining weight and beamed with happiness, but Kukin was getting thinner and more sallow and complained of terrible losses, although business was fairly good during the winter. He coughed at night, and she would make him drink an infusion of raspberries and linden blossoms. rub him with Eau de Cologne and wrap him in her soft shawls.

"What a sweet thing you are!" she would say quite sincerely, smoothing his hair. "My handsome sweet!"

At Lent he left for Moscow to engage a company of actors for the summer season, and she could not sleep with him away. She sat at the window and watched the stars. It occurred to her that she had something in common with the hens: they too stayed awake all night and were disturbed when the cock was absent from the henhouse. Kukin was detained in Moscow, and wrote that he would return by Easter, and in his letters he sent instructions about The Tivoli. But on the Monday of Passion Week, late in the evening, there was a sudden ominous knock at the gate; someone was banging at the wicket as though it were a barrel—boom, boom, boom! The sleepy cook, her bare feet splashing through the puddles, ran to open the gate.

"Open, please!" someone on the other side of the gate was saying in a deep voice. "There's a telegram for you."

Olenka had received telegrams from her husband before, but this time for some reason she was numb with fright. With trembling hands she opened the telegram and read the following:

"Ivan Petrovich died suddenly today awaiting prot instructions tuneral Tuesday."

That is exactly how the telegram had it: "tuneral," and there was also the incomprehensible word "prot"; the signature was that of the director of the comic opera company.

"My precious!" Olenka sobbed. "Vanichka, my precious, my sweet! Why did we ever meet! Why did I get to know you and to love you! To whom can your poor unhappy Olenka turn?"

Kukin was buried on Tuesday in the Vagankovo Cemetery in Moscow. Olenka returned home on Wednesday, and no sooner did she enter her room than she sank onto the bed and sobbed so loudly that she could be heard in the street and in the neighboring courtyards.

"The darling!" said the neighbors, crossing themselves. "Darling Olga Semyonovna! How the poor soul takes on!"

Three months later Olenka was returning from Mass one day in deep mourning and very sad. It happened that one of her neighbors, Vasily Andreich Pustovalov, the manager of Babakayev's lumberyard, who was also returning from church, was walking beside her. He was wearing a straw hat and a white waistcoat, with a gold watch chain, and he looked more like a landowner than a businessman.

"There is order in all things, Olga Semyonovna," he was saying sedately, with a note of sympathy in his voice; "and if one of our dear ones passes on, then it means that this was the will of God, and in that case we must keep ourselves in hand and bear it submissively."

Having seen Olenka to her gate, he took leave of her and went further. All the rest of the day she heard his sedate voice, and as soon as she closed her eyes she had a vision of his dark beard. She liked him very much. And apparently she too had made an impression on him, because a little later a certain elderly lady, whom she scarcely knew, called to have coffee with her, and no sooner was she seated at table than the visitor began to talk about Pustovalov, saying that he was a fine, substantial man, and that any marriageable woman would be glad to go to the altar with him. Three days later Pustovalov himself paid her a visit. He did not stay more than ten minutes and he said little, but Olenka fell in love with him, so deeply that she stayed awake all night burning as with fever, and in the morning she sent for the elderly lady. The match was soon arranged and then came the wedding.

As a married couple Pustovalov and Olenka got on very well together. As a rule he was in the lumberyard till dinnertime, then he went out on business and was replaced by Olenka, who stayed in the office till evening, making out bills and seeing that orders were shipped.

"We pay twenty per cent more for lumber every year," she would say to customers and acquaintances. "Why, we used to deal in local timber, and now Vasichka has to travel to the province of Mogilev for timber regularly. And the freight rates!" she would exclaim, putting her hands to her cheeks in horror. "The freight rates!"

It seemed to her that she had been in the lumber business for ages, that lumber was the most important, the most essential thing in the world, and she found something intimate and touching in the very sound of such words as beam, log, batten, plank, boxboard, lath, scantling, slab. . . .

At night she would dream of whole mountains of boards and planks, of endless caravans of carts hauling lumber out of town to distant points. She would dream that a regiment of beams, 28 feet by 8 inches, standing on end, was marching in the lumberyard, that beams, logs, and slabs were crashing against each other with the hollow sound of dry wood, that they kept tumbling down and rising again, piling themselves on each other. Olenka would scream in her sleep and Pustovalov would say to her tenderly: "Olenka, what's the matter, darling? Cross yourself!"

Whatever ideas her husband had, she adopted as her own. If he thought that the room was hot or that business was slow, she thought so too. Her husband did not care for entertainments and on holidays stayed home—so did she.

"You are always at home or in the office," her friends would say. "You ought to go to the theater, darling, or to the circus."

"Vasichka and I have no time for the theater," she would answer sedately. "We are working people, we're not interested in such foolishness. What good are these theaters?"

On Saturdays the two of them would go to evening service, on holidays they attended early Mass, and returning from the church they walked side by side, their faces wearing a softened expression. There was an agreeable aroma about them, and her silk dress rustled pleasantly. At home they had tea with shortbread, and various kinds of jam, and afterwards they ate pie. Every day at noon, in the yard and on the street just outside the gate, there was a delicious smell of *borshch* and roast lamb or duck, and on fast days there was the odor of fish, and one could not pass the Pustovalov gate without one's mouth watering.

In the office the samovar was always boiling and the customers were treated to tea with doughnuts. Once a week the pair went to the baths and returned side by side, both with red faces.

"Yes, everything goes well with us, thank God," Olenka would say to her friends. "I wish everyone were as happy as Vasichka and I."

When Pustovalov went off to the provinces of Mogilev for timber, she missed him badly and lay awake nights, crying. Sometimes, in the evening, a young army veterinary, by the name of Smirnin, who rented the wing of their house, would call on her. He chatted or played cards with her and that diverted her. What interested her most was what he told her about his domestic life. He had been married and had a son, but was separated from his wife because she had been unfaithful to him, and now he hated her; he sent her forty rubles a month for the maintenance of the child. And listening to him, Olenka would sigh and shake her head: she was sorry for him.

"Well, God keep you," she would say to him as she took leave of him, going to the stairs with him, candle in hand. "Thank you for relieving my boredom, and may the Queen of Heaven give you health!"

She always expressed herself in this sedate and reasonable manner, in imitation of her husband. Just as the veterinary would be closing the door behind him, she would recall him and say:

"You know, Vladimir Platonych, you had better make up with your wife. You ought to forgive her, at least for your son's sake! I am sure the little boy understands everything."

And when Pustovalov came back, she would tell him in low tones about the veterinary and his unhappy domestic life, and both of them would sigh and shake their heads and speak of the boy, who was probably missing his father. Then by a strange association of ideas they would both turn to the icons, bow down to the ground before them and pray that the Lord would grant them children.

Thus the Pustovalovs lived in peace and quiet, in love and harmony for six years. But one winter day, right after having hot tea at the office, Vasily Andreich went out without his cap to see about shipping some lumber, caught a chill and was taken sick. He was treated by the best doctors, but the illness had its own way with him, and he died after four months. Olenka was a widow again.

"To whom can I turn now, my darling?" she sobbed when she had buried her husband. "How can I live without you, wretched and unhappy as I am? Pity me, good people, left all alone in the world—"

She wore a black dress with white cuffs and gave up wearing hat and gloves for good. She hardly ever left the house except to go to church or to visit her husband's grave, and at home she lived like a nun. Only at the end of six months did she take off her widow's weeds and open the shutters. Sometimes in the morning she was seen with her cook going to market for provisions, but how she lived now and what went on in her house could only be guessed. People based their guesses on such facts as that they saw her having tea with the veterinary in her little garden, he reading the newspaper aloud to her, and that, meeting an acquaintance at the post office, she would say:

"There is no proper veterinary inspection in our town, and that's why there is so much illness around. So often you hear of people getting ill from the milk or catching infections from horses and cows. When you come down to it, the health of domestic animals must be as well cared for as the health of human beings."

She now repeated the veterinary's words and held the same opinions about everything that he did. It was plain that she could not live even for one year without an attachment and that she had found new happiness in the wing of her house. Another woman would have been condemned for this, but of Olenka no one could think ill: everything about her was so unequivocal. Neither she nor the veterinary mentioned to anyone the change that had occurred in their relations; indeed, they tried to conceal it, but they didn't succeed, because Olenka could not keep a secret. When he had visitors, his regimental colleagues, she, pouring the tea or serving the supper, would begin to talk of the cattle plague, of the pearl disease, of the municipal slaughterhouses. He would be terribly embarrassed and when the guests had gone, he would grasp her by the arms and hiss angrily:

"I've asked you before not to talk about things that you don't understand! When veterinaries speak among themselves, please don't butt in! It's really annoying!"

She would look at him amazed and alarmed and ask, "But Volodichka, what shall I talk about?"

And with tears in her eyes she would hug him and beg him not to be angry, and both of them were happy.

Yet this happiness did not last long. The veterinary left, left forever, with his regiment, which was moved to some remote place, it may have been Siberia. And Olenka remained alone.

Now she was quite alone. Her father had died long ago, and his armchair stood in the attic, covered with dust and minus one leg. She got thinner and lost her looks, and passers-by in the street did not glance at her and smile as they used to. Obviously, her best years were over, were

behind her, and now a new kind of life was beginning for her, an unfamiliar kind that did not bear thinking of. In the evening Olenka sat on
her porch, and heard the band play at The Tivoli and the rockets go off,
but this no longer suggested anything to her mind. She looked apatheti-
cally at the empty courtyard, thought of nothing, and later, when night
came, she would go to bed and dream of the empty courtyard. She ate
and drank as though involuntarily.

Above all, and worst of all, she no longer had any opinions whatever.
She saw objects about her and understood what was going on, but she
could not form an opinion about anything and did not know what to talk
about. And how terrible it is not to have any opinions! You see, for instance, a bottle, or the rain, or a peasant driving in a cart, but what
is the bottle for, or the rain, or the peasant, what is the meaning of them,
you can't tell, and you couldn't, even if they paid you a thousand rubles.
When Kukin was about, or Pustovalov or, later, the veterinary, Olenka
could explain it all and give her opinions about anything you like, but
now there was the same emptiness in her head and in her heart as in
her courtyard. It was weird, and she felt as bitter as if she had been
eating wormwood.

Little by little the town was extending in all directions. Gypsy Road
was now a regular street, and where The Tivoli had been and the lumber-
yards, houses had sprung up and lanes had multiplied. How swiftly time
passes! Olenka's house had taken on a shabby look, the roof was rusty,
the shed sloped, and the whole yard was invaded by burdock and stinging nettles. Olenka herself had aged and grown homely. In the summer
she sat on the porch, feeling empty and dreary and bitter, as before; in
the winter she sat by the window and stared at the snow. Sometimes at
the first breath of spring or when the wind brought her the chime of
church bells, memories of the past would overwhelm her, her heart would
contract sweetly and her eyes would brim over with tears. But this only
lasted a moment, and then there was again emptiness and once more she
was possessed by a sense of the futility of life; Trot, the black kitten,
rubbed against her and purred softly, but Olenka was not affected by
these feline caresses. Is that what she needed? She needed an affection
that would take possession of her whole being, her soul, her mind, that
would give her ideas, a purpose in life, that would warm her aging
blood. And she would shake the kitten off her lap, and say irritably:
"Scat! Scat! Don't stick to me!"

And so it went, day after day, year after year, and no joy, no opinion!
Whatever Mavra the cook would say was well enough.

One hot July day, toward evening, when the cattle were being driven home and the yard was filled with clouds of dust, suddenly someone knocked at the gate. Olenka herself went to open it and was dumfounded at what she saw: at the gate stood Smirnin, the veterinary, already gray, and wearing civilian clothes. She suddenly recalled everything and, unable to control herself, burst into tears, silently letting her head drop on his breast. She was so agitated that she scarcely noticed how the two of them entered the house and sat down to tea.

"My dear," she murmured, trembling with joy, "Vladimir Platonych, however did you get here?"

"I have come here for good," he explained. "I have retired from the army and want to see what it's like to be on my own and live a settled life. And besides, my son is ready for high school. I have made up with my wife, you know."

"Where is she?"

"She's at the hotel with the boy, and I'm out looking for lodgings."

"Goodness, Vladimir Platonych, take my house! You don't need to look further! Good Lord, and you can have it free," exclaimed Olenka, all in a flutter and beginning to cry again. "You live here in the house, and the wing will do for me. Heavens, I'm so glad!"

The next day they began painting the roof and whitewashing the walls, and Olenka, her arms akimbo, walked about the yard, giving orders. The old smile had come back to her face, and she was lively and spry, as though she had waked from a long sleep. Presently the veterinary's wife arrived, a thin, homely lady with bobbed hair who looked as if she were given to caprices. With her was the little boy, Sasha, small for his age (he was going on ten), chubby, with clear blue eyes and dimples in his cheeks.

No sooner did he walk into the yard than he began chasing the cat, and immediately his eager, joyous laughter rang out.

"Auntie, is that your cat?" he asked Olenka. "When she has little ones, please give us a kitten. Mama is terribly afraid of mice."

Olenka chatted with him, then gave him tea, and her heart suddenly grew warm and contracted sweetly, as if this little boy were her own son. And in the evening, as he sat in the dining room doing his homework, she looked at him with pity and tenderness and whispered:

"My darling, my pretty one, my little one! How blond you are, and so clever!"

"An island," he was reciting from the book, "is a body of land entirely surrounded by water."

"An island is a body of land . . ." she repeated and this was the first opinion she expressed with conviction after so many years of silence and mental vacuity.

She now had opinions of her own, and at supper she had a conversation with Sasha's parents, saying that studying in high school was hard on the children, but that nevertheless the classical course was better than the scientific one because a classical education opened all careers to you: you could be either a doctor or an engineer.

Sasha started going to high school. His mother went off to Kharkov to visit her sister and did not come back; every day his father left town to inspect herds and sometimes he stayed away for three days together, and it seemed to Olenka that Sasha was wholly abandoned, that he was unwanted, that he was being starved, and she moved him into the wing with her and settled him in a little room there.

For six months now Sasha has been living in her wing. Every morning Olenka comes into his room; he is fast asleep, his hand under his cheek, breathing quietly. She is sorry to wake him.

"Sashenka," she says sadly, "get up, my sweet! It's time to go to school."

He gets up, dresses, says his prayers, and sits down to his breakfast: he drinks three glasses of tea and eats two large doughnuts, and half a buttered French roll. He is hardly awake and consequently cross.

"You haven't learned the fable, Sashenka," says Olenka, looking at him as though she were seeing him off on a long journey. "You worry me. You must do your best, darling, study. And pay attention to your teachers."

"Please leave me alone!" says Sasha.

Then he walks down the street to school, a small boy in a big cap, with his books in a rucksack. Olenka follows him noiselessly.

"Sashenka!" she calls after him. He turns around and she thrusts a date or a caramel into his hand. When they turn into the school lane, he feels ashamed at being followed by a tall stout woman; he looks round and says: "You'd better go home, auntie; I can go alone now."

She stands still and stares after him until he disappears at the school entrance. How she loves him! Not one of her former attachments was so deep; never had her soul surrendered itself so unreservedly, so disinterestedly and with such joy as now when her maternal instinct was increasingly asserting itself. For this little boy who was not her own, for the dimples in his cheeks, for his very cap, she would have laid down her life, would have laid it down with joy, with tears of tenderness. Why? But who knows why?

Having seen Sasha off to school, she goes quietly home, contented, tranquil, brimming over with love; her face, grown younger in the last six months, beams with happiness; people meeting her look at her with pleasure and say:

"Good morning, Olga Semyonovna, darling! How are you, darling?"

"They make the children work so hard at high school nowadays," she says, as she does her marketing. "Think of it: yesterday in the first form they had a fable to learn by heart, a Latin translation and a problem for homework. That's entirely too much for a little fellow."

And she talks about the teachers, the lessons, the textbooks—saying just what Sasha says about them.

At three o'clock they have dinner together, in the evening they do the homework together, and cry. When she puts him to bed, she takes a long time making the sign of the cross over him and whispering prayers. Then she goes to bed and thinks of the future, distant and misty, when Sasha, having finished his studies, will become a doctor or an engineer, will have a large house of his own, horses, a carriage, will marry and become a father. She falls asleep and her dreams are of the same thing, and tears flow down her cheeks from her closed eyes. The black kitten lies beside her purring: Purr-purrr-purrr.

Suddenly there is a loud knock at the gate. Olenka wakes up, breathless with fear, her heart palpitating. Half a minute passes, and there is another knock.

"That's a telegram from Kharkov," she thinks, beginning to tremble from head to foot. "Sasha's mother is sending for him from Kharkov—O Lord!"

She is in despair. Her head, her hands, her feet grow chill and it seems to her that she is the most unhappy woman in the whole world. But another minute passes, voices are heard: it's the veterinary returning from the club.

"Well, thank God!" she thinks.

Little by little the load rolls off her heart and she is again at ease; she goes back to bed and thinks of Sasha who is fast asleep in the next room and sometimes shouts in his sleep:

"I'll give it to you! Scram! No fighting!"

Translated by Avrahm Yarmolinsky.

Isaac Singer

1904–

Isaac Bashevis Singer was born in Poland in 1904. He attended a rabbinical seminary in Warsaw and then began to write fiction in Hebrew, later turning to Yiddish. He went to the United States in 1935 and settled in New York. He has been on the staff of the *Jewish Daily Forward* since that time.

Most of Singer's stories, which he has been writing for more than thirty years, have appeared in the *Jewish Daily Forward*, in Yiddish, but they have been translated and have been published in many anthologies. In addition, two collections of his stories have appeared: *Gimpel the Fool and Other Stories* (1957) and *The Spinoza of Market Street and Other Stories* (1961), the title story of which is reprinted here. He is also the author of three novels: *The Family Moskat* (1950), which won the Louis Lamed Prize, *Satan in Goray* (1955), and *The Slave* (1962). The last is an heroic story of a Jew in Poland in the eighteenth century.

Spinoza was a Jew, but aside from that fact he would seem to have little in common with the characters that inhabit most of Singer's stories. These characters are ordinary, often simple folk (though they may be deeply versed in Jewish tradition), on the one hand, and strange demonic creatures of the imagination, on the other. Singer's world is mad and unreal, from one point of view. Witches and mystical forces take on a kind of weird, topsy-turvy life. His heroes and heroines seem to be listening to voices that other people do not hear.

Spinoza was neither ordinary, simple, nor demonic. His thought was complex and powerful, but it was also clear. The clarity and purity of Spinoza's ideas are among the wonders of philosophy.

Nevertheless, Singer has managed to make him a character in the story that follows. At first glance, it might almost seem that Spinoza is another of those strange, half-real figures that people the minds of Singer's heroes. Spinoza seems to be almost as real to the main protagonist of this story, Dr. Fischelson, as the other living people in it. In a score of Singer stories there is a figure that plays much the same role.

But Spinoza in this remarkable story plays another role, too. He is more than a mere figment of the imagination who has, nevertheless, a part in the action. He is also a great philosopher with a compelling view of the world.

What is this view, as Singer, or perhaps only Dr. Fischelson, understands it? Spinoza stands for, and describes with magnificent eloquence, the eternal aspect of our ever changing, muddled, incomprehensible life. That eternal aspect, which is represented in this story by the stars, is not an illusion. But neither is the muddle that is represented in turn by the insects circling "the trembling flame," then by Dr. Fischelson's intestinal troubles, then by the crowd in Market Street seen from Dr. Fischelson's high window, then by the "savage and passionate" cats which offend the hero, and finally by Black Dobbe, Dr. Fischelson's bride.

But the eternal aspect and the muddle do not, at least in this story, merely exist side by side. Perhaps they never do. Here at any rate they are in conflict. At the beginning of the story Dr. Fischelson runs to his window to see the stars in order to escape the heat and the buzzing insects. But at the window he sees not only the eternal stars but also the "half-lit bedlam" below and the "ignorant savage" of a cat. Life cannot be run away from; the muddle attacks Dr. Fischelson even in his own insides. He then, it seems, attempts to make his peace with it. He marries, he becomes a husband, he even, we are given to understand, loves. Yet he rises from his bed on his wedding night and seeks the stars once more. And he cries out to Spinoza, to the permanent, unchanging, eternal universe, that he has become a fool.

His heartfelt words raise many questions. In uttering them, does Dr. Fischelson once and for all renounce the earthbound happiness which may be all that we creatures of the muddle know? Does he turn his back on his love for Black Dobbe and embrace once more the *amor dei intellectualis* [the intellectual love of god]?

Is that one moment of passionate involvement in life to be his last?

Or does he speak those last words with a kind of profound humility and acceptance? Is he saying that there are worse things than to be a fool? Is he asking for forgiveness because he, uniquely, has acted foolishly, or because foolishness is man's eternal lot?

The essence of this memorable tale is to be found in those last murmured words. Perhaps every reader will have to find it, and answer the questions raised by the words, for himself.

The Spinoza
of Market Street

Dr. Nahum Fischelson paced back and forth in his garret room in Market Street, Warsaw. Dr. Fischelson was a short, hunched man with a grayish beard, and was quite bald except for a few wisps of hair remaining at the nape of the neck. His nose was as crooked as a beak and his eyes were large, dark, and fluttering like those of some huge bird. It was a hot summer evening, but Dr. Fischelson wore a black coat which reached to his knees, and he had on a stiff collar and a bow tie. From the door he paced slowly to the dormer window set high in the slanting room and back again. One had to mount several steps to look out. A candle in a brass holder was burning on the table and a variety of insects buzzed around the flame. Now and again one of the creatures would fly too close to the fire and sear its wings, or one would ignite and glow on the wick for an instant. At such moments Dr. Fischelson grimaced. His wrinkled face would twitch and beneath his disheveled moustache he would bite his lips. Finally he took a handkerchief from his pocket and waved it at the insects.

"Away from there, fools and imbeciles," he scolded. "You won't get warm here; you'll only burn yourself."

The insects scattered but a second later returned and once more circled the trembling flame. Dr. Fischelson wiped the sweat from his wrinkled forehead and sighed, "Like men they desire nothing but the pleasure of the moment." On the table lay an open book written in Latin, and on its broad-margined pages were notes and comments printed in small letters by Dr. Fischelson. The book was Spinoza's *Ethics* and Dr. Fischelson had been studying it for the last thirty years. He knew every proposition, every proof, every corollary, every note by heart. When he wanted to find a particular passage, he generally opened to the place immediately without having to search for it. But, nevertheless, he continued to study the *Ethics* for hours every day with a magnifying glass in his bony hand, murmuring and nodding his head in agreement. The truth was that the more Dr. Fischelson studied, the more puzzling sentences, unclear passages, and cryptic remarks he found. Each sentence contained hints unfathomed by any of the students of Spinoza. Actually the philosopher had anticipated all of the criticisms of pure reason made by Kant and his followers. Dr. Fischelson was writing a commentary on the *Ethics*. He had drawers full of notes and drafts, but it didn't seem that he would ever be able to complete his work. The stomach ailment which had plagued him for years was growing worse from day to day. Now he would get pains in his stomach after only a few mouthfuls of oatmeal. "God in Heaven, it's difficult, very difficult," he would say to himself using the same intonation as had his father, the late Rabbi of Tishevitz. "It's very, very hard."

Dr. Fischelson was not afraid of dying. To begin with, he was no longer a young man. Secondly, it is stated in the fourth part of the *Ethics* that "a free man thinks of nothing less than of death and his wisdom is a meditation not of death, but of life." Thirdly, it is also said that "the human mind cannot be absolutely destroyed with the human body but there is some part of it that remains eternal." And yet Dr. Fischelson's ulcer (or perhaps it was a cancer) continued to bother him. His tongue was always coated. He belched frequently and emitted a different foul-smelling gas each time. He suffered from heartburn and cramps. At times he felt like vomiting and at other times he was hungry for garlic, onions, and fried foods. He had long ago discarded the medicines prescribed for him by the doctors and had sought his own remedies. He found it beneficial to take grated radish after meals and lie on his bed, belly down, with his head hanging over the side. But these home remedies offered only temporary relief. Some of the doctors he consulted insisted there was nothing the matter with him. "It's just nerves," they told him. "You could live to be a hundred."

But on this particular hot summer night, Dr. Fischelson felt his strength ebbing. His knees were shaky, his pulse weak. He sat down to read and his vision blurred. The letters on the page turned from green to gold. The lines became waved and jumped over each other, leaving white gaps as if the text had disappeared in some mysterious way. The heat was unbearable, flowing down directly from the tin roof; Dr. Fischelson felt he was inside of an oven. Several times he climbed the four steps to the window and thrust his head out into the cool of the evening breeze. He would remain in that position for so long his knees would become wobbly.

"Oh it's a fine breeze," he would murmur, "really delightful," and he would recall that according to Spinoza, morality and happiness were identical, and that the most moral deed a man could perform was to indulge in some pleasure which was not contrary to reason.

Dr. Fischelson, standing on the top step at the window and looking out, could see into two worlds. Above him were the heavens, thickly strewn with stars. Dr. Fischelson had never seriously studied astronomy but he could differentiate between the planets, those bodies which like the earth, revolve around the sun, and the fixed stars, themselves distant suns, whose light reaches us a hundred or even a thousand years later. He recognized the constellations which mark the path of the earth in space and that nebulous sash, the Milky Way. Dr. Fischelson owned a small telescope he had bought in Switzerland where he had studied and he particularly enjoyed looking at the moon through it. He could clearly make out on the moon's surface the volcanoes bathed in sunlight and the dark, shadowy craters. He never wearied of gazing at these cracks and crevasses. To him they seemed both near and distant, both substantial and insubstantial. Now and then he would see a shooting star trace a wide arc across the sky and disappear, leaving a fiery trail behind it. Dr. Fischelson would know then that a meteorite had reached our atmosphere, and perhaps some unburned fragment of it had fallen into the ocean or had landed in the desert or perhaps even in some inhabited region. Slowly the stars which had appeared from behind Dr. Fischelson's roof rose until they were shining above the house across the street. Yes, when Dr. Fischelson looked up into the heavens, he became aware of that infinite extension which is, according to Spinoza, one of God's attributes. It comforted Dr. Fischelson to think that although he was only a weak, puny man, a changing mode of the absolutely infinite Substance, he was nevertheless a part of the cosmos, made of the same matter as the celestial bodies; to the extent that he was a part of the Godhead, he knew he could not be destroyed. In such moments, Dr. Fischelson experienced the *Amor Dei Intellectualis* which is, according to the philosopher of Amsterdam, the highest perfection of the mind. Dr. Fischelson breathed deeply, lifted his head as high as his stiff collar permitted and actually felt he was whirling in company with the earth, the sun, the stars of the Milky Way, and the infinite host of galaxies known only to infinite thought. His legs became light and weightless and he grasped the window frame with both hands as if afraid he would lose his footing and fly out into eternity.

When Dr. Fischelson tired of observing the sky, his glance dropped to Market Street below. He could see a long strip extending from Yanash's market to Iron Street with the gas lamps lining it merged into a string of fiery dots. Smoke was issuing from the chimneys on the black, tin roofs; the bakers were heating their ovens, and here and there sparks mingled with the black smoke. The street never looked so noisy and crowded as on a summer evening. Thieves, prostitutes, gamblers, and fences loafed in the square which looked from above like a pretzel covered with poppy seeds. The young men laughed coarsely and the girls shrieked. A peddler with a keg of lemonade on his back pierced the general din with his intermittent cries. A watermelon vendor shouted in a savage voice, and the long knife which he used for cutting the fruit dripped with the bloodlike juice. Now and again the street became even more agitated. Fire engines, their heavy wheels clanging, sped by; they were drawn by sturdy black horses which had to be tightly curbed to prevent them from running wild. Next came an ambulance, its siren screaming. Then some thugs had a fight among themselves and the police had to be called. A passer-by was robbed and ran about shouting for help. Some wagons loaded with firewood sought to get through into the courtyards where the bakeries were located but the horses could not lift the wheels over the steep curbs and the drivers berated the animals and lashed them with their whips. Sparks rose from the clanging hoofs. It was now long after seven, which was the prescribed closing time for stores, but actually business had only begun. Customers were led in stealthily through back doors. The Russian policemen on the street, having been paid off, noticed nothing of this. Merchants continued to hawk their wares, each seeking to outshout the others.

"Gold, gold, gold," a woman who dealt in rotten oranges shrieked.

"Sugar, sugar, sugar," croaked a dealer of overripe plums.

"Heads, heads, heads," a boy who sold fishheads roared.

Through the window of a Hasidic study house across the way, Dr. Fischelson could see boys with long sidelocks swaying over holy volumes, grimacing and studying aloud in singsong voices. Butchers, porters, and fruit dealers were drinking beer in the tavern below. Vapor drifted from the tavern's open door like steam from a bathhouse, and there was the sound of loud music. Outside of the tavern, streetwalkers snatched at drunken soldiers and at workers on their way home from the factories. Some of the men carried bundles of wood on their shoulders, reminding Dr. Fischelson of the wicked who are condemned to kindle their own fires in Hell. Husky record players poured out their raspings through open windows. The liturgy of the high holidays alternated with vulgar vaudeville songs.

Dr. Fischelson peered into the half-lit bedlam and cocked his ears. He knew that the behavior of this rabble was the very antithesis of reason. These people were immersed in the vainest of passions, were drunk with emotions, and, according to Spinoza, emotion was never good. Instead of the pleasure they ran after, all they succeeded in obtaining was disease and prison, shame and the suffering that resulted from ignorance. Even the cats which loitered on the roofs here seemed more savage and passionate than those in other parts of the town. They caterwauled with the voices of women in labor, and like demons scampered up walls and leaped onto eaves and balconies. One of the toms paused at Dr. Fischelson's window and let out a howl which made Dr. Fischelson shudder. The doctor stepped from the window and, picking up a broom, brandished it in front of the black beast's glowing, green eyes. "Scat, begone, you ignorant savage!"—and he rapped the broom handle against the roof until the tom ran off.

When Dr. Fischelson had returned to Warsaw from Zürich, where he had studied philosophy, a great future had been predicted for him. His friends had known that he was writing an important book on Spinoza. A Jewish Polish journal had invited him to be a contributor; he had been a frequent guest at several wealthy households and he had been made head librarian at the Warsaw synagogue. Although even then he had been considered an old bachelor, the matchmakers had proposed several rich girls for him. But Dr. Fischelson had not taken advantage of these opportunities. He had wanted to be as independent as Spinoza himself. And he had been. But because of his heretical ideas he had come into conflict with the rabbi and had had to resign his post as librarian. For years after that, he had supported himself by giving private lessons in Hebrew and German. Then, when he had become sick, the Berlin Jewish community had voted him a subsidy of five hundred marks a year. This had been made possible through the intervention of the famous Dr. Hildesheimer with whom he corresponded about philosophy. In order to get by on so small a pension, Dr. Fischelson had moved into the attic room and had begun cooking his own meals on a kerosene stove. He had a cupboard which had many drawers, and each drawer was labeled with the food it contained—buckwheat, rice, barley, onions, carrots, potatoes, mushrooms. Once a week Dr. Fischelson put on his wide-brimmed black hat, took a basket in one hand and Spinoza's *Ethics* in the other, and went off to the market for his provisions. While he was waiting to be served, he would open the *Ethics*. The merchants knew him and would motion him to their stalls.

"A fine piece of cheese, Doctor—just melts in your mouth."

"Fresh mushrooms, Doctor, straight from the woods."

"Make way for the Doctor, ladies," the butcher would shout. "Please don't block the entrance."

During the early years of his sickness, Dr. Fischelson had still gone in the evening to a café which was frequented by Hebrew teachers and other intellectuals. It had been his habit to sit there and play chess while drinking a half a glass of black coffee. Sometimes he would stop at the bookstores on Holy Cross Street where all sorts of old books and magazines could be purchased cheap. On one occasion a former pupil of his had arranged to meet him at a restaurant one evening. When Dr. Fischelson arrived, he had been surprised to find a group of friends and admirers who forced him to sit at the head of the table while they made speeches about him. But these were things that had happened long ago. Now people were no longer interested in him. He had isolated himself completely and had become a forgotten man. The events of 1905 when the boys of Market Street had begun to organize strikes, throw bombs at police stations, and shoot strikebreakers so that the stores were closed even on weekdays had greatly increased his isolation. He began to despise everything associated with the modern Jew—Zionism, socialism, anarchism. The young men in question seemed to him nothing but an ignorant rabble intent on destroying society, society without which no reasonable existence was possible. He still read a Hebrew magazine occasionally, but he felt contempt for modern Hebrew which had no roots in the Bible or the Mishnah. The spelling of Polish words had changed also. Dr. Fischelson concluded that even the so-called spiritual men had abandoned reason and were doing their utmost to pander to the mob. Now and again he still visited a library and browsed through some of the modern histories of philosophy, but he found that the professors did not understand Spinoza, quoted him incorrectly, attributed their own muddled ideas to the philosopher. Although Dr. Fischelson was well aware that anger was an emotion unworthy of those who walk the path of reason, he would become furious, and would quickly close the book and push it from him. "Idiots," he would mutter, "asses, upstarts." And he would vow never again to look at modern philosophy.

Every three months a special mailman who only delivered money orders brought Dr. Fischelson eighty rubles. He expected his quarterly allotment at the beginning of July but as day after day passed and the tall man with the blond moustache and the shiny buttons did not appear, the Doctor grew anxious. He had scarcely a groshen left. Who knows— possibly the Berlin Community had rescinded his subsidy; perhaps Dr. Hildesheimer had died, God forbid; the post office might have made a mistake. Every event has its cause, Dr. Fischelson knew. All was determined, all necessary, and a man of reason had no right to worry. Nevertheless, worry invaded his brain, and buzzed about like the flies. If the worst came to the worst, it occurred to him, he could commit suicide, but then he remembered that Spinoza did not approve of suicide and compared those who took their own lives to the insane.

One day when Dr. Fischelson went out to a store to purchase a composition book, he heard people talking about war. In Serbia somewhere, an Austrian prince had been shot and the Austrians had delivered an ultimatum to the Serbs. The owner of the store, a young man with a yellow beard and shifty yellow eyes, announced, "We are about to have a small war," and he advised Dr. Fischelson to store up food because in the near future there was likely to be a shortage.

Everything happened so quickly. Dr. Fischelson had not even decided whether it was worthwhile to spend four groshen on a newspaper, and already posters had been hung up announcing mobilization. Men were to be seen walking on the street with round, metal tags on their lapels, a sign that they were being drafted. They were followed by their crying wives. One Monday when Dr. Fischelson descended to the street to buy some food with his last kopecks, he found the stores closed. The owners and their wives stood outside and explained that merchandise was unobtainable. But certain special customers were pulled to one side and let in through back doors. On the street all was confusion. Policemen with swords unsheathed could be seen riding on horseback. A large crowd had gathered around the tavern where, at the command of the Tsar, the tavern's stock of whiskey was being poured into the gutter.

Dr. Fischelson went to his old café. Perhaps he would find some acquaintances there who would advise him. But he did not come across a single person he knew. He decided, then, to visit the rabbi of the synagogue where he had once been librarian, but the sexton with the six-sided skull cap informed him that the rabbi and his family had gone off to the spas. Dr. Fischelson had other old friends in town but he found no one at home. His feet ached from so much walking; black and green spots appeared before his eyes and he felt faint. He stopped and waited for the giddiness to pass. The passers-by jostled him. A dark-eyed high school girl tried to give him a coin. Although the war had just started, soldiers eight abreast were marching in full battle dress—the men were covered with dust and were sunburned. Canteens were strapped to their sides and they wore rows of bullets across their chests. The bayonets on their rifles gleamed with a cold, green light. They sang with mournful voices. Along with the men came cannons, each pulled by eight horses; their blind muzzles breathed gloomy terror. Dr. Fischelson felt nauseous. His stomach ached; his intestines seemed about to turn themselves inside out. Cold sweat appeared on his face.

"I'm dying," he thought. "This is the end." Nevertheless, he did manage to drag himself home where he lay down on the iron cot and remained, panting and gasping. He must have dozed off because he imagined that he was in his home town, Tishvitz. He had a sore throat and his mother was busy wrapping a stocking stuffed with hot salt around his neck. He could hear talk going on in the house; something about a candle and about how a frog had bitten him. He wanted to go out into the street but they wouldn't let him because a Catholic procession was passing by. Men in long robes, holding double-edged axes in their hands, were intoning in Latin as they sprinkled holy water. Crosses gleamed; sacred pictures waved in the air. There was an odor of incense and corpses. Suddenly the sky turned a burning red and the whole world started to burn. Bells were ringing; people rushed madly about. Flocks of birds flew overhead, screeching. Dr. Fischelson awoke with a start. His body was covered with sweat and his throat was now actually sore. He tried to meditate about his extraordinary dream, to find its rational connection with what was happening to him and to comprehend it *sub specie eternitatis* [under the aspect of eternity; in its universal form], but none of it made sense. "Alas, the brain is a receptacle for nonsense," Dr. Fischelson thought. "This earth belongs to the mad."

And he once more closed his eyes; once more he dozed; once more he dreamed.

The eternal laws, apparently, had not yet ordained Dr. Fischelson's end.

There was a door to the left of Dr. Fischelson's attic room which opened off a dark corridor, cluttered with boxes and baskets, in which the odor of fried onions and laundry soap was always present. Behind this door lived a spinster whom the neighbors called Black Dobbe. Dobbe was tall and lean, and as black as a baker's shovel. She had a broken nose and there was a moustache on her upper lip. She spoke with the hoarse voice of a man and she wore men's shoes. For years Black Dobbe had sold breads, rolls, and bagels which she had bought from the baker at the gate of the house. But one day she and the baker had quarreled and she had moved her business to the market place and now she dealt in what were called "wrinklers," which was a synonym for cracked eggs. Black Dobbe had no luck with men. Twice she had been engaged to baker's apprentices but in both instances they had returned the engagement contract to her. Some time afterwards she had received an engagement contract from an old man, a glazier who claimed that he was divorced, but it had later come to light that he still had a wife. Black Dobbe had a cousin in America, a shoemaker, and repeatedly she boasted that this cousin was sending her passage, but she remained in Warsaw. She was constantly being teased by the women who would say, "There's no hope for you, Dobbe. You're fated to die an old maid." Dobbe always answered, "I don't intend to be a slave for any man. Let them all rot."

That afternoon Dobbe received a letter from America. Generally she would go to Leizer the Tailor and have him read it to her. However, that day Leizer was out and so Dobbe thought of Dr. Fischelson whom the other tenants considered a convert since he never went to prayer. She knocked on the door of the doctor's room but there was no answer. "The heretic is probably out," Dobbe thought but, nevertheless, she knocked once more, and this time the door moved slightly. She pushed her way in and stood there frightened. Dr. Fischelson lay fully clothed on his bed; his face was as yellow as wax; his Adam's apple stuck out prominently; his beard pointed upward. Dobbe screamed; she was certain that he was dead, but—no—his body moved. Dobbe picked up a glass which stood on the table, ran into the corridor, filled the glass with water from the faucet, hurried back, and threw the water into the face of the unconscious man. Dr. Fischelson shook his head and opened his eyes.

"What's wrong with you?" Dobbe asked. "Are you sick?"

"Thank you very much. No."

"Have you a family? I'll call them."

"No family," Dr. Fischelson said.

Dobbe wanted to fetch the barber from across the street but Dr. Fischelson signified that he didn't wish the barber's assistance. Since Dobbe was not going to the market that day, no "wrinklers" being available, she decided to do a good deed. She assisted the sick man to get off the bed and smoothed down the blanket. Then she undressed Dr. Fischelson and prepared some soup for him on the kerosene stove. The sun never entered Dobbe's room, but here squares of sunlight shimmered on the faded walls. The floor was painted red. Over the bed hung a picture of a man who was wearing a broad frill around his neck and had long hair. "Such an old fellow and yet he keeps his place so nice and clean," Dobbe thought approvingly. Dr. Fischelson asked for the *Ethics,* and she gave it to him disapprovingly. She was certain it was a gentile prayer book. Then she began bustling about, brought in a pail of water, swept the floor. Dr. Fischelson ate; after he had finished, he was much stronger and Dobbe asked him to read her the letter.

He read it slowly, the paper trembling in his hands. It came from New York, from Dobbe's cousin. Once more he wrote that he was about to send her a "really important letter" and a ticket to America. By now, Dobbe knew the story by heart and she helped the old man decipher her cousin's scrawl. "He's lying," Dobbe said. "He forgot about me a long time ago." In the evening, Dobbe came again. A candle in a brass holder was burning on the chair next to the bed. Reddish shadows trembled on the walls and ceiling. Dr. Fischelson sat propped up in bed, reading a book. The candle threw a golden light on his forehead which seemed as if cleft in two. A bird had flown in through the window and was perched on the table. For a moment Dobbe was frightened. This man made her think of witches, of black mirrors and corpses wandering around at night and terrifying women. Nevertheless, she took a few steps toward him and inquired, "How are you? Any better?"

"A little, thank you."

"Are you really a convert?" she asked although she wasn't quite sure what the word meant.

"Me, a convert? No, I'm a Jew like any other Jew," Dr. Fischelson answered.

The doctor's assurances made Dobbe feel more at home. She found the bottle of kerosene and lit the stove, and after that she fetched a glass of milk from her room and began cooking kasha. Dr. Fischelson continued to study the *Ethics,* but that evening he could make no sense of the theorems and proofs with their many references to axioms and definitions and other theorems. With trembling hand he raised the book to his eyes and read, "The idea of each modification of the human body does not involve adequate knowledge of the human body itself. . . . The idea of the idea of each modification of the human mind does not involve adequate knowledge of the human mind."

Dr. Fischelson was certain he would die any day now. He made out his will, leaving all of his books and manuscripts to the synagogue library. His clothing and furniture would go to Dobbe since she had taken care of him. But death did not come. Rather his health improved. Dobbe returned to her business in the market, but she visited the old man several times a day, prepared soup for him, left him a glass of tea, and told him news of the war. The Germans had occupied Kalish, Bendin, and Cestechow, and they were marching on Warsaw. People said that on a quiet morning one could hear the rumblings of the cannon. Dobbe reported that the casualties were heavy. "They're falling like flies," she said. "What a terriblo miofortunc for thc womcn."

She couldn't explain why, but the old man's attic room attracted her. She liked to remove the gold-rimmed books from the bookcase, dust them, and then air them on the window sill. She would climb the few steps to the window and look out through the telescope. She also enjoyed talking to Dr. Fischelson. He told her about Switzerland where he had studied, of the great cities he had passed through, of the high mountains that were covered with snow even in the summer. His father had been a rabbi, he said, and before he, Dr. Fischelson, had become a student, he had attended a yeshiva. She asked him how many languages he knew and it turned out that he could speak and write Hebrew, Russian, German, and French, in addition to Yiddish. He also knew Latin. Dobbe was astonished that such an educated man should live in an attic room on Market Street. But what amazed her most of all was that although he had the title "Doctor," he couldn't write prescriptions. "Why don't you become a real doctor?" she would ask him. "I am a doctor," he would answer. "I'm just not a physician." "What kind of a doctor?" "A doctor of philosophy." Although she had no idea of what this meant, she felt it must be very important. "Oh my blessed mother," she would say, "where did you get such a brain?"

Then one evening after Dobbe had given him his crackers and his glass of tea with milk, he began questioning her about where she came from, who her parents were, and why she had not married. Dobbe was surprised. No one had ever asked her such questions. She told him her story in a quiet voice and stayed until eleven o'clock. Her father had been a porter at the kosher butcher shops. Her mother had plucked chickens in the slaughterhouse. The family had lived in a celler at No. 19 Market Street. When she had been ten, she had become a maid. The man she had worked for had been a fence who bought stolen goods from thieves on the square. Dobbe had had a brother who had gone into the Russian army and had never returned. Her sister had married a coachman in Praga and had died in childbirth. Dobbe told of the battles between the underworld and the revolutionaries in 1905, of blind Itche and his gang and how they collected protection money from the stores, of the thugs who attacked young boys and girls out on Saturday afternoon strolls if they were not paid money for security. She also spoke of the pimps who drove about in carriages and abducted women to be sold in Buenos Aires. Dobbe swore that some men had even sought to inveigle her into a brothel, but that she had run away. She complained of a thousand evils done to her. She had been robbed; her boy friend had been stolen; a competitor had once poured a pint of kerosene into her basket of bagels; her own cousin, the shoemaker, had cheated her out of a hundred rubles before he had left for America. Dr. Fischelson listened to her attentively. He asked her questions, shook his head, and grunted.

"Well, do you believe in God?" he finally asked her.

"I don't know," she answered. "Do you?"

"Yes, I believe."

"Then why don't you go to synagogue?" she asked.

"God is everywhere," he replied. "In the synagogue. In the market place. In this very room. We ourselves are parts of God."

"Don't say such things," Dobbe said. "You frighten me."

She left the room and Dr. Fischelson was certain she had gone to bed. But he wondered why she had not said "good night." "I probably drove her away with my philosophy," he thought. The very next moment he heard her footsteps. She came in carrying a pile of clothing like a peddler.

"I wanted to show you these," she said. "They're my trousseau." And she began to spread out, on the chair, dresses—woolen, silk, velvet. Taking each dress up in turn, she held it to her body. She gave him an account of every item in her trousseau—underwear, shoes, stockings.

"I'm not wasteful," she said. "I'm a saver. I have enough money to go to America."

Then she was silent and her face turned brick-red. She looked at Dr. Fischelson out of the corner of her eyes, timidly, inquisitively. Dr. Fischelson's body suddenly began to shake as if he had the chills. He said, "Very nice, beautiful things." His brow furrowed and he pulled at his beard with two fingers. A sad smile appeared on his toothless mouth and his large fluttering eyes, gazing into the distance through the attic window, also smiled sadly.

The day that Black Dobbe came to the rabbi's chambers and announced that she was to marry Dr. Fischelson, the rabbi's wife thought she had gone mad. But the news had already reached Leizer the Tailor, and had spread to the bakery, as well as to other shops. There were those who thought that the "old maid" was very lucky; the doctor, they said, had a vast hoard of money. But there were others who took the view that he was a run-down degenerate who would give her syphilis. Although Dr. Fischelson had insisted that the wedding be a small, quiet one, a host of guests assembled in the rabbi's rooms. The baker's apprentices who generally went about barefoot, and in their underwear, with paper bags on the tops of their heads, now put on light-colored suits, straw hats, yellow shoes, gaudy ties, and they brought with them huge cakes and pans filled with cookies. They had even managed to find a bottle of vodka although liquor was forbidden in wartime. When the bride and groom entered the rabbi's chamber, a murmur arose from the crowd. The women could not believe their eyes. The woman that they saw was not the one they had known. Dobbe wore a wide-brimmed hat which was amply adorned with cherries, grapes, and plumes, and the dress that she had on was of white silk and was equipped with a train; on her feet were high-heeled shoes, gold in color, and from her thin neck hung a string of imitation pearls. Nor was this all: her fingers sparkled with rings and glittering stones. Her face was veiled. She looked almost like one of those rich brides who were married in the Vienna Hall. The baker's apprentices whistled mockingly. As for Dr. Fischelson, he was wearing his black coat and broad-toed shoes. He was scarcely able to walk; he was leaning on Dobbe. When he saw the crowd from the doorway, he became frightened and began to retreat, but Dobbe's former employer approached him saying, "Come in, come in, bridegroom. Don't be bashful. We are all brethren now."

The ceremony proceeded according to the law. The rabbi, in a worn satin gabardine, wrote the marriage contract and then had the bride and groom touch his handkerchief as a token of agreement; the rabbi wiped the point of the pen on his skullcap. Several porters who had been called from the street to make up the quorum supported the canopy. Dr. Fischelson put on a white robe as a reminder of the day of his death and Dobbe walked around him seven times as custom required. The light from the braided candles flickered on the walls. The shadows wavered. Having poured wine into a goblet, the rabbi chanted the benedictions in a sad melody. Dobbe uttered only a single cry. As for the other women, they took out their lace handkerchiefs and stood with them in their hands, grimacing. When the baker's boys began to whisper wisecracks to each other, the rabbi put a finger to his lips and murmured, *"Eh nu oh,"* as a sign that talking was forbidden. The moment came to slip the wedding ring on the bride's finger, but the bridegroom's hand started to tremble and he had trouble locating Dobbe's index finger. The next thing, according to custom, was the smashing of the glass, but though Dr. Fischelson kicked the goblet several times, it remained unbroken. The girls lowered their heads, pinched each other gleefully, and giggled. Finally one of the apprentices struck the goblet with his heel and it shattered. Even the rabbi could not restrain a smile. After the ceremony the guests drank vodka and ate cookies. Dobbe's former employer came up to Dr. Fischelson and said, "*Mazel tov*, bridegroom. Your luck should be as good as your wife." "Thank you, thank you," Dr. Fischelson murmured, "but I don't look forward to any luck." He was anxious to return as quickly as possible to his attic room. He felt a pressure in his stomach and his chest ached. His face had become greenish. Dobbe had suddenly become angry. She pulled back her veil and called out to the crowd, "What are you laughing at? This isn't a show." And without picking up the cushion cover in which the gifts were wrapped, she returned with her husband to their rooms on the fifth floor.

Dr. Fischelson lay down on the freshly made bed in his room and began reading the *Ethics*. Dobbe had gone back to her own room. The doctor had explained to her that he was an old man, that he was sick and without strength. He had promised her nothing. Nevertheless she returned wearing a silk nightgown, slippers with pompoms, and with her hair hanging down over her shoulders. There was a smile on her face, and she was bashful and hesitant. Dr. Fischelson trembled and the *Ethics* dropped from his hands. The candle went out. Dobbe groped for Dr. Fischelson in the dark and kissed his mouth. "My dear husband," she whispered to him, "*Mazel tov*."

What happened that night could be called a miracle. If Dr. Fischelson hadn't been convinced that every occurrence is in accordance with the laws of nature, he would have thought that Black Dobbe had bewitched him. Powers long dormant awakened in him. Although he had had only a sip of the benediction wine, he was as if intoxicated. He kissed Dobbe and spoke to her of love. Long forgotten quotations from Klopfstock, Lessing, Goethe rose to his lips. The pressures and aches stopped. He embraced Dobbe, pressed her to himself, was again a man as in his youth. Dobbe was faint with delight; crying, she murmured things to him in a Warsaw slang which he did not understand. Later, Dr. Fischelson slipped off into the deep sleep young men know. He dreamed that he was in Switzerland and that he was climbing mountains—running, falling, flying. At dawn he opened his eyes; it seemed to him that someone had blown into his ears. Dobbe was snoring. Dr. Fischelson quietly got out of bed. In his long nightshirt he approached the window, walked up the steps and looked out in wonder. Market Street was asleep, breathing with a deep stillness. The gas lamps were flickering. The black shutters on the stores were fastened with iron bars. A cool breeze was blowing. Dr. Fischelson looked up at the sky. The black arch was thickly sown with stars—there were green, red, yellow, blue stars; there were large ones and small ones, winking and steady ones. There were those that were clustered in dense groups and those that were alone. In the higher sphere, apparently, little notice was taken of the fact that a certain Dr. Fischelson had in his declining days married someone called Black Dobbe. Seen from above even the Great War was nothing but a temporary play of the modes. The myriads of fixed stars continued to travel their destined courses in unbounded space. The comets, planets, satellites, asteroids kept circling these shining centers. Worlds were born and died in cosmic upheavals. In the chaos of nebulae, primeval matter was being formed. Now and again a star tore loose, and swept across the sky, leaving behind it a fiery streak. It was the month of August when there are showers of meteors. Yes, the divine substance was extended and had neither beginning nor end; it was absolute, indivisible, eternal, without duration, infinite in its attributes. Its waves and bubbles danced in the universal cauldron, seething with change, following the unbroken chain of causes and effects, and he, Dr. Fischelson, with his unavoidable fate, was part of this. The doctor closed his eyelids and allowed the breeze to cool the sweat on his forehead and stir the hair of his beard. He breathed deeply of the midnight air, supported his shaky hands on the window sill and murmured, "Divine Spinoza, forgive me. I have become a fool."

Alexander Pushkin

1799–1837

Alexander Pushkin was born in Moscow, on June 6, 1799. His father belonged to the nobility; his mother was descended from an Abyssinian who served Peter the Great. Young Pushkin went to school at Tsarskoe Selo. By 1817 he was attached to the Ministry of Foreign Affairs and writing *Ruslan and Ly'udmila,* a romantic epic. He became a man about town. Before he was twenty-one his outspoken *Ode to Liberty,* handed round in manuscript, got him banished to the south of Russia.

From that day on he was never free of censors and police spies. A series of Byronic poems came out of his six years in the Caucasus. His tragedy *Boris Godunov* later became the rootstock for Mussorgsky's opera. Czar Nicholas I, in the midst of his coronation, ordered the exiled poet brought to Moscow. ". . . it is I who shall be your censor," said the Czar.

In the Dekabrist Rebellion of 1825, Pushkin, who had been mixed up with the conspirators, managed to burn his incriminating papers. During the 1820's and 30's he wrote such narrative poems as *Poltava* and *A Voyage to Arzrum.* By the early 1830's he had finished *Eugen Onegin,* on which the Tschaikovsky opera is based.

Pushkin began his first, unfinished prose works, *The Negro of Peter the Great,* in 1827. Out of the factual *History of the Revolt of Pugachev of 1773* came his only completed novel, *The Captain's Daughter.* In 1831 he married Natalia Goncharov, a Moscow beauty and favorite of the Czar. Pushkin was restored to a job in the Ministry of Foreign Affairs, at 5,000 rubles a year.

The husband of his wife's sister, Baron George Heckeren d'Anthès, adopted son of the Dutch minister, began to pay open court to Natalia. Anonymous letters reached Pushkin. In the duel that followed, Pushkin was wounded. He died two days later, on February 10, 1837.

The *Queen of Spades* was published in 1834. Dostoevsky said that it had created a Russian literary language. Tschaikovsky turned it into the opera *Pique Dame*. Later it became a distinguished motion picture. It was certainly the most popular of Pushkin's stories and took its place among the half-dozen most popular in the whole Romantic movement. Through all these changes it has kept its air of teasing mystery. It is a piece of electric storytelling.

Who is Hermann. the hero or anti-hero? He is a cousin of Stendhal's Julien Sorel, who had appeared earlier in *The Red and the Black*. He is the young man on the make in the hurly-burly of post-Napoleonic Europe. He lives by the will. "A man without morals or religion!" as Pushkin's legend tells us. Petty heir to Napoleon, Hermann is master of a cool self-possession in every action. And this is his mark: he acts.

He wants power. Money is the most available kind of power. Moved by a casual story, he resolves to make money gambling. But honest gambling is by definition chance. Hermann is not interested in chance. He wants a sure thing. To believe in a sure thing, we must believe (a) that the cards fall in a certain rigidly predictable order, and (b) that this order can be known and acted on. Hermann does believe this, and for the term of the story Pushkin asks us to believe it too.

The young officer of engineers is convinced that the aged Countess Anna Fedotovna knows this secret. We are told that it has already worked twice: once when it enabled Anna Fedotovna to pay off her gambling debts, and once when she gave it to young Chaplitzky. And where did she get it? It was given to her by the Count St.-Germain (a real personage, who served Louis XV as an envoy, claimed to have found the elixir of life, and was one of the most famous occultists of his time). So, almost from the first, we are edged over into that shadowy region where what is believable merges with what we wish to believe.

Rosemary Edmonds, one of Pushkin's translators, has remarked that this is "a psychological tale without psychology." That is, we are not told what the character is thinking; we are allowed to deduce it from his acts. But we are left with a residue of mystery, placed there, for our entertainment, by the author himself. If Hermann had not played the wrong card, would he have won again? And *why* did he play the wrong card? Was it because he was tricked into punishing himself for the guilt he felt at the old woman's death? Or was he, in fact, perhaps a little deranged? Was it all delusion—Anna Fedotovna's phantom, the three cards, her distorted face in the queen of spades? Or should we believe—in terms of the story, at least—that the old woman had got her revenge for the indignity of her death? In that case, why had she given him the names of all three winning cards?

The Queen
of Spades

The Queen of Spades signifies secret ill-will.
New Fortune-Teller

When bleak was the weather,
The friends came together
To play.
The stakes, they were doubled;
The sly ones, untroubled,
Were gay.
They all had their innings,
And chalked up their winnings,
And so
They kept busy together
Throughout the bleak weather,
Oho!

There was a card-party at the rooms of Narumov of the Horse
Guards. The long winter night passed away imperceptibly, and it was
five o'clock in the morning before the company sat down to supper.
Those who had won ate with a good appetite; the others sat staring absently at their empty plates. When the champagne appeared, however,
the conversation became more animated, and all took a part in it.

"And how did you fare, Surin?" asked the host.

"Oh, I lost, as usual. I must confess that I am unlucky: I never raise the
original stakes, I always keep cool, I never allow anything to put me out,
and yet I always lose!"

"And you have never been tempted? You have never staked on several cards in succession? . . . Your firmness astonishes me."

"But what do you think of Hermann?" said one of the guests, pointing to a young engineer. "He has never had a card in his hand in his life, he has never in his life doubled the stake, and yet he sits here till five o'clock in the morning watching our play."

"Play interests me very much," said Hermann, "but I am not in the position to sacrifice the necessary in the hope of winning the superfluous."

"Hermann is a German; he is prudent—that is all!" observed Tomsky. "But if there is one person that I cannot understand, it is my grandmother, the Countess Anna Fedotovna."

"How? What?" cried the guests.

"I cannot understand," continued Tomsky, "how it is that my grandmother does not punt."

"What is there remarkable about an old lady of eighty not gambling?" said Narumov.

"Then you know nothing about her?"

"No, really, haven't the faintest idea."

"Oh! then listen. You must know that, about sixty years ago, my grandmother went to Paris, where she created quite a sensation. People used to run after her to catch a glimpse of *la Vénus moscovite*. Richelieu courted her, and my grandmother maintains that he almost blew out his brains in consequence of her cruelty. At that time ladies used to play faro. On one occasion at the Court, she lost a very considerable sum to the Duke of Orleans. On returning home, my grandmother removed the patches from her face, took off her hoops, informed my grandfather of her loss at the gaming table, and ordered him to pay the money. My deceased grandfather, as far as I remember, was a sort of butler to my grandmother. He dreaded her like fire; but, on hearing of such a heavy loss, he almost went out of his mind; he calculated the various sums she had lost, and pointed out to her that in six months she had spent half a million, that neither their Moscow nor Saratov estates were near Paris, and finally refused point-blank to pay the debt. My grandmother slapped his face and slept by herself as a sign of her displeasure. The next day she sent for her husband, hoping that this domestic punishment had produced an effect upon him, but she found him inflexible. For the first time in her life, she condescended to offer reasons and explanations. She thought she could convince him by pointing out to him that there are debts and debts, and that there is a great difference between a prince and a coachmaker. But it was all in vain; grandfather was in revolt. He

said 'no,' and that was all. My grandmother did not know what to do.
She was on friendly terms with a very remarkable man. You have heard
of Count St. Germain, about whom so many marvellous stories are told.
You know that he represented himself as the Wandering Jew, as the dis-
coverer of the elixir of life, of the philosopher's stone, and so forth. Some
laughed at him as a charlatan; but Casanova, in his memoirs, says that he
was a spy. But be that as it may, St. Germain, in spite of the mystery
surrounding him, was a man of decent appearance and had an amiable
manner in company. Even to this day my grandmother is in love with
him, and becomes quite angry if anyone speaks disrespectfully of him.
My grandmother knew that St Germain had large sums of money at his
disposal. She resolved to have recourse to him, and she wrote a letter to
him asking him to come to her without delay. The queer old man immediately waited upon her and found her overwhelmed with grief. She described to him in the blackest colours the barbarity of her husband, and
ended by declaring that she placed all her hopes in his friendship and
graciousness.

"St. Germain reflected. 'I could advance you the sum you want,' said
he; 'but I know that you would not rest easy until you had paid me back,
and I should not like to bring fresh troubles upon you. But there is another way of getting out of your difficulty: you can win back your
money.'

"'But, my dear Count,' replied my grandmother, 'I tell you that we
haven't any money left.'

"'Money is not necessary,' replied St. Germain. 'Be pleased to listen
to me.'

"Then he revealed to her a secret, for which each of us would give a
good deal . . ."

The young gamblers listened with increased attention. Tomsky lit his
pipe, pulled at it, and continued:

"That same evening my grandmother went to Versailles *au jeu de la
Reine* [to the game of the Queen]. The Duke of Orleans kept the bank;
my grandmother excused herself in an offhanded manner for not having
yet paid her debt, by inventing some little story, and then began to play
against him. She chose three cards and played them one after the other:
all three won at the start and my grandmother recovered all that she had
lost."

"Mere chance!" said one of the guests.

"A fairy tale!" observed Hermann.

"Perhaps they were marked cards!" said a third.

"I do not think so," replied Tomsky gravely.

"What!" said Narumov. "You have a grandmother who knows how to hit upon three lucky cards in succession, and you have never yet succeeded in getting the secret of it out of her?"

"That's the deuce of it!" replied Tomsky. "She had four sons, one of whom was my father; all four are desperate gamblers, and yet not to one of them did she ever reveal her secret, although it would not have been a bad thing either for them or for me. But this is what I heard from my uncle, Count Ivan Ilyich, and he assured me, on his honour, that it was true. The late Chaplitzky—the same who died in poverty after having squandered millions—once lost, in his youth, about three hundred thousand roubles—to Zorich, if I remember rightly. He was in despair. My grandmother, who was always very hard on extravagant young men, took pity, however, upon Chaplitzky. She mentioned to him three cards, telling him to play them one after the other, at the same time exacting from him a solemn promise that he would never play cards again as long as he lived. Chaplitzky then went to his victorious opponent, and they began a fresh game. On the first card he staked fifty thousand roubles and won at once; he doubled the stake and won again, doubled it again, and won, not only all he had lost, but something over and above that. . .

"But it is time to go to bed: it is a quarter to six already."

And indeed it was already beginning to dawn; the young men emptied their glasses and then took leave of one another.

II

—Il paraît que monsieur est
décidément pour les suivantes.
—Que voulez-vous, madame? Elles
sont plus fraîches.

["It appears, monsieur, that you
decidedly favour the lady's maids."
"Of course, madame; they're fresher."]
                                        Society Talk

The old Countess X. was seated in her dressing-room in front of her looking-glass. Three maids stood around her. One held a small pot of rouge, another a box of hairpins, and the third a tall cap with bright red ribbons. The Countess had no longer the slightest pretensions to beauty—hers had faded long ago—but she still preserved all the habits of her youth, dressed in strict accordance with the fashion of the seventies, and made as long and as careful a toilette as she would have done sixty years previously. Near the window, at an embroidery frame, sat a young lady, her ward.

"Good morning, *Grand'maman*," said a young officer, entering the room. "*Bonjour, Mademoiselle Lise. Grand'maman*, I have a favour to ask of you."

"What is it, Paul?"

"I want you to let me introduce one of my friends to you, and to allow me to bring him to the ball on Friday."

"Bring him direct to the ball and introduce him to me there. Were you at N.'s yesterday?"

"Yes; everything went off very pleasantly, and dancing kept up until five o'clock. How beautiful Mme Yeletzkaya was!"

"But, my dear, what is there beautiful about her? You should have seen her grandmother, Princess Darya Petrovna! By the way, she must have aged very much, Princess Darya Petrovna."

"How do you mean, aged?" cried Tomsky thoughtlessly. "She died seven years ago."

The young lady raised her head and made a sign to the young man. He then remembered that the old Countess was never to be informed of the death of any of her contemporaries, and he bit his lip. But the Countess heard the news with the greatest indifference.

"Died!" said she. "And I did not know it. We were appointed maids of honour at the same time, and when we were being presented, the Empress . . ."

And the Countess for the hundredth time related the anecdote to her grandson.

"Come, Paul," said she, when she had finished her story, "help me to get up. Lizanka, where is my snuff-box?"

And the Countess with her three maids went behind a screen to finish her toilette. Tomsky was left alone with the young lady.

"Who is the gentleman you wish to introduce to the Countess?" asked Lizaveta Ivanovna in a whisper.

"Narumov. Do you know him?"

"No. Is he in the army or is he a civilian?"

"In the army."

"Is he in the Engineers?"

"No, in the Cavalry. What made you think that he was in the Engineers?"

The young lady smiled, but made no reply.

"Paul," cried the Countess, from behind the screen, "send me some new novel, only, pray, not the kind they write nowadays."

"What do you mean, *Grand'maman?*"

"That is, a novel in which the hero strangles neither his father nor his mother, and in which there are no drowned bodies. I have a great horror of them."

"There are no such novels nowadays. Would you like a Russian one?"

"Are there any Russian novels? Send me one, my dear, please send me one!"

"Good-bye, *Grand'maman*, I am in a hurry. . . . . Good-bye, Lizaveta Ivanovna. What, then, made you think that Narumov was in the Engineers?"

And Tomsky withdrew from the dressing-room.

Lizaveta Ivanovna was left alone; she laid aside her work and began to look out of the window. A few moments afterwards, from behind a corner house on the other side of the street, a young officer appeared. A deep blush covered her cheeks; she took up her work again and bent her head over the frame. At the same moment the Countess returned, completely dressed.

"Order the carriage, Lizaveta," said she; "we will go out for a drive."

Lizaveta arose from the frame and began to put away her work.

"What is the matter with you, my dear, are you deaf?" cried the Countess. "Order the carriage to be got ready at once."

"I will do so this moment," replied the young lady, and ran into the ante-room.

A servant entered and gave the Countess some books from Prince Pavel Alexandrovich.

"Tell him that I am much obliged to him," said the Countess. "Lizaveta! Lizaveta! Where are you running to?"

"I am going to dress."

"There is plenty of time, my dear. Sit down here. Open the first volume and read aloud to me."

Her companion took the book and read a few lines.

"Louder," said the Countess. "What is the matter with you, my dear? Have you lost your voice? Wait—give me that footstool—a little nearer—that will do!"

Lizaveta read two more pages. The Countess yawned.

"Put the book down," said she. "What a lot of nonsense! Send it back to Prince Pavel with my thanks. . . . . But where is the carriage?"

"The carriage is ready," said Lizaveta, looking out into the street.

"How is it that you are not dressed?" said the Countess. "I must always wait for you. It is intolerable, my dear!"

Liza hastened to her room. She had not been there two minutes before the Countess began to ring with all her might. The three maids came running in at one door and the valet at another.

"How is it that you don't come when I ring for you?" said the Countess. "Tell Lizaveta Ivanovna that I am waiting for her."

Lizaveta returned with her hat and cloak on.

"At last you are here!" said the Countess. "But why such an elaborate toilette? Whom do you intend to captivate? What sort of weather is it? It seems rather windy."

"No, Your Ladyship, it is very calm," replied the valet.

"You always speak thoughtlessly. Open the window. So it is: windy and bitterly cold. Unharness the horses. Lizaveta, we won't go out—there was no need for you to deck yourself out like that."

"And that's my life!" thought Lizaveta Ivanovna.

And, in truth, Lizaveta Ivanovna was a very unfortunate creature. "It is bitter to eat the bread of another," says Dante, "and hard to climb his stair." But who can know what the bitterness of dependence is so well as the poor companion of an old lady of quality? The Countess X. had by no means a bad heart, but she was capricious, like a woman who had been spoiled by the world, as well as avaricious and sunk in cold egoism, like all old people who are no longer capable of affection, and whose thoughts are with the past and not the present. She participated in all the vanities of the great world. went to balls, where she sat in a corner, painted and dressed in old-fashioned style, like an ugly but indispensable ornament of the ballroom; the guests on entering approached her and bowed profoundly, as if in accordance with a set ceremony, but after that nobody took any further notice of her. She received the whole town at her house, and observed the strictest etiquette, although she could no longer recognize people. Her numerous domestics, growing fat and old in her antechamber and servants' hall, did just as they liked, and vied with each other in robbing the moribund old woman. Lizaveta Ivanovna was the martyr of the household. She poured tea, and was reprimanded for using too much sugar; she read novels aloud to the Countess, and the faults of the author were visited upon her head; she accompanied the Countess in her walks, and was held answerable for the weather or the state of the pavement. A salary was attached to the post, but she very rarely received it, although she was expected to dress like everybody else, that is to say, like very few indeed. In society she played the most pitiable role. Everybody knew her, and nobody paid her any attention. At balls she danced only when a partner was wanted, and ladies would only take hold of her arm when it was necessary to lead her out of the room to attend to their dresses. She had a great deal of *amour propre* [self-esteem], and felt her position keenly, and she looked about her with impatience for a deliverer to come to her rescue; but the young men, calculating in their giddiness, did not condescend to pay her any attention, although Lizaveta Ivanovna was a hundred times prettier than the barefaced and cold-hearted marriageable girls around whom they hovered. Many a time did she quietly slink away from the dull and elegant drawing-room, to go and cry in her own poor little room, in which stood a screen, a chest of drawers, a looking-glass and a painted bedstead, and where a tallow candle burned feebly in a copper candlestick.

One morning—this was about two days after the card-party described at the beginning of this story, and a week previous to the scene at which we have just assisted—Lizaveta Ivanovna was seated near the window at her embroidery frame, when, happening to look out into the street, she caught sight of a young officer of the Engineers, standing motionless with his eyes fixed upon her window. She lowered her head and went on again with her work. About five minutes afterwards she looked out again —the young officer was still standing in the same place. Not being in the habit of coquetting with passing officers, she did not continue to gaze out into the street, but went on sewing for a couple of hours, without raising her head. Dinner was announced. She rose up and began to put her embroidery away, but glancing casually out the window, she perceived the officer again. This seemed to her very strange. After dinner she went to the window with a certain feeling of uneasiness, but the officer was no longer there—and she thought no more about him.

A couple of days afterwards, just as she was stepping into the carriage with the Countess, she saw him again. He was standing close to the entrance, with his face half-concealed by his beaver collar, his black eyes flashing beneath his hat. Lizaveta felt alarmed, though she knew not why, and she trembled as she seated herself in the carriage.

On returning home, she hastened to the window—the officer was standing in his accustomed place, with his eyes fixed upon her. She drew back, a prey to curiosity and agitated by a feeling which was quite new to her.

From that time on not a day passed without the young officer making his appearance under the window at the customary hour. A spontaneous relationship was established between them. Sitting in her place at work, she would feel his approach; and raising her head, she would look at him longer and longer each day. The young man seemed to be very grateful to her for it: she saw with the sharp eye of youth how a sudden flush covered his pale cheeks each time that their glances met. By the end of the week she smiled at him. . . .

When Tomsky asked permission of his grandmother the Countess to present one of his friends to her, the young girl's heart beat violently. But hearing that Narumov was not an Engineer, but in the Horse Guards, she regretted that by her indiscreet question, she had betrayed her secret to the volatile Tomsky.

Hermann was the son of a Russified German from whom he had inherited a small fortune. Being firmly convinced of the necessity of ensuring his independence, Hermann did not touch even the interest on his capital, but lived on his pay, without allowing himself the slightest luxury. Moreover, he was reserved and ambitious, and his companions rarely had an opportunity of making merry at the expense of his excessive parsimony. He had strong passions and an ardent imagination, but his firmness of disposition preserved him from the ordinary errors of youth. Thus, though a gambler at heart, he never touched a card, for he considered his position did not allow him—as he said—"to risk the necessary in the hope of winning the superfluous," yet he would sit for nights together at the card-table and follow with feverish excitement the various turns of the game.

The story of the three cards had produced a powerful impression upon his imagination, and all night long he could think of nothing else. "If only," he thought to himself the following evening, as he wandered through St. Petersburg, "if only the old Countess would reveal her secret to me! If she would only tell me the names of the three winning cards! Why should I not try my fortune? I must get introduced to her and win her favour—perhaps become her lover. . . . But all that will take time, and she is eighty-seven years old: she might be dead in a week, in a couple of days even! . . . And the story itself: is it credible? . . . No! Prudence, moderation and work: those are my three winning cards; that is what will increase my capital threefold, sevenfold, and procure for me ease and independence."

Musing in this manner, he walked on until he found himself in one of the principal streets of St. Petersburg, in front of a house of old-fashioned architecture. The street was blocked with carriages; one after the other they rolled up in front of the illuminated entrance. Every minute there emerged from the coaches the shapely foot of a young beauty, a spurred boot, a striped stocking above a diplomatic shoe. Fur coats and cloaks whisked past the majestic porter.

Hermann stopped. "Whose house is this?" he asked the watchman at the corner.

"The Countess X.'s," replied the watchman.

Hermann trembled. The strange story of the three cards again presented itself to his imagination. He began walking up and down before the house, thinking of its owner and her marvellous gift. Returning late to his modest lodging, he could not go to sleep for a long time, and when at last he did doze off, he could dream of nothing but cards, green tables, piles of bank-notes and heaps of gold coins. He played card after card, firmly turning down the corners, and won uninterruptedly, raking in the gold and filling his pockets with the notes. Waking up late the next morning, he sighed over the loss of his imaginary wealth, then went out again to wander about the streets, and found himself once more in front of the Countess's house. Some unknown power seemed to draw him thither. He stopped and began to stare at the windows. In one of these he saw the head of a black-haired woman, which was bent probably over some book or handwork. The head was raised. Hermann saw a fresh-cheeked face and a pair of black eyes. That moment decided his fate.

III

Vous m'écrivez, mon ange, des lettres de
quatre pages plus vite que je ne puis les lire.

[You write me four-page letters, my angel, faster than I can read them.]
                                        A Correspondence

Lizaveta Ivanovna had scarcely taken off her hat and cloak, when the Countess sent for her and again ordered the carriage. The vehicle drew up before the door, and they prepared to take their seats. Just at the moment when two footmen were assisting the old lady into the carriage, Lizaveta saw her Engineer close beside the wheel; he grasped her hand; alarm caused her to lose her presence of mind, and the young man disappeared—but not before leaving a letter in her hand. She concealed it in her glove, and during the whole of the drive she neither saw nor heard anything. It was the custom of the Countess, when out for an airing in her carriage to be constantly asking such questions as: "Who was that person that met us just now? What is the name of this bridge? What is written on that sign-board?" On this occasion, however, Lizaveta returned such vague and absurd answers that the Countess became angry with her.

"What is the matter with you, my dear?" she exclaimed. "Have you taken leave of your senses, or what is it? Do you not hear me or understand what I say? . . . Heaven be thanked, I am still in my right mind and speak plainly enough!"

Lizaveta Ivanovna did not hear her. On returning home she ran to her room, and drew the letter out of her glove: it was not sealed. Lizaveta read it. The letter contained a declaration of love; it was tender, respectful, and copied word for word from a German novel. But Lizaveta did not know anything of the German language, and she was quite delighted with the letter.

For all that, it troubled her exceedingly. For the first time in her life she was entering into secret and intimate relations with a young man. His boldness horrified her. She reproached herself for her imprudent behaviour, and knew not what to do. Should she cease to sit at the window and, by assuming an appearance of indifference toward him, put a check upon the young officer's desire to pursue her further? Should she send his letter back to him, or should she answer him in a cold and resolute manner? There was nobody to whom she could turn in her perplexity, for she had neither female friend nor adviser. . . . At length she resolved to reply to him.

She sat down at her little writing-table, took pen and paper, and began to think. Several times she began her letter, and then tore it up: the way she had expressed herself seemed to her either too indulgent or too severe. At last she succeeded in writing a few lines with which she felt satisfied.

"I am convinced," she wrote, "that your intentions are honourable, and that you do not wish to offend me by any imprudent action, but our acquaintance should not have begun in such a manner. I return you your letter, and I hope that I shall never have any cause to complain of undeserved disrespect."

The next day, as soon as Hermann made his appearance, Lizaveta rose from her embroidery, went into the drawing-room, opened the wicket and threw the letter into the street, trusting to the young officer's alertness.

Hermann hastened forward, picked it up and then repaired to a confectioner's shop. Breaking the seal of the envelope, he found inside it his own letter and Lizaveta's reply. He had expected this, and he returned home, very much taken up with his intrigue.

Three days afterwards, a bright-eyed young girl from a milliner's estab-

lishment brought Lizaveta a letter. Lizaveta opened it with great uneasiness, fearing that it was a demand for money, when suddenly she
recognized Hermann's handwriting.

"You have made a mistake, my dear," said she; "this letter is not
for me."

"Oh, yes, it is for you," replied the pert girl, without concealing a sly
smile. "Have the goodness to read it."

Lizaveta glanced at the letter. Hermann requested an interview.

"It cannot be," said Lizaveta Ivanovna, alarmed both at the haste with
which he had made his request, and the manner in which it had been
transmitted. "This letter is certainly not for me."

And she tore it into fragments.

"If the letter was not for you, why have you torn it up?" said the girl.
"I should have given it back to the person who sent it."

"Be good enough, my dear," said Lizaveta, disconcerted by this remark, "not to bring me any more letters in future and tell the person
who sent you that he ought to be ashamed. . . ."

But Hermann was not the man to be thus put off. Every day Lizaveta
received from him a letter, sent now in this way, now in that. They were
no longer translated from the German. Hermann wrote them under the
inspiration of passion. and spoke in his own language, and they bore full
testimony to the inflexibility of his desire and the disordered condition
of his uncontrollable imagination. Lizaveta no longer thought of sending
them back to him: she became intoxicated with them and began to reply
to them, and little by little her answers became longer and more affectionate. At last she threw out of the window to him the following letter:

"This evening there is going to be a ball at the X. Embassy. The Countess will be there. We shall remain until two o'clock. This is your opportunity of seeing me alone. As soon as the Countess is gone, the servants
will very probably go out, and there will be nobody left but the porter,
but he, too, usually retires to his lodge. Come at half past eleven. Walk
straight upstairs. If you meet anybody in the ante-room, ask if the Countess is at home. If you are told she is not, there will be nothing left for you
to do but to go away and return another time. But it is most probable
that you will meet nobody. The maidservants all sit together in one room.
On leaving the ante-room, turn to the left, and walk straight on until you
reach the Countess' bedroom. In the bedroom, behind a screen, you will
find two small doors: the one on the right leads to a study, which the
Countess never enters; the one on the left leads to a corridor, at the end
of which is a narrow winding staircase; this leads to my room."

Hermann quivered like a tiger as he waited for the appointed time. At ten o'clock in the evening he was already in front of the Countess' house. The weather was terrible; the wind was howling; the sleety snow fell in large flakes; the lamps emitted a feeble light, the streets were deserted; from time to time a sledge, drawn by a sorry-looking hack, passed by, the driver on the look out for a belated fare. Hermann stood there wearing nothing but his jacket, yet he felt neither the wind nor the snow.

At last the Countess' carriage drew up. Hermann saw two footmen carry out in their arms the bent form of the old lady, wrapped in sables, and immediately behind her, clad in a light mantle, and with a wreath of fresh flowers on her head, followed Lizaveta. The door was closed. The carriage rolled away heavily through the yielding snow. The porter shut the street door; the windows became dark.

Hermann began walking up and down near the deserted house; at length he stopped under a lamp, and glanced at his watch: it was twenty minutes past eleven. He remained standing under the lamp, his eyes fixed upon the watch, impatiently waiting for the remaining minutes to pass. At half past eleven precisely, Hermann ascended the steps of the house, and made his way into the brightly illuminated vestibule. The porter was not there. Hermann ran up the stairs, opened the door of the ante-room and saw a footman sitting asleep in an antique soiled armchair, under a lamp. With a light firm step Hermann walked past him. The reception room and the drawing-room were in semi-darkness. They were lit feebly by a lamp in the ante-room.

Hermann entered the bedroom. Before an icon case, filled with ancient icons, a golden sanctuary lamp was burning. Armchairs, upholstered in faded brocade, and sofas, the gilding of which was worn off and which were piled with down cushions, stood in melancholy symmetry around the room, the walls of which were hung with China silk. On the wall hung two portraits painted in Paris by Madame Lebrun. One of them represented a plump, pink-cheeked man of about forty in a light-green uniform and with a star on his breast; the other—a beautiful young woman, with an aquiline nose, curls at her temples, and a rose in her powdered hair. In all the corners stood porcelain shepherds and shepherdesses, clocks from the workshop of the celebrated Leroy, boxes, roulettes, fans, and the various gewgaws for ladies that were invented at the end of the last century, together with Montgolfier's balloon and Mesmer's magnetism. Hermann stepped behind the screen. Behind it stood a little iron bed; on the right was the door which led to the study; on the left—the other which led to the corridor. He opened the latter, and saw the little winding staircase which led to the room of the poor ward. . . . But he retraced his steps and entered the dark study.

The time passed slowly. All was still. The clock in the drawing-room struck twelve; in all the rooms, one clock after another marked the hour, and everything was quiet again. Hermann stood leaning against the cold stove. He was calm; his heart beat regularly, like that of a man resolved upon a dangerous but inevitable undertaking. The clock struck one, then two; and he heard the distant rumbling of carriage wheels. In spite of himself, excitement seized him. The carriage drew near and stopped. He heard the sound of the carriage step being let down. All was bustle within the house. The servants were running hither and thither, voices were heard, and the house was lit up. Three antiquated chambermaids entered the bedroom, and they were shortly afterwards followed by the Countess who, more dead than alive, sank into an arm-chair. Hermann peeped through a chink. Lizaveta Ivanovna passed close by him, and he heard her steps as she hurried up her staircase. For a moment his heart was assailed by something like remorse, but the emotion was only transitory. He stood petrified.

The Countess began to undress before her looking-glass. Her cap, decorated with roses, was unpinned, and then her powdered wig was removed from off her white and closely cropped head. Hairpins fell in showers around her. Her yellow satin dress, embroidered with silver, fell down at her swollen feet.

Herman witnessed the repulsive mysteries of her toilette; at last the Countess was in her night-cap and night-gown, and in this costume, more suitable to her age, she appeared less hideous and terrifying.

Like all old people in general, the Countess suffered from sleeplessness. Having undressed, she seated herself at the window in an arm-chair and dismissed her maids. The candles were taken away, and once more the room was lit only by the sanctuary lamp. The Countess sat there looking quite yellow, moving her flaccid lips and swaying from side to side. Her dull eyes expressed complete vacancy of mind, and, looking at her, one would have thought that the rocking of her body was not voluntary, but was produced by the action of some concealed galvanic mechanism.

Suddenly the deathlike face changed incredibly. The lips ceased to move, the eyes became animated: before the Countess stood a stranger.

"Do not be alarmed, for Heaven's sake, do not be alarmed!" said he in a low but distinct voice. "I have no intention of doing you any harm, I have only come to ask a favour of you."

The old woman looked at him in silence, as if she had not heard what he had said. Hermann thought that she was deaf, and, bending down toward her ear, he repeated what he had said. The old woman remained silent as before.

"You can ensure the happiness of my life," continued Hermann, "and it will cost you nothing. I know that you can name three cards in succession—"

Hermann stopped. The Countess appeared now to understand what was asked of her; she seemed to be seeking words with which to reply.

"It was a joke," she replied at last. "I swear it was only a joke."

"This is no joking matter," replied Hermann angrily. "Remember Chaplitzky, whom you helped to win back what he had lost."

The Countess became visibly uneasy. Her features expressed strong emotion, but she soon lapsed into her former insensibility.

"Can you not name me these three winning cards?" continued Hermann.

The Countess remained silent; Hermann continued: "For whom are you preserving your secret? For your grandsons? They are rich enough without it; they do not know the worth of money. Your cards would be of no use to a spendthrift. He who cannot preserve his paternal inheritance will die in want, even though he had a demon at his service. I am not a man of that sort; I know the value of money. Your three cards will not be wasted on me. Come!"

He paused and tremblingly awaited her reply. The Countess remained silent; Hermann fell upon his knees.

"If your heart has ever known the feeling of love," said he, "if you remember its rapture, if you have ever smiled at the cry of your new-born child, if your breast has ever throbbed with any human feeling, I entreat you by the feelings of a wife, a lover, a mother, by all that is most sacred in life, not to reject my plea. Reveal to me your secret. Of what use is it to you? . . . Maybe it is connected with some terrible sin, the loss of eternal bliss, some bargain with the devil. . . . Consider—you are old; you have not long to live—I am ready to take your sins upon my soul. Only reveal to me your secret. Remember that the happiness of a man is in your hands, that not only I, but my children, grandchildren, and great-grandchildren, will bless your memory and reverence it as something sacred. . . ."

The old woman answered not a word.

Hermann rose to his feet.

"You old witch!" he exclaimed, clenching his teeth. "Then I will make you answer!"

With these words he drew a pistol from his pocket.

At the sight of the pistol, the Countess for the second time exhibited strong emotion. She shook her head and raised her hands as if to protect herself from the shot . . . then she fell backward and remained motionless.

"Come, an end to this childish nonsense!" said Hermann, taking hold of her hand. "I ask you for the last time: will you tell me the names of your three cards, or will you not?"

The Countess made no reply. Hermann perceived that she was dead!

IV

7 mai, 18 — —
Homme sans moeurs et sans religion!

[A man without morals or religion!]
A Correspondence

Lizaveta Ivanovna was sitting in her room, still in her ball dress, lost in deep thought. On returning home, she had hastily dismissed the sleepy maid, who reluctantly came forward to assist her, saying that she would undress herself, and with a trembling heart had gone up to her own room, hoping to find Hermann there, but yet desiring not to find him. At the first glance she convinced herself that he was not there, and she thanked her fate for the obstacle which had prevented their meeting. She sat down without undressing, and began to recall to mind all the circumstances which in so short a time had carried her so far. It was not three weeks since the time when she had first seen the young man from the window—and she already was in correspondence with him, and he had succeeded in inducing her to grant him a nocturnal tryst! She knew his name only through his having written it at the bottom of some of his letters; she had never spoken to him, had never heard his voice, and had never heard anything of him until that evening. But, strange to say, that very evening at the ball, Tomsky, being piqued with the young Princess Pauline N., who, contrary to her usual custom, did not flirt with him, wished to revenge himself by assuming an air of indifference: he therefore engaged Lizaveta Ivanovna and danced an endless mazurka with her. All the time he kept teasing her about her partiality for officers in the Engineers; he assured her that he knew far more than she could have supposed, and some of his jests were so happily aimed, that Lizaveta thought several times that her secret was known to him.

"From whom have you learned all this?" she asked, smiling.

"From a friend of a person very well known to you," replied Tomsky, "from a very remarkable man."

"And who is this remarkable man?"

"His name is Hermann."

Lizaveta made no reply; but her hands and feet turned to ice.

"This Hermann," continued Tomsky, "is a truly romantic character. He has the profile of a Napoleon, and the soul of a Mephistopheles. I believe that he has at least three crimes upon his conscience. . . . How pale you are!"

"I have a headache. . . . But what did this Hermann—or whatever his name is—tell you?"

"Hermann is very much dissatisfied with his friend: he says that in his place he would act very differently. . . . I even think that Hermann himself has designs upon you; at least, he listens not indifferently to his friend's enamoured exclamations."

"But where has he seen me?"

"In church, perhaps; or promenading—God alone knows where. It may have been in your room, while you were asleep, for he is capable of it."

Three ladies approaching him with the question: "*Oubli ou regret* [Forgetfulness or regret]?" interrupted the conversation, which had become so tantalizingly interesting to Lizaveta.

The lady chosen by Tomsky was the Princess Pauline herself. She succeeded in effecting a reconciliation with him by making an extra turn in the dance and managing to delay resuming her seat. On returning to his place, Tomsky thought no more either of Hermann or Lizaveta. She longed to renew the interrupted conversation, but the mazurka came to an end, and shortly afterwards the old Countess took her departure.

Tomsky's words were nothing more than the small talk of the mazurka, but they sank deep into the soul of the young dreamer. The portrait, sketched by Tomsky, agreed with the picture she had formed in her own mind, and that image, rendered commonplace by current novels, terrified and fascinated her imagination. She was now sitting with her bare arms crossed and her head, still adorned with flowers, was bowed over her half-uncovered breast. Suddenly the door opened and Hermann entered. She shuddered.

"Where have you been?" she asked in a frightened whisper.

"In the old Countess' bedroom," replied Hermann. "I have just left her. The Countess is dead."

"My God! What are you saying?"

"And I am afraid," added Hermann, "that I am the cause of her death."

Lizaveta looked at him, and Tomsky's words found an echo in her soul: "This man has at least three crimes upon his conscience!" Hermann sat down by the window near her, and related all that had happened.

Lizaveta listened to him in terror. So all those passionate letters, those ardent demands, this bold obstinate pursuit—all this was not love! Money —that was what his soul yearned for! She could not satisfy his desire and make him happy! The poor girl had been nothing but the blind accomplice of a robber, of the murderer of her aged benefactress! . . . She wept bitter tears of belated, agonized repentance. Hermann gazed at her in silence: his heart, too, was tormented, but neither the tears of the poor girl, nor the wonderful charm of her beauty, enhanced by her grief, could produce any impression upon his hardened soul. He felt no pricking of conscience at the thought of the dead old woman. One thing only horrified him: the irreparable loss of the secret which he had expected would bring him wealth.

"You are a monster!" said Lizaveta at last.

"I did not wish her death," replied Hermann: "my pistol is not loaded."

Both grew silent.

The day began to dawn. Lizaveta extinguished her candle: a pale light illumined her room. She wiped her tear-stained eyes and raised them toward Hermann: he was sitting on the window-sill, with his arms folded and frowning fiercely. In this attitude he bore a striking resemblance to the portrait of Napoleon. This resemblance struck even Lizaveta Ivanovna.

"How shall I get you out of the house?" said she at last. "I thought of conducting you down the secret staircase, but in that case it would be necessary to go through the Countess' bedroom, and I am afraid."

"Tell me how to find this secret staircase—I will go alone."

Lizaveta arose, took from her drawer a key, handed it to Hermann and gave him the necessary instructions. Hermann pressed her cold, unresponsive hand, kissed her bowed head, and left the room.

He descended the winding staircase, and once more entered the Countess' bedroom. The dead old woman sat as if petrified; her face expressed profound tranquillity. Hermann stopped before her, and gazed long and earnestly at her, as if he wished to convince himself of the terrible reality; at last he entered the study, felt behind the tapestry for the door, and then began to descend the dark staircase, agitated by strange emotions. "At this very hour," thought he, "some sixty years ago, a young gallant, who has long been mouldering in his grave, may have stolen down this very staircase, perhaps coming from the very same bedroom, wearing an embroidered caftan, with his hair dressed à l'oiseau royal and pressing to his heart his three-cornered hat, and the heart of his aged mistress has only today ceased to beat. . . ."

At the bottom of the staircase Hermann found a door, which he opened with the same key, and found himself in a corridor which led him into the street.

V

That night the deceased Baroness von W. appeared to me. She was clad all in white and said to me: "How are you, Mr. Councilor?"

Swedenborg

Three days after the fatal night, at nine o'clock in the morning, Hermann repaired to the Convent of ——, where the burial service for the deceased Countess was to be held. Although feeling no remorse, he could not altogether stifle the voice of conscience, which kept repeating to him: "You are the murderer of the old woman!" While he had little true faith, he was very superstitious; and believing that the dead Countess might exercise an evil influence on his life, he resolved to be present at her funeral in order to ask her pardon.

The church was full. It was with difficulty that Hermann made his way through the crowd. The coffin stood on a sumptuous catafalque under a velvet baldachin. The deceased lay within it, her hands crossed upon her breast, and wearing a lace cap and a white satin gown. Around the catafalque stood the members of her household: the servants in black caftans, with armorial ribbons upon their shoulders, and candles in their hands; the relatives—children, grandchildren, and great-grandchildren—in deep mourning.

Nobody wept; tears would have been *une affectation*. The Countess was so old that her death could have surprised nobody, and her relatives had long looked upon her as not among the living. A famous preacher delivered the funeral oration. In simple and touching words he described the peaceful passing away of the saintly woman whose long life had been a serene, moving preparation for a Christian end. "The angel of death found her," said the preacher, "engaged in pious meditation and waiting for the midnight bridegroom."

The service concluded in an atmosphere of melancholy decorum. The relatives went forward first to bid farewell to the deceased. Then followed the numerous acquaintances, who had come to render the last homage to her who for so many years had participated in their frivolous amusements. After these followed the members of the Countess' household. The last of these was the old housekeeper who was of the same age as the deceased. Two young women led her forward, supporting her by the arms. She had not strength enough to bow down to the ground—she was the only one to shed a few tears and kiss the cold hand of her mistress.

Hermann now resolved to approach the coffin. He bowed down to the ground and for several minutes lay on the cold floor, which was strewn with fir boughs; at last he arose, as pale as the deceased Countess herself, ascended the steps of the catafalque and bent over the corpse. . . . At that moment it seemed to him that the dead woman darted a mocking look at him and winked with one eye. Hermann started back, took a false step and fell to the ground. He was lifted up. At the same moment Lizaveta Ivanovna was carried into the vestibule of the church in a faint. This episode disturbed for some minutes the solemnity of the gloomy ceremony. Among the congregation arose a muffled murmur, and the lean chamberlain, a near relative of the deceased, whispered in the ear of an Englishman who was standing near him, that the young officer was a natural son of the Countess, to which the Englishman coldly replied: "Oh!"

During the whole of that day, Hermann was exceedingly perturbed. Dining in an out-of-the-way restaurant, he drank a great deal of wine, contrary to his usual custom, in the hope of allaying his inward agitation. But the wine only served to excite his imagination still more. On returning home, he threw himself upon his bed without undressing, and fell into a deep sleep.

When he woke up it was already night, and the moon was shining into the room. He looked at his watch: it was a quarter to three. Sleep had left him; he sat down upon his bed and thought of the funeral of the old Countess.

At that moment somebody in the street looked in at his window, and immediately passed on again. Hermann paid no attention to this incident. A few moments afterwards he heard the door of the ante-room open. Hermann thought that it was his orderly, drunk as usual, returning from some nocturnal expedition, but presently he heard footsteps that were unknown to him: somebody was shuffling softly across the floor in slippers. The door opened, and a woman, dressed in white, entered the room. Hermann mistook her for his old nurse, and wondered what could bring her there at that hour of the night. But the white woman glided rapidly across the room and stood before him—and Hermann recognized the Countess!

"I have come to you against my will," she said in a firm voice: "but I have been ordered to grant your request. Three, seven, ace will win for you if played in succession, but only on these conditions: that you do not play more than one card in twenty-four hours, and that you never play again during the rest of your life. I forgive you my death, on condition that you marry my ward, Lizaveta Ivanovna."

With these words she turned round very quietly, walked with a shuffling gait toward the door and disappeared. Hermann heard the street door bang, and he saw someone look in at him through the window again.

For a long time Hermann could not recover himself. Then he went into the next room. His orderly was asleep upon the floor, and he had much difficulty in waking him. The orderly was drunk as usual, and nothing could be got out of him. The street door was locked. Hermann returned to his room, lit his candle, and set down an account of his vision.

V I

"Attendez!"

"How dare you say *attendez* to me?"

"Your Excellency, I said: 'Attendez, Sir.' "

Two fixed ideas can no more exist together in the moral world than two bodies can occupy one and the same place in the physical world. "Three, seven, ace" soon drove out of Hermann's mind the thought of the dead Countess. "Three, seven, ace" were perpetually running through his head and continually on his lips. If he saw a young girl, he would say: "How slender she is! Quite like the three of hearts." If anybody asked: "What is the time?" he would reply: "Five minutes to seven." Every stout man that he saw reminded him of the ace. "Three, seven, ace" haunted him in his sleep, and assumed all possible shapes. The three bloomed before him in the form of a magnificent flower, the seven was represented by a Gothic portal, and the ace became transformed into a gigantic spider. One thought alone occupied his whole mind—to make use of the secret which he had purchased so dearly. He thought of applying for a furlough so as to travel abroad. He wanted to go to Paris and force fortune to yield a treasure to him in the public gambling houses there. Chance spared him all this trouble.

There was in Moscow a society of wealthy gamblers, presided over by the celebrated Chekalinsky, who had passed all his life at the card table and had amassed millions, accepting bills of exchange for his winnings and paying his losses in ready money. His long experience secured for him the confidence of his companions, and his open house, his famous cook, and his agreeable and cheerful manner gained for him the respect of the public. He came to St. Petersburg. The young men of the capital flocked to his rooms, forgetting balls for cards, and preferring the temptations of faro to the seductions of flirting. Narumov conducted Hermann to Chekalinsky's residence.

They passed through a suite of magnificent rooms, filled with courteous attendants. Several generals and privy counsellors were playing whist; young men were lolling carelessly upon the velvet-covered sofas, eating ices and smoking pipes. In the drawing room, at the head of a long table, around which crowded about a score of players, sat the master of the house keeping the bank. He was a man of about sixty years of age, of a very dignified appearance; his head was covered with silvery-white hair; his full, florid countenance expressed good nature, and his eyes twinkled with a perpetual smile. Narumov introduced Hermann to him. Chekalinsky shook him by the hand in a friendly manner, requested him not to stand on ceremony, and then went on dealing.

The game lasted a long time. On the table lay more than thirty cards. Chekalinsky paused after each throw, in order to give the players time to arrange their cards and note down their losses, listened politely to their requests, and more politely still, straightened out the corners of cards that some absent-minded player's hand had turned down. At last the game was finished. Chekalinsky shuffled the cards and prepared to deal again.

"Allow me to play a card," said Hermann, stretching out his hand from behind a stout gentleman who was punting.

Chekalinsky smiled and bowed silently, as a sign of acquiescence. Narumov laughingly congratulated Hermann on ending his long abstention from cards, and wished him a lucky beginning.

"Here goes!" said Hermann. writing the figure with chalk on the back of his card.

"How much, sir?" asked the banker, screwing up his eyes. "Excuse me, I cannot see quite clearly."

"Forty-seven thousand," replied Hermann.

At these words every head in the room turned suddenly round, and all eyes were fixed upon Hermann.

"He has taken leave of his senses!" thought Narumov.

"Allow me to observe," said Chekalinsky, with his eternal smile, "that that is a very high stake; nobody here has ever staked more than two hundred and seventy-five roubles at a time."

"Well," retorted Hermann, "do you accept my card or not?"

Chekalinsky bowed with the same look of humble acquiescence.

"I only wish to inform you," said he, "that enjoying the full confidence of my partners, I can only play for ready money. For my own part, I am, of course, quite convinced that your word is sufficient, but for the sake of order, and because of the accounts, I must ask you to put the money on your card."

Hermann drew from his pocket a banknote and handed it to Chekalinsky, who, after examining it in a cursory manner, placed it on Hermann's card.

He began to deal. On the right a nine turned up, and on the left a three.

"I win!" said Hermann, showing his card.

A murmur of astonishment arose among the players. Chekalinsky frowned, but the smile quickly returned to his face.

"Do you wish me to settle with you?" he said to Hermann.

"If you please," replied the latter.

Chekalinsky drew from his pocket a number of banknotes and paid up at once. Hermann took his money and left the table. Narumov could not recover from his astonishment. Hermann drank a glass of lemonade and went home.

The next evening he again appeared at Chekalinsky's. The host was dealing. Hermann walked up to the table; the punters immediately made room for him. Chekalinsky greeted him with a gracious bow.

Hermann waited for the next game, took a card and placed upon it his forty-seven thousand roubles, together with his winnings of the previous evening.

Chekalinsky began to deal. A knave turned up on the right, a seven on the left.

Hermann showed his seven.

There was a general exclamation. Chekalinsky was obviously disturbed, but he counted out the ninety-four thousand roubles and handed them over to Hermann, who pocketed them in the coolest manner possible and immediately left the house.

The next evening Hermann appeared again at the table. Everyone was expecting him. The generals and privy counselors left their whist in order to watch such extraordinary play. The young officers jumped up from their sofas, and even the servants crowded into the room. All pressed round Hermann. The other players left off punting, impatient to see how it would end. Hermann stood at the table and prepared to play alone against the pale but still smiling Chekalinsky. Each opened a new pack of cards. Chekalinsky shuffled. Hermann took a card and covered it with a pile of banknotes. It was like a duel. Deep silence reigned.

Chekalinsky began to deal; his hands trembled. On the right a queen turned up, and on the left an ace.

"Ace wins!" cried Hermann, showing his card.

"Your queen has lost," said Chekalinsky sweetly.

Hermann started; instead of an ace, there lay before him the queen of spades! He could not believe his eyes, nor could he understand how he had made such a mistake.

At that moment it seemed to him that the queen of spades screwed up her eyes and sneered. He was struck by the remarkable resemblance. . . .

"The old woman!" he exclaimed, in terror.

Chekalinsky gathered up his winnings. For some time Hermann remained perfectly motionless. When at last he left the table, the room buzzed with loud talk.

"Splendidly punted!" said the players. Chekalinsky shuffled the cards afresh, and the game went on as usual.

CONCLUSION

Hermann went out of his mind. He is now confined in room Number 17 of the Obukhov Hospital. He never answers any questions, but he constantly mutters with unusual rapidity: "Three, seven, ace! Three, seven, queen!"

Lizaveta Ivanovna has married a very amiable young man, a son of the former steward of the old Countess. He is a civil servant, and has a considerable fortune. Lizaveta is bringing up a poor relative.

Tomsky has been promoted to the rank of captain, and is marrying Princess Pauline.

Translated by T. Keane.

D. H. Lawrence

1885–1930

D. H. (David Herbert) Lawrence was born in Nottinghamshire, England, on September 11, 1885. He was the son of a Midlands coal miner. The younger Lawrence taught school, and attended University College in Nottingham. His reputation built up slowly with the publication of *The White Peacock* in 1911, followed by *The Trespasser* the next year and *Sons and Lovers* in 1913. On July 13, 1914, he became the third husband of Frieda von Richthofen, whose brother ranked as the most famous German fighter pilot in World War I.

The English edition of Lawrence's novel *The Rainbow* was prosecuted for obscenity in 1915. After 1919 he took up the wandering life of the international artist in the 1920's. "There's nothing like keeping on the move," he said in one of his letters. But he wrote wherever he went—the Italian mainland, Capri, Sicily, and Austria up to 1922; Ceylon, Australia, New Mexico, and Mexico in the years 1922–23; England, France, and Germany in the following year; then back to New Mexico and Mexico. He remained in Europe after 1925.

In his own decidedly individual way, he was a complete man of letters who worked in many forms. Much of his poetry, from *Amores* to the posthumous work, takes high rank. His *Studies in Classic American Literature* made some important revaluations in

---

Notes from the artist: ". . . Lawrence's portrait emphasizes his monumental stature as a writer and at the same time suggests his delicate physical appearance. The two phoenixes entwining his figure are Lawrence's own personally selected symbols; a similar motif is used to decorate the Lawrence Memorial Chapel at Taos, New Mexico."

that field. In partial dissent from Freud, two of his books examined the role of the unconscious. He wrote *The Widowing of Mrs. Holroyd* and other plays, and such penetrating travel books as *Mornings in Mexico* and *Sea and Sardinia*. He translated the stories of Giovanni Verga.

He is best known, however, for his own stories, and for such novels or novelettes as *Women in Love, St. Mawr, The Lost Girl, The Plumed Serpent,* and *The Virgin and the Gypsy*. In 1928 the first edition of *Lady Chatterley's Lover* was privately printed in Florence. Some thirty years later it was cleared of obscenity charges in British and American courts. As the 1920's ended, Lawrence's health gradually declined. He died of bronchial tuberculosis in Vence, France, on March 2, 1930.

T*he Rocking-Horse Winner* first appeared in the 1920's in Lady Cynthia Asquith's *The Ghost Book*. In 1949 it was made into an English motion picture written and directed by Anthony Pelissier.

It is perhaps Lawrence's best-known short story, and one of his finest. It has that touch of the dark sorcerer which we have learned to look for in his most impressive work. He did not need to sign it. His mark is on every word. No one else in English literature could have written it. No one else could have given us that unique mingling of qualities—a style so simple, so apparently offhand in its colloquial ease; the uneasy theme that catches us at once; the particular detail about one family that somehow expands into whole classes in many countries; and the tone of fever, of tension, rising to a shrill pitch in the climax.

What is *The Rocking-Horse Winner* about? We may take it first on a perfectly everyday level. It is a story about a family that needs money. ". . . your father has no luck," the small boy's mother tells him. He decides that *he* has luck. He will get money for her. He will play the races. He does, and wins. That is all. Or is it? How does he win? He is driven by the soundless voices in the house: "There must be more money! There must be more money!" Like a demented child jockey, he rides his rocking horse in a symbolic race. If he can ride hard enough and "get there," he will "know" which of the real horses is going to win. When he "knows," his horse always comes in.

So we begin to understand that, on the second or social level, this is a story about the epidemic anxiety of the contemporary world: money worry. Here it communicates itself from the unloving mother to her children, so that the whole house is whispering with it. That this is not real need, that it is anxiety rooted in other sources, Lawrence shows us in a single sardonic touch. Through his uncle, the boy arranges to transfer a considerable sum of money to his mother. Does this quiet the voices? No. They scream now "in a sort of ecstasy: 'There must be more money!'" We know there will be no end to it.

We recognize too the theme of luck. The mother has communicated to her son the belief that luck is the key, the one hope of relief. So he does not ride merely to win money. Money is the magic key that will release his mother's and his own unbearable anxiety. If he can do this, he will win her love. He gets the money for her and he sees that it does not work. There is nothing to do but try again, to ride and ride until he can bring the winning horse in. We are reminded of that other story of money and luck and magic powers, Pushkin's *The Queen of Spades*.[1]

Lawrence's handling of his many-sided symbol is nowhere so masterly as in his muted intimations of love and sexual excitement. We are aware of his doctrine that true sexuality is the live core of human feeling. In the small boy's anxiety we catch the note of childish sexuality described by Freud. We recognize the familiar Freudian triangle: the son challenging the father for the mother's love. But Lawrence brings them all together—anxiety, money, luck, love, sexuality—in that last blazing instant when the mother turns on the light in her son's room.

---

[1] See Vol. 3, pp. 484–507, in this set.

The Rocking-Horse Winner

There was a woman who was beautiful, who started with all the advantages, yet she had no luck. She married for love, and the love turned to dust. She had bonny children, yet she felt they had been thrust upon her, and she could not love them. They looked at her coldly, as if they were finding fault with her. And hurriedly she felt she must cover up some fault in herself. Yet what it was that she must cover up she never knew. Nevertheless, when her children were present, she always felt the centre of her heart go hard. This troubled her, and in her manner she was all the more gentle and anxious for her children, as if she loved them very much. Only she herself knew that at the centre of her heart was a hard little place that could not feel love, no, not for anybody. Everybody else said of her: "She is such a good mother. She adores her children." Only she herself, and her children themselves, knew it was not so. They read it in each other's eyes.

There were a boy and two little girls. They lived in a pleasant house, with a garden, and they had discreet servants, and felt themselves superior to anyone in the neighbourhood.

Although they lived in style, they felt always an anxiety in the house. There was never enough money. The mother had a small income, and the father had a small income, but not nearly enough for the social position which they had to keep up. The father went into town to some office. But though he had good prospects, these prospects never materialized. There was always the grinding sense of the shortage of money, though the style was always kept up.

At last the mother said: "I will see if I can't make something." But she did not know where to begin. She racked her brains, and tried this thing and the other, but could not find anything successful. The failure made deep lines come into her face. Her children were growing up, they would have to go to school. There must be more money, there must be more money. The father, who was always very handsome and expensive in his tastes, seemed as if he never would be able to do anything worth doing. And the mother, who had a great belief in herself, did not succeed any better, and her tastes were just as expensive.

And so the house came to be haunted by the unspoken phrase: There must be more money! There must be more money! The children could hear it all the time, though nobody said it aloud. They heard it at Christmas, when the expensive and splendid toys filled the nursery. Behind the shining modern rocking-horse, behind the smart doll's house, a voice would start whispering: "There must be more money! There must be more money!" And the children would stop playing, to listen for a moment. They would look into each other's eyes, to see if they had all heard. And each one saw in the eyes of the other two that they too had heard. "There must be more money! There must be more money!"

It came whispering from the springs of the still-swaying rocking-horse, and even the horse, bending his wooden, champing head, heard it. The big doll, sitting so pink and smirking in her new pram, could hear it quite plainly, and seemed to be smirking all the more self-consciously because of it. The foolish puppy, too, that took the place of the teddy-bear, he was looking so extraordinarily foolish for no other reason but that he heard the secret whisper all over the house: "There must be more money!"

Yet nobody ever said it aloud. The whisper was everywhere, and therefore no one spoke it. Just as no one ever says: "We are breathing!" in spite of the fact that breath is coming and going all the time.

"Mother," said the boy Paul one day, "why don't we keep a car of our own? Why do we always use uncle's, or else a taxi?"

"Because we're the poor members of the family," said the mother.

"But why are we, mother?"

"Well—I suppose," she said slowly and bitterly, "it's because your father has no luck."

The boy was silent for some time.

"Is luck money, mother?" he asked, rather timidly.

"No, Paul. Not quite. It's what causes you to have money."

"Oh!" said Paul vaguely. "I thought when Uncle Oscar said filthy lucker, it meant money."

"Filthy lucre does mean money," said the mother. "But it's lucre, not luck."

"Oh!" said the boy. "Then what is luck, mother?"

"It's what causes you to have money. If you're lucky you have money. That's why it's better to be born lucky than rich. If you're rich, you may lose your money. But if you're lucky, you will always get more money."

"Oh! Will you? And is father not lucky?"

"Very unlucky, I should say," she said bitterly.

The boy watched her with unsure eyes.

"Why?" he asked.

"I don't know. Nobody ever knows why one person is lucky and another unlucky."

"Don't they? Nobody at all? Does nobody know?"

"Perhaps God. But He never tells."

"He ought to, then. And aren't you lucky either, mother?"

"I can't be, if I married an unlucky husband."

"But by yourself, aren't you?"

"I used to think I was, before I married. Now I think I am very unlucky indeed."

"Why?"

"Well—never mind! Perhaps I'm not really," she said.

The child looked at her, to see if she meant it. But he saw, by the lines of her mouth, that she was only trying to hide something from him.

"Well, anyhow," he said stoutly, "I'm a lucky person."

"Why?" said his mother, with a sudden laugh.

He stared at her. He didn't even know why he had said it.

"God told me," he asserted, brazening it out.

"I hope He did, dear!" she said, again with a laugh, but rather bitter.

"He did, mother!"

"Excellent!" said the mother, using one of her husband's exclamations.

The boy saw she did not believe him; or, rather, that she paid no attention to his assertion. This angered him somewhat, and made him want to compel her attention.

He went off by himself, vaguely, in a childish way, seeking for the clue to "luck." Absorbed, taking no heed of other people, he went about with a sort of stealth, seeking inwardly for luck. He wanted luck, he wanted it, he wanted it. When the two girls were playing dolls in the nursery, he would sit on his big rocking-horse, charging madly into space, with a frenzy that made the little girls peer at him uneasily. Wildly the horse careered, the waving dark hair of the boy tossed, his eyes had a strange glare in them. The little girls dared not speak to him.

When he had ridden to the end of his mad little journey, he climbed down and stood in front of his rocking-horse, staring fixedly into its lowered face. Its red mouth was slightly open, its big eye was wide and glassy-bright.

"Now!" he would silently command the snorting steed. "Now, take me to where there is luck! Now take me!"

And he would slash the horse on the neck with the little whip he had asked Uncle Oscar for. He knew the horse could take him to where there was luck, if only he forced it. So he would mount again, and start on his furious ride, hoping at last to get there. He knew he could get there.

"You'll break your horse, Paul!" said the nurse.

"He's always riding like that! I wish he'd leave off!" said his elder sister Joan.

But he only glared down on them in silence. Nurse gave him up. She could make nothing of him. Anyhow he was growing beyond her.

One day his mother and his Uncle Oscar came in when he was on one of his furious rides. He did not speak to them.

"Hallo, you young jockey! Riding a winner?" said his uncle.

"Aren't you growing too big for a rocking-horse? You're not a very little boy any longer, you know," said his mother.

But Paul only gave a blue glare from his big, rather close-set eyes. He would speak to nobody when he was in full tilt. His mother watched him with an anxious expression on her face.

At last he suddenly stopped forcing his horse into the mechanical gallop, and slid down.

"Well, I got there!" he announced fiercely, his blue eyes still flaring, and his sturdy long legs straddling apart.

"Where did you get to?" asked his mother.

"Where I wanted to go," he flared back at her.

"That's right, son!" said Uncle Oscar. "Don't you stop till you get there. What's the horse's name?"

"He doesn't have a name," said the boy.

"Gets on without all right?" asked the uncle.

"Well, he has different names. He was called Sansovino last week."

"Sansovino, eh? Won the Ascot. How did you know his name?"

"He always talks about horse-races with Bassett," said Joan.

The uncle was delighted to find that his small nephew was posted with all the racing news. Bassett, the young gardener, who had been wounded in the left foot in the war and had got his present job through Oscar Cresswell, whose batman he had been, was a perfect blade of the "turf." He lived in the racing events, and the small boy lived with him.

Oscar Cresswell got it all from Bassett.

"Master Paul comes and asks me, so I can't do more than tell him, sir," said Bassett, his face terribly serious, as if he were speaking of religious matters.

"And does he ever put anything on a horse he fancies?"

"Well—I don't want to give him away—he's a young sport, a fine sport, sir. Would you mind asking him yourself? He sort of takes a pleasure in it, and perhaps he'd feel I was giving him away, sir, if you don't mind."

Bassett was serious as a church.

The uncle went back to his nephew, and took him off for a ride in the car.

"Say, Paul, old man, do you ever put anything on a horse?" the uncle asked.

The boy watched the handsome man closely.

"Why, do you think I oughtn't to?" he parried.

"Not a bit of it! I thought perhaps you might give me a tip for the Lincoln."

The car sped on into the country, going down to Uncle Oscar's place in Hampshire.

"Honour bright?" said the nephew.

"Honour bright, son!" said the uncle.

"Well, then, Daffodil."

"Daffodil! I doubt it, sonny. What about Mirza?"

"I only know the winner," said the boy. "That's Daffodil."

"Daffodil, eh?"

There was a pause. Daffodil was an obscure horse comparatively.

"Uncle!"

"Yes, son?"

"You won't let it go any further, will you? I promised Bassett."

"Bassett be damned, old man! What's he got to do with it?"

"We're partners. We've been partners from the first. Uncle, he lent me my first five shillings, which I lost. I promised him, honour bright, it was only between me and him; only you gave me that ten-shilling note I started winning with, so I thought you were lucky. You won't let it go any further, will you?"

The boy gazed at his uncle from those big, hot, blue eyes, set rather close together. The uncle stirred and laughed uneasily.

"Right you are, son! I'll keep your tip private. Daffodil, eh? How much are you putting on him?"

"All except twenty pounds," said the boy. "I keep that in reserve."

The uncle thought it a good joke.

"You keep twenty pounds in reserve, do you, you young romancer? What are you betting, then?"

"I'm betting three hundred," said the boy gravely. "But it's between you and me, Uncle Oscar! Honour bright?"

The uncle burst into a roar of laughter.

"It's between you and me all right, you young Nat Gould," he said, laughing. "But where's your three hundred?"

"Bassett keeps it for me. We're partners."

"You are, are you? And what is Bassett putting on Daffodil?"

"He won't go quite as high as I do, I expect. Perhaps he'll go a hundred and fifty."

"What, pennies?" laughed the uncle.

"Pounds," said the child, with a surprised look at his uncle. "Bassett keeps a bigger reserve than I do."

Between wonder and amusement Uncle Oscar was silent. He pursued the matter no further, but he determined to take his nephew with him to the Lincoln races.

"Now, son," he said, "I'm putting twenty on Mirza, and I'll put five for you on any horse you fancy. What's your pick?"

"Daffodil, uncle."

"No, not the fiver on Daffodil!"

"I should if it was my own fiver," said the child.

"Good! Good! Right you are! A fiver for me and a fiver for you on Daffodil."

The child had never been to a race-meeting before, and his eyes were blue fire. He pursed his mouth tight, and watched. A Frenchman just in front had put his money on Lancelot. Wild with excitement, he flayed his arms up and down, yelling "Lancelot! Lancelot!" in his French accent.

Daffodil came in first, Lancelot second, Mirza third. The child, flushed and with eyes blazing, was curiously serene. His uncle brought him four five-pound notes, four to one.

"What am I to do with these?" he cried, waving them before the boy's eyes.

"I suppose we'll talk to Bassett," said the boy. "I expect I have fifteen hundred now; and twenty in reserve; and this twenty."

His uncle studied him for some moments.

"Look here, son!" he said. "You're not serious about Bassett and that fifteen hundred, are you?"

"Yes, I am. But it's between you and me, uncle. Honour bright!"

"Honour bright all right, son! But I must talk to Bassett."

"If you'd like to be a partner, uncle, with Bassett and me, we could all be partners. Only, you'd have to promise, honour bright, uncle, not to let it go beyond us three. Bassett and I are lucky, and you must be lucky, because it was your ten shillings I started winning with. . . ."

Uncle Oscar took both Bassett and Paul into Richmond Park for an afternoon, and there they talked.

"It's like this, you see, sir," Bassett said. "Master Paul would get me talking about racing events, spinning yarns, you know, sir. And he was always keen on knowing if I'd made or if I'd lost. It's about a year since, now, that I put five shillings on Blush of Dawn for him—and we lost. Then the luck turned, with that ten shillings he had from you, that we put on Singhalese. And since that time, it's been pretty steady, all things considering. What do you say, Master Paul?"

"We're all right when we're sure," said Paul. "It's when we're not quite sure that we go down."

"Oh, but we're careful then," said Bassett.

"But when are you sure?" smiled Uncle Oscar.

"It's Master Paul, sir," said Bassett, in a secret, religious voice. "It's as if he had it from heaven. Like Daffodil, now, for the Lincoln. That was as sure as eggs."

"Did you put anything on Daffodil?" asked Oscar Cresswell.

"Yes, sir. I made my bit."

"And my nephew?"

Bassett was obstinately silent, looking at Paul.

"I made twelve hundred, didn't I, Bassett? I told uncle I was putting three hundred on Daffodil."

"That's right," said Bassett, nodding.

"But where's the money?" asked the uncle.

"I keep it safe locked up, sir. Master Paul he can have it any minute he likes to ask for it."

"What, fifteen hundred pounds?"

"And twenty! And forty, that is, with the twenty he made on the course."

"It's amazing!" said the uncle.

"If Master Paul offers you to be partners, sir, I would, if I were you; if you'll excuse me," said Bassett.

Oscar Cresswell thought about it.

"I'll see the money," he said.

They drove home again, and sure enough, Bassett came round to the garden-house with fifteen hundred pounds in notes. The twenty pounds reserve was left with Joe Glee, in the Turf Commission deposit.

"You see, it's all right, uncle, when I'm sure! Then we go strong, for all we're worth. Don't we, Bassett?"

"We do that, Master Paul."

"And when are you sure?" said the uncle, laughing.

"Oh, well, sometimes I'm absolutely sure, like about Daffodil," said the boy; "and sometimes I have an idea; and sometimes I haven't even an idea, have I, Bassett? Then we're careful, because we mostly go down."

"You do, do you! And when you're sure, like about Daffodil, what makes you sure, sonny?"

"Oh, well, I don't know," said the boy uneasily. "I'm sure, you know, uncle; that's all."

"It's as if he had it from heaven, sir," Bassett reiterated.

"I should say so!" said the uncle.

But he became a partner. And when the Leger was coming on, Paul was "sure" about Lively Spark, which was a quite inconsiderable horse. The boy insisted on putting a thousand on the horse, Bassett went for five hundred, and Oscar Cresswell two hundred. Lively Spark came in first, and the betting had been ten to one against him. Paul had made ten thousand.

"You see," he said. "I was absolutely sure of him."

Even Oscar Cresswell had cleared two thousand.

"Look here, son," he said, "this sort of thing makes me nervous."

"It needn't, uncle! Perhaps I shan't be sure again for a long time."

"But what are you going to do with your money?" asked the uncle.

"Of course," said the boy, "I started it for mother. She said she had no luck, because father is unlucky, so I thought if I was lucky, it might stop whispering."

"What might stop whispering?"

"Our house. I hate our house for whispering."

"What does it whisper?"

"Why—why"—the boy fidgeted—"why, I don't know. But it's always short of money, you know, uncle."

"I know it, son, I know it."

"You know people send mother writs, don't you, uncle?"

"I'm afraid I do," said the uncle.

"And then the house whispers, like people laughing at you behind your back. It's awful, that is! I thought if I was lucky . . ."

"You might stop it," added the uncle.

The boy watched him with big blue eyes that had an uncanny cold fire in them, and he said never a word.

"Well, then!" said the uncle. "What are we doing?"

"I shouldn't like mother to know I was lucky," said the boy.

"Why not, son?"

"She'd stop me."

"I don't think she would."

"Oh!"—and the boy writhed in an odd way—"I don't want her to know, uncle."

"All right, son! We'll manage it without her knowing."

They managed it very easily. Paul, at the other's suggestion, handed over five thousand pounds to his uncle, who deposited it with the family lawyer, who was then to inform Paul's mother that a relative had put five thousand pounds into his hands, which sum was to be paid out a thousand pounds at a time, on the mother's birthday, for the next five years.

"So she'll have a birthday present of a thousand pounds for five successive years," said Uncle Oscar. "I hope it won't make it all the harder for her later."

Paul's mother had her birthday in November. The house had been "whispering" worse than ever lately, and, even in spite of his luck, Paul could not bear up against it. He was very anxious to see the effect of the birthday letter, telling his mother about the thousand pounds.

When there were no visitors, Paul now took his meals with his parents, as he was beyond the nursery control. His mother went into town nearly every day. She had discovered that she had an odd knack of sketching furs and dress materials, so she worked secretly in the studio of a friend who was the chief "artist" for the leading drapers. She drew the figures of ladies in furs and ladies in silk and sequins for the newspaper advertisements. This young woman artist earned several thousand pounds a year, but Paul's mother only made several hundreds, and she was again dissatisfied. She so wanted to be first in something, and she did not succeed, even in making sketches for drapery advertisements.

She was down to breakfast on the morning of her birthday. Paul watched her face as she read her letters. He knew the lawyer's letter. As his mother read it, her face hardened and became more expressionless. Then a cold, determined look came on her mouth. She hid the letter under the pile of others and said not a word about it.

"Didn't you have anything nice in the post for your birthday, mother?" said Paul.

"Quite moderately nice," she said, her voice cold and absent.

She went away to town without saying more.

But in the afternoon Uncle Oscar appeared. He said Paul's mother had had a long interview with the lawyer, asking if the whole five thousand could be advanced at once, as she was in debt.

"What do you think, uncle?" said the boy.

"I leave it to you, son."

"Oh, let her have it, then! We can get some more with the other," said the boy.

"A bird in the hand is worth two in the bush, laddie!"

"But I'm sure to know for the Grand National; or the Lincolnshire; or else the Derby. I'm sure to know for one of them," said Paul.

So Uncle Oscar signed the agreement, and Paul's mother touched the whole five thousand. Then something very curious happened. The voices in the house suddenly went mad, like a chorus of frogs on a spring evening. There were certain new furnishings, and Paul had a tutor. He was really going to Eton, his father's school, in the following autumn. There were flowers in the winter, and a blossoming of the luxury Paul's mother had been used to. And yet the voices in the house, behind the sprays of mimosa and almond blossom, and from under the piles of iridescent cushions, simply trilled and screamed in a sort of ecstasy: "There must be more money! Oh-h-h, there must be more money. Oh, now, now-w! Now-w-w—there must be more money!—more than ever! More than ever!"

It frightened Paul terribly. He studied away at his Latin and Greek with his tutors. But his intense hours were spent with Bassett. The Grand National had gone by: he had not "known," and had lost a hundred pounds. Summer was at hand. He was in agony for the Lincoln. But even for the Lincoln he didn't "know" and he lost fifty pounds. He became wild-eyed and strange, as if something were going to explode in him.

"Let it alone, son! Don't you bother about it!" urged Uncle Oscar. But it was as if the boy couldn't really hear what his uncle was saying.

"I've got to know for the Derby! I've got to know for the Derby!" the child reiterated, his big blue eyes blazing with a sort of madness.

His mother noticed how overwrought he was.

"You'd better go to the seaside. Wouldn't you like to go now to the seaside, instead of waiting? I think you'd better," she said, looking down at him anxiously, her heart curiously heavy because of him.

But the child lifted his uncanny blue eyes.

"I couldn't possibly go before the Derby, mother!" he said. "I couldn't possibly!"

"Why not?" she said, her voice becoming heavy when she was opposed. "Why not? You can still go from the seaside to see the Derby with your Uncle Oscar, if that's what you wish. No need for you to wait here. Besides, I think you care too much about these races. It's a bad sign. My family has been a gambling family, and you won't know till you grow up how much damage it has done. But it has done damage. I shall have to send Bassett away, and ask Uncle Oscar not to talk racing to you, unless you promise to be reasonable about it; go away to the seaside and forget it. You're all nerves!"

"I'll do what you like, mother, so long as you don't send me away till after the Derby," the boy said.

"Send you away from where? Just from this house?"

"Yes," he said, gazing at her.

"Why, you curious child, what makes you care about this house so much, suddenly? I never knew you loved it."

He gazed at her without speaking. He had a secret within a secret, something he had not divulged, even to Bassett or to his Uncle Oscar.

But his mother, after standing undecided and a little bit sullen for some moments, said:

"Very well, then! Don't go to the seaside till after the Derby, if you don't wish it. But promise me you won't let your nerves go to pieces. Promise you won't think so much about horse-racing and events, as you call them!"

"Oh, no," said the boy casually. "I won't think much about them, mother. You needn't worry. I wouldn't worry, mother, if I were you."

"If you were me and I were you," said his mother, "I wonder what we should do!"

"But you know you needn't worry, mother, don't you?" the boy repeated.

"I should be awfully glad to know it," she said wearily.

"Oh, well, you can, you know. I mean, you ought to know you needn't worry," he insisted.

"Ought I? Then I'll see about it," she said.

Paul's secret of secrets was his wooden horse, that which had no name. Since he was emancipated from a nurse and a nursery-governess, he had had his rocking-horse removed to his own bedroom at the top of the house.

"Surely, you're too big for a rocking-horse!" his mother had remonstrated.

"Well, you see, mother, till I can have a real horse, I like to have some sort of animal about," had been his quaint answer.

"Do you feel he keeps you company?" she laughed.

"Oh, yes! He's very good, he always keeps me company, when I'm there," said Paul.

So the horse, rather shabby, stood in an arrested prance in the boy's bedroom.

The Derby was drawing near, and the boy grew more and more tense. He hardly heard what was spoken to him, he was very frail, and his eyes were really uncanny. His mother had sudden seizures of uneasiness about him. Sometimes, for half an hour, she would feel a sudden anxiety about him that was almost anguish. She wanted to rush to him at once, and know he was safe.

Two nights before the Derby, she was at a big party in town, when one of her rushes of anxiety about her boy, her first-born, gripped her heart till she could hardly speak. She fought with the feeling, might and main, for she believed in common sense. But it was too strong. She had to leave the dance and go downstairs to telephone to the country. The children's nursery-governess was terribly surprised and startled at being rung up in the night.

"Are the children all right, Miss Wilmot?"

"Oh, yes, they are quite all right."

"Master Paul? Is he all right?"

"He went to bed as right as a trivet. Shall I run up and look at him?"

"No," said Paul's mother reluctantly. "No! Don't trouble. It's all right. Don't sit up. We shall be home fairly soon." She did not want her son's privacy intruded upon.

"Very good," said the governess.

It was about one o'clock when Paul's mother and father drove up to their house. All was still. Paul's mother went to her room and slipped off her white fur cloak. She had told her maid not to wait up for her. She heard her husband downstairs, mixing a whisky-and-soda.

And then, because of the strange anxiety at her heart, she stole upstairs to her son's room. Noiselessly she went along the upper corridor. Was there a faint noise? What was it?

She stood, with arrested muscles, outside his door, listening. There was a strange, heavy, and yet not loud noise. Her heart stood still. It was a soundless noise, yet rushing and powerful. Something huge, in violent, hushed motion. What was it? What in God's name was it? She ought to know. She felt that she knew the noise. She knew what it was.

Yet she could not place it. She couldn't say what it was. And on and on it went, like a madness.

Softly, frozen with anxiety and fear, she turned the door-handle.

The room was dark. Yet in the space near the window, she heard and saw something plunging to and fro. She gazed in fear and amazement.

Then suddenly she switched on the light, and saw her son, in his green pyjamas, madly surging on the rocking-horse. The blaze of light suddenly lit him up, as he urged the wooden horse, and lit her up, as she stood, blonde, in her dress of pale green and crystal, in the doorway.

"Paul!" she cried. "Whatever are you doing?"

"It's Malabar!" he screamed, in a powerful, strange voice. "It's Malabar."

His eyes blazed at her for one strange and senseless second, as he ceased urging his wooden horse. Then he fell with a crash to the ground, and she, all her tormented motherhood flooding upon her, rushed to gather him up.

But he was unconscious, and unconscious he remained, with some brain-fever. He talked and tossed, and his mother sat stonily by his side.

"Malabar! It's Malabar! Bassett, Bassett, I know! It's Malabar!"

So the child tried, trying to get up and urge the rocking-horse that gave him his inspiration.

"What does he mean by Malabar?" asked the heart-frozen mother.

"I don't know," said the father stonily.

"What does he mean by Malabar?" she asked her brother Oscar.

"It's one of the horses running for the Derby," was the answer.

And, in spite of himself, Oscar Cresswell spoke to Bassett, and himself put a thousand on Malabar: at fourteen to one.

The third day of the illness was critical: they were waiting for a change. The boy, with his rather long, curly hair, was tossing ceaselessly on the pillow. He neither slept nor regained consciousness, and his eyes were like blue stones. His mother sat, feeling her heart had gone, turned actually into a stone.

In the evening, Oscar Cresswell did not come, but Bassett sent a message, saying could he come up for one moment, just one moment? Paul's mother was very angry at the intrusion, but on second thought she agreed. The boy was the same. Perhaps Bassett might bring him to consciousness.

The gardener, a shortish fellow with a little brown moustache, and sharp little brown eyes, tiptoed into the room, touched his imaginary cap to Paul's mother, and stole to the bedside, staring with glittering, smallish eyes, at the tossing, dying child.

"Master Paul!" he whispered. "Master Paul! Malabar come in first all right, a clean win. I did as you told me. You've made over seventy thousand pounds, you have; you've got over eighty thousand. Malabar came in all right, Master Paul!"

"Malabar! Malabar! Did I say Malabar, mother? Did I say Malabar? Do you think I'm lucky, mother? I knew Malabar, didn't I? Over eighty thousand pounds! I call that lucky, don't you, mother? Over eighty thousand pounds! I knew, didn't I know I knew? Malabar came in all right. If I ride my horse till I'm sure, then I tell you, Bassett, you can go as high as you like. Did you go for all you were worth, Bassett?"

"I went a thousand on it, Master Paul."

"I never told you, mother, that if I can ride my horse, and get there, then I'm absolutely sure—oh, absolutely! Mother, did I ever tell you? I am lucky."

"No, you never did," said the mother.

But the boy died in the night.

And even as he lay dead, his mother heard her brother's voice saying to her: "My God, Hester, you're eighty-odd thousand to the good and a poor devil of a son to the bad. But, poor devil, poor devil, he's best gone out of a life where he rides his rocking-horse to find a winner."

Henry James

1843–1916

Henry James was born in New York City, on April 15, 1843. He was the second son of the Swedenborgian philosopher Henry James, Sr., and brother of the psychologist William James. In the year of his birth the future novelist made his first visit to Europe. He grew up largely in Albany, New York, and New York City. His education was a planned succession of governesses, tutors, schools, and travel experiences in the United States, Switzerland, Germany, France, and England.

In 1860–62 he lived in Newport, Rhode Island. A spinal injury incurred with a volunteer fire company probably kept him out of the Civil War and forced him to leave Harvard Law School. In Boston he wrote criticism, travel articles, and short stories. By 1875 he had decided to live in Europe. He settled first in Paris, where Turgenev, Flaubert, Maupassant, and Zola became his friends. In the following year he moved to London.

His first full-length novel, *Roderick Hudson*, was published in 1876. During this early period he wrote *The American, The Portrait of a Lady* (said to have been studied from his beloved cousin, Minny Temple, who died young), *Daisy Miller, Washington*

Notes from the artist: ". . . James as a boy—his head spinning— in an otherwise 'period' portrait with his father, complete with elaborate Victorian frame. The deliberate shock in this generally sedate family portrait was intended to suggest the restlessness of the artist, both as a youth who resisted formal education and as the mature writer who would dissect some of the tragedy that lay beneath the apparent calm of turn-of-the-century society."

Square, and *The Aspern Papers.* He made extended visits to the United States, France, and Italy. Beginning in 1889, he tried hard but unsuccessfully to break into the theater. Only two plays of his were produced: *The American* and *Guy Domville.*

In the 1890's he published a long row of such distinguished works as *The Tragic Muse, What Maisie Knew, The Lesson of the Master,* and *The Turn of the Screw.* He moved to Lamb House in Rye, Sussex. *The American Scene* came out of a visit to the United States in 1904–05. *The Wings of the Dove, The Ambassadors,* and *The Golden Bowl* belong among the great novels of his final period. During World War I he became a naturalized British subject and was awarded the Order of Merit. He died on February 28, 1916.

I n one of the prefaces to the New York Edition of his works, Henry James tells how the suggestion for *The Pupil* came to him. On a summer day, he writes, "in a very hot Italian railway-carriage," a physician friend "happened to speak to me of a wonderful American family, an odd, adventurous, extravagant band, the most interesting member of which was a small boy, acute and precocious, afflicted with a heart of weak action. . . ."

Its imaginative power, James adds, might well have come out of "an old latent and dormant impression, a buried germ, implanted by experience and then forgotten. . . ." Van Wyck Brooks suggests that this must have been a recollection of the Sargent family—its most famous member was the painter John Singer Sargent—who "wandered like gypsies all over Europe, from Biarritz to Venice, to Switzerland, to Paris, 'living one year like ambassadors and the next like paupers,' as Henry James was to describe them in his story 'The Pupil'. . . ."

If this is so, the Sargents must have undergone a striking change when James turned them into the Moreens. They became what the Sargents had probably never been— "a houseful of Bohemians who wanted tremendously to be Philistines." And what is a Philistine? A prosperous conservative who has no use for artists. Out of the Moreens' desire to be fashionable and secure, without having the means for it, comes all the falseness that Morgan and his young American tutor find in them.

They try to present a solvent and conventional face to the world. They are Bohemians only in private and by necessity. This gives them a resemblance to a troupe of actors who must never be off guard, who must never forget to pretend that they are not acting. James makes an amusing thing of it. In a series of light touches he gives us Mr. Moreen, with his white mustache and his "ribbon of a foreign order"; the eternal macaroni and coffee; the talk about "good places"—"as if they had been pickpockets or strolling players"; and the villa at Nice with "a carriage, a piano and a banjo. . . ."

But the story hinges on the friendship between Pemberton, the tutor, and young Morgan Moreen. Morgan himself—because he is "a genius," as his mother says? because he has a weak heart?—is treated with "a genuine tenderness, an artless admiration. . . ." By that very sign he is an outsider. He is not privy to the family secrets. He must find them out for himself—and does. He and Pemberton make a small union of outsiders. They are at once ironic spectators and hopelessly involved. They have a common longing to escape; but there is no future for them outside the trap of the family.

Do we have misgivings of a sort that James, for once, does not seem to have anticipated? "I think a position in society is a legitimate object of ambition," he remarked once. So we are a little dismayed perhaps when young Morgan and his tutor assume the right to judge "such people" as the Moreens. Pemberton, in fact, reflected that "they were adventurers because they were toadies and snobs." Perhaps they are "toadies and snobs" by nature. But they are adventurers because they have no money, or too little to be any use to them. They live like prospective heirs borrowing against an inheritance that will never come.

The Pupil

The poor young man hesitated and procrastinated: it cost him such an effort to broach the subject of terms, to speak of money to a person who spoke only of feelings and, as it were, of the aristocracy. Yet he was unwilling to take leave, treating his engagement as settled, without some more conventional glance in that direction than he could find an opening for in the manner of the large affable lady who sat there drawing a pair of soiled *gants de Suède* [suede gloves] through a fat jewelled hand and, at once pressing and gliding, repeated over and over everything but the thing he would have liked to hear. He would have liked to hear the figure of his salary; but just as he was nervously about to sound that note the little boy came back—the little boy Mrs. Moreen had sent out of the room to fetch her fan. He came back without the fan, only with the casual observation that he couldn't find it. As he dropped this cynical confession he looked straight and hard at the candidate for the honour of taking his education in hand. This personage reflected somewhat grimly that the first thing he should have to teach his little charge would be to appear to address himself to his mother when he spoke to her—especially not to make her such an improper answer as that.

When Mrs. Moreen bethought herself of this pretext for getting rid of their companion, Pemberton supposed it was precisely to approach the delicate subject of his remuneration. But it had been only to say some things about her son that it was better a boy of eleven shouldn't catch. They were extravagantly to his advantage save when she lowered her voice to sigh, tapping her left side familiarly, "And all overclouded by *this*, you know; all at the mercy of a weakness—!" Pemberton gathered that the weakness was in the region of the heart. He had known the poor child was not robust: this was the basis on which he had been invited to treat, through an English lady, an Oxford acquaintance, then at Nice, who happened to know both his needs and those of the amiable American family looking out for something really superior in the way of a resident tutor.

The young man's impression of his prospective pupil, who had come into the room as if to see for himself the moment Pemberton was admitted, was not quite the soft solicitation the visitor had taken for granted. Morgan Moreen was somehow sickly without being "delicate," and that he looked intelligent—it is true Pemberton wouldn't have enjoyed his being stupid—only added to the suggestion that, as with his big mouth and big ears he really couldn't be called pretty, he might too utterly fail to please. Pemberton was modest, was even timid; and the chance that his small scholar would prove cleverer than himself had quite figured, to his anxiety, among the dangers of an untried experiment. He reflected, however, that these were risks one had to run when one accepted a position, as it was called, in a private family; when as yet one's university honours had, pecuniarily speaking, remained barren. At any rate when Mrs. Moreen got up as to intimate that, since it was understood he would enter upon his duties within the week, she would let him off now, he succeeded, in spite of the presence of the child, in squeezing out a phrase about the rate of payment. It was not the fault of the conscious smile which seemed a reference to the lady's expensive identity, it was not the fault of this demonstration, which had, in a sort, both vagueness and point, if the allusion didn't sound rather vulgar. This was exactly because she became still more gracious to reply: "Oh I can assure you that all that will be quite regular."

Pemberton only wondered, while he took up his hat, what "all that" was to amount to—people had such different ideas. Mrs. Moreen's words, however, seemed to commit the family to a pledge definite enough to elicit from the child a strange little comment in the shape of the mocking foreign ejaculation "Oh la-la!"

Pemberton, in some confusion, glanced at him as he walked slowly to the window with his back turned, his hands in his pockets and the air in his elderly shoulders of a boy who didn't play. The young man wondered if he should be able to teach him to play, though his mother had said it would never do and that this was why school was impossible. Mrs. Moreen exhibited no discomfiture; she only continued blandly: "Mr. Moreen will be delighted to meet your wishes. As I told you, he has been called to London for a week. As soon as he comes back you shall have it out with him."

This was so frank and friendly that the young man could only reply, laughing as his hostess laughed: "Oh I don't imagine we shall have much of a battle."

"They'll give you anything you like," the boy remarked unexpectedly, returning from the window. "We don't mind what anything costs—we live awfully well."

"My darling, you're too quaint!" his mother exclaimed, putting out to caress him a practised but ineffectual hand. He slipped out of it, but looked with intelligent innocent eyes at Pemberton, who had already had time to notice that from one moment to the other his small satiric face seemed to change its time of life. At this moment it was infantine, yet it appeared also to be under the influence of curious intuitions and knowledges. Pemberton rather disliked precocity and was disappointed to find gleams of it in a disciple not yet in his teens. Nevertheless he divined on the spot that Morgan wouldn't prove a bore. He would prove on the contrary a source of agitation. This idea held the young man, in spite of a certain repulsion.

"You pompous little person! We're not extravagant!" Mrs. Moreen gaily protested, making another unsuccessful attempt to draw the boy to her side. "You must know what to expect," she went on to Pemberton.

"The less you expect the better!" her companion interposed. "But we *are* people of fashion."

"Only so far as *you* make us so!" Mrs. Moreen tenderly mocked. "Well then, on Friday—don't tell me you're superstitious—and mind you don't fail us. Then you'll see us all. I'm so sorry the girls are out. I guess you'll like the girls. And, you know, I've another son, quite different from this one."

"He tries to imitate me," Morgan said to their friend.

"He tries? Why he's twenty years old!" cried Mrs. Moreen.

"You're very witty," Pemberton remarked to the child—a proposition his mother echoed with enthusiasm, declaring Morgan's sallies to be the delight of the house.

The boy paid no heed to this; he only enquired abruptly of the visitor, who was surprised afterwards that he hadn't struck him as offensively forward: "Do you *want* very much to come?"

"Can you doubt it after such a description of what I shall hear?" Pemberton replied. Yet he didn't want to come at all; he was coming because he had to go somewhere, thanks to the collapse of his fortune at the end of a year abroad spent on the system of putting his scant patrimony into a single full wave of experience. He had had his full wave but couldn't pay the score at his inn. Moreover he had caught in the boy's eyes the glimpse of a far-off appeal.

"Well, I'll do the best I can for you," said Morgan; with which he turned away again. He passed out of one of the long windows; Pember-

ton saw him go and lean on the parapet of the terrace. He remained
there while the young man took leave of his mother, who, on Pemberton's
looking as if he expected a farewell from him, interposed with: "Leave
him, leave him; he's so strange!" Pemberton supposed her to fear something he might say. "He's a genius—you'll love him," she added. "He's
much the most interesting person in the family." And before he could
invent some civility to oppose to this she wound up with: "But we're all
good, you know!"

"He's a genius—you'll love him!" were words that recurred to our
aspirant before the Friday, suggesting among many things that geniuses
were not invariably lovable. However, it was all the better if there was
an element that would make tutorship absorbing: he had perhaps taken
too much for granted it would only disgust him. As he left the villa after
his interview he looked up at the balcony and saw the child leaning over
it. "We shall have great larks!" he called up.

Morgan hung fire a moment and then gaily returned: "By the time you
come back I shall have thought of something witty!"

This made Pemberton say to himself "After all he's rather nice."

On the Friday he saw them all, as Mrs. Moreen had promised, for her
husband had come back and the girls and the other son were at home.
Mr. Moreen had a white moustache, a confiding manner and, in his button-hole, the ribbon of a foreign order—bestowed, as Pemberton eventually learned, for services. For what services he never clearly ascer-
tained: this was a point—one of a larger number—that Mr. Moreen's
manner never confided. What it emphatically did confide was that he
was even more a man of the world than you might first make out. Ulick,
the first-born, was in visible training for the same profession—under the
disadvantage as yet, however, of a button-hole but feebly floral and a
moustache with no pretensions to type. The girls had hair and figures and
manners and small fat feet, but had never been out alone. As for Mrs.
Moreen, Pemberton saw on a nearer view that her elegance was intermittent and her parts didn't always match. Her husband, as she had
promised, met with enthusiasm Pemberton's ideas in regard to a salary.
The young man had endeavoured to keep these stammerings modest,
and Mr. Moreen made it no secret that *he* found them wanting in
"style." He further mentioned that he aspired to be intimate with his
children, to be their best friend, and that he was always looking out for
them. That was what he went off for, to London and other places—to
look out; and this vigilance was the theory of life, as well as the real

occupation, of the whole family. They all looked out, for they were very frank on the subject of its being necessary. They desired it to be understood that they were earnest people, and also that their fortune, though quite adequate for earnest people, required the most careful administration. Mr. Moreen, as the parent bird, sought sustenance for the nest. Ulick invoked support mainly at the club, where Pemberton guessed that it was usually served on green cloth. The girls used to do up their hair and their frocks themselves, and our young man felt appealed to to be glad, in regard to Morgan's education, that, though it must naturally be of the best, it didn't cost too much. After a little he *was* glad, forgetting at times his own needs in the interest inspired by the child's character and culture and the pleasure of making easy terms for him.

During the first weeks of their acquaintance Morgan had been as puzzling as a page in an unknown language—altogether different from the obvious little Anglo-Saxons who had misrepresented childhood to Pemberton. Indeed the whole mystic volume in which the boy had been amateurishly bound demanded some practice in translation. Today, after a considerable interval, there is something phantasmagoric, like a prismatic reflection or a serial novel, in Pemberton's memory of the queerness of the Moreens. If it were not for a few tangible tokens—a lock of Morgan's hair cut by his own hand, and the half-dozen letters received from him when they were disjoined—the whole episode and the figures peopling it would seem too inconsequent for anything but dreamland. Their supreme quaintness was their success—as it appeared to him for a while at the time; since he had never seen a family so brilliantly equipped for failure. Wasn't it success to have kept him so hatefully long? Wasn't it success to have drawn him in that first morning at *déjeuner* [lunch], the Friday he came—it was enough to *make* one superstitious—so that he utterly committed himself, and this not by calculation or on a signal, but from a happy instinct which made them, like a band of gipsies, work so neatly together? They amused him as much as if they had really been a band of gipsies. He was still young and had not seen much of the world—his English years had been properly arid; therefore the reversed conventions of the Moreens—for they had *their* desperate properties—struck him as topsy-turvy. He had encountered nothing like them at Oxford; still less had any such note been struck to his younger American ear during the four years at Yale in which he had richly supposed himself to be reacting against a Puritan strain. The reaction of the Moreens, at any rate, went ever so much further. He had thought himself very sharp that first day in hitting them all off in his mind with the "cosmopolite" label. Later it seemed feeble and colour-less—confessedly helplessly provisional.

He yet when he first applied it felt a glow of joy—for an instructor he was still empirical—rise from the apprehension that living with them would really be to see life. Their sociable strangeness was an imitation of that—their chatter of tongues, their gaiety and good humour, their in-finite dawdling (they were always getting themselves up, but it took for ever, and Pemberton had once found Mr. Moreen shaving in the draw-ing-room), their French, their Italian and, cropping up in the foreign fluencies, their cold tough slices of American. They lived on macaroni and coffee—they had these articles prepared in perfection—but they knew recipes for a hundred other dishes. They overflowed with music and song, were always humming and catching each other up, and had a sort of professional acquaintance with Continental cities. They talked of "good places" as if they had been pickpockets or strolling players. They had at Nice a villa, a carriage, a piano and a banjo, and they went to official parties. They were a perfect calendar of the "days" of their friends, which Pemberton knew them, when they were indisposed, to get out of bed to go to, and which made the week larger than life when Mrs. Moreen talked of them with Paula and Amy. Their initiations gave their new inmate at first an almost dazzling sense of culture. Mrs. Moreen had translated something at some former period—an author whom it made Pemberton feel *borné* [limited] never to have heard of. They could imitate Venetian and sing Neapolitan, and when they wanted to say something very particular communicated with each other in an ingenious dialect of their own, an elastic spoken cipher which Pemberton at first took for some *patois* of one of their countries, but which he "caught on to" as he would not have grasped provincial development of Spanish or German.

"It's the family language—Ultramoreen," Morgan explained to him drolly enough; but the boy rarely condescended to use it himself, though he dealt in colloquial Latin as if he had been a little prelate.

Among all the "days" with which Mrs. Moreen's memory was taxed she managed to squeeze in one of her own, which her friends sometimes forgot. But the house drew a frequented air from the number of fine peo-ple who were freely named there and from several mysterious men with foreign titles and English clothes whom Morgan called the Princes and who, on sofas with the girls, talked French very loud—though sometimes

with some oddity of accent—as if to show they were saying nothing improper. Pemberton wondered how the Princes could ever propose in that
tone and so publicly: he took for granted cynically that this was what
was desired of them. Then he recognized that even for the chance of such
an advantage Mrs. Moreen would never allow Paula and Amy to receive
alone. These young ladies were not at all timid, but it was just the safe-
guards that made them so candidly free. It was a houseful of Bohemians
who wanted tremendously to be Philistines.

In one respect, however, certainly, they achieved no rigour—they were
wonderfully amiable and ecstatic about Morgan. It was a genuine tenderness, an artless admiration, equally strong in each. They even praised
his beauty. which was small, and were as afraid of him as if they felt him
of finer clay. They spoke of him as a little angel and a prodigy—they
touched on his want of health with long, vague faces. Pemberton feared
at first an extravagance that might make him hate the boy, but before
this happened he had become extravagant himself. Later, when he had
grown rather to hate the others, it was a bribe to patience for him that
they were at any rate nice about Morgan, going on tiptoe if they fancied
he was showing symptoms, and even giving up somebody's "day" to procure him a pleasure. Mixed with this too was the oddest wish to make
him independent, as if they had felt themselves not good enough for him.
They passed him over to the new members of their circle very much as
if wishing to force some charity of adoption on so free an agent and get
rid of their own charge. They were delighted when they saw Morgan
take so to his kind playfellow, and could think of no higher praise for
the young man. It was strange how they contrived to reconcile the appearance, and indeed the essential fact, of adoring the child with their
eagerness to wash their hands of him. Did they want to get rid of him
before he should find them out? Pemberton was finding them out month
by month. The boy's fond family, however this might be, turned their
backs with exaggerated delicacy, as if to avoid the reproach of inter-
fering. Seeing in time how little he had in common with them—it was
by *them* he first observed it; they proclaimed it with complete humility—
his companion was moved to speculate on the mysteries of transmission,
the far jumps of heredity. Where his detachment from most of the things
they represented had come from was more than an observer could say—
it certainly had burrowed under two or three generations.

As for Pemberton's own estimate of his pupil, it was a good while before he got the point of view, so little had he been prepared for it by the

smug young barbarians to whom the tradition of tutorship, as hitherto revealed to him, had been adjusted. Morgan was scrappy and surprising, deficient in many properties supposed common to the *genus* and abounding in others that were the portion only of the supernaturally clever. One day his friend made a great stride: it cleared up the question to perceive that Morgan *was* supernaturally clever and that, though the formula was temporarily meagre, this would be the only assumption on which one could successfully deal with him. He had the general quality of a child for whom life had not been simplified by school, a kind of home-bred sensibility which might have been bad for himself but was charming for others, and a whole range of refinement and perception— little musical vibrations as taking as picked-up airs—begotten by wandering about Europe at the tail of his migratory tribe. This might not have been an education to recommend in advance, but its results with so special a subject were as appreciable as the marks on a piece of fine porcelain. There was at the same time in him a small strain of stoicism, doubtless the fruit of having had to begin early to bear pain, which counted for pluck and made it of less consequence that he might have been thought at school rather a polyglot little beast. Pemberton indeed quickly found himself rejoicing that school was out of the question: in any million of boys it was probably good for all but one, and Morgan was that millionth. It would have made him comparative and superior—it might have made him really require kicking. Pemberton would try to be school himself—a bigger seminary than five hundred grazing donkeys, so that, winning no prizes, the boy would remain unconscious and irresponsible and amusing—amusing, because, though life was already intense in his childish nature, freshness still made there a strong draught for jokes. It turned out that even in the still air of Morgan's various disabilities jokes flourished greatly. He was a pale lean acute undeveloped little cosmopolite, who liked intellectual gymnastics and who also, as regards the behaviour of mankind, had noticed more things than you might suppose, but who nevertheless had his proper playroom of superstitions, where he smashed a dozen toys a day.

At Nice once, toward evening, as the pair rested in the open air after a walk, and looked over the sea at the pink western lights, he said suddenly to his comrade: "Do you like it, you know—being with us all in this intimate way?"

"My dear fellow, why should I stay if I didn't?"

"How do I know you'll stay? I'm almost sure you won't, very long."

"I hope you don't mean to dismiss me," said Pemberton.

Morgan debated, looking at the sunset. "I think if I did right I ought to."

"Well, I know I'm supposed to instruct you in virtue; but in that case don't do right."

"You're very young—fortunately," Morgan went on, turning to him again.

"Oh yes, compared with you!"

"Therefore it won't matter so much if you do lose a lot of time."

"That's the way to look at it," said Pemberton accommodatingly.

They were silent a minute; after which the boy asked: "Do you like my father and my mother very much?"

"Dear me, yes. Charming people."

Morgan received this with another silence; then unexpectedly, familiarly, but at the same time affectionately, he remarked: "You're a jolly old humbug!"

For a particular reason the words made our young man change colour. The boy noticed in an instant that he had turned red, whereupon he turned red himself and pupil and master exchanged a longish glance in which there was a consciousness of many more things than are usually touched upon, even tacitly, in such a relation. It produced for Pemberton an embarrassment; it raised in a shadowy form a question—this was the first glimpse of it—destined to play a singular and, as he imagined, owing to the altogether peculiar conditions, an unprecedented part in his intercourse with his little companion. Later, when he found himself talking with the youngster in a way in which few youngsters could ever have been talked with, he thought of that clumsy moment on the bench at Nice as the dawn of an understanding that had broadened. What had added to the clumsiness then was that he thought it his duty to declare to Morgan that he might abuse him, Pemberton, as much as he liked, but must never abuse his parents. To this Morgan had the easy retort that he hadn't dreamed of abusing them; which appeared to be true: it put Pemberton in the wrong.

"Then why am I a humbug for saying *I* think them charming?" the young man asked, conscious of a certain rashness.

"Well—they're not your parents."

"They love you better than anything in the world—never forget that," said Pemberton.

"Is that why you like them so much?"

"They're very kind to me," Pemberton replied evasively.

"You *are* a humbug!" laughed Morgan, passing an arm into his tutor's. He leaned against him looking off at the sea again and swinging his long thin legs.

"Don't kick my shins," said Pemberton while he reflected "Hang it, I can't complain of them to the child!"

"There's another reason too," Morgan went on, keeping his legs still.

"Another reason for what?"

"Besides their not being your parents."

"I don't understand you," said Pemberton.

"Well, you will before long. All right!"

He did understand fully before long, but he made a fight even with himself before he confessed it. He thought it the oddest thing to have a struggle with the child about. He wondered he didn't hate the hope of the Moreens for bringing the struggle on. But by the time it began any such sentiment for that scion was closed to him. Morgan was a special case, and to know him was to accept him on his own odd terms. Pemberton had spent his aversion to special cases before arriving at knowledge. When at last he did arrive his quandary was great. Against every interest he had attached himself. They would have to meet things together. Before they went home that evening at Nice the boy had said, clinging to his arm:

"Well, at any rate you'll hang on to the last."

"To the last?"

"Till you're fairly beaten."

"*You* ought to be fairly beaten!" cried the young man, drawing him closer.

A year after he had come to live with them Mr. and Mrs. Moreen suddenly gave up the villa at Nice. Pemberton had got used to suddenness, having seen it practised on a considerable scale during two jerky little tours—one in Switzerland the first summer, and the other late in the winter, when they all ran down to Florence and then, at the end of ten days, liking it much less than they had intended, straggled back in mysterious depression. They had returned to Nice "for ever," as they said; but this didn't prevent their squeezing, one rainy muggy May night, into a second-class railway carriage—you could never tell by which class they would travel—where Pemberton helped them to stow away a wonderful collection of bundles and bags. The explanation of this manoeuvre was that they had determined to spend the summer "in some bracing place", but in Paris they dropped into a small furnished apartment—a fourth floor in a third-rate avenue, where there was a smell on the staircase and the *portier* was hateful—and passed the next four months in blank indigence.

The better part of this baffled sojourn was for the preceptor and his pupil, who, visiting the Invalides and Notre Dame, the Conciergerie and all the museums, took a hundred remunerative rambles. They learned to know their Paris, which was useful, for they came back another year for a longer stay, the general character of which in Pemberton's memory today mixes pitiably and confusedly with that of the first. He sees Morgan's shabby knickerbockers—the everlasting pair that didn't match his blouse and that as he grew longer could only grow faded. He remembers the particular holes in his three or four pair of coloured stockings.

Morgan was dear to his mother, but he never was better dressed than was absolutely necessary—partly, no doubt, by his own fault, for he was as indifferent to his appearance as a German philosopher. "My dear fellow, you *are* coming to pieces," Pemberton would say to him in sceptical remonstrance; to which the child would reply, looking at him serenely up and down: "My dear fellow, so are you! I don't want to cast you in the shade." Pemberton could have no rejoinder for this—the assertion so closely represented the fact. If however the deficiencies of his own wardrobe were a chapter by themselves he didn't like his little charge to look too poor. Later he used to say, "Well, if we're poor, why, after all, shouldn't we look it?" and he consoled himself with thinking there was something rather elderly and gentlemanly in Morgan's disrepair—it differed from the untidiness of the urchin who plays and spoils his things. He could trace perfectly the degrees by which, in proportion as her little son confined himself to his tutor for society, Mrs. Moreen shrewdly forbore to renew his garments. She did nothing that didn't show, neglected him because he escaped notice, and then, as he illustrated this clever policy, discouraged at home his public appearances. Her position was logical enough—those members of her family who did show had to be showy.

During this period and several others Pemberton was quite aware of how he and his comrade might strike people; wandering languidly through the Jardin des Plantes as if they had nowhere to go, sitting on the winter days in the galleries of the Louvre, so splendidly ironical to the homeless, as if for the advantage of the *calorifère* [stove]. They joked about it sometimes: it was the sort of joke that was perfectly within the boy's compass. They figured themselves as part of the vast vague hand-to-mouth multitude of the enormous city and pretended they were

proud of their position in it—it showed them "such a lot of life" and made
them conscious of a democratic brotherhood. If Pemberton couldn't feel a
sympathy in destitution with his small companion—for after all Morgan's
fond parents would never have let him really suffer—the boy would at
least feel it with him, so it came to the same thing. He used sometimes
to wonder what people would think they were—to fancy they were
looked askance at, as if it might be a suspected case of kidnapping. Morgan wouldn't be taken for a young patrician with a preceptor—he wasn't
smart enough; though he might pass for his companion's sickly little
brother. Now and then he had a five-franc piece, and except once, when
they bought a couple of lovely neck-ties, one of which he made Pemberton accept, they laid it out scientifically in old books. This was sure to be
a great day, always spent on the quays, in a rummage of the dusty boxes
that garnish the parapets. Such occasions helped them to live, for their
books ran low very soon after the beginning of their acquaintance. Pemberton had a good many in England, but he was obliged to write to a
friend and ask him kindly to get some fellow to give him something for
them.

If they had to relinquish that summer the advantage of the bracing
climate the young man couldn't but suspect this failure of the cup when
at their very lips to have been the effect of a rude jostle of his own.
This had represented his first blow-out, as he called it, with his patrons;
his first successful attempt—though there was little other success about it
—to bring them to a consideration of his impossible position. As the ostensible eve of a costly journey the moment had struck him as favourable to
an earnest protest, the presentation of an ultimatum. Ridiculous as it
sounded, he had never yet been able to compass an uninterrupted private
interview with the elder pair or with either of them singly. They were
always flanked by their elder children, and poor Pemberton usually had
his own little charge at his side. He was conscious of its being a house
in which the surface of one's delicacy got rather smudged; nevertheless
he had preserved the bloom of his scruple against announcing to Mr. and
Mrs. Moreen with publicity that he shouldn't be able to go on longer
without a little money. He was still simple enough to suppose Ulick and
Paula and Amy might not know that since his arrival he had only had a
hundred and forty francs; and he was magnanimous enough to wish not
to compromise their parents in their eyes. Mr. Moreen now listened to
him, as he listened to every one and to every thing, like a man of the
world, and seemed to appeal to him—though not of course too grossly
—to try and be a little more of one himself. Pemberton recognized in fact

the importance of the character—from the advantage it gave Mr. Moreen. He was not even confused or embarrassed, whereas the young man in his service was more so than there was any reason for. Neither was he surprised—at least any more than a gentleman had to be who freely confessed himself a little shocked—though not perhaps strictly at Pemberton.

"We must go into this, mustn't we, dear?" he said to his wife. He assured his young friend that tho matter should have his very best attention; and he melted into space as elusively as if, at the door, he were taking an inevitable but deprecatory precedence. When, the next moment, Pemberton found himself alone with Mrs. Moreen it was to hear her say, "I see, I see"—stroking the roundness of her chin and looking as if she were only hesitating between a dozen easy remedies. If they didn't make their push Mr. Moreen could at least disappear for several days. During his absence his wife took up the subject again spontaneously, but her contribution to it was merely that she had thought all the while they were getting on so beautifully. Pemberton's reply to this revelation was that unless they immediately put down something on account he would leave them on the spot and for ever. He knew she would wonder how he would get away, and for a moment expected her to enquire. She didn't for which he was almost grateful to her, so little was he in a position to tell.

"You won't, you *know* you won't—you're too interested," she said. "You *are* interested, you know you are, you dear kind man!" She laughed with almost condemnatory archness, as if it were a reproach—though she wouldn't insist; and flirted a soiled pocket-handkerchief at him.

Pemberton's mind was fully made up to take his step the following week. This would give him time to get an answer to a letter he had dispatched to England. If he did in the event nothing of the sort—that is if he stayed another year and then went away only for three months—it was not merely because before the answer to his letter came (most unsatisfactory when it did arrive) Mr. Moreen generously counted out to him, and again with the sacrifice to "form" of a marked man of the world, three hundred francs in elegant ringing gold. He was irritated to find that Mrs. Moreen was right, that he couldn't at the pinch bear to leave the child. This stood out clearer for the very reason that, the night of his desperate appeal to his patrons, he had seen fully for the first time where he was. Wasn't it another proof of the success with which those patrons practised their arts that they had managed to avert for so long the illuminating flash? It descended on our friend with a breadth of effect which perhaps would have struck a spectator as comical, after he had returne

to his little servile room, which looked into a close court where a bare
dirty opposite wall took, with the sound of shrill clatter, the reflection
of lighted back windows. He had simply given himself away to a band
of adventurers. The idea, the word itself, wore a romantic horror for him
—he had always lived on such safe lines. Later it assumed a more interesting, almost a soothing, sense: it pointed a moral, and Pemberton
could enjoy a moral. The Moreens were adventurers not merely because
they didn't pay their debts, because they lived on society, but because
their whole view of life, dim and confused and instinctive, like that of
clever colour-blind animals, was speculative and rapacious and mean. Oh
they were "respectable," and that only made them more *immondes* [igno-
ble]! The young man's analysis, while he brooded, put it at last very simply—they were adventurers because they were toadies and snobs. That
was the completest account of them—it was the law of their being. Even
when this truth became vivid to their ingenious inmate he remained unconscious of how much his mind had been prepared for it by the extraordinary little boy who had now become such a complication in his life.
Much less could he then calculate on the information he was still to owe
the extraordinary little boy.

But it was during the ensuing time that the real problem came up—
the problem of how far it was excusable to discuss the turpitude of parents with a child of twelve, of thirteen, of fourteen. Absolutely inexcus-
able and quite impossible it of course at first appeared; and indeed the
question didn't press for some time after Pemberton had received his
three hundred francs. They produced a temporary lull, a relief from the
sharpest pressure. The young man frugally amended his wardrobe and
even had a few francs in his pocket. He thought the Moreens looked at
him as if he were almost too smart, as if they ought to take care not to
spoil him. If Mr. Moreen hadn't been such a man of the world he would
perhaps have spoken of the freedom of such neck-ties on the part of a
subordinate. But Mr. Moreen was always enough a man of the world to
let things pass—he had certainly shown that. It was singular how Pemberton guessed that Morgan, though saying nothing about it, knew something had happened. But three hundred francs, especially when one
owed money, couldn't last for ever; and when the treasure was gone—
the boy knew when it had failed—Morgan did break ground. The party
had returned to Nice at the beginning of the winter, but not to the
charming villa. They went to a hotel, where they stayed three months,
and then moved to another establishment, explaining that they had left

the first because, after waiting and waiting, they couldn't get the rooms they wanted. These apartments, the rooms they wanted, were generally very splendid; but fortunately they never *could* get them—fortunately, I mean, for Pemberton, who reflected always that if they had got them there would have been a still scanter educational fund. What Morgan said at last was said suddenly, irrelevantly, when the moment came, in the middle of a lesson, and consisted of the apparently unfeeling words: "You ought to *filer,* you know—you really ought."

Pemberton stared. He had learnt enough French slang from Morgan to know that to *filer* meant to cut sticks. "Ah my dear fellow, don't turn me off!"

Morgan pulled a Greek lexicon toward him—he used a Greek-German —to look out a word, instead of asking it of Pemberton. "You can't go on like this, you know."

"Like what, my boy?"

"You know they don't pay you up," said Morgan, blushing and turning his leaves.

"Don't pay me?" Pemberton stared again and feigned amazement. "What on earth put that into your head?"

"It has been there a long time," the boy replied, rummaging his book.

Pemberton was silent, then he went on: "I say, what are you hunting for? They pay me beautifully."

"I'm hunting for the Greek for awful whopper," Morgan dropped.

"Find that rather for gross impertinence and disabuse your mind. What do I want of money?"

"Oh, that's another question!"

Pemberton wavered—he was drawn in different ways. The severely correct thing would have been to tell the boy that such a matter was none of his business and bid him go on with his lines. But they were really too intimate for that; it was not the way he was in the habit of treating him; there had been no reason it should be. On the other hand Morgan had quite lighted on the truth—he really shouldn't be able to keep it up much longer; therefore why not let him know one's real motive for forsaking him? At the same time it wasn't decent to abuse to one's pupil the family of one's pupil; it was better to misrepresent than to do that. So in reply to his comrade's last exclamation he just declared, to dismiss the subject, that he had received several payments.

"I say—I say!" the boy ejaculated, laughing.

"That's all right," Pemberton insisted. "Give me your written rendering."

Morgan pushed a copybook across the table, and he began to read the page, but with something running in his head that made it no sense. Looking up after a minute or two he found the child's eyes fixed on him and felt in them something strange. Then Morgan said: "I'm not afraid of the stern reality."

"I haven't yet seen the thing you *are* afraid of—I'll do you that justice!"

This came out with a jump—it was perfectly true—and evidently gave Morgan pleasure. "I've thought of it a long time," he presently resumed.

"Well, don't think of it any more."

The boy appeared to comply, and they had a comfortable and even an amusing hour. They had a theory that they were very thorough, and yet they seemed always to be in the amusing part of lessons, the intervals between the dull dark tunnels, where there were waysides and jolly views. Yet the morning was brought to a violent end by Morgan's suddenly leaning his arms on the table, burying his head in them and bursting into tears: at which Pemberton was the more startled that, as it then came over him, it was the first time he had ever seen the boy cry and that the impression was consequently quite awful.

The next day, after much thought, he took a decision and, believing it to be just, immediately acted on it. He cornered Mr. and Mrs. Moreen again and let them know that if on the spot they didn't pay him all they owed him he wouldn't only leave their house but would tell Morgan exactly what had brought him to it.

"Oh you *haven't* told him?" cried Mrs. Moreen with a pacifying hand on her well-dressed bosom.

"Without warning you? For what do you take me?" the young man returned.

Mr. and Mrs. Moreen looked at each other; he could see that they appreciated, as tending to their security, his superstition of delicacy, and yet that there was a certain alarm in their relief. "My dear fellow," Mr. Moreen demanded, "what use *can* you have, leading the quiet life we all do, for such a lot of money?"—a question to which Pemberton made no answer, occupied as he was in noting that what passed in the mind of his patrons was something like: "Oh then, if we've felt that the child, dear little angel, has judged us and how he regards us, and we haven't been betrayed, he must have guessed—and in short it's *general!*" an inference that rather stirred up Mr. and Mrs. Moreen, as Pemberton had desired it should. At the same time, if he had supposed his threat would do something towards bringing them round, he was disappointed to find them taking for granted—how vulgar their perception *had* been!—that he had already given them away. There was a mystic uneasiness in their parental breasts, and that had been the inferior sense of it. None the less, however, his threat did touch them; for if they had escaped it was only to meet a new danger. Mr. Moreen appealed to him, on every precedent, as a man of the world; but his wife had recourse, for the first time since his domestication with them, to a fine *hauteur*, reminding him that a devoted mother, with her child, had arts that protected her against gross misrepresentation.

"I should misrepresent you grossly if I accused you of common honesty!" our friend replied; but as he closed the door behind him sharply, thinking he had not done himself much good, while Mr. Moreen lighted another cigarette, he heard his hostess shout after him more touchingly:

"Oh you do, you *do,* put the knife to one's throat!"

The next morning, very early, she came to his room. He recognized her knock, but had no hope she brought him money; as to which he was wrong, for she had fifty francs in her hand. She squeezed forward in her dressing-gown, and he received her in his own, between his bath-tub and his bed. He had been tolerably schooled by this time to the "foreign ways" of his hosts. Mrs. Moreen was ardent, and when she was ardent she didn't care what she did; so she now sat down on his bed, his clothes being on the chairs, and, in her preoccupation, forgot, as she glanced round, to be ashamed of giving him such a horrid room. What Mrs. Moreen's ardour now bore upon was the design of persuading him that in the first place she was very good-natured to bring him fifty francs, and that in the second, if he would only see it, he was really too absurd to expect to be *paid*. Wasn't he paid enough without perpetual money—wasn't he paid by the comfortable luxurious home he enjoyed with them all, without a care, an anxiety, a solitary want? Wasn't he sure of his position, and wasn't that everything to a young man like him, quite unknown, with singularly little to show, the ground of whose exorbitant pretensions it had never been easy to discover? Wasn't he paid above all by the sweet relation he had established with Morgan—quite ideal as from master to pupil—and by the simple privilege of knowing and living with so amazingly gifted a child; than whom really (and she meant literally what she said) there was no better company in Europe? Mrs. Moreen herself took to appealing to him as a man of the world; she said, "*Voyons, mon cher,*" and "My dear man, look here now"; and urged him to be reasonable, putting it before him that it was truly a chance for him. She spoke as if, according as he *should* be reasonable, he would prove himself worthy to be her son's tutor and of the extraordinary confidence they had placed in him.

After all, Pemberton reflected, it was only a difference of theory and the theory didn't matter much. They had hitherto gone on that of remunerated, as now they would go on that of gratuitous, service; but why should they have so many words about it? Mrs. Moreen at all events continued to be convincing; sitting there with her fifty francs she talked and reiterated as women reiterate, and bored and irritated him, while he leaned against the wall with his hands in the pockets of his wrapper, drawing it together round his legs and looking over the head of his visitor at the grey negations of his window. She wound up with saying: "You see I bring you a definite proposal."

"A definite proposal?"

"To make our relations regular, as it were—to put them on a comfortable footing."

"I see—it's a system," said Pemberton. "A kind of organized blackmail."

Mrs. Moreen bounded up, which was exactly what he wanted. "What do you mean by that?"

"You practise on one's fears—one's fears about the child if one should go away."

"And pray what would happen to him in that event?" she demanded with majesty.

"Why he'd be alone with *you.*"

"And pray with whom *should* a child be but with those whom he loves most?"

"If you think that, why don't you dismiss me?"

"Do you pretend he loves you more than he loves *us?*" cried Mrs. Moreen.

"I think he ought to. I make sacrifices for him. Though I've heard of those *you* make I don't see them."

Mrs. Moreen stared a moment; then with emotion she grasped her inmate's hand. "*Will* you make it—the sacrifice?"

He burst out laughing. "I'll see. I'll do what I can. I'll stay a little longer. Your calculation's just—I *do* hate intensely to give him up; I'm fond of him and he thoroughly interests me, in spite of the inconvenience I suffer. You know my situation perfectly. I haven't a penny in the world and, occupied as you see me with Morgan, am unable to earn money."

Mrs. Moreen tapped her undressed arm with her folded bank-note. "Can't you write articles? Can't you translate as *I* do?"

"I don't know about translating; it's wretchedly paid."

"I'm glad to earn what I can," said Mrs. Moreen with prodigious virtue.

"You ought to tell me who you do it for." Pemberton paused a moment, and she said nothing; so he added: "I've tried to turn off some little sketches, but the magazines won't have them—they're declined with thanks."

"You see then you're not such a phoenix," his visitor pointedly smiled —"to pretend to abilities you're sacrificing for our sake."

"I haven't time to do things properly," he ruefully went on. Then as it came over him that he was almost abjectly good-natured to give these explanations he added: "If I stay on longer it must be on one condition— that Morgan shall know distinctly on what footing I am."

Mrs. Moreen demurred. "Surely you don't want to show off to a child?"

"To show *you* off, do you mean?"

Again she cast about, but this time it was to produce a still finer flower. "And *you* talk of blackmail!"

"You can easily prevent it," said Pemberton.

"And *you* talk of practising on fears!" she bravely pushed on.

"Yes, there's no doubt I'm a great scoundrel."

His patroness met his eyes—it was clear she was in straits. Then she thrust out her money at him. "Mr. Moreen desired me to give you this on account."

"I'm much obliged to Mr. Moreen, but we *have* no account."

"You won't take it?"

"That leaves me more free," said Pemberton.

"To poison my darling's mind?" groaned Mrs. Moreen.

"Oh your darling's mind—!" the young man laughed.

She fixed him a moment, and he thought she was going to break out tormentedly, pleadingly: "For God's sake, tell me what *is* in it!" But she checked this impulse—another was stronger. She pocketed the money— the crudity of the alternative was comical—and swept out of the room with the desperate concession: "You may tell him any horror you like!"

A couple of days after this, during which he had failed to profit by so free a permission, he had been for a quarter of an hour walking with his charge in silence when the boy became sociable again with the remark: "I'll tell you how I know it; I know it through Zénobie."

"Zénobie? Who in the world is *she?*"

"A nurse I used to have—ever so many years ago. A charming woman. I liked her awfully, and she liked me."

"There's no accounting for tastes. What is it you know through her?"

"Why what their idea is. She went away because they didn't fork out. She did like me awfully, and she stayed two years. She told me all about it—that at last she could never get her wages. As soon as they saw how much she liked me they stopped giving her anything. They thought she'd stay for nothing—just *because*, don't you know?" And Morgan had a queer little conscious lucid look. "She did stay ever so long—as long as she could. She was only a poor girl. She used to send money to her mother. At last she couldn't afford it any longer, and went away in a fearful rage one night—I mean of course in a rage against *them*. She cried over me tremendously, she hugged me nearly to death. She told me all about it," the boy repeated. "She told me it was their idea. So I guessed, ever so long ago, that they have had the same idea with you."

"Zénobie was very sharp," said Pemberton. "And she made you so."

"Oh that wasn't Zénobie; that was nature. And experience!" Morgan laughed.

"Well, Zénobie was a part of your experience."

"Certainly I was a part of hers, poor dear!" the boy wisely sighed. "And I'm part of yours."

"A very important part. But I don't see how you know I've been treated like Zénobie."

"Do you take me for the biggest dunce you've known?" Morgan asked. "Haven't I been conscious of what we've been through together?"

"What we've been through?"

"Our privations—our dark days."

"Oh our days have been bright enough."

Morgan went on in silence for a moment. Then he said: "My dear chap, you're a hero!"

"Well, you're another!" Pemberton retorted.

"No, I'm not, but I ain't a baby. I won't stand it any longer. You must get some occupation that pays. I'm ashamed, I'm ashamed!" quavered the boy with a ring of passion, like some high silver note from a small cathedral chorister, that deeply touched his friend.

"We ought to go off and live somewhere together," the young man said.

"I'll go like a shot if you'll take me."

"I'd get some work that would keep us both afloat," Pemberton continued.

"So would I. Why shouldn't *I* work? I ain't such a beastly little muff as *that* comes to."

"The difficulty is that your parents wouldn't hear of it. They'd never part with you; they worship the ground you tread on. Don't you see the proof of it?" Pemberton developed. "They don't dislike me; they wish me no harm; they're very amiable people; but they're perfectly ready to expose me to any awkwardness in life for your sake."

The silence in which Morgan received his fond sophistry struck Pemberton somehow as expressive. After a moment the child repeated: "You *are* a hero!" Then he added: "They leave me with you altogether. You've all the responsibility. They put me off on you from morning till night. Why then should they object to my taking up with you completely? I'd help you."

"They're not particularly keen about my being helped, and they delight in thinking of you as *theirs*. They're tremendously proud of you."

"I'm not proud of *them*. But you know that," Morgan returned.

"Except for the little matter we speak of they're charming people," said Pemberton, not taking up the point made for his intelligence, but wondering greatly at the boy's own, and especially at this fresh reminder of something he had been conscious of from the first—the strangest thing in his friend's large little composition, a temper, a sensibility, even a private ideal, which made him as privately disown the stuff his people were made of. Morgan had in secret a small loftiness which made him acute about betrayed meanness; as well as a critical sense for the manners immediately surrounding him that was quite without precedent in a juvenile nature, especially when one noted that it had not made this nature "old-fashioned," as the word is of children—quaint or wizened or offensive. It was as if he had been a little gentleman and had paid the penalty by discovering that he was the only such person in his family. This comparison didn't make him vain, but it could make him melancholy and a trifle austere. While Pemberton guessed at these dim young things, shadows of shadows, he was partly drawn on and partly checked, as for a scruple, by the charm of attempting to sound the little cool shallows that were so quickly growing deeper. When he tried to figure to himself the morning twilight of childhood, so as to deal with it safely, he saw it was never fixed, never arrested, that ignorance, at the instant he touched it, was already flushing faintly into knowledge, that there was nothing that at a given moment you could say an intelligent child didn't know. It seemed to him that he himself knew too much to imagine Morgan's simplicity and too little to disembroil his tangle.

The boy paid no heed to his last remark; he only went on: "I'd have spoken to them about their idea, as I call it, long ago, if I hadn't been sure what they'd say."

"And what would they say?"

"Just what they said about what poor Zénobie told me—that it was a horrid dreadful story, that they had paid her every penny they owed her."

"Well, perhaps they had," said Pemberton.

"Perhaps they've paid you!"

"Let us pretend they have, and *n'en parlons plus* [speak no more about it]."

"They accused her of lying and cheating"—Morgan stuck to historic truth. "That's why I don't want to speak to them."

"Lest they should accuse me too?" To this Morgan made no answer, and his companion, looking down at him—the boy turned away his eyes, which had filled—saw that he couldn't have trusted himself to utter. "You're right. Don't worry them," Pemberton pursued. "Except for that, they *are* charming people."

"Except for *their* lying and *their* cheating?"

"I say—I say!" cried Pemberton, imitating a little tone of the lad's which was itself an imitation.

"We must be frank, at the last; we *must* come to an understanding," said Morgan with the importance of the small boy who lets himself think he is arranging great affairs—almost playing at shipwreck or at Indians. "I know all about everything."

"I dare say your father has his reasons," Pemberton replied, but too vaguely, as he was aware.

"For lying and cheating?"

"For saving and managing and turning his means to the best account. He has plenty to do with his money. You're an expensive family."

"Yes, I'm very expensive," Morgan concurred in a manner that made his preceptor burst out laughing.

"He's saving for *you*," said Pemberton. "They think of you in everything they do."

"He might, while he's about it, save a little—" The boy paused, and his friend waited to hear what. Then Morgan brought out oddly: "A little reputation."

"Oh there's plenty of that. That's all right!"

"Enough of it for the people they know, no doubt. The people they know are awful."

"Do you mean the princes? We mustn't abuse the princes."

"Why not? They haven't married Paula—they haven't married Amy. They only clean out Ulick."

"You *do* know everything!" Pemberton declared.

"No, I don't after all. I don't know what they live on, or how they live, or *why* they live! What have they got and how did they get it? Are they rich, are they poor, or have they a *modeste aisance* [moderate wherewithal]? Why are they always chiveying me about—living one year like ambassadors and the next like paupers? Who are they, anyway, and what are they? I've thought of all that—I've thought of a lot of things. They're so beastly worldly. That's what I hate most—oh, I've *seen* it! All they care about is to make an appearance and to pass for something or other. What the dickens do they want to pass for? What *do* they, Mr. Pemberton?"

"You pause for a reply," said Pemberton, treating the question as a joke, yet wondering too and greatly struck with his mate's intense if imperfect vision. "I haven't the least idea."

"And what good does it do? Haven't I seen the way people treat them —the 'nice' people, the ones they want to know? They'll take anything from them—they'll lie down and be trampled on. The nice ones hate that —they just sicken them. You're the only really nice person we know."

"Are you sure? They don't lie down for me!"

"Well, you shan't lie down for them. You've got to go—that's what you've got to do," said Morgan.

"And what will become of you?"

"Oh I'm growing up. I shall get off before long. I'll see you later."

"You had better let me finish you," Pemberton urged, lending himself to the child's strange superiority.

Morgan stopped in their walk, looking up at him. He had to look up much less than a couple of years before—he had grown, in his loose leanness, so long and high. "Finish me?" he echoed.

"There are such a lot of jolly things we can do together yet I want to turn you out—I want you to do me credit."

Morgan continued to look at him. "To give you credit—do you mean?"

"My dear fellow, you're too clever to live."

"That's just what I'm afraid you think. No, no; it isn't fair—I can't endure it. We'll separate next week. The sooner it's over the sooner to sleep."

"If I hear of anything—any other chance—I promise to go," Pemberton said.

Morgan consented to consider this. "But you'll be honest," he demanded; "you won't pretend you haven't heard?"

"I'm much more likely to pretend I have."

"But what can you hear of, this way, stuck in a hole with us? You ought to be on the spot, to go to England—you ought to go to America."

"One would think you were *my* tutor!" said Pemberton.

Morgan walked on and after a little had begun again: "Well, now that you know I know and that we look at the facts and keep nothing back—it's much more comfortable, isn't it?"

"My dear boy, it's so amusing, so interesting, that it will surely be quite impossible for me to forego such hours as these."

This made Morgan stop once more. "You *do* keep something back. Oh you're not straight—*I* am!"

"How am I not straight?"

"Oh you've got your idea!"

"My idea?"

"Why that I probably shan't make old—make older—bones, and that you can stick it out till I'm removed."

"You *are* too clever to live!" Pemberton repeated.

"I call it a mean idea," Morgan pursued. "But I shall punish you by the way I hang on."

"Look out or I'll poison you!" Pemberton laughed.

"I'm stronger and better every year. Haven't you noticed that there hasn't been a doctor near me since you came?"

"*I'm* your doctor," said the young man, taking his arm and drawing him tenderly on again.

Morgan proceeded and after a few steps gave a sigh of mingled weariness and relief. "Ah, now that we look at the facts it's all right!"

They looked at the facts a good deal after this; and one of the first consequences of their doing so was that Pemberton stuck it out, in his friend's parlance, for the purpose. Morgan made the facts so vivid and so droll, and at the same time so bald and so ugly, that there was fascination in talking them over with him, just as there would have been heartlessness in leaving him alone with them. Now that the pair had such perceptions in common it was useless for them to pretend they didn't judge such people; but the very judgment and the exchange of perceptions created another tie. Morgan had never been so interesting as now that he himself was made plainer by the sidelight of these confidences. What came out in it most was the small fine passion of his pride. He had plenty of that, Pemberton felt—so much that one might perhaps wisely wish for it some early bruises. He would have liked his people to have a spirit and had waked up to the sense of their perpetually eating humble pie. His mother would consume any amount, and his father would consume even more than his mother. He had a theory that Ulick had wriggled out of an "affair" at Nice: there had once been a flurry at home, a regular panic, after which they all went to bed and took medicine, not to be accounted for on any other supposition. Morgan had a romantic imagination, fed by poetry and history, and he would have liked those who "bore his name"—as he used to say to Pemberton with the humour that made his queer delicacies manly—to carry themselves with an air. But their one idea was to get in with people who didn't want them and to take snubs as if they were honourable scars. Why people didn't want them more he didn't know—that was people's own affair; after all they weren't superficially repulsive, they were a hundred times cleverer than most of the dreary grandees, the "poor swells" they rushed about Europe to catch up with. "After all they *are* amusing—they are!" he used to pronounce with the wisdom of the ages. To which Pemberton always replied: "Amusing—the great Moreen troupe? Why they're altogether delightful; and if it weren't for the hitch that you and I (feeble performers!) make in the *ensemble* they'd carry everything before them."

What the boy couldn't get over was the fact that this particular blight seemed, in a tradition of self-respect, so undeserved and so arbitrary. No doubt people had a right to take the line they liked; but why should *his* people have liked the line of pushing and toadying and lying and cheating? What had their forefathers—all decent folk, so far as he knew —done to them, or what had *he* done to them? Who had poisoned their blood with the fifth-rate social ideal, the fixed idea of making smart acquaintances and getting into the *monde chic* [fashionable world], especially when it was foredoomed to failure and exposure? They showed so what they were after; that was what made the people they wanted not want *them*. And never a wince for dignity, never a throb of shame at looking each other in the face, never any independence or resentment or disgust. If his father or his brother would only knock some one down once or twice a year! Clever as they were they never guessed the impression they made. They were good-natured, yes—as good-natured as Jews at the doors of clothing shops! But was that the model one wanted one's family to follow? Morgan had dim memories of an old grandfather, the maternal, in New York, whom he had been taken across the ocean at the age of five to see: a gentleman with a high neckcloth and a good deal of pronunciation, who wore a dress-coat in the morning, which made one wonder what he wore in the evening, and had, or was supposed to have, "property" and something to do with the Bible Society. It couldn't have been but that *he* was a good type. Pemberton himself remembered Mrs. Clancy, a widowed sister of Mr. Moreen's, who was as irritating as a moral

tale and had paid a fortnight's visit to the family at Nice shortly after he
came to live with them. She was "pure and refined," as Amy said over
the banjo, and had the air of not knowing what they meant when they
talked, and of keeping something rather important back. Pemberton
judged that what she kept back was an approval of many of their ways;
therefore it was to be supposed that she too was of a good type, and that
Mr. and Mrs. Moreen and Ulick and Paula and Amy might easily have
been of a better one if they would.

But that they wouldn't was more and more perceptible from day to
day. They continued to "chivey," as Morgan called it, and in due time
became aware of a variety of reasons for proceeding to Venice. They
mentioned a great many of them—they were always strikingly frank and
had the brightest friendly chatter, at the late foreign breakfast in especial, before the ladies had made up their faces, when they leaned their
arms on the table, had something to follow the *demi-tasse,* and, in the
heat of familiar discussion as to what they "really ought" to do, fell
inevitably into the languages in which they could *tutoyer.*[1] Even Pemberton liked them then; he could endure even Ulick when he heard him
give his little flat voice for the "sweet sea-city." That was what made him
have a sneaking kindness for them—that they were so out of the workaday world and kept him so out of it. The summer had waned when, with
cries of ecstasy, they all passed out on the balcony that overhung the
Grand Canal. The sunsets then were splendid and the Dorringtons had
arrived. The Dorringtons were the only reason they hadn't talked of at
breakfast; but the reasons they didn't talk of at breakfast always came
out in the end. The Dorringtons on the other hand came out very little;
or else when they did they stayed—as was natural—for hours, during
which periods Mrs. Moreen and the girls sometimes called at their hotel
(to see if they had returned) as many as three times running. The gon-
dola was for the ladies, as in Venice too there were "days," which Mrs.
Moreen knew in their order an hour after she arrived. She immediately
took one herself, to which the Dorringtons never came, though on a certain occasion when Pemberton and his pupil were together at Saint
Mark's—where, taking the best walks they had ever had and haunting a
hundred churches, they spent a great deal of time—they saw the old
lord turn up with Mr. Moreen and Ulick, who showed him the dim ba-
silica as if it belonged to them. Pemberton noted how much less, among
its curiosities, Lord Dorrington carried himself as a man of the world;

1. Address one another in the familiar second person; *e.g.,* French *tu,* German
du [Ed.].

wondering too whether, for such services, his companions took a fee from him. The autumn at any rate waned, the Dorringtons departed, and Lord Verschoyle, the eldest son, had proposed neither for Amy nor for Paula.

One sad November day, while the wind roared round the old palace and the rain lashed the lagoon, Pemberton, for exercise and even somewhat for warmth—the Moreens were horribly frugal about fires; It was a cause of suffering to their inmate—walked up and down the big bare *sala* with his pupil. The scagliola floor was cold, the high battered casements shook in the storm, and the stately decay of the place was unrelieved by a particle of furniture. Pemberton's spirits were low, and it came over him that the fortune of the Moreens was now even lower. A blast of desolation, a portent of disgrace and disaster, seemed to draw through the comfortless hall. Mr. Moreen and Ulick were in the Piazza, looking out for something, strolling drearily, in mackintoshes, under the arcades; but still, in spite of mackintoshes, unmistakable men of the world. Paula and Amy were in bed—it might have been thought they were staying there to keep warm. Pemberton looked askance at the boy at his side, to see to what extent he was conscious of these dark omens. But Morgan, luckily for him, was now mainly conscious of growing taller and stronger and indeed of being in his fifteenth year. This fact was intensely interesting to him and the basis of a private theory—which, however, he had imparted to his tutor—that in a little while he should stand on his own feet. He considered that the situation would change—that in short he should be "finished," grown up, producible in the world of affairs and ready to prove himself of sterling ability. Sharply as he was capable at times of analysing, as he called it, his life, there were happy hours when he remained, as he also called it—and as the name, really, of their right ideal—"jolly" superficial; the proof of which was his fundamental assumption that he should presently go to Oxford, to Pemberton's college, and aided and abetted by Pemberton, do the most wonderful things. It depressed the young man to see how little in such a project he took account of ways and means: in other connections he mostly kept to the measure. Pemberton tried to imagine the Moreens at Oxford and fortunately failed; yet unless they were to adopt it as a residence there would be no *modus vivendi* for Morgan. How could he live without an allowance, and where was the allowance to come from? He, Pemberton, might live on Morgan; but how could Morgan live on *him*? What was to become of him anyhow? Somehow the fact that he was a big boy now, with better prospects of health, made the question of his future more difficult. So long as he was markedly frail the great consideration he inspired seemed enough of an answer to it. But at the bottom of Pemberton's heart was the recognition of his probably being strong enough to live and not yet strong enough to struggle or to thrive. Morgan himself at any rate was in the first flush of the rosiest consciousness of adolescence, so that the beating of the tempest seemed to him after all but the voice of life and the challenge of fate. He had on his shabby little overcoat, with the collar up, but was enjoying his walk.

It was interrupted at last by the appearance of his mother at the end of the *sala*. She beckoned him to come to her, and while Pemberton saw him, complaisant, pass down the long vista and over the damp false marble, he wondered what was in the air. Mrs. Moreen said a word to the boy and made him go into the room she had quitted. Then, having closed the door after him, she directed her steps swiftly to Pemberton. There *was* something in the air, but his wildest flight of fancy wouldn't have suggested what it proved to be. She signified that she had made a pretext to get Morgan out of the way, and then she enquired—without hesitation—if the young man could favour her with the loan of three louis. While, before bursting into a laugh, he stared at her with surprise, she declared that she was awfully pressed for the money; she was desperate for it—it would save her life.

"Dear lady, *c'est trop fort* [this is too much]!" Pemberton laughed in the manner and with the borrowed grace of idiom that marked the best colloquial, the best anecdotic, moments of his friends themselves. "Where in the world do you suppose I should get three louis, *du train dont vous allez* [at the rate you're going]?"

"I thought you worked—wrote things. Don't they pay you?"

"Not a penny."

"Are you such a fool as to work for nothing?"

"You ought surely to know that."

Mrs. Moreen stared, then she coloured a little. Pemberton saw she had quite forgotten the terms—if "terms" they could be called—that he had ended by accepting from herself; they had burdened her memory as little as her conscience. "Oh yes, I see what you mean—you've been very nice about that; but why drag it in so often?" She had been perfectly urbane with him ever since the rough scene of explanation in his room the morning he made her accept *his* "terms"—the necessity of his making his case known to Morgan. She had felt no resentment after seeing there was no danger Morgan would take the matter up with her. Indeed, attributing this immunity to the good taste of his influence with the boy, she had once said to Pemberton, "My dear fellow, it's an immense comfort you're a gentleman." She repeated this in substance now. "Of course you're a gentleman—that's a bother the less!" Pemberton reminded her that he had not "dragged in" anything that wasn't already in as much as his foot was in his shoe; and she also repeated her prayer that, somewhere and somehow, he would find her sixty francs. He took the liberty of hinting that if he could find them it wouldn't be to lend them to *her*—as to which he consciously did himself injustice, knowing that if he had them he would certainly put them at her disposal. He accused himself, at bottom and not unveraciously, of a fantastic, a demoralized sympathy with her. If misery made strange bedfellows it also made strange sympathies. It was moreover a part of the abasement of living with such people that one had to make vulgar retorts, quite out of one's own tradition of good manners. "Morgan, Morgan, to what pass have I come for you?" he groaned while Mrs. Moreen floated voluminously down the *sala* again to liberate the boy, wailing as she went that everything was too odious.

Before their young friend was liberated there came a thump at the door communicating with the staircase, followed by the apparition of a dripping youth who poked in his head. Pemberton recognized him as the bearer of a telegram and recognized the telegram as addressed to himself. Morgan came back as, after glancing at the signature—that of a relative in London—he was reading the words: "Found jolly job for you, engagement to coach opulent youth on own terms. Come at once." The answer happily was paid and the messenger waited. Morgan. who had drawn near, waited too and looked hard at Pemberton; and Pemberton, after a moment, having met his look, handed him the telegram. It was really by wise looks—they knew each other so well now—that, while the telegraph boy, in his waterproof cape, made a great puddle on the floor, the thing was settled between them. Pemberton wrote the answer with a pencil against the frescoed wall, and the messenger departed. When he had gone the young man explained himself.

"I'll make a tremendous charge; I'll earn a lot of money in a short time, and we'll live on it."

"Well, I hope the opulent youth will be a dismal dunce—he probably will," Morgan parenthesized—"and keep you a long time a-hammering of it in."

"Of course the longer he keeps me the more we shall have for our old age."

"But suppose *they* don't pay you!" Morgan awfully suggested.

"Oh, there are not two such—!" But Pemberton pulled up; he had been on the point of using too invidious a term. Instead of this he said "Two such fatalities."

Morgan flushed—the tears came to his eyes. "*Dites toujours* [go ahead and say] two such rascally crews!" Then in a different tone he added: "Happy opulent youth!"

"Not if he's a dismal dunce."

"Oh, they're happier then. But you can't have everything, can you?" the boy smiled.

Pemberton held him fast, hands on his shoulders—he had never loved him so. "What will become of *you,* what will you do?" He thought of Mrs. Moreen, desperate for sixty francs.

"I shall become an *homme fait* [grown-up man]." And then as if he recognized all the bearings of Pemberton's allusion: "I shall get on with them better when you're not here."

"Ah don't say that—it sounds as if I set you against them!"

"You do—the sight of you. It's all right; you know what I mean. I shall be beautiful. I'll take their affairs in hand; I'll marry my sisters."

"You'll marry yourself!" joked Pemberton; as high, rather tense pleasantry would evidently be the right, or the safest, tone for their separation.

It was, however, not purely in this strain that Morgan suddenly asked: "But I say—how will you get to your jolly job? You'll have to telegraph to the opulent youth for money to come on."

Pemberton bethought himself. "They won't like that, will they?"

"Oh look out for them!"

Then Pemberton brought out his remedy. "I'll go to the American Consul; I'll borrow some money of him—just for the few days, on the strength of the telegram."

Morgan was hilarious. "Show him the telegram—then collar the money and stay!"

Pemberton entered into the joke sufficiently to reply that for Morgan he was really capable of that; but the boy, growing more serious, and to prove he hadn't meant what he said, not only hurried him off to the Consulate—since he was to start that evening, as he had wired to his friend—but made sure of their affair by going with him. They splashed through the tortuous perforations and over the hump-backed bridges, and they passed through the Piazza, where they saw Mr. Moreen and Ulick go into a jeweller's shop. The Consul proved accommodating—Pemberton said it wasn't the letter, but Morgan's grand air—and on their way back they went into Saint Mark's for a hushed ten minutes. Later they took up and kept up the fun of it to the very end; and it seemed to Pemberton a part of that fun that Mrs. Moreen, who was very angry when he had announced her his intention, should charge him, grotesquely and vulgarly and in reference to the loan she had vainly endeavoured to effect, with bolting lest they should "get something out" of him. On the other hand he had to do Mr. Moreen and Ulick the justice to recognize that when on coming in *they* heard the cruel news they took it like perfect men of the world.

When he got at work with the opulent youth, who was to be taken in hand for Balliol, he found himself unable to say if this aspirant had really such poor parts or if the appearance were only begotten of his own long association with an intensely living little mind. From Morgan he heard half a dozen times: the boy wrote charming young letters, a patchwork of tongues, with indulgent postscripts in the family Volapuk and, in little squares and rounds and crannies of the text, the drollest illustrations—letters that he was divided between the impulse to show his present charge as a vain, a wasted incentive, and the sense of something in them that publicity would profane. The opulent youth went up in due course and failed to pass; but it seemed to add to the presumption that brilliancy was not expected of him all at once that his parents, condoning the lapse, which they good-naturedly treated as little as possible as if it were Pemberton's, should have sounded the rally again, begged the young coach to renew the siege.

The young coach was now in a position to lend Mrs. Moreen three louis, and he sent her a post-office order even for a larger amount. In return for his favour he received a frantic scribbled line from her: "Implore you to come back instantly—Morgan dreadfully ill." They were on the rebound, once more in Paris—often as Pemberton had seen them depressed he had never seen them crushed—and communication was therefore rapid. He wrote to the boy to ascertain the state of his health, but awaited the answer in vain. He accordingly, after three days, took an abrupt leave of the opulent youth and, crossing the Channel, alighted at the small hotel, in the quarter of the Champs Élysées, of which Mrs. Moreen had given him the address. A deep if dumb dissatisfaction with this lady and her companions bore him company: they couldn't be vulgarly honest, but they could live at hotels, in velvety entresols, amid a smell of burnt pastilles, surrounded by the most expensive city in Europe. When he had left them in Venice it was with an irrepressible suspicion that something was going to happen; but the only thing that could have taken place was again their masterly retreat. "How is he? where is he?" he asked of Mrs. Moreen; but before she could speak these questions were answered by the pressure round his neck of a pair of arms, in shrunken sleeves, which still were perfectly capable of an effusive young foreign squeeze.

"Dreadfully ill—I don't see it!" the young man cried. And then to Morgan: "Why on earth didn't you relieve me? Why didn't you answer my letter?"

Mrs. Moreen declared that when she wrote he was very bad, and Pemberton learned at the same time from the boy that he had answered every letter he had received. This led to the clear inference that Pemberton's note had been kept from him so that the game to be practised should not be interfered with. Mrs. Moreen was prepared to see the fact exposed, as Pemberton saw the moment he faced her that she was prepared for a good many other things. She was prepared above all to maintain that she had acted from a sense of duty, that she was enchanted she had got him over, whatever they might say, and that it was useless of him to pretend he didn't know in all his bones that his place at such a time was with Morgan. He had taken the boy away from them and now had no right to abandon him. He had created for himself the gravest responsibilities and must at least abide by what he had done.

"Taken him away from you?" Pemberton exclaimed indignantly.

"Do it—do it for pity's sake; that's just what I want. I can't stand *this* —and such scenes. They're awful frauds—poor dears!" These words broke from Morgan, who had intermitted his embrace, in a key which made Pemberton turn quickly to him and see that he had suddenly seated himself, was breathing in great pain and was very pale.

"*Now* do you say he's not in a state, my precious pet?" shouted his mother, dropping on her knees before him with clasped hands, but touching him no more than if he had been a gilded idol. "It will pass—it's only for an instant; but don't say such dreadful things!"

"I'm all right—all right," Morgan panted to Pemberton, whom he sat looking up at with a strange smile, his hands resting on either side on the sofa.

"Now do you pretend I've been dishonest, that I've deceived?" Mrs. Moreen flashed at Pemberton as she got up.

"It isn't *he* says it, it's I!" the boy returned, apparently easier but sinking back against the wall; while his restored friend, who had sat down beside him, took his hand and bent over him.

"Darling child, one does what one can; there are so many things to consider," urged Mrs. Moreen. "It's his *place*—his only place. You see *you* think it is now."

"Take me away—take me away," Morgan went on, smiling to Pemberton with his white face.

"Where shall I take you, and how—oh *how*, my boy?" the young man stammered, thinking of the rude way in which his friends in London held that, for his convenience, with no assurance of prompt return, he had thrown them over; of the just resentment with which they would already have called in a successor, and of the scant help to finding fresh employment that resided for him in the grossness of his having failed to pass his pupil.

"Oh, we'll settle that. You used to talk about it," said Morgan. "If we can only go all the rest's a detail."

"Talk about it as much as you like, but don't think you can attempt it. Mr. Moreen would never consent—it would be so *very* hand to mouth," Pemberton's hostess beautifully explained to him. Then to Morgan she made it clearer: "It would destroy our peace, it would break our hearts. Now that he's back it will be all the same again. You'll have your life, your work and your freedom, and we'll all be happy as we used to be. You'll bloom and grow perfectly well, and we won't have any more silly experiments, will we? They're too absurd. It's Mr. Pemberton's place— every one in his place. You in yours, your papa in his, me in mine— *n'est-ce pas, chéri* [isn't that so, my dear]? We'll all forget how foolish we've been and have lovely times."

She continued to talk and to surge vaguely about the little draped stuffy salon while Pemberton sat with the boy, whose colour gradually came back; and she mixed up her reasons, hinting that there were going to be changes, that the other children might scatter (who knew?—Paula had her ideas) and that then it might be fancied how much the poor old parent birds would want the little nestling. Morgan looked at Pemberton, who wouldn't let him move; and Pemberton knew exactly how he felt at hearing himself called a little nestling. He admitted that he had had one or two bad days, but he protested afresh against the wrong of his mother's having made them the ground of an appeal to poor Pemberton. Poor Pemberton could laugh now, apart from the comicality of Mrs. Moreen's mustering so much philosophy for her defence—she seemed to shake it out of her agitated petticoats, which knocked over the light gilt chairs—so little did their young companion, *marked*, unmistakably marked at the best, strike him as qualified to repudiate any advantage.

He himself was in for it at any rate. He should have Morgan on his hands again indefinitely; though indeed he saw the lad had a private theory to produce which would be intended to smooth this down. He was obliged to him for it in advance; but the suggested amendment didn't keep his heart rather from sinking, any more than it prevented him from accepting the prospect on the spot, with some confidence moreover that he should do even better if he could have a little supper. Mrs. Moreen threw out more hints about the changes that were to be looked for, but she was such a mixture of smiles and shudders—she confessed she was very nervous—that he couldn't tell if she were in high feather or only in hysterics. If the family was really at last going to pieces why shouldn't she recognize the necessity of pitching Morgan into some sort of life-boat? This presumption was fostered by the fact that they were established in luxurious quarters in the capital of pleasure; that was exactly where they naturally *would* be established in view of going to pieces. Moreover didn't she mention that Mr. Moreen and the others were enjoying themselves at the opera with Mr. Granger, and wasn't *that* also precisely where one would look for them on the eve of a smash? Pemberton gathered that Mr. Granger was a rich vacant American—a big bill with a flourishy heading and no items; so that one of Paula's "ideas" was probably that this time she hadn't missed fire—by which straight shot indeed she would have shattered the general cohesion. And if the cohesion was to crumble what would become of poor Pemberton? He felt quite enough bound up with them to figure to his alarm as a dislodged block in the edifice.

It was Morgan who eventually asked if no supper had been ordered for him; sitting with him below, later, at the dim delayed meal, in the presence of a great deal of corded green plush, a plate of ornamental biscuit and an aloofness marked on the part of the waiter. Mrs. Moreen had explained that they had been obliged to secure a room for the visitor out of the house; and Morgan's consolation—he offered it while Pemberton reflected on the nastiness of lukewarm sauces—proved to be, largely, that this circumstance would facilitate their escape. He talked of their escape —recurring to it often afterwards—as if they were making up a "boy's book" together. But he likewise expressed his sense that there was something in the air, that the Moreens couldn't keep it up much longer. In point of fact, as Pemberton was to see, they kept it up for five or six months. All the while, however, Morgan's contention was designed to cheer him. Mr. Moreen and Ulick, whom he had met the day after his return, accepted that return like perfect men of the world. If Paula and Amy treated it even with less formality an allowance was to be made for them, inasmuch as Mr. Granger hadn't come to the opera after all. He had only placed his box at their service, with a bouquet for each of the party; there was even one apiece, embittering the thought of his profusion, for Mr. Moreen and Ulick. "They're all like that," was Morgan's comment; "at the very last, just when we think we've landed them they're back in the deep sea!"

Morgan's comments in these days were more and more free; they even included a large recognition of the extraordinary tenderness with which he had been treated while Pemberton was away. Oh yes, they couldn't do enough to be nice to him, to show him they had him on their mind and make up for his loss. That was just what made the whole thing so sad and caused him to rejoice after all in Pemberton's return—he had to keep thinking of their affection less, had less sense of obligation. Pemberton laughed out at this last reason, and Morgan blushed and said "Well, dash it, you know what I mean." Pemberton knew perfectly what he meant; but there were a good many things that—dash it too!—it didn't make any clearer. This episode of his second sojourn in Paris stretched itself out wearily, with their resumed readings and wanderings and maunderings, their potterings on the quays, their hauntings of the museums, their occasional lingerings in the Palais Royal when the first sharp weather came on and there was a comfort in warm emanations, before Chevet's wonderful succulent window. Morgan wanted to hear all about the opulent youth—he took an immense interest in him. Some of the details of his opulence—Pemberton could spare him none of them—evidently fed the boy's appreciation of all his friend had given up to come back to him; but in addition to the greater reciprocity established by that heroism he had always his little brooding theory, in which there was a frivolous gaiety too, that their long probation was drawing to a close. Morgan's conviction that the Moreens couldn't go on much longer kept pace with the unexpended impetus with which, from month to month, they did go on. Three weeks after Pemberton had rejoined them they went on to another hotel, a dingier one than the first; but Morgan rejoiced that his tutor had at least still not sacrificed the advantage of a room outside. He clung to the romantic utility of this when the day, or rather the night, should arrive for their escape.

For the first time, in this complicated connection, our friend felt his collar gall him. It was, as he had said to Mrs. Moreen in Venice, *trop fort*—everything was *trop fort*. He could neither really throw off his blighting burden nor find in it the benefit of a pacified conscience or of a rewarded affection. He had spent all the money accruing to him in Eng-

land, and he saw his youth going and that he was getting nothing back
for it. It was all very well of Morgan to count it for reparation that he
should now settle on him permanently—there was an irritating flaw in
such a view. He saw what the boy had in his mind; the conception that
as his friend had had the generosity to come back he must show his
gratitude by giving him his life. But the poor friend didn't desire the gift
—what could he do with Morgan's dreadful little life? Of course at the
same time that Pemberton was irritated he remembered the reason,
which was very honourable to Morgan and which dwelt simply in his
making one so forget that he was no more than a patched urchin. If one
dealt with him on a different basis one's misadventures were one's own
fault. So Pemberton waited in a queer confusion of yearning and alarm
for the catastrophe which was held to hang over the house of Moreen, of
which he certainly at moments felt the symptoms brush his cheek and as
to which he wondered much in what form it would find its liveliest effect.

Perhaps it would take the form of sudden dispersal—a frightened
sauve qui peut [rout], a scuttling into selfish corners. Certainly they
were less elastic than of yore; they were evidently looking for something
they didn't find. The Dorringtons hadn't reappeared, the princes had
scattered; wasn't that the beginning of the end? Mrs. Moreen had lost her
reckoning of the famous "days"; her social calendar was blurred—it had
turned its face to the wall. Pemberton suspected that the great, the cruel
discomfiture had been the unspeakable behaviour of Mr. Granger, who
seemed not to know what he wanted, or, what was much worse, what
they wanted. He kept sending flowers, as if to bestrew the path of his retreat, which was never the path of a return. Flowers were all very well,
but—Pemberton could complete the proposition. It was now positively
conspicuous that in the long run the Moreens were a social failure; so that
the young man was almost grateful the run had not been short. Mr.
Moreen indeed was still occasionally able to get away on business and,
what was more surprising, was likewise able to get back. Ulick had no
club, but you couldn't have discovered it from his appearance, which was
as much as ever that of a person looking at life from the window of
such an institution; therefore Pemberton was doubly surprised at an answer he once heard him make his mother in the desperate tone of a man
familiar with the worst privations. Her question Pemberton had not quite
caught; it appeared to be an appeal for a suggestion as to whom they
might get to take Amy. "Let the Devil take her!" Ulick snapped; so that
Pemberton could see that they had not only lost their amiability but had
ceased to believe in themselves. He could also see that if Mrs. Moreen

was trying to get people to take her children she might be regarded as closing the hatches for the storm. But Morgan would be the last she would part with.

One winter afternoon—it was a Sunday—he and the boy walked far together in the Bois de Boulogne. The evening was so splendid, the cold lemon-coloured sunset so clear, the stream of carriages and pedestrians so amusing and the fascination of Paris so great that they stayed out later than usual and became aware that they should have to hurry home to arrive in time for dinner. They hurried accordingly, arm-in-arm, good-humoured and hungry, agreeing that there was nothing like Paris after all and that after everything too that had come and gone they were not yet sated with innocent pleasures. When they reached the hotel they found that, though scandalously late, they were in time for all the dinner they were likely to sit down to. Confusion reigned in the apartments of the Moreens—very shabby ones this time, but the best in the house—and before the interrupted service of the table, with objects displaced almost as if there had been a scuffle and a great wine stain from an overturned bottle, Pemberton couldn't blink the fact that there had been a scene of the last proprietary firmness. The storm had come—they were all seeking refuge. The hatches were down, Paula and Amy were invisible —they had never tried the most casual art upon Pemberton, but he felt they had enough of an eye to him not to wish to meet him as young ladies whose frocks had been confiscated—and Ulick appeared to have jumped overboard. The host and his staff, in a word, had ceased to "go on" at the pace of their guests, and the air of embarrassed detention, thanks to a pile of gaping trunks in the passage, was strangely commingled with the air of indignant withdrawal.

When Morgan took all this in—and he took it in very quickly—he coloured to the roots of his hair. He had walked from his infancy among difficulties and dangers, but he had never seen a public exposure. Pemberton noticed in a second glance at him that the tears had rushed into his eyes and that they were tears of a new and untasted bitterness. He wondered an instant, for the boy's sake, whether he might successfully pretend not to understand. Not successfully, he felt, as Mr. and Mrs. Moreen, dinnerless by their extinguished hearth, rose before him in their little dishonoured salon, casting about with glassy eyes for the nearest port in such a storm. They were not prostrate but were horribly white, and Mrs. Moreen had evidently been crying. Pemberton quickly learned however that her grief was not for the loss of her dinner, much as she usually enjoyed it, but the fruit of a blow that struck even deeper, as she made all haste to explain. He would see for himself, so far as that went, how the great change had come, the dreadful bolt had fallen, and how they would now all have to turn themselves about. Therefore cruel as it was to them to part with their darling she must look to him to carry a little further the influence he had so fortunately acquired with the boy —to induce his young charge to follow him into some modest retreat. They depended on him—that was the fact—to take their delightful child temporarily under his protection: it would leave Mr. Moreen and herself so much more free to give the proper attention (too little, alas! had been given) to the readjustment of their affairs.

"We trust you—we feel we *can*," said Mrs. Moreen, slowly rubbing her plump white hands and looking with compunction hard at Morgan, whose chin, not to take liberties, her husband stroked with a tentative paternal forefinger.

"Oh yes—we feel that we *can*. We trust Mr. Pemberton fully, Morgan," Mr. Moreen pursued.

Pemberton wondered again if he might pretend not to understand; but everything good gave way to the intensity of Morgan's understanding. "Do you mean he may take me to live with him for ever and ever?" cried the boy. "May take me away, away, anywhere he likes?"

"For ever and ever? *Comme vous-y-allez* [How you go on]!" Mr. Moreen laughed indulgently. "For as long as Mr. Pemberton may be so good."

"We've struggled, we've suffered," his wife went on; "but you've made him so your own that we've already been through the worst of the sacrifice."

Morgan had turned away from his father—he stood looking at Pemberton with a light in his face. His sense of shame for their common humiliated state had dropped; the case had another side—the thing was to clutch at *that*. He had a moment of boyish joy, scarcely mitigated by the reflection that with this unexpected consecration of his hope—too sudden and too violent; the turn taken was away from a *good* boy's book—the "escape" was left on their hands. The boyish joy was there an instant, and Pemberton was almost scared at the rush of gratitude and affection that broke through his first abasement. When he stammered "My dear fellow, what do you say to *that?*" how could one not say something enthusiastic? But there was more need for courage at something else that immediately followed and that made the lad sit down quickly on the nearest chair. He had turned quite livid and had raised his hand to his left side. They were all three looking at him, but Mrs. Moreen suddenly bounded forward. "Ah his darling little heart!" she broke out; and this time, on her knees before him and without respect for the idol, she caught him ardently in her arms. "You walked him too far, you hurried him too fast!" she hurled over her shoulder at Pemberton. Her son made no protest, and the next instant, still holding him, she sprang up with her face convulsed and with the terrified cry "Help, help! he's going, he's gone!" Pemberton saw with equal horror, by Morgan's own stricken face, that he was beyond their wildest recall. He pulled him half out of his mother's hands, and for a moment, while they held him together, they looked all their dismay into each other's eyes. "He couldn't stand it with his weak organ," said Pemberton—"the shock, the whole scene, the violent emotion."

"But I thought he *wanted* to go to you!" wailed Mrs. Moreen.

"I *told* you he didn't, my dear," her husband made answer. Mr. Moreen was trembling all over and was in his way as deeply affected as his wife. But after the very first he took his bereavement as a man of the world.

Thomas Mann

1875–1955

Thomas Mann was born in Lübeck, Germany, on June 6, 1875. His father was a grain merchant and senator of the city, his mother descended from Portuguese-Creole Brazilian ancestors. Young Mann, who detested school, was a writer almost from the first. After his father's death, he worked as an insurance clerk and attended the university in Munich. With his brother Heinrich, also a writer, he spent a year in Rome. A first book of stories, *Little Herr Friede- mann*, was published in 1898.

In Palestrina, near Rome. he began his first novel, *Buddenbrooks,* and finished it later while he was working as an editor on the satirical journal *Simplicissimus* in Munich. Slow to take hold, in a year *Buddenbrooks* made its author the most famous young writer in Germany. *Tristan,* which included *Tonio Kröger* and other tales, came out in 1903, and the play *Fiorenza* in 1906. That same year he married the daughter of the mathematician Alfred Pringsheim. They had six children.

Mann's second novel, *Royal Highness,* appeared in 1909, and was followed by one of his best-known works, *Death in Venice.* During World War I he published a book of stories and *Reflections of a Nonpolitical Man.* At the same time he was working on *The Magic Mountain.* Brought out in 1924, this great novel established its author as a world figure. In 1929 he was awarded the Nobel Prize for literature.

Mann left Germany in 1933, the year Hitler came to power. That same year he published the first volume of his massive biblical tetralogy, *Joseph and His Brothers.* It was finished ten years later. He lived for a while in Switzerland, then moved to Princeton, New Jersey, and in 1941 to Pacific Palisades, California. In 1944 he became an American citizen. During this period he wrote *The Be-loved Returns, Doctor Faustus,* and *The Holy Sinner.* In essays, speeches, and radio addresses, he spoke out strongly for human liberty. In the early 1950's he settled near Zurich, Switzerland, where he wrote the book-length *Confessions of Felix Krull, Confidence Man.* He was one of the great composers of form in literature, dedicated, as he said, to the task of "marrying the daemonic with the formal, the private and Bohemian with the official and representative. . . ." He died on August 12, 1955.

In *A Sketch of My Life,* Mann tells how he wrote *Mario and the Magician.* During the summer of 1929 he took his wife and younger children to Rauschen, a Baltic seaside resort. He had, as he says, "no talent for unoccupied recreation"; and the manuscript of *Joseph* was too bulky to carry with him. So he decided to work on something that could be written without notes, "an incident of a previous holiday in Forte dei Marmi, near Viareggio," Italy.

He tried to work in his room. But "the feeling that the sea was waiting" forced him outside. In a wicker chair at the water's edge, with a pad on his knee, tranquil amidst the animation of the bathing hour, he found that "the fable, all unexpectedly, grew out of the anecdote, the intellectualized literary form out of mere 'story-telling'; the personal turned into the symbolic and ethical."

How well he understood what he was doing—and how well he has done it! In the opening sentence—"The atmosphere of Torre di Venere remains unpleasant in the memory"—the tone is set. First we are given a broad view of the resort. Then two or three "unpleasantnesses." Oh, nothing much—a shade of discrimination at the Grand Hotel, the highhandedness of the Principessa. These are relieved at once by the good nature of Signora Angiolieri, one-time companion of the actress Eleonora Duse.

But almost at once the irritations, offset here and there by a touch of humor, begin again. The children are puzzled by phrases "about

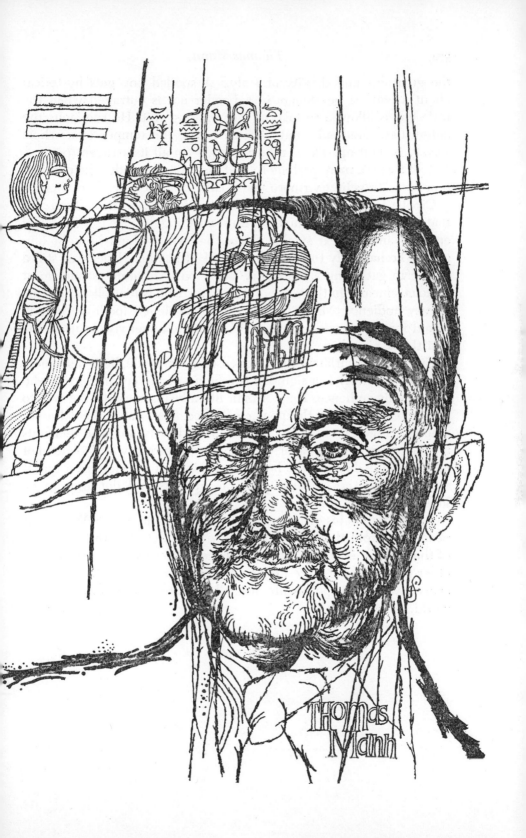

Thomas Mann

the greatness and dignity of Italy." A spoiled boy gets hysterical about a crab. A gentleman in a bowler hat is outraged when the little girl is allowed to take off her bathing suit. He summons the authorities. Gradually, out of such trivia, the temper of a whole society is built up. The sun burns down "in all its arrogant power." But all this is a mere prelude to that last evening under the domination of a "traveling virtuoso" who calls himself Cavaliere Cipolla.

Cipolla bills himself as *"forzatore, illusionista, prestidigitatore"*— that is, compeller or dominator, illusionist, juggler. He is a masterful creation and a great symbol. Note that when Mann brought him to life, he had only the lesser model of Mussolini. Hitler was still a politician gathering a following. Using only the quietest and most judicious means, in the voice of a narrator who is himself part of the uneasy audience, Mann creates the malevolent Cipolla with such naked force that we ourselves feel a hostile anger rise in us at the whistle of his whip.

Cipolla is a charlatan. Like Stevenson's Mr. Hyde, he is deformed, and his deformity is a sign. He is a figure of the corrupt artist who debases his audience. He is a man literally insane with the will to power. His power is the power of Circe. He is an animal trainer who turns men into beasts. He is the kind of tyrant who demands not mere service but eager co-operation; a tyrant who violates not merely the bodies but the hearts and minds of his victims; a tyrant who destroys the personality of his subjects and demands to be loved for it.

He believes in his own terrible will and in nothing else. We do not need to be told that Mann, like Lawrence, detested this imposing of the will, by fear or fraud or violence or mere superior power, on other human beings. We may coin a term for it—Cipolla's Evil. In everyday living or public life, it is all too often still powerful in our world.

Mario and
the Magician

The atmosphere of Torre di Venere remains unpleasant in the memory. From the first moment the air of the place made us uneasy, we felt irritable, on edge; then at the end came the shocking business of Cipolla, that dreadful being who seemed to incorporate, in so fateful and so humanly impressive a way, all the peculiar evilness of the situation as a whole. Looking back, we had the feeling that the horrible end of the affair had been preordained and lay in the nature of things; that the children had to be present at it was an added impropriety, due to the false colors in which the weird creature presented himself. Luckily for them, they did not know where the comedy left off and the tragedy began; and we let them remain in their happy belief that the whole thing had been a play up till the end.

Torre di Venere lies some fifteen kilometers from Portoclemente, one of the most popular summer resorts on the Tyrrhenian Sea. Portoclemente is urban and elegant and full to overflowing for months on end. Its gay and busy main street of shops and hotels runs down to a wide sandy beach covered with tents and pennanted sand castles and sunburnt humanity, where at all times a lively social bustle reigns, and much noise. But this same spacious and inviting fine-sanded beach, this same border of pine grove and, near, presiding mountains, continues all the way along the coast. No wonder then that some competition of a quiet kind should have sprung up further on. Torre di Venere—the tower that gave the town its name is gone long since, one looks for it in vain—is an offshoot of the larger resort, and for some years remained an idyll for the few, a refuge for more unworldly spirits. But the usual history of such places repeated itself: peace has had to retire further along the coast, to Marina Petriera and dear knows where else. We all know how the world at once seeks peace and puts her to flight—rushing upon her in the fond idea that they two will wed, and where she is, there it can be at home. It will even set up its Vanity Fair in a spot and be capable of thinking that peace is still by its side. Thus Torre—though its atmosphere so far is more modest and contemplative than that of Portoclemente—has been quite taken up, by both Italians and foreigners. It is no longer the thing to go to Portoclemente—though still so much the thing that it is as noisy and crowded as ever. One goes next door, so to speak: to Torre. So much more refined, even, and cheaper to boot. And the attractiveness of these qualities persists, though the qualities themselves long ago ceased to be evident. Torre has got a Grand Hotel. Numerous pensions have sprung up, some modest, some pretentious. The people who own or rent the villas and pinetas overlooking the sea no longer have it all their own way on the beach. In July and August it looks just like the beach at Portoclemente: it swarms with a screaming, squabbling, merrymaking crowd, and the sun, blazing down like mad, peels the skin off their necks. Garish little flat-bottomed boats rock on the glittering blue, manned by children, whose mothers hover afar and fill the air with anxious cries of Nino! and Sandro! and Bice! and Maria! Peddlers step across the legs of recumbent sun bathers, selling flowers and corals, oysters, lemonade, and *cornetti al burro* [buttered croissants], and crying their wares in the breathy, full-throated southern voice.

Such was the scene that greeted our arrival in Torre: pleasant enough, but after all, we thought, we had come too soon. It was the middle of August, the Italian season was still at its height, scarcely the moment for strangers to learn to love the special charms of the place. What an afternoon crowd in the cafés on the front! For instance, in the Esquisito, where we sometimes sat and were served by Mario, that very Mario of whom I shall have presently to tell. It is well-nigh impossible to find a table; and the various orchestras contend together in the midst of one's conversation with bewildering effect. Of course, it is in the afternoon that people come over from Portoclemente. The excursion is a favorite one for the restless denizens of that pleasure resort, and a Fiat motorbus plies to and fro, coating inch-thick with dust the oleander and laurel hedges along the highroad—a notable if repulsive sight.

Yes, decidedly one should go to Torre in September, when the great public has left. Or else in May, before the water is warm enough to tempt the Southerner to bathe. Even in the before and after seasons Torre is not empty, but life is less national and more subdued. English, French, and German prevail under the tent awnings and in the pension dining rooms; whereas in August—in the Grand Hotel, at least, where, in default of

private addresses, we had engaged rooms—the stranger finds the field so
occupied by Florentine and Roman society that he feels quite isolated
and even temporarily *déclassé*.

We had, rather to our annoyance, this experience on the evening we
arrived, when we went in to dinner and were shown to our table by the
waiter in charge. As a table, it had nothing against it, save that we had
already fixed our eyes upon those on the veranda beyond, built out over
the water, where little red-shaded lamps glowed—and there were still
some tables empty, though it was as full as the dining room within. The
children went into raptures at the festive sight, and without more ado
we announced our intention to take our meals by preference in the veranda. Our words, it appeared, were prompted by ignorance; for we
were informed, with somewhat embarrassed politeness, that the cosy
nook outside was reserved for the clients of the hotel: *ai nostri clienti*.
Their clients? But we were their clients. We were not tourists or trippers,
but boarders for a stay of some three or four weeks. However, we forbore to press for an explanation of the difference between the likes of us
and that clientele to whom it was vouchsafed to eat out there in the glow
of the red lamps, and took our dinner by the prosaic common light of
the dining-room chandelier—a thoroughly ordinary and monotonous
hotel bill of fare, be it said. In Pensione Eleonora, a few steps landward,
the table, as we were to discover, was much better.

And thither it was that we moved, three or four days later, before we
had had time to settle in properly at the Grand Hotel. Not on account of
the veranda and the lamps. The children, straightway on the best of terms
with waiters and pages, absorbed in the joys of life on the beach,
promptly forgot those colorful seductions. But now there arose, between
ourselves and the veranda clientele—or perhaps more correctly with the
compliant management—one of those little unpleasantnesses which can
quite spoil the pleasure of a holiday. Among the guests were some high
Roman aristocracy, a Principe X and his family. These grand folk occupied rooms close to our own, and the Principessa, a great and a passionately maternal lady, was thrown into a panic by the vestiges of a whooping cough which our little ones had lately got over, but which now and
then still faintly troubled the unshatterable slumbers of our youngest-
born. The nature of this illness is not clear, leaving some play for the
imagination. So we took no offense at our elegant neighbor for clinging
to the widely held view that whooping cough is acoustically contagious
and quite simply fearing lest her children yield to the bad example set
by ours. In the fullness of her feminine self-confidence she protested to the

management, which then, in the person of the proverbial frock-coated manager, hastened to represent to us, with many expressions of regret, that under the circumstances they were obliged to transfer us to the annex. We did our best to assure him that the disease was in its very last stages, that it was actually over, and presented no danger of infection to anybody. All that we gained was permission to bring the case before the hotel physician—not one chosen by us—by whose verdict we must then abide. We agreed, convinced that thus we should at once pacify the Princess and escape the trouble of moving. The doctor appeared, and behaved like a faithful and honest servant of science. He examined the child and gave his opinion: the disease was quite over, no danger of contagion was present. We drew a long breath and considered the incident closed—until the manager announced that despite the doctor's verdict it would still be necessary for us to give up our rooms and retire to the dependence. Byzantinism like this outraged us. It is not likely that the Principessa was responsible for the willful breach of faith. Very likely the fawning management had not even dared to tell her what the physician said. Anyhow, we made it clear to his understanding that we preferred to leave the hotel altogether and at once—and packed our trunks. We could do so with a light heart, having already set up casual friendly relations with Casa Eleonora. We had noticed its pleasant exterior and formed the acquaintance of its proprietor, Signora Angiolieri, and her husband: she slender and black-haired, Tuscan in type, probably at the beginning of the thirties, with the dead ivory complexion of the southern woman, he quiet and bald and carefully dressed. They owned a larger establishment in Florence and presided only in summer and early autumn over the branch in Torre di Venere. But earlier, before her marriage, our new landlady had been companion, fellow traveler, wardrobe mistress, yes, friend, of Eleonora Duse and manifestly regarded that period as the crown of her career. Even at our first visit she spoke of it with animation. Numerous photographs of the great actress, with affectionate inscriptions, were displayed about the drawing room, and other souvenirs of their life together adorned the little tables and *étagères*. This cult of a so interesting past was calculated, of course, to heighten the advantages of the signora's present business. Nevertheless our pleasure and interest were quite genuine as we were conducted through the house by its owner and listened to her sonorous and staccato Tuscan voice relating anecdotes of that immortal mistress, depicting her suffering saintliness, her genius, her profound delicacy of feeling.

Thither, then, we moved our effects, to the dismay of the staff of the

Grand Hotel, who, like all Italians, were very good to children. Our new quarters were retired and pleasant, we were within easy reach of the sea through the avenue of young plane trees that ran down to the esplanade. In the clean, cool dining room Signora Angiolieri daily served the soup with her own hands, the service was attentive and good, the table capital. We even discovered some Viennese acquaintances, and enjoyed chatting with them after luncheon, in front of the house. They, in their turn, were the means of our finding others—in short, all seemed for the best, and we were heartily glad of the change we had made. Nothing was now wanting to a holiday of the most gratifying kind.

And yet no proper gratification ensued. Perhaps the stupid occasion of our change of quarters pursued us to the new ones we had found. Personally, I admit that I do not easily forget these collisions with ordinary humanity, the naïve misuse of power, the injustice, the sycophantic corruption. I dwelt upon the incident too much, it irritated me in retrospect —quite futilely, of course, since such phenomena are only all too natural and all too much the rule. And we had not broken off relations with the Grand Hotel. The children were as friendly as ever there, the porter mended their toys, and we sometimes took tea in the garden. We even saw the Principessa. She would come out, with her firm and delicate tread, her lips emphatically corallined, to look after her children, playing under the supervision of their English governess. She did not dream that we were anywhere near, for so soon as she appeared in the offing we sternly forbade our little one even to clear his throat.

The heat—if I may bring it in evidence—was extreme. It was African. The power of the sun, directly one left the border of the indigo-blue wave, was so frightful, so relentless, that the mere thought of the few steps between the beach and luncheon was a burden, clad though one might be only in pajamas. Do you care for that sort of thing? Weeks on end? Yes, of course, it is proper to the south, it is classic weather, the sun of Homer, the climate wherein human culture came to flower—and all the rest of it. But after a while it is too much for me, I reach a point where I begin to find it dull. The burning void of the sky, day after day, weighs one down; the high coloration, the enormous naïveté of the unrefracted light—they do, I dare say, induce lightheartedness, a carefree mood born of immunity from downpours and other meteorological caprices. But slowly, slowly, there makes itself felt a lack: the deeper, more complex needs of the northern soul remain unsatisfied. You are left barren— even it may be, in time, a little contemptuous. True without that stupid business of the whooping cough I might not have been feeling these things. I was annoyed, very likely I wanted to feel them and so half-unconsciously seized upon an idea lying ready to hand to induce, or if not to induce, at least to justify and strengthen, my attitude. Up to this point, then, if you like, let us grant some ill will on our part. But the sea; and the mornings spent extended upon the fine sand in face of its eternal splendors—no, the sea could not conceivably induce such feelings. Yet it was none the less true that, despite all previous experience, we were not at home on the beach, we were not happy.

It was too soon, too soon. The beach, as I have said, was still in the hands of the middle-class native. It is a pleasing breed to look at, and among the young we saw much shapeliness and charm. Still, we were necessarily surrounded by a great deal of very average humanity—a middle-class mob, which, you will admit, is not more charming under this sun than under one's own native sky. The voices these women have! It was sometimes hard to believe that we were in the land which is the western cradle of the art of song. *"Fuggièro!"* I can still hear that cry, as for twenty mornings long I heard it close behind me, breathy, full-throated, hideously stressed, with a harsh open *e*, uttered in accents of mechanical despair. *"Fuggièro! Rispondi almeno* [Well, answer then]!" Answer when I call you! The *sp* in *rispondi* was pronounced like *shp*, as Germans pronounce it; and this, on top of what I felt already, vexed my sensitive soul. The cry was addressed to a repulsive youngster whose sunburn had made disgusting raw sores on his shoulders. He outdid anything I have ever seen for ill breeding, refractoriness, and temper and was a great coward to boot, putting the whole beach in an uproar, one day, because of his outrageous sensitiveness to the slightest pain. A sand crab had pinched his toe in the water, and the minute injury made him set up a cry of heroic proportions—the shout of an antique hero in his agony—that pierced one to the marrow and called up visions of some frightful tragedy. Evidently he considered himself not only wounded but poisoned as well; he crawled out on the sand and lay in apparently intolerable anguish, groaning *"Ohi!"* and *"Ohimè!"* and threshing about with arms and legs to ward off his mother's tragic appeals and the questions of the bystanders. An audience gathered round. A doctor was fetched—the same who had pronounced objective judgment on our whooping cough —and here again acquitted himself like a man of science. Good-naturedly he reassured the boy, telling him that he was not hurt at all, he should simply go into the water again to relieve the smart. Instead of which, Fuggièro was borne off the beach, followed by a concourse of people. But he did not fail to appear next morning, nor did he leave off spoiling our children's sand castles. Of course, always by accident. In short, a perfect terror.

And this twelve-year-old lad was prominent among the influences that, imperceptibly at first, combined to spoil our holiday and render it unwholesome. Somehow or other, there was a stiffness, a lack of innocent enjoyment. These people stood on their dignity—just why, and in what spirit, it was not easy at first to tell. They displayed much self-respectingness; towards each other and towards the foreigner their bearing was that of a person newly conscious of a sense of honor. And wherefore? Gradually we realized the political implications and understood that we were in the presence of a national ideal. The beach, in fact, was alive with patriotic children—a phenomenon as unnatural as it was depressing. Children are a human species and a society apart, a nation of their own, so to speak. On the basis of their common form of life, they find each other out with the greatest ease, no matter how different their small vocabularies. Ours soon played with natives and foreigners alike. Yet they were plainly both puzzled and disappointed at times. There were wounded sensibilities, displays of assertiveness—or rather hardly assertiveness, for it was too self-conscious and too didactic to deserve the name. There were quarrels over flags, disputes about authority and precedence. Grownups joined in, not so much to pacify as to render judgment and enunciate principles. Phrases were dropped about the greatness and dignity of Italy, solemn phrases that spoiled the fun. We saw our two little ones retreat, puzzled and hurt, and were put to it to explain the situation. These people, we told them, were just passing through a certain stage, something rather like an illness, perhaps; not very pleasant, but probably unavoidable.

We had only our own carelessness to thank that we came to blows in the end with this "stage"—which, after all, we had seen and sized up long before now. Yes, it came to another "cross-purposes," so evidently the earlier ones had not been sheer accident. In a word, we became an offense to the public morals. Our small daughter—eight years old, but in physical development a good year younger and thin as a chicken—had had a good long bathe and gone playing in the warm sun in her wet costume. We told her that she might take off her bathing suit, which was stiff with sand, rinse it in the sea, and put it on again, after which she must take care to keep it cleaner. Off goes the costume and she runs down naked to the sea, rinses her little jersey, and comes back. Ought we to have foreseen the outburst of anger and resentment which her conduct, and thus our conduct, called forth? Without delivering a homily on the subject, I may say that in the last decade our attitude towards the nude body and our feelings regarding it have undergone, all over the world, a fundamental change. There are things we "never think about" any more, and among them is the freedom we had permitted to this by no means provocative little childish body. But in these parts it was taken as a challenge. The patriotic children hooted. Fuggièro whistled on his fingers. The sudden buzz of conversation among the grown people in our neighborhood boded no good. A gentleman in city togs, with a not very apropos bowler hat on the back of his head, was assuring his outraged womenfolk that he proposed to take punitive measures; he stepped up to us, and a philippic descended on our unworthy heads, in which all the emotionalism of the sense-loving south spoke in the service of morality and discipline. The offense against decency of which we had been guilty was, he said, the more to be condemned because it was also a gross ingratitude and an insulting breach of his country's hospitality. We had criminally injured not only the letter and spirit of the public bathing regulations but also the honor of Italy; he, the gentleman in the city togs, knew how to defend that honor and proposed to see to it that our offense against the national dignity should not go unpunished.

We did our best, bowing respectfully, to give ear to this eloquence. To contradict the man, overheated as he was, would probably be to fall from one error into another. On the tips of our tongues we had various answers: as, that the word "hospitality," in its strictest sense, was not quite the right one, taking all the circumstances into consideration. We were not literally the guests of Italy, but of Signora Angiolieri, who had assumed the role of dispenser of hospitality some years ago on laying down that of familiar friend to Eleonora Duse. We longed to say that surely this beautiful country had not sunk so low as to be reduced to a state of hypersensitive prudishness. But we confined ourselves to assuring the gentleman that any lack of respect, any provocation on our parts, had been the furthest from our thoughts. And as a mitigating circumstance we pointed out the tender age and physical slightness of the little culprit. In vain. Our protests were waved away, he did not believe in them; our defense would not hold water. We must be made an example of. The authorities were notified, by telephone, I believe, and their representatives appeared on the beach. He said the case was *"molto grave."* We had to go with him to the Municipio up in the Piazza, where a higher official confirmed the previous verdict of *"molto grave,"* launched into a stream of the usual didactic phrases—the selfsame tune and words as the man in the bowler hat—and levied a fine and ransom of fifty lire. We felt that the adventure must willy-nilly be worth to us this much of a contribution to the economy of the Italian government; paid, and left. Ought we not at this point to have left Torre as well?

If we only had! We should thus have escaped that fatal Cipolla. But circumstances combined to prevent us from making up our minds to a change. A certain poet says that it is indolence that makes us endure uncomfortable situations. The *aperçu* may serve as an explanation for our inaction. Anyhow, one dislikes voiding the field immediately upon such an event. Especially if sympathy from other quarters encourages one to defy it. And in the Villa Eleonora they pronounced as with one voice upon the injustice of our punishment. Some Italian after-dinner acquaintances found that the episode put their country in a very bad light, and proposed taking the man in the bowler hat to task, as one fellow citizen to another. But the next day he and his party had vanished from the beach. Not on our account, of course. Though it might be that the consciousness of his impending departure had added energy to his rebuke; in any case his going was a relief. And, furthermore, we stayed because our stay had by now become remarkable in our own eyes, which is worth something in itself, quite apart from the comfort or discomfort involved. Shall we strike sail, avoid a certain experience so soon as it seems not expressly calculated to increase our enjoyment or our self-esteem? Shall we go away whenever life looks like turning in the slightest uncanny, or not quite normal, or even rather painful and mortifying? No, surely not. Rather stay and look matters in the face, brave them out; perhaps precisely in so doing lies a lesson for us to learn. We stayed on and reaped as the awful reward of our constancy the unholy and staggering experience with Cipolla.

I have not mentioned that the after-season had begun, almost on the very day we were disciplined by the city authorities. The worshipful gentleman in the bowler hat, our denouncer, was not the only person to leave the resort. There was a regular exodus, on every hand you saw luggage carts on their way to the station. The beach denationalized itself. Life in Torre, in the cafés and the pinetas, became more homelike and more European. Very likely we might even have eaten at a table in the glass veranda, but we refrained, being content at Signora Angiolieri's— as content, that is, as our evil star would let us be. But at the same time with this turn for the better came a change in the weather: almost to an hour it showed itself in harmony with the holiday calendar of the general public. The sky was overcast; not that it grew any cooler, but the unclouded heat of the entire eighteen days since our arrival, and probably long before that, gave place to a stifling sirocco air, while from time to time a little ineffectual rain sprinkled the velvety surface of the beach. Add to which that two-thirds of our intended stay at Torre had passed. The colorless, lazy sea, with sluggish jellyfish floating in its shallows, was at least a change. And it would have been silly to feel retrospective longings after a sun that had caused us so many sighs when it burned down in all its arrogant power.

At this juncture, then, it was that Cipolla announced himself. Cavaliere Cipolla he was called on the posters that appeared one day stuck up everywhere, even in the dining room of Pensione Eleonora. A traveling virtuoso, an entertainer, *"forzatore* [conjuror], *illusionista, prestidigitatore,"* as he called himself, who proposed to wait upon the highly respectable population of Torre di Venere with a display of extraordinary phenomena of a mysterious and staggering kind. A conjuror! The bare announcement was enough to turn our children's heads. They had never seen anything of the sort, and now our present holiday was to afford them this new excitement. From that moment on they besieged us with prayers to take tickets for the performance. We had doubts, from the first, on the score of the lateness of the hour, nine o'clock; but gave way, in the idea that we might see a little of what Cipolla had to offer, probably no great matter, and then go home. Besides, of course, the children could sleep late next day. We bought four tickets of Signora Angiolieri herself, she having taken a number of the stalls on commission to sell them to her guests. She could not vouch for the man's performance, and we had no great expectations. But we were conscious of a need for diversion, and the children's violent curiosity proved catching.

The Cavaliere's performance was to take place in a hall where during the season there had been a cinema with a weekly program. We had never been there. You reached it by following the main street under the wall of the *"palazzo,"* a ruin with a "For sale" sign, that suggested a castle and had obviously been built in lordlier days. In the same street were the druggist, the hairdresser, and all the better shops; it led, so to speak, from the feudal past the bourgeois into the proletarian, for it ended off between two rows of poor fishing huts, where old women sat mending nets before the doors. And here, among the proletariat, was the hall, not much more, actually, than a wooden shed, though a large one, with a turreted entrance, plastered on either side with layers of gay placards. Some while after dinner, then, on the appointed evening, we wended our way thither in the dark, the children dressed in their best and blissful with the sense of so much irregularity. It was sultry, as it had been for days; there was heat lightning now and then, and a little rain; we proceeded under umbrellas. It took us a quarter of an hour.

Our tickets were collected at the entrance, our places we had to find ourselves. They were in the third row left, and as we sat down we saw that, late though the hour was for the performance, it was to be interpreted with even more laxity. Only very slowly did an audience—who seemed to be relied upon to come late—begin to fill the stalls. These comprised the whole auditorium; there were no boxes. This tardiness gave us some concern. The children's checks were already flushed as much with fatigue as with excitement. But even when we entered, the standing room at the back and in the side aisles was already well occupied. There stood the manhood of Torre di Venere, all and sundry, fisherfolk, rough-and-ready youths with bare forearms crossed over their striped jerseys. We were well pleased with the presence of this native assemblage, which always adds color and animation to occasions like the present; and the children were frankly delighted. For they had friends among these people—acquaintances picked up on afternoon strolls to the further ends of the beach. We would be turning homeward, at the hour when the sun dropped into the sea, spent with the huge effort it had made and gilding with reddish gold the oncoming surf; and we would come upon barelegged fisherfolk standing in rows, bracing and hauling with long-drawn cries as they drew in the nets and harvested in dripping baskets their catch, often so scanty, of *frutto di mare*. The children looked on, helped to pull, brought out their little stock of Italian words, made friends. So now they exchanged nods with the "standing room" clientele; there was Guiscardo, there Antonio, they knew them by name and waved and called across in half whispers, getting answering nods and smiles that displayed rows of healthy white teeth. Look, there is even Mario, Mario from the Esquisito, who brings us the chocolate. He wants to see the conjuror, too, and he must have come early, for he is almost in front; but he does not see us, he is not paying attention; that is a way he has, even though he is a waiter. So we wave instead to the man who lets out the little boats on the beach; he is there too, standing at the back.

It had got to a quarter past nine, it got to almost half past. It was natural that we should be nervous. When would the children get to bed? It had been a mistake to bring them, for now it would be very hard to suggest breaking off their enjoyment before it had got well under way. The stalls had filled in time; all Torre, apparently, was there: the guests of the Grand Hotel, the guests of Villa Eleonora, familiar faces from the beach. We heard English and German and the sort of French that Rumanians speak with Italians. Madame Angiolieri herself sat two rows behind us, with her quiet, bald-headed spouse, who kept stroking his mustache with the two middle fingers of his right hand. Everybody had come late, but nobody too late. Cipolla made us wait for him.

He made us wait. That is probably the way to put it. He heightened the suspense by his delay in appearing. And we could see the point of this, too—only not when it was carried to extremes. Towards half past nine the audience began to clap—an amiable way of expressing justifiable impatience, evincing as it does an eagerness to applaud. For the little ones, this was a joy in itself—all children love to clap. From the popular sphere came loud cries of *"Pronti!" "Cominciamo!"* And lo, it seemed now as easy to begin as before it had been hard. A gong sounded, greeted by the standing rows with a many-voiced "Ah-h!" and the curtains parted. They revealed a platform furnished more like a schoolroom than like the theater of a conjuring performance—largely because of the blackboard in the left foreground. There was a common yellow hatstand, a few ordinary straw-bottomed chairs, and further back a little round table holding a water carafe and glass, also a tray with a liqueur glass and a flask of pale yellow liquid. We had still a few seconds of time to let these things sink in. Then, with no darkening of the house, Cavaliere Cipolla made his entry.

He came forward with a rapid step that expressed his eagerness to appear before his public and gave rise to the illusion that he had already come a long way to put himself at their service—whereas, of course, he had only been standing in the wings. His costume supported the fiction. A man of an age hard to determine, but by no means young; with a sharp, ravaged face, piercing eyes, compressed lips, small black waxed mustache, and a so-called imperial in the curve between mouth and chin. He was dressed for the street with a sort of complicated evening elegance, in a wide black pelerine with velvet collar and satin lining; which, in the hampered state of his arms, he held together in front with his white-gloved hands. He had a white scarf round his neck; a top hat with a curving brim sat far back on his head. Perhaps more than anywhere else the eighteenth century is still alive in Italy, and with it the charlatan and mountebank type so characteristic of the period. Only there, at any rate, does one still encounter really well-preserved specimens. Cipolla had in his whole appearance much of the historic type; his very clothes helped to conjure up the traditional figure with its blatantly, fantastically foppish air. His pretentious costume sat upon him, or rather hung upon him, most curiously, being in one place drawn too tight, in another a mass of awkward folds. There was something not quite in order about his figure, both front and back—that was plain later on. But I must emphasize the fact that there was not a trace of personal jocularity or clownishness in his pose, manner, or behavior. On the contrary, there was complete seriousness, an absence of any humorous appeal; occasionally even a cross-grained pride, along with that curious, self-satisfied air so characteristic of the deformed. None of all this, however, prevented his appearance from being greeted with laughter from more than one quarter of the hall.

All the eagerness had left his manner. The swift entry had been merely an expression of energy, not of zeal. Standing at the footlights he negligently drew off his gloves, to display long yellow hands, one of them adorned with a seal ring with a lapis lazuli in a high setting. As he stood there, his small hard eyes, with flabby pouches beneath them, roved appraisingly about the hall, not quickly, rather in a considered examination, pausing here and there upon a face with his lips clipped together, not speaking a word. Then with a display of skill as surprising as it was casual, he rolled his gloves into a ball and tossed them across a considerable distance into the glass on the table. Next from an inner pocket he drew forth a packet of cigarettes; you could see by the wrapper that they were the cheapest sort the government sells. With his fingertips he pulled out a cigarette and lighted it, without looking, from a quick-firing benzine lighter. He drew the smoke deep into his lungs and let it out again, tapping his foot, with both lips drawn in an arrogant grimace and the gray smoke streaming out between broken and saw-edged teeth.

With a keenness equal to his own his audience eyed him. The youths at the rear scowled as they peered at this cocksure creature to search out his secret weaknesses. He betrayed none. In fetching out and putting back the cigarettes his clothes got in his way. He had to turn back his pelerine, and in so doing revealed a riding whip with a silver claw handle that hung by a leather thong from his left forearm and looked decidedly out of place. You could see that he had on not evening clothes but a frock coat, and under this, as he lifted it to get at his pocket, could be seen a striped sash worn about the body. Somebody behind me whispered that this sash went with his title of Cavaliere. I give the information for what it may be worth—personally, I never heard that the title carried such insignia with it. Perhaps the sash was sheer pose, like the way he stood there, without a word, casually and arrogantly puffing smoke into his audience's face.

People laughed, as I said. The merriment had become almost general when somebody in the "standing seats," in a loud, dry voice, remarked: *"Buona sera."*

Cipolla cocked his head. "Who was that?" asked he, as though he had been dared. "Who was that just spoke? Well? First so bold and now so modest? *Paura,* eh?" He spoke with a rather high, asthmatic voice, which yet had a metallic quality. He waited.

"That was me," a youth at the rear broke into the stillness, seeing himself thus challenged. He was not far from us, a handsome fellow in a woolen shirt, with his coat hanging over one shoulder. He wore his surly, wiry hair in a high, disheveled mop, the style affected by the youth of the awakened Fatherland; it gave him an African appearance that rather spoiled his looks. *"Bè!* That was me. It was your business to say it first, but I was trying to be friendly."

More laughter. The chap had a tongue in his head. *"Ha sciolto lo scilinguagnolo* [He has a quick tongue]," I heard near me. After all, the retort was deserved.

"Ah, bravo!" answered Cipolla. "I like you, *giovanotto* [young man]. Trust me, I've had my eye on you for some time. People like you are just in my line. I can use them. And you are the pick of the lot, that's plain to see. You do what you like. Or is it possible you have ever not done what you liked—or even, maybe, what you didn't like? What somebody else liked, in short? Hark ye, my friend, that might be a pleasant change for you, to divide up the willing and the doing and stop tackling both jobs at once. Division of labor, *sistema americano, sa!* For instance, suppose you were to show your tongue to this select and honorable audience here— your whole tongue, right down to the roots?"

"No, I won't," said the youth, hostilely. "Sticking out your tongue shows a bad bringing-up."

"Nothing of the sort," retorted Cipolla. "You would only be *doing* it. With all due respect to your bringing-up, I suggest that before I count ten, you will perform a right turn and stick out your tongue at the company here further than you knew yourself that you could stick it out."

He gazed at the youth, and his piercing eyes seemed to sink deeper into their sockets. *"Uno!"* said he. He had let his riding whip slide down his arm and made it whistle once through the air. The boy faced about and put out his tongue, so long, so extendedly, that you could see it was the very uttermost in tongue which he had to offer. Then turned back, stony-faced, to his former position.

"That was me," mocked Cipolla, with a jerk of his head towards the youth. "*Bè!* That was me." Leaving the audience to enjoy its sensations, he turned towards the little round table, lifted the bottle, poured out a small glass of what was obviously cognac, and tipped it up with a practiced hand.

The children laughed with all their hearts. They had understood practically nothing of what had been said, but it pleased them hugely that something so funny should happen, straightaway, between that queer man up there and somebody out of the audience. They had no preconception of what an "evening" would be like and were quite ready to find this a priceless beginning. As for us, we exchanged a glance and I remember that involuntarily I made with my lips the sound that Cipolla's whip had made when it cut the air. For the rest, it was plain that people did not know what to make of a preposterous beginning like this to a sleight-of-hand performance. They could not see why the *giovanotto*, who after all in a way had been their spokesman, should suddenly have turned on them to vent his incivility. They felt that he had behaved like a silly ass and withdrew their countenances from him in favor of the artist, who now came back from his refreshment table and addressed them as follows:

"Ladies and gentlemen," said he, in his wheezing, metallic voice, "you saw just now that I was rather sensitive on the score of the rebuke this hopeful young linguist saw fit to give me"—"*questo linguista di belle speranze*" [this hopeful linguist] was what he said, and we all laughed at the pun [on *lingua*, the tongue]. "I am a man who sets some store by himself, you may take it from me. And I see no point in being wished a good evening unless it is done courteously and in all seriousness. For anything else there is no occasion. When a man wishes me a good evening he wishes himself one, for the audience will have one only if I do. So this lady-killer of Torre di Venere" (another thrust) "did well to testify that I have one tonight and that I can dispense with any wishes of his in the matter. I can boast of having good evenings almost without exception. One not so good does come my way now and again, but very seldom. My calling is hard and my health not of the best. I have a little physical defect which prevented me from doing my bit in the war for the greater glory of the Fatherland. It is perforce with my mental and spiritual parts that I conquer life—which after all only means conquering oneself. And I flatter myself that my achievements have aroused interest and respect among the educated public. The leading newspapers have lauded me, the *Corriere della Sera* did me the courtesy of calling me a phenomenon, and in Rome the brother of the *Duce* honored me by his presence at one of my evenings. I should not have thought that in a relatively less important place" (laughter here, at the expense of poor little Torre) "I should have to give up the small personal habits which brilliant and elevated audiences had been ready to overlook. Nor did I think I had to stand being heckled by a person who seems to have been rather spoiled by the favors of the fair sex." All this of course at the expense of the youth whom Cipolla never tired of presenting in the guise of *donnaiuolo* [lover] and rustic Don Juan. His persistent thin-skinnedness and animosity were in striking contrast to the self-confidence and the worldly success he boasted of. One might have assumed that the *giovanotto* was merely the chosen butt of Cipolla's customary professional sallies had not the very pointed witticisms betrayed a genuine antagonism. No one looking at the physical parts of the two men need have been at a loss for the explanation, even if the deformed man had not constantly played on the other's supposed success with the fair sex. "Well," Cipolla went on, "before beginning our entertainment this evening, perhaps you will permit me to make myself comfortable."

And he went towards the hatstand to take off his things.

"*Parla benissimo* [He talks beautifully]," asserted somebody in our neighborhood. So far, the man had done nothing; but what he had said was accepted as an achievement, by means of that he had made an impression. Among southern peoples speech is a constituent part of the pleasure of living, it enjoys far livelier social esteem than in the north. That national cement, the mother tongue, is paid symbolic honors down here, and there is something blithely symbolical in the pleasure people take in their respect for its forms and phonetics. They enjoy speaking, they enjoy listening; and they listen with discrimination. For the way a man speaks serves as a measure of his personal rank; carelessness and clumsiness are greeted with scorn; elegance and mastery are rewarded with social éclat. Wherefore the small man too, where it is a question of getting his effect, chooses his phrase nicely and turns it with care. On this count, then, at least, Cipolla had won his audience; though he by no means belonged to the class of men which the Italian, in a singular mixture of moral and aesthetic judgments, labels "*simpatico*."

After removing his hat, scarf, and mantle he came to the front of the stage, settling his coat, pulling down his cuffs with their large cuff buttons, adjusting his absurd sash. He had very ugly hair; the top of his head, that is, was almost bald, while a narrow, black-varnished frizz of curls ran from front to back as though stuck on; the side hair, likewise blackened, was brushed forward to the corners of the eyes—it was, in short, the hairdressing of an old-fashioned circus director, fantastic, but entirely suited to his outmoded personal type and worn with so much assurance as to take the edge off the public's sense of humor. The little physical defect of which he had warned us was now all too visible, though the nature of it was even now not very clear; the chest was too high, as is usual in such cases, but the corresponding malformation of the back did not sit between the shoulders; it took the form of a sort of hips or buttocks hump, which did not indeed hinder his movements but gave him a grotesque and dipping stride at every step he took. However, by mentioning his deformity beforehand he had broken the shock of it, and a delicate propriety of feeling appeared to reign throughout the hall.

"At your service," said Cipolla. "With your kind permission, we will begin the evening with some arithmetical tests."

Arithmetic? That did not sound much like sleight of hand. We began to have our suspicions that the man was sailing under a false flag, only we did not yet know which was the right one. I felt sorry on the children's account; but for the moment they were content simply to be there.

The numerical test which Cipolla now introduced was as simple as it was baffling. He began by fastening a piece of paper to the upper right-hand corner of the blackboard; then lifting it up, he wrote something underneath. He talked all the while, relieving the dryness of his offering by a constant flow of words, and showed himself a practiced speaker, never at a loss for conversational turns of phrase. It was in keeping with the nature of his performance, and at the same time vastly entertained the children, that he went on to eliminate the gap between stage and audience, which had already been bridged over by the curious skirmish with the fisher lad; he had representatives from the audience mount the stage, and himself descended the wooden steps to seek personal contact with his public. And again, with individuals, he fell into his former taunting tone. I do not know how far that was a deliberate feature of his system; he preserved a serious, even a peevish, air, but his audience, at least the more popular section, seemed convinced that that was all part of the game. So then, after he had written something and covered the writing by the paper, he desired that two persons should come up on the platform and help to perform the calculations. They would not be difficult, even for people not clever at figures. As usual, nobody volunteered, and Cipolla took care not to molest the more select portion of his audience. He kept to the populace. Turning to two sturdy young louts standing behind us, he beckoned them to the front, encouraging and scolding by turns. They should not stand there gaping, he said, unwilling to oblige the company. Actually he got them in motion; with clumsy tread they came down the middle aisle, climbed the steps, and stood in front of the black-board, grinning sheepishly at their comrades' shouts and applause. Cipolla joked with them for a few minutes, praised their heroic firmness of limb and the size of their hands, so well calculated to do this service for the public. Then he handed one of them the chalk and told him to write down the numbers as they were called out. But now the creature declared that he could not write! *"Non so scrivere,"* said he in his gruff voice, and his companion added that neither did he.

God knows whether they told the truth or whether they wanted to make game of Cipolla. Anyhow, the latter was far from sharing the general merriment which their confession aroused. He was insulted and disgusted. He sat there on a straw-bottomed chair in the center of the stage with his legs crossed, smoking a fresh cigarette out of his cheap packet; obviously it tasted the better for the cognac he had indulged in while the yokels were stumping up the steps. Again he inhaled the smoke and let it stream out between curling lips. Swinging his leg, with his gaze sternly averted from the two shamelessly chuckling creatures and from the audience as well, he stared into space as one who withdraws himself and his dignity from the contemplation of an utterly despicable phenomenon.

"Scandalous," said he, in a sort of icy snarl. "Go back to your places! In Italy everybody can write—in all her greatness there is no room for ignorance and unenlightenment. To accuse her of them, in the hearing of this international company, is a cheap joke, in which you yourselves cut a very poor figure and humiliate the government and the whole country as well. If it is true that Torre di Venere is indeed the last refuge of such ignorance, then I must blush to have visited the place—being, as I already was, aware of its inferiority to Rome in more than one respect—"

Here Cipolla was interrupted by the youth with the Nubian coiffure and his jacket across his shoulder. His fighting spirit, as we now saw, had only abdicated temporarily, and he now flung himself into the breach in defense of his native heath. "That will do," said he loudly. "That's enough jokes about Torre. We all come from the place and we won't stand strangers making fun of it. These two chaps are our friends. Maybe they are no scholars, but even so they may be straighter than some folks in the room who are so free with their boasts about Rome, though they did not build it either."

That was capital. The young man had certainly cut his eye teeth. And this sort of spectacle was good fun, even though it still further delayed the regular performance. It is always fascinating to listen to an altercation. Some people it simply amuses; they take a sort of kill-joy pleasure in not being principals. Others feel upset and uneasy, and my sympathies are with these latter, although on the present occasion I was under the impression that all this was part of the show—the analphabetic yokels no less than the *giovanotto* with the jacket. The children listened well pleased. They understood not at all, but the sound of the voices made them hold their breath. So this was a "magic evening"—at least it was the kind they have in Italy. They expressly found it "lovely." Cipolla had stood up and with two of his scooping strides was at the footlights.

"Well, well, see who's here!" said he with grim cordiality. "An old acquaintance! A young man with his heart at the end of his tongue" (he used the word *linguaccia,* which means a coated tongue, and gave rise to much hilarity). "That will do, my friends," he turned to the yokels. "I do not need you now, I have business with this deserving young man here, *con questo torregiano di Venere,* this tower of Venus, who no doubt expects the gratitude of the fair as a reward for his prowess—"

"*Ah, non scherziamo* [Let's not joke now]! We're talking earnest," cried out the youth. His eyes flashed, and he actually made as though to pull off his jacket and proceed to direct methods of settlement.

Cipolla did not take him too seriously. We had exchanged apprehensive glances; but he was dealing with a fellow countryman and had his native soil beneath his feet. He kept quite cool and showed complete mastery of the situation. He looked at his audience, smiled, and made a sideways motion of the head towards the young cockerel as though calling the public to witness how the man's bumptiousness only served to betray the simplicity of his mind. And then, for the second time, something strange happened, which set Cipolla's calm superiority in an uncanny light, and in some mysterious and irritating way turned all the explosiveness latent in the air into matter for laughter.

Cipolla drew still nearer to the fellow, looking him in the eye with a peculiar gaze. He even came halfway down the steps that led into the auditorium on our left, so that he stood directly in front of the troublemaker, on slightly higher ground. The riding whip hung from his arm.

"My son, you do not feel much like joking," he said. "It is only too natural, for anyone can see that you are not feeling too well. Even your tongue, which leaves something to be desired on the score of cleanliness, indicates acute disorder of the gastric system. An evening entertainment is no place for people in your state; you yourself, I can tell, were of several minds whether you would not do better to put on a flannel bandage and go to bed. It was not good judgment to drink so much of that very sour white wine this afternoon. Now you have such a colic you would like to double up with the pain. Go ahead, don't be embarrassed. There is a distinct relief that comes from bending over in cases of intestinal cramp."

He spoke thus, word for word, with quiet impressiveness and a kind of stern sympathy, and his eyes, plunged the while deep in the young man's, seemed to grow very tired and at the same time burning above their enlarged tear ducts—they were the strangest eyes; you could tell that not manly pride alone was preventing the young adversary from withdrawing his gaze. And presently, indeed, all trace of its former arrogance was gone from the bronzed young face. He looked openmouthed at the Cavaliere and the open mouth was drawn in a rueful smile.

"Double over," repeated Cipolla. "What else can you do? With a colic like that you *must* bend. Surely you will not struggle against the performance of a perfectly natural action just because somebody suggests it to you?"

Slowly the youth lifted his forearms, folded and squeezed them across his body; it turned a little sideways, then bent, lower and lower, the feet shifted, the knees turned inward, until he had become a picture of writhing pain, until he all but groveled upon the ground. Cipolla let him stand for some seconds thus, then made a short cut through the air with his whip and went with his scooping stride back to the little table, where he poured himself out a cognac.

"*Il boit beaucoup* [He drinks a lot]," asserted a lady behind us. Was that the only thing that struck her? We could not tell how far the audience grasped the situation. The fellow was standing upright again, with a sheepish grin—he looked as though he scarcely knew how it had all happened. The scene had been followed with tense interest and applauded at the end; there were shouts of "*Bravo, Cipolla!*" and "*Bravo, giovanotto!*" Apparently the issue of the duel was not looked upon as a personal defeat for the young man. Rather the audience encouraged him as one does an actor who succeeds in an unsympathetic role. Certainly his way of screwing himself up with cramp had been highly picturesque, its appeal was directly calculated to impress the gallery—in short, a fine dramatic performance. But I am not sure how far the audience were moved by that natural tactfulness in which the south excels, or how far it penetrated into the nature of what was going on.

The Cavaliere, refreshed, had lighted another cigarette. The numerical tests might now proceed. A young man was easily found in the back row who was willing to write down on the blackboard the numbers as they were dictated to him. Him too we knew; the whole entertainment had taken on an intimate character through our acquaintance with so many of the actors. This was the man who worked at the greengrocer's in the main street; he had served us several times, with neatness and dispatch. He wielded the chalk with clerkly confidence, while Cipolla descended to our level and walked with his deformed gait through the audience, collecting numbers as they were given, in two, three, and four places, and calling them out to the grocer's assistant, who wrote them down in a column. In all this, everything on both sides was calculated to amuse, with its jokes and its oratorical asides. The artist could not fail to hit on foreigners, who were not ready with their figures, and with them he was elaborately patient and chivalrous, to the great amusement of the natives, whom he reduced to confusion in their turn, by making them translate numbers that were given in English or French. Some people gave dates concerned with great events in Italian history. Cipolla took them up at once and made patriotic comments. Somebody shouted "Number one!" The Cavaliere, incensed at this as at every attempt to make game of him, retorted over his shoulder that he could not take less than two-place figures. Whereupon another joker cried out "Number two!" and was greeted with the applause and laughter which every reference to natural functions is sure to win among southerners.

When fifteen numbers stood in a long straggling row on the board, Cipolla called for a general adding match. Ready reckoners might add in their heads, but pencil and paper were not forbidden. Cipolla, while the work went on, sat on his chair near the blackboard, smoked and grimaced, with the complacent, pompous air cripples so often have. The five-place addition was soon done. Somebody announced the answer, somebody else confirmed it, a third had arrived at a slightly different result, but the fourth agreed with the first and second. Cipolla got up, tapped some ash from his coat, and lifted the paper at the upper right-hand corner of the board to display the writing. The correct answer, a sum close on a million, stood there; he had written it down beforehand.

Astonishment, and loud applause. The children were overwhelmed. How had he done that, they wanted to know. We told them it was a trick, not easily explainable offhand. In short, the man was a conjuror. This was what a sleight-of-hand evening was like, so now they knew. First the fisherman had cramp, and then the right answer was written down beforehand—it was all simply glorious, and we saw with dismay that despite the hot eyes and the hand of the clock at almost half past ten, it would be very hard to get them away. There would be tears. And yet it was plain that this magician did not "magick"—at least not in the accepted sense of manual dexterity—and that the entertainment was not at all suitable for children. Again, I do not know, either, what the audience really thought. Obviously there was grave doubt whether its answers had been given of "free choice"; here and there an individual might have answered of his own motion, but on the whole Cipolla certainly selected his people and thus kept the whole procedure in his own hands and directed it towards the given result. Even so, one had to admire the quickness of his calculations, however much one felt disinclined to admire anything else about the performance. Then his patriotism, his irritable sense of dignity—the Cavaliere's own countrymen might feel in their element with all that and continue in a laughing mood; but the combination certainly gave us outsiders food for thought.

Cipolla himself saw to it—though without giving them a name—that the nature of his powers should be clear beyond a doubt to even the least-instructed person. He alluded to them, of course, in his talk—and he talked without stopping—but only in vague, boastful, self-advertising phrases. He went on awhile with experiments on the same lines as the first, merely making them more complicated by introducing operations in multiplying, subtracting, and dividing; then he simplified them to the last degree in order to bring out the method. He simply had numbers "guessed" which were previously written under the paper; and the guess was nearly always right. One guesser admitted that he had had in mind to give a certain number, when Cipolla's whip went whistling through the air, and a quite different one slipped out, which proved to be the "right" one. Cipolla's shoulders shook. He pretended admiration for the powers of the people he questioned. But in all his compliments there was something fleering and derogatory; the victims could scarcely have relished them much, although they smiled, and although they might easily have set down some part of the applause to their own credit. Moreover, I had not the impression that the artist was popular with his public. A certain ill will and reluctance were in the air, but courtesy kept such feelings in check, as did Cipolla's competency and his stern self-confidence. Even the riding whip, I think, did much to keep rebellion from becoming overt.

From tricks with numbers he passed to tricks with cards. There were two packs, which he drew out of his pockets, and so much I still remember, that the basis of the tricks he played with them was as follows: From the first pack he drew three cards and thrust them without looking at them inside his coat. Another person then drew three out of the second

pack, and these turned out to be the same as the first three—not invariably all the three, for it did happen that only two were the same. But in
the majority of cases Cipolla triumphed, showing his three cards with a
little bow in acknowledgment of the applause with which his audience
conceded his possession of strange powers—strange whether for good or
evil. A young man in the front row, to our right, an Italian, with proud,
finely chiseled features, rose up and said that he intended to assert his
own will in his choice and consciously to resist any influence, of whatever
sort. Under these circumstances, what did Cipolla think would be the result? "You will," answered the Cavaliere, "make my task somewhat more
difficult thereby. As for the result, your resistance will not alter it in the
least. Freedom exists, and also the will exists; but freedom of the will does
not exist, for a will that aims at its own freedom aims at the unknown.
You are free to draw or not to draw. But if you draw, you will draw the
right cards—the more certainly, the more willfully obstinate your behavior."

One must admit that he could not have chosen his words better, to
trouble the waters and confuse the mind. The refractory youth hesitated
before drawing. Then he pulled out a card and at once demanded to see
if it was among the chosen three. "But why?" queried Cipolla. "Why do
things by halves?" Then, as the other defiantly insisted, *"E servito,"* said
the juggler, with a gesture of exaggerated servility; and held out the three
cards fanwise, without looking at them himself. The left-hand card was
the one drawn.

Amid general applause, the apostle of freedom sat down. How far
Cipolla employed small tricks and manual dexterity to help out his natural talents, the deuce only knew. But even without them the result would
have been the same: the curiosity of the entire audience was unbounded
and universal, everybody both enjoyed the amazing character of the
entertainment and unanimously conceded the professional skill of the
performer. *"Lavora bene* [He works well]," we heard, here and there in
our neighborhood; it signified the triumph of objective judgment over
antipathy and repressed resentment.

After his last, incomplete, yet so much the more telling, success, Cipolla
had at once fortified himself with another cognac. Truly he did "drink a
lot," and the fact made a bad impression. But obviously he needed the
liquor and the cigarettes for the replenishment of his energy, upon which,
as he himself said, heavy demands were made in all directions. Certainly
in the intervals he looked very ill, exhausted and hollow-eyed. Then the
little glassful would redress the balance, and the flow of lively, self-

confident chatter run on, while the smoke he inhaled gushed out gray from his lungs. I clearly recall that he passed from the card tricks to parlor games—the kind based on certain powers which in human nature are higher or else lower than human reason: on intuition and "magnetic" transmission; in short, upon a low type of manifestation. What I do not remember is the precise order things came in. And I will not bore you with a description of these experiments; everybody knows them, everybody has at one time or another taken part in this finding of hidden articles, this blind carrying out of a series of acts, directed by a force that proceeds from organism to organism by unexplored paths. Everybody has had his little glimpse into the equivocal, impure, inexplicable nature of the occult, has been conscious of both curiosity and contempt, has shaken his head over the human tendency of those who deal in it to help themselves out with humbuggery, though, after all, the humbuggery is no disproof whatever of the genuiness of the other elements in the dubious amalgam. I can only say here that each single circumstance gains in weight and the whole greatly in impressiveness when it is a man like Cipolla who is the chief actor and guiding spirit in the sinister business. He sat smoking at the rear of the stage, his back to the audience while they conferred. The object passed from hand to hand which it was his task to find, with which he was to perform some action agreed upon beforehand. Then he would start to move zigzag through the hall, with his head thrown back and one hand outstretched, the other clasped in that of a guide who was in the secret but enjoined to keep himself perfectly passive, with his thoughts directed upon the agreed goal. Cipolla moved with the bearing typical in these experiments: now groping upon a false start, now with a quick forward thrust, now pausing as though to listen and by sudden inspiration correcting his course. The roles seemed reversed, the stream of influence was moving in the contrary direction, as the artist himself pointed out, in his ceaseless flow of discourse. The suffering, receptive, performing part was now his, the will he had before imposed on others was shut out, he acted in obedience to a voiceless common will which was in the air. But he made it perfectly clear that it all came to the same thing. The capacity for self-surrender, he said, for becoming a tool, for the most unconditional and utter self-abnegation, was but the reverse side of that other power to will and to command. Commanding and obeying formed together one single principle, one indissoluble unity; he who knew how to obey knew also how to command, and conversely; the one idea was comprehended in the other, as people and leader were comprehended in one another. But that which was *done,* the highly exacting and exhausting performance, was in every case his, the leader's and mover's, in whom the will became obedience, the obedience will, whose person was the cradle and womb of both, and who thus suffered enormous hardship. Repeatedly he emphasized the fact that his lot was a hard one—presumably to account for his need of stimulant and his frequent recourse to the little glass.

Thus he groped his way forward, like a blind seer, led and sustained by the mysterious common will. He drew a pin set with a stone out of its hiding place in an Englishwoman's shoe, carried it, halting and pressing on by turns, to another lady—Signora Angiolieri—and handed it to her on bended knee, with the words it had been agreed he was to utter. "I present you with this in token of my respect" was the sentence. Their sense was obvious, but the words themselves not easy to hit upon, for the reason that they had been agreed on in French; the language complication seemed to us a little malicious, implying as it did a conflict between the audience's natural interest in the success of the miracle and their desire to witness the humiliation of this presumptuous man. It was a strange sight: Cipolla on his knees before the Signora, wrestling, amid efforts at speech, after knowledge of the preordained words. "I must say something," he said, "and I feel clearly what it is I must say. But I also feel that if it passed my lips it would be wrong. Be careful not to help me unintentionally!" he cried out, though very likely that was precisely what he was hoping for. "*Pensez très fort* [Think very hard]," he cried all at once, in bad French, and then burst out with the required words—in Italian, indeed, but with the final substantive pronounced in the sister tongue, in which he was probably far from fluent: he said *vénération* instead of *venerazione,* with an impossible nasal. And this partial success, after the complete success before it, the finding of the pin, the presentation of it on his knees to the right person—was almost more impressive than if he had got the sentence exactly right, and evoked bursts of admiring applause.

Cipolla got up from his knees and wiped the perspiration from his brow. You understand that this experiment with the pin was a single case, which I describe because it sticks in my memory. But he changed his method several times and improvised a number of variations suggested by his contact with his audience; a good deal of time thus went by. He seemed to get particular inspiration from the person of our landlady; she drew him on to the most extraordinary displays of clairvoyance. "It does not escape me, madame," he said to her, "that there is something unusual about you, some special and honorable distinction. He who has eyes to see descries about your lovely brow an aureola—if I mistake not, it once was stronger than now—a slowly paling radiance . . . hush, not a word! Don't help me. Beside you sits your husband—yes?" He turned towards the silent Signor Angiolieri. "You are the husband of this lady, and your happiness is complete. But in the midst of this happiness memories rise . . . the past, Signora, so it seems to me, plays an important part in your present. You knew a king . . . has not a king crossed your path in bygone days?"

"No," breathed the dispenser of our midday soup, her golden-brown eyes gleaming in the noble pallor of her face.

"No? No, not a king; I meant that generally, I did not mean literally a king. Not a king, not a prince, and a prince after all, a king of a loftier realm; it was a great artist, at whose side you once—you would contradict me, and yet I am not wholly wrong. Well, then! It was a woman, a great, a world-renowned woman artist, whose friendship you enjoyed in your tender years, whose sacred memory overshadows and transfigures your whole existence. Her name? Need I utter it, whose fame has long been bound up with the Fatherland's, immortal as its own? Eleonora Duse," he finished, softly and with much solemnity.

The little woman bowed her head, overcome. The applause was like a patriotic demonstration. Nearly everyone there knew about Signora Angiolieri's wonderful past; they were all able to confirm the Cavaliere's intuition—not least the present guests of Casa Eleonora. But we wondered how much of the truth he had learned as the result of professional inquiries made on his arrival. Yet I see no reason at all to cast doubt, on rational grounds, upon powers which, before our very eyes, became fatal to their possessor.

At this point there was an intermission. Our lord and master withdrew. Now I confess that almost ever since the beginning of my tale I have looked forward with dread to this moment in it. The thoughts of men are mostly not hard to read; in this case they are very easy. You are sure to ask why we did not choose this moment to go away—and I must continue to owe you an answer. I do not know why. I cannot defend myself. By this time it was certainly eleven, probably later. The children were asleep. The last series of tests had been too long, nature had had her way. They were sleeping in our laps, the little one on mine, the boy on his mother's. That was, in a way, a consolation; but at the same time it was also ground for compassion and a clear leading to take them home to bed. And I give you my word that we wanted to obey this touching admonition, we seriously wanted to. We roused the poor things and told them it was now high time to go. But they were no sooner conscious than they began to resist and implore—you know how horrified children are at the thought of leaving before the end of a thing. No cajoling has any effect; you have to use force. It was so lovely, they wailed. How did we know what was coming next? Surely we could not leave until after the intermission; they liked a little nap now and again—only not go home, only not go to bed, while the beautiful evening was still going on!

We yielded, but only for the moment, of course—so far as we knew—only for a little while, just a few minutes longer. I cannot excuse our staying, scarcely can I even understand it. Did we think, having once said A, we had to say B—having once brought the children hither we had to let them stay? No, it is not good enough. Were we ourselves so highly entertained? Yes, and no. Our feelings for Cavaliere Cipolla were of a very mixed kind, but so were the feelings of the whole audience, if I mistake not, and nobody left. Were we under the sway of a fascination which emanated from this man who took so strange a way to earn his bread; a fascination which he gave out independently of the program and even between the tricks and which paralyzed our resolve? Again, sheer curiosity may account for something. One was curious to know how such an evening turned out; Cipolla in his remarks having all along hinted that he had tricks in his bag stranger than any he had yet produced.

But all that is not it—or at least it is not all of it. More correct it would be to answer the first question with another. Why had we not left Torre di Venere itself before now? To me the two questions are one and the same, and in order to get out of the impasse I might simply say that I had answered it already. For, as things had been in Torre in general: queer, uncomfortable, troublesome, tense, oppressive, so precisely they were here in this hall tonight. Yes, more than precisely. For it seemed to be the fountainhead of all the uncanniness and all the strained feelings which had oppressed the atmosphere of our holiday. This man whose return to the stage we were awaiting was the personification of all that; and, as we had not gone away in general, so to speak, it would have been inconsistent to do it in the particular case. You may call this an explanation, you may call it inertia, as you see fit. Any argument more to the purpose I simply do not know how to adduce.

Well, there was an interval of ten minutes, which grew into nearly twenty. The children remained awake. They were enchanted by our compliance, and filled the break to their own satisfaction by renewing relations with the popular sphere, with Antonio, Guiscardo, and the canoe man. They put their hands to their mouths and called messages across, appealing to us for the Italian words. "Hope you have a good catch tomorrow, a whole netful!" They called to Mario, Esquisito Mario: *"Mario, una cioccolata e biscotti* [a chocolate and biscuits]!" And this time he heeded and answered with a smile: *"Subito, signorini* [Right away ladies]!" Later we had reason to recall this kindly, if rather absent and pensive, smile.

Thus the interval passed, the gong sounded. The audience, which had scattered in conversation, took their places again; the children sat up straight in their chairs with their hands in their laps. The curtain had not been dropped. Cipolla came forward again, with his dipping stride, and began to introduce the second half of the program with a lecture.

Let me state once for all that this self-confident cripple was the most powerful hypnotist I have ever seen in my life. It was pretty plain now that he threw dust in the public eye and advertised himself as a presti-digitator on account of police regulations which would have prevented him from making his living by the exercise of his powers. Perhaps this eyewash is the usual thing in Italy; it may be permitted or even connived at by the authorities. Certainly the man had from the beginning made little concealment of the actual nature of his operations; and this second half of the program was quite frankly and exclusively devoted to one sort of experiment. While he still practiced some rhetorical circumlocutions, the tests themselves were one long series of attacks upon the will power, the loss or compulsion of volition. Comic, exciting, amazing by turns, by midnight they were still in full swing; we ran the gamut of all the phenomena this natural-unnatural field has to show, from the unimpressive at one end of the scale to the monstrous at the other. The audience laughed and applauded as they followed the grotesque details; shook their heads, clapped their knees, fell very frankly under the spell of this stern, self-assured personality. At the same time I saw signs that they were not quite complacent, not quite unconscious of the peculiar ignominy which lay, for the individual and for the general, in Cipolla's triumphs.

Two main features were constant in all the experiments: the liqueur glass and the claw-handled riding whip. The first was always invoked to add fuel to his demoniac fires; without it, apparently, they might have burned out. On this score we might even have felt pity for the man; but the whistle of his scourge, the insulting symbol of his domination, before which we all cowered, drowned out every sensation save a dazed and outbraved submission to his power. Did he then lay claim to our sympathy to boot? I was struck by a remark he made—it suggested no less. At the climax of his experiments, by stroking and breathing upon a certain young man who had offered himself as a subject and already proved himself a particularly susceptible one, he had not only put him into the condition known as deep trance and extended his insensible body by neck and feet across the backs of two chairs, but had actually sat down on the rigid form as on a bench, without making it yield. The sight of this unholy figure in a frock coat squatted on the stiff body was horrible and incredible; the audience, convinced that the victim of this scientific diversion must be suffering, expressed its sympathy: *"Ah, poveretto!"* Poor soul, poor soul! *"Poor soul!"* Cipolla mocked them, with some bitterness. "Ladies and gentlemen, you are barking up the wrong tree. *Sono io il poveretto.* I am the person who is suffering, I am the one to be pitied." We pocketed the information. Very good. Maybe the experiment was at his expense, maybe it was he who had suffered the cramp when the *giovanotto* over there had made the faces. But appearances were all against it; and one does not feel like saying *poveretto* to a man who is suffering to bring about the humiliation of others.

I have got ahead of my story and lost sight of the sequence of events. To this day my mind is full of the Cavaliere's feats of endurance; only I do not recall them in their order—which does not matter. So much I do know: that the longer and more circumstantial tests, which got the most applause, impressed me less than some of the small ones which passed quickly over. I remember the young man whose body Cipolla converted into a board, only because of the accompanying remarks which I have quoted. An elderly lady in a cane-seated chair was lulled by Cipolla in the delusion that she was on a voyage to India and gave a voluble account of her adventures by land and sea. But I found this phenomenon less impressive than one which followed immediately after the intermission. A tall, well-built, soldierly man was unable to lift his arm after the hunchback had told him that he could not and given a cut through the air with his whip. I can still see the face of that stately. mustachioed colonel smiling and clenching his teeth as he struggled to regain his lost freedom of action. A staggering performance! He seemed to be exerting his will, and in vain; the trouble, however, was probably simply that he could not will. There was involved here that recoil of the will upon itself which paralyzes choice—as our tyrant had previously explained to the Roman gentleman.

Still less can I forget the touching scene, at once comic and horrible, with Signora Angiolieri. The Cavaliere, probably in his first bold survey of the room, had spied out her ethereal lack of resistance to his power.

For actually he bewitched her, literally drew her out of her seat, out of her row, and away with him whither he willed. And in order to enhance his effect, he bade Signor Angiolieri call upon his wife by her name, to throw, as it were, all the weight of his existence and his rights in her into the scale, to rouse by the voice of her husband everything in his spouse's soul which could shield her virtue against the evil assaults of magic. And how vain it all was! Cipolla was standing at some distance from the couple, when he made a single cut with his whip through the air. It caused our landlady to shudder violently and turn her face towards him. "Sofronia!" cried Signor Angiolieri—we had not known that Signora Angiolieri's name was Sofronia. And he did well to call; everybody saw that there was no time to lose. His wife kept her face turned in the direction of the diabolical Cavaliere, who with his ten long yellow fingers was making passes at his victim, moving backwards as he did so, step by step. Then Signora Angiolieri, her pale face gleaming, rose up from her seat, turned right round, and began to glide after him. Fatal and forbidding sight! Her face as though moon-struck, stiff-armed, her lovely hands lifted a little at the wrists, the feet as it were together, she seemed to float slowly out of her row and after the tempter. "Call her, sir, keep on calling," prompted the redoubtable man. And Signor Angiolieri, in a weak voice, called: "Sofronia!" Ah, again and again he called; as his wife went further off he even curved one hand round his lips and beckoned with the other as he called. But the poor voice of love and duty echoed unheard, in vain, behind the lost one's back; the Signora swayed along, moon-struck, deaf, enslaved; she glided into the middle aisle and down it towards the fingering hunchback, towards the door. We were driven to the conviction that she would have followed her master, had he so willed it, to the ends of the earth.

"*Accidente!*" cried out Signor Angiolieri, in genuine affright, springing up as the exit was reached. But at the same moment the Cavaliere put aside, as it were, the triumphal crown and broke off. "Enough, Signora, I thank you," he said, and offered his arm to lead her back to her husband. "Signor," he greeted the latter, "here is your wife. Unharmed, with my compliments, I give her into your hands. Cherish with all the strength of your manhood a treasure which is so wholly yours, and let your zeal be quickened by knowing that there are powers stronger than reason or virtue, and not always so magnanimously ready to relinquish their prey!"

Poor Signor Angiolieri, so quiet, so bald! He did not look as though he would know how to defend his happiness, even against powers much less demoniac than these which were now adding mockery to frightfulness.

Solemnly and pompously the Cavaliere retired to the stage, amid applause to which his eloquence gave double strength. It was this particular episode, I feel sure, that set the seal upon his ascendancy. For now he made them dance, yes, literally; and the dancing lent a dissolute, abandoned, topsy-turvy air to the scene, a drunken abdication of the critical spirit which had so long resisted the spell of this man. Yes, he had had to fight to get the upper hand—for instance against the animosity of the young Roman gentleman, whose rebellious spirit threatened to serve others as a rallying point. But it was precisely upon the importance of example that the Cavaliere was so strong. He had the wit to make his attack at the weakest point and to choose as his first victim that feeble, ecstatic youth whom he had previously made into a board. The master had but to look at him, when this young man would fling himself back as though struck by lightning, place his hands rigidly at his sides, and fall into a state of military somnambulism, in which it was plain to any eye that he was open to the most absurd suggestion that might be made to him. He seemed quite content in his abject state, quite pleased to be relieved of the burden of voluntary choice. Again and again he offered himself as a subject and gloried in the model facility he had in losing consciousness. So now he mounted the platform, and a single cut of the whip was enough to make him dance to the Cavaliere's orders, in a kind of complacent ecstasy, eyes closed, head nodding, lank limbs flying in all directions.

It looked unmistakably like enjoyment, and other recruits were not long in coming forward: two other young men, one humbly and one well dressed, were soon jigging alongside the first. But now the gentleman from Rome bobbed up again, asking defiantly if the Cavaliere would engage to make him dance too, even against his will.

"Even against your will," answered Cipolla, in unforgettable accents. That frightful *"anche se non vuole"* still rings in my ears. The struggle began. After Cipolla had taken another little glass and lighted a fresh cigarette he stationed the Roman at a point in the middle aisle and himself took up a position some distance behind, making his whip whistle through the air as he gave the order: *"Balla!"* His opponent did not stir. *"Balla!"* repeated the Cavaliere incisively, and snapped his whip. You saw the young man move his neck round in his collar; at the same time one hand lifted slightly at the wrist, one ankle turned outward. But that was all, for the time at least; merely a tendency to twitch, now sternly repressed, now seeming about to get the upper hand. It escaped nobody that here a heroic obstinacy, a fixed resolve to resist, must needs be conquered; we were beholding a gallant effort to strike out and save the honor of the human race. He twitched but danced not; and the struggle was so prolonged that the Cavaliere had to divide his attention between it and the stage, turning now and then to make his riding whip whistle in the direction of the dancers, as it were to keep them in leash. At the same time he advised the audience that no fatigue was involved in such activities, however long they went on, since it was not the automatons up there who danced, but himself. Then once more his eye would bore itself into the back of the Roman's neck and lay siege to the strength of purpose which defied him.

One saw it waver, that strength of purpose, beneath the repeated summons and whipcrackings. Saw with an objective interest which yet was not quite free from traces of sympathetic emotion—from pity, even from a cruel kind of pleasure. If I understand what was going on, it was the negative character of the young man's fighting position which was his undoing. It is likely that not willing is not a practicable state of mind; *not* to want to do something may be in the long run a mental content impossible to subsist on. Between not willing a certain thing and not willing at all—in other words, yielding to another person's will—there may lie too small a space for the idea of freedom to squeeze into. Again, there were the Cavaliere's persuasive words, woven in among the whipcrackings and commands, as he mingled effects that were his own secret with others of a bewilderingly psychological kind. "*Balla!*" said he. "Who wants to torture himself like that? Is forcing yourself your idea of freedom? *Una ballatina!* Why, your arms and legs are aching for it. What a relief to give way to them—there, you are dancing already! That is no struggle any more, it is a pleasure!" And so it was. The jerking and twitching of the refractory youth's limbs had at last got the upper hand; he lifted his arms, then his knees, his joints quite suddenly relaxed, he flung his legs and danced, and amid bursts of applause the Cavaliere led him to join the row of puppets on the stage. Up there we could see his face as he "enjoyed" himself; it was clothed in a broad grin and the eyes were half shut. In a way, it was consoling to see that he was having a better time than he had had in the hour of his pride.

His "fall" was, I may say, an epoch. The ice was completely broken. Cipolla's triumph had reached its height. The Circe's wand, that whistling leather whip with the claw handle, held absolute sway. At one time —it must have been well after midnight—not only were there eight or ten persons dancing on the little stage, but in the hall below a varied animation reigned, and a long-toothed Anglo-Saxoness in a pince-nez left

her seat of her own motion to perform a tarantella in the center aisle.
Cipolla was lounging in a cane-seated chair at the left of the stage, gulp-
ing down the smoke of a cigarette and breathing it impudently out
through his bad teeth. He tapped his foot and shrugged his shoulders,
looking down upon the abandoned scene in the hall; now and then he
snapped his whip backwards at a laggard upon the stage. The children
were awake at the moment. With shame I speak of them. For it was
not good to be here, least of all for them; that we had not taken them
away can only be explained by saying that we had caught the general
devil-may-careness of the hour. By that time it was all one. Anyhow,
thank goodness, they lacked understanding for the disreputable side of
the entertainment, and in their innocence were perpetually charmed by
the unheard-of indulgence which permitted them to be present at such
a thing as a magician's "evening." Whole quarter hours at a time they
drowsed on our laps, waking refreshed and rosy-cheeked, with sleep-
drunken eyes, to laugh to bursting at the leaps and jumps the magician
made those people up there make. They had not thought it would be so
jolly; they joined with their clumsy little hands in every round of applause. And jumped for joy upon their chairs, as was their wont, when
Cipolla beckoned to their friend Mario from the Esquisito, beckoned to
him just like a picture in a book, holding his hand in front of his nose
and bending and straightening the forefinger by turns.

Mario obeyed. I can see him now going up the stairs to Cipolla, who
continued to beckon him, in that droll, picture-book sort of way. He hesitated for a moment at first; that, too, I recall quite clearly. During the
whole evening he had lounged against a wooden pillar at the side entrance, with his arms folded, or else with his hands thrust into his jacket
pockets. He was on our left, near the youth with the militant hair, and
had followed the performance attentively, so far as we had seen, if with
no particular animation and God knows how much comprehension. He
could not much relish being summoned thus, at the end of the evening.
But it was only too easy to see why he obeyed. After all, obedience was
his calling in life; and then, how should a simple lad like him find it
within his human capacity to refuse compliance to a man so throned and
crowned as Cipolla at that hour? Willy-nilly he left his column and with
a word of thanks to those making way for him he mounted the steps with
a doubtful smile on his full lips.

Picture a thickset youth of twenty years, with clipped hair, a low forehead, and heavy-lidded eyes of an indefinite gray, shot with green and
yellow. These things I knew from having spoken with him, as we often

had. There was a saddle of freckles on the flat nose, the whole upper half
of the face retreated behind the lower, and that again was dominated by
thick lips that parted to show the salivated teeth. These thick lips and
the veiled look of the eyes lent the whole face a primitive melancholy—
it was that which had drawn us to him from the first. In it was not the
faintest trace of brutality—indeed, his hands would have given the lie to
such an idea, being unusually slender and delicate even for a southerner.
They were hands by which one liked being served.

We knew him humanly without knowing him personally, if I may make
that distinction. We saw him nearly every day, and felt a certain kindness
for his dreamy ways, which might at times be actual inattentiveness, suddenly transformed into a redeeming zeal to serve. His mien was serious;
only the children could bring a smile to his face. It was not sulky, but
uningratiating, without intentional effort to please—or, rather, it seemed
to give up being pleasant in the conviction that it could not succeed. We
should have remembered Mario in any case, as one of those homely recollections of travel which often stick in the mind better than more important ones. But of his circumstances we knew no more than that his father
was a petty clerk in the Municipio and his mother took in washing.

His white waiter's-coat became him better than the faded striped suit
he wore, with a gay colored scarf instead of a collar, the ends tucked
into his jacket. He neared Cipolla, who however did not leave off that
motion of his finger before his nose, so that Mario had to come still closer,
right up to the chair seat and the master's legs. Whereupon the latter
spread out his elbows and seized the lad, turning him so that we had a
view of his face. Then gazed him briskly up and down, with a careless,
commanding eye.

"Well, *ragazzo mio* [my boy], how comes it we make acquaintance so
late in the day? But believe me, I made yours long ago. Yes, yes, I've had
you in my eye this long while and known what good stuff you were made
of. How could I go and forget you again? Well, I've had a good deal to
think about. . . . Now tell me, what is your name? The first name, that's
all I want."

"My name is Mario," the young man answered, in a low voice.

"Ah, Mario. Very good. Yes, yes, there is such a name, quite a common
name, a classic name too, one of those which preserve the heroic tradi-
tions of the Fatherland. *Bravo! Salve!*" And he flung up his arm slantingly
above his crooked shoulder, palm outward, in the Roman salute. He may
have been slightly tipsy by now, and no wonder; but he spoke as before,
clearly, fluently, and with emphasis. Though about this time there had

crept into his voice a gross, autocratic note, and a kind of arrogance was in his sprawl.

"Well, now, Mario *mio*," he went on, "it's a good thing you came this evening, and that's a pretty scarf you've got on; it is becoming to your style of beauty. It must stand you in good stead with the girls, the pretty pretty girls of Torre—"

From the row of youths, close by the place where Mario had been standing, sounded a laugh. It came from the youth with the militant hair. He stood there, his jacket over his shoulder, and laughed outright, rudely and scornfully.

Mario gave a start. I think it was a shrug, but he may have started and then hastened to cover the movement by shrugging his shoulders, as much as to say that the neckerchief and the fair sex were matters of equal indifference to him.

The Cavaliere gave a downward glance.

"We needn't trouble about him," he said. "He is jealous, because your scarf is so popular with the girls, maybe partly because you and I are so friendly up here. Perhaps he'd like me to put him in mind of his colic— I could do it free of charge. Tell me, Mario. You've come here this evening for a bit of fun—and in the daytime you work in an ironmonger's shop?"

"In a café," corrected the youth.

"Oh, in a café. That's where Cipolla nearly came a cropper! What you are is a cupbearer, a Ganymede—I like that, it is another classical allusion—*Salvietta!*" Again the Cavaliere saluted, to the huge gratification of his audience.

Mario smiled too. "But before that," he interpolated, in the interest of accuracy, "I worked for a while in a shop in Portoclemente." He seemed visited by a natural desire to assist the prophecy by dredging out its essential features.

"There, didn't I say so? In an ironmonger's shop?"

"They kept combs and brushes," Mario got round it.

"Didn't I say that you were not always a Ganymede? Not always at the sign of the serviette? Even when Cipolla makes a mistake, it is a kind that makes you believe in him. Now tell me: Do you believe in me?"

An indefinite gesture.

"A halfway answer," commented the Cavaliere. "Probably it is not easy to win your confidence. Even for me, I can see, it is not so easy. I see in your features a reserve, a sadness, *un tratto di malinconia* [a trace of melancholy] . . . tell me" (he seized Mario's hand persuasively) "have you troubles?"

"*Nossignore*," answered Mario, promptly and decidedly.

"You *have* troubles," insisted the Cavaliere, bearing down the denial by the weight of his authority. "Can't I see? Trying to pull the wool over Cipolla's eyes, are you? Of course, about the girls—it is a girl, isn't it? You have love troubles?"

Mario gave a vigorous headshake. And again the *giovanotto's* brutal laugh rang out. The Cavaliere gave heed. His eyes were roving about somewhere in the air: but he cocked an ear to the sound, then swung his whip backwards, as he had once or twice before in his conversation with Mario, that none of his puppets might flag in their zeal. The gesture had nearly cost him his new prey: Mario gave a sudden start in the direction of the steps. But Cipolla had him in his clutch.

"Not so fast," said he. "That would be fine, wouldn't it? So you want to skip, do you, Ganymede, right in the middle of the fun, or, rather, when it is just beginning? Stay with me, I'll show you something nice. I'll convince you. You have no reason to worry, I promise you. This girl— you know her and others know her too—what's her name? Wait! I read the name in your eyes, it is on the tip of my tongue and yours too—"

"Silvestra!" shouted the *giovanotto* from below.

The Cavaliere's face did not change.

"Aren't there the forward people?" he asked, not looking down, more as in undisturbed converse with Mario. "Aren't there the young fighting cocks that crow in season and out? Takes the word out of your mouth, the conceited fool, and seems to think he has some special right to it. Let him be. But Silvestra, your Silvestra—ah, what a girl that is! What a prize! Brings your heart into your mouth to see her walk or laugh or breathe, she is so lovely. And her round arms when she washes, and tosses her head back to get the hair out of her eyes! An angel from paradise!"

Mario started at him, his head thrust forward. He seemed to have forgotten the audience, forgotten where he was. The red rings round his eyes had got larger, they looked as though they were painted on. His thick lips parted.

"And she makes you suffer, this angel," went on Cipolla, "or, rather, you make yourself suffer for her—there is a difference, my lad, a most important difference, let me tell you. There are misunderstandings in love, maybe nowhere else in the world are there so many. I know what you are thinking: what does this Cipolla, with his little physical defect, know about love? Wrong, all wrong, he knows a lot. He has a wide and powerful understanding of its workings, and it pays to listen to his advice. But let's leave Cipolla out, cut him out altogether and think only of Silvestra, your peerless Silvestra! What! Is she to give any young gamecock the preference, so that he can laugh while you cry? To prefer him to a chap like you, so full of feeling and so sympathetic? Not very likely, is it? It is impossible—we know better, Cipolla and she. If I were to put myself in her place and choose between the two of you, a tarry lout like that—a codfish, a sea urchin—and a Mario, a knight of the serviette, who moves among gentlefolk and hands round refreshments with an air—my word, but my heart would speak in no uncertain tones—it knows to whom I gave it long ago. It is time that he should see and understand, my chosen one! It is time that you see me and recognize me, Mario, my beloved! Tell me, who am I?"

It was grisly, the way the betrayer made himself irresistible, wreathed and coquetted with his crooked shoulder, languished with the puffy eyes, and showed his splintered teeth in a sickly smile. And alas, at his beguiling words, what was come of our Mario? It is hard for me to tell, hard as it was for me to see; for here was nothing less than an utter abandonment of the inmost soul, a public exposure of timid and deluded passion and rapture. He put his hands across his mouth, his shoulders rose and fell with his pantings. He could not, it was plain, trust his eyes and ears for joy, and the one thing he forgot was precisely that he could not trust them. "Silvestra!" he breathed, from the very depths of his vanquished heart.

"Kiss me!" said the hunchback. "Trust me, I love thee. Kiss me here." And with the tip of his index finger, hand, arm, and little finger outspread, he pointed to his cheek, near the mouth. And Mario bent and kissed him.

It had grown very still in the room. That was a monstrous moment, grotesque and thrilling, the moment of Mario's bliss. In that evil span of time, crowded with a sense of the illusiveness of all joy, one sound became audible, and that not quite at once, but on the instant of the melancholy and ribald meeting between Mario's lips and the repulsive flesh which thrust itself forward for his caress. It was the sound of a laugh, from the *giovanotto* on our left. It broke into the dramatic suspense of the moment, coarse, mocking, and yet—or I must have been grossly mistaken—with an undertone of compassion for the poor, bewildered, victimized creature. It had a faint ring of that *"Poveretto"* which Cipolla had declared was wasted on the wrong person, when he claimed the pity for his own.

The laugh still rang in the air when the recipient of the caress gave his whip a little swish, low down, close to his chair leg, and Mario started up and flung himself back. He stood in that posture staring, his hands one over the other on those desecrated lips. Then he beat his temples with his clenched fists, over and over; turned and staggered down the steps, while the audience applauded, and Cipolla sat there with his hands in his lap, his shoulders shaking. Once below, and even while in full retreat, Mario hurled himself round with legs flung wide apart; one arm flew up, and two flat shattering detonations crashed through applause and laughter.

There was instant silence. Even the dancers came to a full stop and stared about, struck dumb. Cipolla bounded from his seat. He stood with his arms spread out, slanting as though to ward everybody off, as though next moment he would cry out: "Stop! Keep back! Silence! What was that?" Then, in that instant, he sank back in his seat, his head rolling on his chest; in the next he had fallen sideways to the floor, where he lay motionless, a huddled heap of clothing, with limbs awry.

The commotion was indescribable. Ladies hid their faces, shuddering, on the breasts of their escorts. There were shouts for a doctor, for the police. People flung themselves on Mario in a mob, to disarm him, to take away the weapon that hung from his fingers—that small, dull-metal, scarcely pistol-shaped tool with hardly any barrel—in how strange and unexpected a direction had fate leveled it!

And now—now finally, at last—we took the children and led them towards the exit, past the pair of *carabinieri* just entering. Was that the end, they wanted to know, that they might go in peace? Yes, we assured them, that was the end. An end of horror, a fatal end. And yet a liberation—for I could not, and I cannot, but find it so!

Isak Dinesen

1885–1962

Isak Dinesen (pen name of Karen Dinesen, later Baroness Blixen) was born in Denmark in 1885. Her father was a venturesome naval officer who lived for a while as a trapper among the Indians in Minnesota. She grew up near the sea and said later that she could not remember when she had first sailed a boat. In the years before World War I, she studied painting in Copenhagen, Paris, and Rome. She recalled that time as a period of free and youthful gaiety.

In 1914 she married Baron Bror von Blixen and went with him to British East Africa, later Kenya Colony. There, largely with capital borrowed from her family, they bought a big coffee plantation. It prospered. When they were divorced in 1921, Baroness Blixen took over the management of the estate. Much of the time she saw no fellow Europeans. She lived alone with the crews of fieldworkers and her household servants.

She began to write, as she said, "to amuse myself in the rainy season." Her Kikuyu servants would bow respectfully and ask "what God had now inspired me to write." In 1931, when the bottom fell out of the world coffee market, she gave up the plantation and went back to live with her mother on the family estate at Rungstedlund, Denmark.

She wrote *Seven Gothic Tales* in English. It was published in 1934. In *Out of Africa,* an account of her life on that continent, she returned to Danish. The English translation appeared in 1938. This was followed in 1943 by *Winter's Tales,* which contained the remarkable *Sorrow-Acre* (see below). During the Nazi occupation of Denmark in World War II, a novel by one "Pierre Andrézel" was published. Censors passed it as a harmless "Gothic romance," but the more knowing Danes recognized a satire on the invaders. In

1947 it came out in English, as *The Angelic Avengers,* under the proper pen name of its author, Isak Dinesen. She died in Denmark on September 7, 1962.

The Danish stories of Isak Dinesen take us back to the half-feudal world of Sigrid Undset and Giovanni Verga, or to Turgenev's *A Sportsman's Sketches.* In all these works, what we feel is the feudal spirit. The story, in fact, might conceivably happen at any time from, say, the twelfth century to World War I. But in *Sorrow-Acre* the period is clearly suggested. Heavy four-horse coaches, young Adam's hair caught with a ribbon, the powder in Sophie Magdalena's hair—what can this be but the late eighteenth century, or at most the early nineteenth?

Sorrow-Acre is no more than the story of a single day at a great Danish manor house, but it presents us with a human problem of such complexity that we can hardly be sure we understand it on first reading. Not that the story itself is difficult. Far from it. Indeed, it stirs us at once. Like Adam at first, we conceive a hot sympathy for the old woman and brush away all objections to it.

Perhaps we are right. Why not? we ask ourselves. Certainly what happens to Anne-Marie bears no likeness to any sort of justice we know. We go over the facts again, as the old lord tells them to Adam. Someone has burned down the barn at Rødmose-gaard. Two men bring the boy Goske to the old lord and charge that they saw him near the barn that night. They are known to be hostile to him. He protests that he is innocent.

The old lord orders him to be locked up. But the judge, he says, "is a fool, and would naturally do nothing but what he thought I wished him to do." At this point the widow Anne-Marie, Goske's mother, makes a weeping appeal for her son. Very well, says the old lord. If you can, between sunrise and sunset, reap this field of rye

---

Notes from the artist: "Isak Dinesen draped in the hooded black garments she affected and which gave her the appearance of being a character in one of her Seven Gothic Tales. *Her residence in Africa and use of it as a locale for some of her work suggested the drawings at left, which are derived from Bushman cave art."*

that we stand in with your own hands, your son may go free. And he adds that "the mowing of that field is a day's work to three men, or three days' work to one man." A little later he murmurs the strangest sentence of all: "We are not quibbling with the law, Anne-Marie and I."

Monstrous! we say to ourselves. What sort of cat-and-mouse game is this? And what was it the old lord had said earlier—that "power is in itself the supreme virtue"? We remember that he too has lost his only son, taken from him by a power against which there is no appeal. We begin to piece things together, as Adam did. We do not have Adam's reasons for love or gratitude. So, more quickly perhaps than Adam, we guess the secret. The old lord is playing god.

And what kind of god? Perhaps, as he has hinted, a god like the Roman Jove, who knows nothing of good or evil because the nature of his own being is the necessity of the world. What if this necessity includes setting some old woman an all-but-impossible task if she wishes to save the life of her son? Like Adam, we listen to the old lord's discourse on tragedy as "the right of human beings" and comedy as "a condescension of the divine to the world of man. . . ."

The old lord has made a decree. The old woman accepts it. Both have the sense that what is decreed must be. But there are compensations: like Adam, we hear the words of the little French song: "To die for what one loves/This is too sweet an effort. . . ." We reflect that a mother may welcome the chance to sacrifice herself for her son, and that other people may find in it a great community of feeling. Is this what the old lord meant? Perhaps. But behind all this, we glimpse for a moment, as Adam does, the freedom of the New World, where every man has the right to his own feelings.

Sorrow-Acre

T he low, undulating Danish landscape was silent and serene, mysteriously wide awake, in the hour before sunrise. There was not a cloud in the pale sky, not a shadow along the dim, pearly fields, hills, and woods. The mist was lifting from the valleys and hollows, the air was cool, the grass and the foliage dripping wet with morning dew. Unwatched by the eyes of man, and undisturbed by his activity, the country breathed a timeless life, to which language was inadequate.

All the same, a human race had lived on this land for a thousand years, had been formed by its soil and weather, and had marked it with its thoughts, so that now no one could tell where the existence of the one ceased and the other began. The thin grey line of a road, winding across the plain and up and down hills, was the fixed materialization of human longing, and of the human notion that it is better to be in one place than another.

A child of the country would read this open landscape like a book. The irregular mosaic of meadows and cornlands was a picture, in timid green and yellow, of the people's struggle for its daily bread; the centuries had taught it to plough and sow in this way. On a distant hill the immovable wings of a windmill, in a small blue cross against the sky, delineated a later stage in the career of bread. The blurred outline of thatched roofs—a low, brown growth of the earth—where the huts of the village thronged together, told the history, from his cradle to his grave of the peasant, the creature nearest to the soil and dependent on it, prospering in a fertile year and dying in years of drought and pests.

A little higher up, with the faint horizontal line of the white cemetery-wall round it, and the vertical contour of tall poplars by its side, the red-tiled church bore witness, as far as the eye reached, that this was a Christian country. The child of the land knew it as a strange house, inhabited only for a few hours every seventh day, but with a strong, clear

615

voice in it to give out the joys and sorrows of the land: a plain, square embodiment of the nation's trust in the justice and mercy of heaven. But where, amongst cupular woods and groves, the lordly, pyramidal silhouette of the cut lime avenues rose in the air, there a big country house lay.

The child of the land would read much within these elegant, geometrical ciphers on the hazy blue. They spoke of power, the lime trees paraded round a stronghold. Up here was decided the destiny of the surrounding land and of the men and beasts upon it, and the peasant lifted his eyes to the green pyramids with awe. They spoke of dignity, decorum and taste. Danish soil grew no finer flower than the mansion to which the long avenue led. In its lofty rooms life and death bore themselves with stately grace. The country house did not gaze upward, like the church, nor down to the ground like the huts; it had a wider earthly horizon than they, and was related to much noble architecture all over Europe. Foreign artisans had been called in to panel and stucco it, and its own inhabitants travelled and brought back ideas, fashions and things of beauty. Paintings, tapestries, silver and glass from distant countries had been made to feel at home here, and now formed part of Danish country life.

The big house stood as firmly rooted in the soil of Denmark as the peasants' huts, and was as faithfully allied to her four winds and her changing seasons, to her animal life, trees and flowers. Only its interests lay in a higher plane. Within the domain of the lime trees it was no longer cows, goats and pigs on which the minds and the talk ran, but horses and dogs. The wild fauna, the game of the land, that the peasant shook his fist at, when he saw it on his young green rye or in his ripening wheat field, to the residents of the country houses were the main pursuit and the joy of existence.

The writing in the sky solemnly proclaimed continuance, a worldly immortality. The great country houses had held their ground through many generations. The families who lived in them revered the past as they honoured themselves, for the history of Denmark was their own history.

A Rosenkrantz had sat at Rosenholm, a Juel at Hverringe, a Skeel at Gammel-Estrup as long as people remembered. They had seen kings and schools of style succeed one another and, proudly and humbly, had made over their personal existence to that of their land, so that amongst their equals and with the peasants they passed by its name: Rosenholm, Hverringe, Gammel-Estrup. To the King and the country, to his family and to the individual lord of the manor himself it was a matter of minor consequence which particular Rosenkrantz, Juel or Skeel, out of a long

row of fathers and sons, at the moment in his person incarnated the fields
and woods, the peasants, cattle and game of the estate. Many duties
rested on the shoulders of the big landowners—towards God in heaven,
towards the King, his neighbour and himself—and they were all harmo-
niously consolidated into the idea of his duties towards his land. Highest
amongst these ranked his obligation to uphold the sacred continuance,
and to produce a new Rosenkrantz, Juel or Skeel for the service of Rosenholm, Hverringe and Gammel-Estrup.

Female grace was prized in the manors. Together with good hunting
and fine wine it was the flower and emblem of the higher existence led
there, and in many ways the families prided themselves more on their
daughters than on their sons.

The ladies who promenaded in the lime avenues, or drove through
them in heavy coaches with four horses, carried the future of the name in
their laps and were, like dignified and debonair caryatides, holding up
the houses. They were themselves conscious of their value, kept up
their price, and moved in a sphere of pretty worship and self-worship.
They might even be thought to add to it, on their own, a graceful, arch,
paradoxical haughtiness. For how free were they, how powerful! Their
lords might rule the country, and allow themselves many liberties, but
when it came to that supreme matter of legitimacy which was the vital
principle of their world, the centre of gravity lay with them.

The lime trees were in bloom. But in the early morning only a faint
fragrance drifted through the garden, an airy message, an aromatic echo
of the dreams during the short summer night.

In a long avenue that led from the house all the way to the end of the
garden, where, from a small white pavilion in the classic style, there was
a great view over the fields, a young man walked. He was plainly dressed
in brown, with pretty linen and lace, bareheaded, with his hair tied by a
ribbon. He was dark, a strong and sturdy figure with fine eyes and hands;
he limped a little on one leg.

The big house at the top of the avenue, the garden and the fields had
been his childhood's paradise. But he had travelled and lived out of Denmark, in Rome and Paris, and he was at present appointed to the Danish
Legation to the Court of King George, the brother of the late, unfortunate young Danish Queen. He had not seen his ancestral home for nine
years. It made him laugh to find, now, everything so much smaller than
he remembered it, and at the same time he was strangely moved by
meeting it again. Dead people came towards him and smiled at him; a
small boy in a ruff ran past him with his hoop and kite, in passing gave

him a clear glance and laughingly asked: "Do you mean to tell me that you are I?" He tried to catch him in the flight, and to answer him: "Yes, I assure you that I am you," but the light figure did not wait for a reply.

The young man, whose name was Adam, stood in a particular relation to the house and the land. For six months he had been heir to all; nominally he was so even at this moment. It was this circumstance which had brought him from England, and on which his mind was dwelling, as he walked along slowly.

The old lord up at the manor, his father's brother, had had much misfortune in his domestic life. His wife had died young, and two of his children in infancy. The one son then left to him, his cousin's playmate, was a sickly and morose boy. For ten years the father travelled with him from one watering place to another, in Germany and Italy, hardly ever in other company than that of his silent, dying child, sheltering the faint flame of life with both hands, until such time as it could be passed over to a new bearer of the name. At the same time another misfortune had struck him: he fell into disfavour at Court, where till now he had held a fine position. He was about to rehabilitate his family's prestige through the marriage which he had arranged for his son, when before it could take place the bridegroom died, not yet twenty years old.

Adam learned of his cousin's death, and his own changed fortune, in England, through his ambitious and triumphant mother. He sat with her letter in his hand and did not know what to think about it.

If this, he reflected, had happened to him while he was still a boy, in Denmark, it would have meant all the world to him. It would be so now with his friends and schoolfellows, if they were in his place, and they would, at this moment, be congratulating or envying him. But he was neither covetous nor vain by nature; he had faith in his own talents and had been content to know that his success in life depended on his personal ability. His slight infirmity had always set him a little apart from other boys; it had, perhaps, given him a keener sensibility of many things in life, and he did not, now, deem it quite right that the head of the family should limp on one leg. He did not even see his prospects in the same light as his people at home. In England he had met with greater wealth and magnificence than they dreamed of; he had been in love with, and made happy by, an English lady of such rank and fortune that to her, he felt, the finest estate of Denmark would look but like a child's toy farm.

And in England, too, he had come in touch with the great new ideas of the age: of nature, of the right and freedom of man, of justice and beauty. The universe, through them, had become infinitely wider to him; he wanted to find out still more about it and was planning to travel to America, to the new world. For a moment he felt trapped and imprisoned, as if the dead people of his name, from the family vault at home, were stretching out their parched arms for him.

But at the same time he began to dream at night of the old house and garden. He had walked in these avenues in dream, and had smelled the scent of the flowering limes. When at Ranelagh an old gypsy woman looked at his hand and told him that a son of his was to sit in the seat of his fathers, he felt a sudden, deep satisfaction, queer in a young man who till now had never given his sons a thought.

Then, six months later, his mother again wrote to tell him that his uncle had himself married the girl intended for his dead son. The head of the family was still in his best age, not over sixty, and although Adam remembered him as a small, slight man, he was a vigorous person; it was likely that his young wife would bear him sons.

Adam's mother in her disappointment lay the blame on him. If he had returned to Denmark, she told him, his uncle might have come to look upon him as a son, and would not have married; nay, he might have handed the bride over to him. Adam knew better. The family estate, differing from the neighbouring properties, had gone down from father to son ever since a man of their name first sat there. The tradition of direct succession was the pride of the clan and a sacred dogma to his uncle; he would surely call for a son of his own flesh and bone.

But at the news the young man was seized by a strange, deep, aching remorse towards his old home in Denmark. It was as if he had been making light of a friendly and generous gesture, and disloyal to someone unfailingly loyal to him. It would be but just, he thought, if from now the place should disown and forget him. Nostalgia, which before he had never known, caught hold of him; for the first time he walked in the streets and parks of London as a stranger.

He wrote to his uncle and asked if he might come and stay with him, begged leave from the Legation and took ship for Denmark. He had come to the house to make his peace with it; he had slept little in the night, and was up so early and walking in the garden, to explain himself, and to be forgiven.

While he walked, the still garden slowly took up its day's work. A big snail, of the kind that his grandfather had brought back from France, and which he remembered eating in the house as a child, was already, with dignity, dragging a silver train down the avenue. The birds began to sing; in an old tree under which he stopped a number of them were worrying an owl; the rule of the night was over.

He stood at the end of the avenue and saw the sky lightening. An ecstatic clarity filled the world; in half an hour the sun would rise. A rye field here ran along the garden; two roe-deer were moving in it and looked roseate in the dawn. He gazed out over the fields, where as a small boy he had ridden his pony, and towards the wood where he had killed his first stag. He remembered the old servants who had taught him; some of them were now in their graves.

The ties which bound him to this place, he reflected, were of a mystic nature. He might never again come back to it, and it would make no difference. As long as a man of his own blood and name should sit in the house, hunt in the fields and be obeyed by the people in the huts, wherever he travelled on earth, in England or amongst the red Indians of America, he himself would still be safe, would still have a home, and would carry weight in the world.

His eyes rested on the church. In old days, before the time of Martin Luther, younger sons of great families, he knew, had entered the Church of Rome, and had given up individual wealth and happiness to serve the greater ideals. They, too, had bestowed honour upon their homes and were remembered in its registers. In the solitude of the morning half in jest he let his mind run as it listed; it seemed to him that he might speak to the land as to a person, as to the mother of his race. "Is it only my body that you want," he asked her, "while you reject my imagination, energy and emotions? If the world might be brought to acknowledge that the virtue of our name does not belong to the past only, will it give you no satisfaction?" The landscape was so still that he could not tell whether it answered him yes or no.

After a while he walked on, and came to the new French rose garden laid out for the young mistress of the house. In England he had acquired a freer taste in gardening, and he wondered if he could liberate these blushing captives, and make them thrive outside their cut hedges. Perhaps, he meditated, the elegantly conventional garden would be a floral portrait of his young aunt from Court, whom he had not yet seen.

As once more he came to the pavilion at the end of the avenue his eyes were caught by a bouquet of delicate colours which could not possibly belong to the Danish summer morning. It was in fact his uncle himself, powdered and silk-stockinged, but still in a brocade dressing-gown, and obviously sunk in deep thought. "And what business, or what meditations," Adam asked himself, "drags a connoisseur of the beautiful, but three months married to a wife of seventeen, from his bed into his garden before sunrise?" He walked up to the small, slim, straight figure.

His uncle on his side showed no surprise at seeing him, but then he rarely seemed surprised at anything. He greeted him, with a compliment on his matutinality, as kindly as he had done on his arrival last evening. After a moment he looked to the sky, and solemnly proclaimed: "It will be a hot day." Adam, as a child, had often been impressed by the grand, ceremonial manner in which the old lord would state the common happenings of existence; it looked as if nothing had changed here, but all was what it used to be.

The uncle offered the nephew a pinch of snuff. "No, thank you, Uncle," said Adam, "it would ruin my nose to the scent of your garden, which is as fresh as the Garden of Eden, newly created." "From every tree of which," said his uncle, smiling, "thou, my Adam, mayest freely eat." They slowly walked up the avenue together.

The hidden sun was now already gilding the top of the tallest trees. Adam talked of the beauties of nature, and of the greatness of Nordic scenery, less marked by the hand of man than that of Italy. His uncle took the praise of the landscape as a personal compliment, and congratulated him because he had not, in likeness to many young travellers in foreign countries, learned to despise his native land. No, said Adam, he had lately in England longed for the fields and woods of his Danish home. And he had there become acquainted with a new piece of Danish poetry which had enchanted him more than any English or French work. He named the author, Johannes Ewald, and quoted a few of the mighty, turbulent verses.

"And I have wondered, while I read," he went on after a pause, still moved by the lines he himself had declaimed, "that we have not till now understood how much our Nordic mythology in moral greatness surpasses that of Greece and Rome. If it had not been for the physical beauty of the ancient gods, which has come down to us in marble, no modern mind could hold them worthy of worship. They were mean, capricious and treacherous. The gods of our Danish forefathers are as much more divine than they as the Druid is nobler than the Augur. For the fair gods of Asgaard did possess the sublime human virtues; they were righteous, trustworthy, benevolent and even, within a barbaric age, chivalrous." His uncle here for the first time appeared to take any real interest in the conversation. He stopped, his majestic nose a little in the air. "Ah, it was easier to them," he said.

"What do you mean, Uncle?" Adam asked. "It was a great deal easier," said his uncle, "to the northern gods than to those of Greece to be, as you will have it, righteous and benevolent. To my mind it even reveals a weakness in the souls of our ancient Danes that they should consent to adore such divinities." "My dear Uncle," said Adam, smiling, "I have always felt that you would be familiar with the modes of Olympus. Now please let me share your insight, and tell me why virtue should come easier to our Danish gods than to those of milder climates." "They were not as powerful," said his uncle.

"And does power," Adam again asked, "stand in the way of virtue?" "Nay," said his uncle gravely. "Nay, power is in itself the supreme virtue. But the gods of which you speak were never all-powerful. They had, at all times, by their side those darker powers which they named the Jotuns, and who worked the suffering, the disasters, the ruin of our world. They might safely give themselves up to temperance and kindness. The omnipotent gods," he went on, "have no such facilitation. With their omnipotence they take over the woe of the universe."

They had walked up the avenue till they were in view of the house. The old lord stopped and ran his eyes over it. The stately building was the same as ever; behind the two tall front windows, Adam knew, was now his young aunt's room. His uncle turned and walked back.

"Chivalry," he said, "chivalry, of which you were speaking, is not a virtue of the omnipotent. It must needs imply mighty rival powers for the knight to defy. With a dragon inferior to him in strength, what figure will St. George cut? The knight who finds no superior forces ready to hand must invent them, and combat windmills; his knighthood itself stipulates dangers, vileness, darkness on all sides of him. Nay, believe me, my nephew, in spite of his moral worth, your chivalrous Odin of Asgaard as a Regent must take rank below that of Jove who avowed his sovereignty, and accepted the world which he ruled. But you are young," he added, "and the experience of the aged to you will sound pedantic."

He stood immovable for a moment and then with deep gravity proclaimed: "The sun is up."

The sun did indeed rise above the horizon. The wide landscape was suddenly animated by its splendour, and the dewy grass shone in a thousand gleams.

"I have listened to you, Uncle," said Adam, "with great interest. But while we have talked you yourself have seemed to me preoccupied; your eyes have rested on the field outside the garden, as if something of great moment, a matter of life and death, was going on there. Now that the sun is up, I see the mowers in the rye and hear them whetting their sickles. It is, I remember you telling me, the first day of the harvest. That is a great day to a landowner and enough to take his mind away from the gods. It is very fine weather, and I wish you a full barn."

The elder man stood still, his hands on his walking-stick. "There is indeed," he said at last, "something going on in that field, a matter of life and death. Come, let us sit down here, and I will tell you the whole story." They sat down on the seat that ran all along the pavilion, and while he spoke the old lord of the land did not take his eyes off the rye field.

"A week ago, on Thursday night," he said, "someone set fire to my barn at Rødmosegaard—you know the place, close to the moor—and burned it all down. For two or three days we could not lay hands on the offender. Then on Monday morning the keeper at Rødmose, with the wheelwright over there, came up to the house; they dragged with them a boy, Goske Piil, a widow's son, and they made their Bible oath that he had done it; they had themselves seen him sneaking round the barn by nightfall on Thursday. Goske had no good name on the farm; the keeper bore him a grudge upon an old matter of poaching, and the wheelwright did not like him either, for he did, I believe, suspect him with his young wife. The boy, when I talked to him, swore to his innocence, but he could not hold his own against the two old men. So I had him locked up, and meant to send him in to our judge of the district, with a letter.

"The judge is a fool, and would naturally do nothing but what he thought I wished him to do. He might have the boy sent to the convict prison for arson, or put amongst the soldiers as a bad character and a poacher. Or again, if he thought that that was what I wanted, he could let him off.

"I was out riding in the fields, looking at the corn that was soon ripe to be mowed, when a woman, the widow, Goske's mother, was brought up before me, and begged to speak to me. Anne-Marie is her name. You will remember her; she lives in the small house east of the village. She has not got a good name in the place either. They tell as a girl she had a child and did away with it.

"From five days' weeping her voice was so cracked that it was difficult for me to understand what she said. Her son, she told me at last, had indeed been over at Rødmose on Thursday, but for no ill purpose; he had gone to see someone. He was her only son, she called the Lord God to witness on his innocence, and she wrung her hands to me that I should save the boy for her.

"We were in the rye field that you and I are looking at now. That gave me an idea. I said to the widow: 'If in one day, between sunrise and sunset, with your own hands you can mow this field, and it be well done, I will let the case drop and you shall keep your son. But if you cannot do it, he must go, and it is not likely that you will then ever see him again.'

"She stood up then and gazed over the field. She kissed my riding boot in gratitude for the favour shown to her."

The old lord here made a pause, and Adam said: "Her son meant much to her?" "He is her only child," said his uncle. "He means to her her daily bread and support in old age. It may be said that she holds him as dear as her own life. As," he added, "within a higher order of life, a son to his father means the name and the race, and he holds him as dear as life everlasting. Yes, her son means much to her. For the mowing of that field is a day's work to three men, or three days' work to one man. Today, as the sun rose, she set to her task. And down there, by the end of the field, you will see her now, in a blue head-cloth, with the man I have set to follow her and to ascertain that she does the work unassisted, and with two or three friends by her, who are comforting her."

Adam looked down, and did indeed see a woman in a blue head-cloth, and a few other figures in the corn.

They sat for a while in silence. "Do you yourself," Adam then said, "believe the boy to be innocent?" "I cannot tell," said his uncle. "There is no proof. The word of the keeper and the wheelwright stand against the boy's word. If indeed I did believe the one thing or the other, it would be merely a matter of chance, or maybe of sympathy. The boy," he said after a moment, "was my son's playmate, the only other child that I ever knew him to like or to get on with." "Do you," Adam again asked, "hold it possible to her to fulfil your condition?" "Nay, I cannot tell," said the old lord. "To an ordinary person it would not be possible. No ordinary person would ever have taken it on at all. I chose it so. We are not quibbling with the law, Anne-Marie and I."

Adam for a few minutes followed the movement of the small group in the rye. "Will you walk back?" he asked. "No," said his uncle, "I think that I shall stay here till I have seen the end of the thing." "Until sunset?" Adam asked with surprise. "Yes," said the old lord. Adam said: "It will be a long day." "Yes," said his uncle, "a long day. But," he added, as Adam rose to walk away, "if, as you said, you have got that tragedy of which you spoke in your pocket, be as kind as to leave it here, to keep me company." Adam handed him the book.

In the avenue he met two footmen who carried the old lord's morning chocolate down to the pavilion on large silver trays.

As now the sun rose in the sky, and the day grew hot, the lime trees gave forth their exuberance of scent, and the garden was filled with unsurpassed, unbelievable sweetness. Toward the still hour of midday the long avenue reverberated like a soundboard with a low, incessant murmur: the humming of a million bees that clung to the pendulous, thronging clusters of blossoms and were drunk with bliss.

In all the short lifetime of Danish summer there is no richer or more luscious moment than that week wherein the lime trees flower. The heavenly scent goes to the head and to the heart; it seems to unite the fields of Denmark with those of Elysium; it contains both hay, honey and holy incense, and is half fairyland and half apothecary's locker. The avenue was changed into a mystic edifice, a dryad's cathedral, outward from summit to base lavishly adorned, set with multitudinous ornaments, and golden in the sun. But behind the walls the vaults were benignly cool and sombre, like ambrosial sanctuaries in a dazzling and burning world, and in here the ground was still moist.

Up in the house, behind the silk curtains of the two front windows, the young mistress of the estate from the wide bed stuck her feet into two little high-heeled slippers. Her lace-trimmed nightgown had slid up above her knee and down from the shoulder; her hair, done up in curling-pins for the night, was still frosty with the powder of yesterday, her round face flushed with sleep. She stepped out to the middle of the floor and stood there, looking extremely grave and thoughtful, yet she did not think at all. But through her head a long procession of pictures marched, and she was unconsciously endeavouring to put them in order, as the pictures of her existence had used to be.

She had grown up at Court; it was her world, and there was probably not in the whole country a small creature more exquisitely and innocently drilled to the stately measure of a palace. By favour of the old Dowager Queen she bore her name and that of the King's sister, the Queen of Sweden: Sophie Magdalena. It was with a view to these things that her husband, when he wished to restore his status in high places, had chosen her as a bride, first for his son and then for himself. But her own father, who held an office in the Royal Household and belonged to the new Court aristocracy, in his day had done the same thing the other way round, and had married a country lady, to get a foothold within the old nobility of Denmark. The little girl had her mother's blood in her veins. The country to her had been an immense surprise and delight.

To get into her castle court she must drive through the farm-yard, through the heavy stone gateway in the barn itself, wherein the rolling of her coach for a few seconds re-echoed like thunder. She must drive past the stables and the timber-mare, from which sometimes a miscreant would follow her with sad eyes, and might here startle a long string of squalling geese, or pass the heavy, scowling bull, led on by a ring in his nose and kneading the earth in dumb fury. At first this had been to her, every time, a slight shock and a jest. But after a while all these creatures and things, which belonged to her, seemed to become part of herself. Her mothers, the old Danish country ladies, were robust persons, undismayed by any kind of weather; now she herself had walked in the rain and had laughed and glowed in it like a green tree.

She had taken her great new home in possession at a time when all the world was unfolding, mating and propagating. Flowers, which she had known only in bouquets and festoons, sprung from the earth round her; birds sang in all the trees. The new-born lambs seemed to her daintier than her dolls had been. From her husband's Hanoverian stud, foals were brought to her to give names; she stood and watched as they poked their soft noses into their mothers' bellies to drink. Of this strange process she had till now only vaguely heard. She had happened to witness, from a path in the park, the rearing and screeching stallion on the mare. All this luxuriance, lust and fecundity was displayed before her eyes, as for her pleasure.

And for her own part, in the midst of it, she was given an old husband who treated her with punctilious respect because she was to bear him a son. Such was the compact; she had known of it from the beginning. Her husband, she found, was doing his best to fulfil his part of it, and she herself was loyal by nature and strictly brought up. She would not shirk her obligation. Only she was vaguely aware of a discord or an incompatibility within her majestic existence, which prevented her from being as happy as she had expected to be.

After a time her chagrin took a strange form: as the consciousness of an absence. Someone ought to have been with her who was not. She had no experience in analyzing her feelings; there had not been time for that at Court. Now, as she was more often left to herself, she vaguely probed her own mind. She tried to set her father in that void place, her sisters, her music master, an Italian singer whom she had admired; but none of them would fill it for her. At times she felt lighter at heart, and believed the misfortune to have left her. And then again it would happen, if she were alone, or in her husband's company, and even within his embrace, that everything round her would cry out: Where? Where? so that she let her wild eyes run about the room in search for the being who should have been there, and who had not come.

When, six months ago, she was informed that her first young bridegroom had died and that she was to marry his father in his place, she had not been sorry. Her youthful suitor, the one time she had seen him, had appeared to her infantile and insipid; the father would make a statelier consort. Now she had sometimes thought of the dead boy, and wondered whether with him life would have been more joyful. But she soon again dismissed the picture, and that was the sad youth's last recall to the stage of this world.

Upon one wall of her room there hung a long mirror. As she gazed into it new images came along. The day before, driving with her husband, she had seen. at a distance, a party of village girls bathe in the river, and the sun shining on them. All her life she had moved amongst naked marble deities, but it had till now never occurred to her that the people she knew should themselves be naked under their bodices and trains, waistcoats and satin breeches, that indeed she herself felt naked within her clothes. Now, in front of the looking-glass, she tardily untied the ribbons of her nightgown, and let it drop to the floor.

The room was dim behind the drawn curtains. In the mirror her body was silvery like a white rose; only her cheeks and mouth, and the tips of her fingers and breasts had a faint carmine. Her slender torso was formed by the whalebones that had clasped it tightly from her childhood; above the slim, dimpled knee a gentle narrowness marked the place of the garter. Her limbs were rounded as if, at whatever place they might be cut through with a sharp knife, a perfectly circular transverse incision would be obtained. The side and belly were so smooth that her own gaze slipped and glided, and grasped for a hold. She was not altogether like a statue, she found, and lifted her arms above her head. She turned to get a view of her back, the curves below the waistline were still blushing from the pressure of the bed. She called to mind a few tales about nymphs and goddesses, but they all seemed a long way off, so her mind returned to the peasant girls in the river. They were, for a few minutes, idealized into playmates, or sisters even, since they belonged to her as did the meadow and the blue river itself. And within the next moment the sense of forlornness once more came upon her, a *horror vaccui* like a physical pain. Surely, surely someone should have been with her now, her other self, like the image in the glass, but nearer, stronger, alive. There was no one, the universe was empty round her.

A sudden, keen itching under her knee took her out of her reveries, and awoke in her the hunting instincts of her breed. She wetted a finger on her tongue, slowly brought it down and quickly slapped it to the spot. She felt the diminutive, sharp body of the insect against the silky skin, pressed the thumb to it, and triumphantly lifted up the small prisoner between her fingertips. She stood quite still, as if meditating upon the fact that a flea was the only creature risking its life for her smoothness and sweet blood.

Her maid opened the door and came in, loaded with the attire of the day—shift, stays, hoop and petticoats. She remembered that she had a guest in the house, the new nephew arrived from England. Her husband had instructed her to be kind to their young kinsman, disinherited, so to say, by her presence in the house. They would ride out on the land together.

In the afternoon the sky was no longer blue as in the morning. Large clouds slowly towered up on it, and the great vault itself was colourless, as if diffused into vapours round the white-hot sun in zenith. A low thunder ran along the western horizon; once or twice the dust of the roads rose in tall spirals. But the fields, the hills and the woods were as still as a painted landscape.

Adam walked down the avenue to the pavilion, and found his uncle there, fully dressed, his hands upon his walking-stick and his eyes on the rye field. The book that Adam had given him lay by his side. The field now seemed alive with people. Small groups stood here and there in it, and a long row of men and women were slowly advancing towards the garden in the line of the swath.

The old lord nodded to his nephew, but did not speak or change his position. Adam stood by him as still as himself.

The day to him had been strangely disquieting. At the meeting again with old places the sweet melodies of the past had filled his senses and his mind, and had mingled with new, bewitching tunes of the present. He was back in Denmark, no longer a child but a youth, with a keener sense of the beautiful, with tales of other countries to tell, and still a true son of his own land and enchanted by its loveliness as he had never been before.

But through all these harmonies the tragic and cruel tale which the old lord had told him in the morning, and the sad contest which he knew to be going on so near by, the cornfield, had re-echoed, like the recurrent, hollow throbbing of a muffled drum, a redoubtable sound. It came back time after time, so that he had felt himself to change colour and to answer absently. It brought with it a deeper sense of pity with all that lived than he had ever known. When he had been riding with his young aunt, and their road ran along the scene of the drama, he had taken care to ride between her and the field, so that she should not see what was going on there, or question him about it. He had chosen the way home through the deep, green wood for the same reason.

More dominantly even than the figure of the woman struggling with her sickle for her son's life, the old man's figure, as he had seen it at sunrise, kept him company through the day. He came to ponder on the part which that lonely, determinate form had played in his own life. From the time when his father died, it had impersonated to the boy law and order, wisdom of life and kind guardianship. What was he to do, he thought, if after eighteen years these filial feelings must change, and his second father's figure take on to him a horrible aspect, as a symbol of the tyranny and oppression of the world? What was he to do if ever the two should come to stand in opposition to each other as adversaries?

At the same time an unaccountable, a sinister alarm and dread on behalf of the old man himself took hold of him. For surely here the Goddess Nemesis could not be far away. This man had ruled the world round him for a longer period than Adam's own lifetime and had never been gainsaid by anyone. During the years when he had wandered through Europe with a sick boy of his own blood as his sole companion he had learned to set himself apart from his surroundings, and to close himself up to all outer life, and he had become insusceptible to the ideas and feelings of other human beings. Strange fancies might there have run in his mind, so that in the end he had seen himself as the only person really existing, and the world as a poor and vain shadow-play, which had no substance to it.

Now, in senile wilfulness, he would take in his hand the life of those simpler and weaker than himself, of a woman, using it to his own ends, and he feared of no retributive justice. Did he not know, the young man thought, that there were powers in the world, different from and more formidable than the short-lived might of a despot?

With the sultry heat of the day this foreboding of impending disaster grew upon him, until he felt ruin threatening not the old lord only, but the house, the name and himself with him. It seemed to him that he must cry out a warning to the man he had loved, before it was too late.

But as now he was once more in his uncle's company, the green calm of the garden was so deep that he did not find his voice to cry out. Instead a little French air which his aunt had sung to him up in the house kept

running in his mind—"*C'est un trop doux effort . . .*" He had good
knowledge of music; he had heard the air before, in Paris, but not so
sweetly sung.

After a time he asked: "Will the woman fulfil her bargain?" His uncle
unfolded his hands. "It is an extraordinary thing," he said animatedly,
"that it looks as if she might fulfil it. If you count the hours from sunrise
till now, and from now till sunset, you will find the time left her to be
half of that already gone. And see! She has now mowed two-thirds of the
field. But then we will naturally have to reckon with her strength
declining as she works on. All in all, it is an idle pursuit in you or me to
bet on the issue of the matter; we must wait and see. Sit down, and keep
me company in my watch." In two minds Adam sat down.

"And here," said his uncle, and took up the book from the seat, "is your
book, which has passed the time finely. It is great poetry, ambrosia to the
ear and the heart. And it has, with our discourse on divinity this morning,
given me stuff for thought. I have been reflecting upon the law of retributive justice." He took a pinch of snuff, and went on. "A new age," he said,
"has made to itself a god in its own image, an emotional god. And now
you are already writing a tragedy on your god."

Adam had no wish to begin a debate on poetry with his uncle, but he
also somehow dreaded a silence, and said: "It may be, then, that we hold
tragedy to be, in the scheme of life, a noble, a divine phenomenon."

"Aye," said his uncle solemnly, "a noble phenomenon. the noblest on
earth. But of the earth only, and never divine. Tragedy is the privilege of
man, his highest privilege. The God of the Christian Church Himself,
when He wished to experience tragedy, had to assume human form. And
even at that," he added thoughtfully, "the tragedy was not wholly
valid, as it would have become had the hero of it been, in very truth, a
man. The divinity of Christ conveyed to it a divine note, the moment of
comedy. The real tragic part, by the nature of things, fell to the executors,
not to the victim. Nay, my nephew, we should not adulterate the pure
elements of the cosmos. Tragedy should remain the right of human
beings, subject, in their conditions or in their own nature, to the dire law
of necessity. To them it is salvation and beatification. But the gods, whom
we must believe to be unacquainted with and incomprehensive of necessity, can have no knowledge of the tragic. When they are brought face to
face with it they will, according to my experience, have the good taste
and decorum to keep still, and not interfere.

"No," he said after a pause, "the true art of the gods is the comic. The
comic is a condescension of the divine to the world of man; it is the

sublime vision, which cannot be studied, but must ever be celestially granted. In the comic the gods see their own being reflected as in a mirror, and while the tragic poet is bound by strict laws, they will allow the comic artist a freedom as unlimited as their own. They do not even withhold their own existence from his sports. Jove may favour Lucianos of Samosata. As long as your mockery is in true godly taste you may mock at the gods and still remain a sound devotee. But in pitying, or condoling with your god, you deny and annihilate him, and such is the most horrible of atheisms.

"And here on earth, too," he went on, "we, who stand in lieu of the gods and have emancipated ourselves from the tyranny of necessity, should leave to our vassals their monopoly of tragedy, and for ourselves accept the comic with grace. Only a boorish and cruel master—a parvenu, in fact—will make a jest of his servants' necessity, or force the comic upon them. Only a timid and pedantic ruler, a *petit-maître*, will fear the ludicrous on his own behalf. Indeed," he finished his long speech, "the very same fatality, which, in striking the burgher or peasant, will become tragedy, with the aristocrat is exalted to the comic. By the grace and wit of our acceptance hereof our aristocracy is known."

Adam could not help smiling a little as he heard the apotheosis of the comic on the lips of the erect, ceremonious prophet. In this ironic smile he was, for the first time, estranging himself from the head of his house.

A shadow fell across the landscape. A cloud had crept over the sun; the country changed colour beneath it, faded and bleached, and even all sounds for a minute seemed to die out of it.

"Ah, now," said the old lord, "if it is going to rain, and the rye gets wet, Anne-Marie will not be able to finish in time. And who comes there?" he added, and turned his head a little.

Preceded by a lackey a man in riding-boots and a striped waistcoat with silver buttons, and with his hat in his hand, came down the avenue. He bowed deeply, first to the old lord and then to Adam.

"My bailiff," said the old lord. "Good afternoon, Bailiff. What news have you to bring?" The bailiff made a sad gesture. "Poor news only, my lord," he said. "And how poor news?" asked his master. "There is," said the bailiff with weight, "not a soul at work on the land, and not a sickle going except that of Anne-Marie in this rye field. The mowing has stopped; they are all at her heels. It is a poor day for a first day of the harvest." "Yes, I see," said the old lord. The bailiff went on. "I have spoken kindly to them," he said, "and I have sworn at them; it is all one. They might as well all be deaf."

"Good Bailiff," said the old lord, "leave them in peace; let them do as they like. This day may, all the same, do them more good than many others. Where is Goske, the boy, Anne-Marie's son?" "We have set him in the small room by the barn," said the bailiff. "Nay, let him be brought down," said the old lord; "let him see his mother at work. But what do you say—will she get the field mowed in time?" "If you ask me, my lord," said the bailiff, "I believe that she will. Who would have thought so? She is only a small woman. It is as hot a day today as, well, as I do ever remember. I myself, you yourself, my lord, could not have done what Anne-Marie has done today." "Nay, nay, we could not, Bailiff," said the old lord.

The bailiff pulled out a red handkerchief and wiped his brow, somewhat calmed by venting his wrath. "If," he remarked with bitterness, "they would all work as the widow works now, we would make a profit on the land." "Yes," said the old lord, and fell into thought, as if calculating the profit it might make. "Still," he said, "as to the question of profit and loss, that is more intricate than it looks. I will tell you something that you may not know: The most famous tissue ever woven was ravelled out again every night. But come," he added, "she is close by now. We will go and have a look at her work ourselves." With these words he rose and set his hat on.

The cloud had drawn away again; the rays of the sun once more burned the wide landscape, and as the small party walked out from under the shade of the trees the dead-still heat was heavy as lead; the sweat sprang out on their faces and their eyelids smarted. On the narrow path they had to go one by one, the old lord stepping along first, all black, and the footman, in his bright livery, bringing up the rear.

The field was indeed filled with people like a market-place; there were probably a hundred or more men and women in it. To Adam the scene recalled pictures from his Bible: the meeting between Esau and Jacob in Edom, or Boaz's reapers in his barley field near Bethlehem. Some were standing by the side of the field, others pressed in small groups close to the mowing woman, and a few followed in her wake, binding up sheaves where she had cut the corn, as if thereby they thought to help her, or as if by all means they meant to have part in her work. A younger woman with a pail on her head kept close to her side, and with her a number of half-grown children. One of these first caught sight of the lord of the estate and his suite, and pointed to him. The binders let their sheaves drop, and as the old man stood still many of the onlookers drew close round him.

The woman on whom till now the eyes of the whole field had rested— a small figure on the large stage—was advancing slowly and unevenly, bent double as if she were walking on her knees, and stumbling as she walked. Her blue head-cloth had slipped back from her head; the grey hair was plastered to the skull with sweat, dusty and stuck with straw. She was obviously totally unaware of the multitude round her; neither did she now once turn her head or her gaze towards the new arrivals.

Absorbed in her work she again and again stretched out her left hand to grasp a handful of corn, and her right hand with the sickle in it to cut it off close to the soil, in wavering, groping pulls, like a tired swimmer's strokes. Her course took her so close to the feet of the old lord that his shadow fell on her. Just then she staggered and swayed sideways, and the woman who followed her lifted the pail from her head and held it to her lips. Anne-Marie drank without leaving her hold on her sickle, and the water ran from the corners of her mouth. A boy, close to her, quickly bent one knee, seized her hands in his own and, steadying and guiding them, cut off a gripe of rye. "No, no," said the old lord, "you must not do that, boy. Leave Anne-Marie in peace to her work." At the sound of his voice the woman, falteringly, lifted her face in his direction.

The bony and tanned face was streaked with sweat and dust; the eyes were dimmed. But there was not in its expression the slightest trace of fear or pain. Indeed amongst all the grave and concerned faces of the field hers was the only one perfectly calm, peaceful and mild. The mouth was drawn together in a thin line, a prim, keen, patient little smile, such as will be seen in the face of an old woman at her spinning-wheel or her knitting, eager on her work, and happy in it. And as the younger woman lifted back the pail, she immediately again fell to her mowing, with an ardent, tender craving, like that of a mother who lays a baby to the nipple. Like an insect that bustles along in high grass, or like a small vessel in a heavy sea, she butted her way on, her quiet face once more bent upon her task.

The whole throng of onlookers, and with them the small group from the pavilion, advanced as she advanced, slowly and as if drawn by a string. The bailiff, who felt the intense silence of the field heavy on him, said to the old lord: "The rye will yield better this year than last," and got no reply. He repeated his remark to Adam, and at last to the footman, who felt himself above a discussion on agriculture, and only cleared his throat in answer. In a while the bailiff again broke the silence. "There is the boy," he said and pointed with his thumb. "They have brought him down." At that moment the woman fell forward on her face and was lifted up by those nearest to her.

Adam suddenly stopped on the path, and covered his eyes with his hand. The old lord without turning asked him if he felt incommoded by the heat. "No," said Adam, "but stay. Let me speak to you." His uncle stopped, with his hand on the stick and looking ahead, as if regretful of being held back.

"In the name of God," cried the young man in French, "force not this woman to continue." There was a short pause. "But I force her not, my friend," said his uncle in the same language. "She is free to finish at any moment." "At the cost of her child only," again cried Adam. "Do you not see that she is dying? You know not what you are doing, or what it may bring upon you."

The old lord, perplexed by this unexpected animadversion, after a second turned all round, and his pale, clear eyes sought his nephew's face with stately surprise. His long, waxen face, with two symmetrical curls at the sides, had something of the mien of an idealized and ennobled old sheep or ram. He made sign to the bailiff to go on. The footman also withdrew a little, and the uncle and nephew were, so to say, alone on the path. For a minute neither of them spoke.

"In this very place where we now stand," said the old lord, then, with hauteur, "I gave Anne-Marie my word."

"My uncle!" said Adam. "A life is a greater thing even than a word. Recall that word, I beseech you, which was given in caprice, as a whim. I am praying you more for your sake than for my own, yet I shall be grateful to you all my life if you will grant me my prayer."

"You will have learned in school," said his uncle, "that in the beginning was the word. It may have been pronounced in caprice, as a whim, the Scripture tells us nothing about it. It is still the principle of our world, its law of gravitation. My own humble word has been the principle of the land on which we stand, for an age of man. My father's word was the same, before my day."

"You are mistaken," cried Adam. "The word is creative—it is imagination, daring and passion. By it the world was made. How much greater are these powers which bring into being than any restricting or controlling law! You wish the land on which we look to produce and propagate; you should not banish from it the forces which cause, and which keep up life, nor turn it into a desert by dominance of law. And when you look at the people, simpler than we and nearer to the heart of nature, who do not analyze their feelings, whose life is one with the life of the earth, do they not inspire in you tenderness, respect, reverence even? This woman is ready to die for her son; will it ever happen to you or me that a woman willingly gives up her life for us? And if it did indeed come to pass, should we make so light of it as not to give up a dogma in return?"

"You are young," said the old lord. "A new age will undoubtedly applaud you. I am old-fashioned, I have been quoting to you texts a thousand years old. We do not, perhaps, quite understand one another. But with my own people I am, I believe, in good understanding. Anne-Marie might well feel that I am making light of her exploit, if now, at the eleventh hour, I did nullify it by a second word. I myself should feel so in her place. Yes, my nephew, it is possible, did I grant you your prayer and pronounce such an amnesty, that I should find it void against her faithfulness, and that we would still see her at her work, unable to give it up, as a shuttle in the rye field, until she had it all mowed. But she would then be a shocking, a horrible sight, a figure of unseemly fun, like a small planet running wild in the sky, when the law of gravitation had been done away with."

"And if she dies at her task," Adam exclaimed, "her death, and its consequences will come upon your head."

The old lord took off his hat and gently ran his hand over his powdered head. "Upon my head?" he said. "I have kept up my head in many weathers. Even," he added proudly, "against the cold wind from high places. In what shape will it come upon my head, my nephew?" "I cannot tell," cried Adam in despair. "I have spoken to warn you. God only knows." "Amen," said the old lord with a little delicate smile. "Come, we will walk on." Adam drew in his breath deeply.

"No," he said in Danish. "I cannot come with you. This field is yours; things will happen here as you decide. But I myself must go away. I beg you to let me have, this evening, a coach as far as town. For I could not sleep another night under your roof, which I have honoured beyond any on earth." So many conflicting feelings at his own speech thronged in his breast that it would have been impossible for him to give them words.

The old lord, who had already begun to walk on, stood still, and with him the lackey. He did not speak for a minute, as if to give Adam time to collect his mind. But the young man's mind was in uproar and would not be collected.

"Must we," the old man asked, in Danish, "take leave here, in the rye field? I have held you dear, next to my own son. I have followed your career in life from year to year, and have been proud of you. I was happy when you wrote to say that you were coming back. If now you will go away, I wish you well." He shifted his walking-stick from the right hand to the left and gravely looked his nephew in the face.

Adam did not meet his eyes. He was gazing out over the landscape.

In the late mellow afternoon it was resuming its colours, like a painting brought into proper light; in the meadows the little black stacks of peat stood gravely distinct upon the green sward. On this same morning he had greeted it all, like a child running laughingly to its mother's bosom; now already he must tear himself from it, in discordance, and forever. And at the moment of parting it seemed infinitely dearer than any time before, so much beautified and solemnized by the coming separation that it looked like the place in a dream, a landscape out of paradise, and he wondered if it was really the same. But, yes—there before him was, once more, the hunting-ground of long ago. And there was the road on which he had ridden today.

"But tell me where you mean to go from here," said the old lord slowly. "I myself have travelled a good deal in my days. I know the word of leaving, the wish to go away. But I have learned by experience that, in reality, the word has a meaning only to the place and the people which one leaves. When you have left my house—although it will see you go with sadness—as far as it is concerned the matter is finished and done with. But to the person who goes away it is a different thing, and not so simple. At the moment that he leaves one place he will be already, by the laws of life, on his way to another, upon this earth. Let me know, then, for the sake of our old acquaintance, to which place you are going when you leave here. To England?"

"No," said Adam. He felt in his heart that he could never again go back to England or to his easy and carefree life there. It was not far enough away; deeper waters than the North Sea must now be laid between him and Denmark. "No, not to England," he said. "I shall go to America, to the new world." For a moment he shut his eyes, trying to form to himself a picture of existence in America, with the grey Atlantic Ocean between him and these fields and woods.

"To America?" said his uncle and drew up his eyebrows. "Yes, I have heard of America. They have got freedom there, a big waterfall, savage red men. They shoot turkeys, I have read, as we shoot partridges. Well, if it be your wish, go to America, Adam, and be happy in the new world."

He stood for some time, sunk in thought, as if he had already sent off the young man to America, and had done with him. When at last he spoke, his words had the character of a monologue, enunciated by the person who watches things come and go, and himself stays on.

"Take service, there," he said, "with the power which will give you an easier bargain than this: That with your own life you may buy the life of your son."

Adam had not listened to his uncle's remarks about America, but the conclusive, solemn words caught his ear. He looked up. As if for the first time in his life, he saw the old man's figure as a whole, and conceived how small it was, so much smaller than himself, pale, a thin black anchorite upon his own land. A thought ran through his head: "How terrible to be old!" The abhorrence of the tyrant, and the sinister dread on his behalf, which had followed him all day, seemed to die out of him, and his pity with all creation to extend even to the sombre form before him.

His whole being had cried out for harmony. Now, with the possibility of forgiving, of a reconciliation, a sense of relief went through him; confusedly he bethought himself of Anne-Marie drinking the water held to her lips. He took off his hat, as his uncle had done a moment ago, so that to a beholder at a distance it would seem tha⁺ the two dark-clad gentlemen on the path were repeatedly and respectfully saluting one another, and brushed the hair from his forehead. Once more the tune of the garden-room rang in his mind:

> "*Mourir pour ce qu'on aime*
> *C'est un trop doux effort . . .*"
>
> [To die for what one loves,
> This is too sweet an effort . . .]

He stood for a long time immobile and dumb. He broke off a few ears of rye, kept them in his hand and looked at them.

He saw the ways of life, he thought, as a twined and tangled design, complicated and mazy; it was not given him or any mortal to command or control it. Life and death, happiness and woe, the past and the present, were interlaced within the pattern. Yet to the initiated it might be read as easily as our ciphers—which to the savage must seem confused and incomprehensible—will be read by the schoolboy. And out of the contrasting elements concord rose. All that lived must suffer; the old man, whom he had judged hardly, had suffered, as he had watched his son die, and had dreaded the obliteration of his being. He himself would come to know ache, tears and remorse, and, even through these, the fullness of life. So might now, to the woman in the rye field, her ordeal be a triumphant procession. For to die for the one you loved was an effort too sweet for words.

As now he thought of it, he knew that all his life he had sought the unity of things, the secret which connects the phenomena of existence. It was this strife, this dim presage, which had sometimes made him stand still and inert in the midst of the games of his playfellows, or which had, at other moments—on moonlight nights, or in his little boat on the sea— lifted the boy to ecstatic happiness. Where other young people, in their pleasures or their amours, had searched for contrast and variety, he himself had yearned only to comprehend in full the oneness of the world. If things had come differently to him, if his young cousin had not died, and the events that followed his death had not brought him to Denmark, his search for understanding and harmony might have taken him to America, and he might have found them there, in the virgin forests of a new world. Now they have been disclosed to him today, in the place where he had played as a child. As the song is one with the voice that sings it, as the road is one with the goal, as lovers are made one in their embrace, so is man one with his destiny, and he shall love it as himself.

He looked up again, towards the horizon. If he wished to, he felt, he might find out what it was that had brought to him, here, the sudden conception of the unity of the universe. When this same morning he had philosophized, lightly and for his own sake, on his feeling of belonging to this land and soil, it had been the beginning of it. But since then it had grown; it had become a mightier thing, a revelation to his soul. Some time he would look into it, for the law of cause and effect was a wonderful and fascinating study. But not now. This hour was consecrated to greater emotions, to a surrender to fate and to the will of life.

"No," he said at last. "If you wish it I shall not go. I shall stay here."

At that moment a long, loud roll of thunder broke the stillness of the afternoon. It re-echoed for a while amongst the low hills, and it reverberated within the young man's breast as powerfully as if he had been seized and shaken by hands. The landscape had spoken. He remembered that twelve hours ago he had put a question to it, half in jest, and not knowing what he did. Here it gave him its answer.

What it contained he did not know; neither did he inquire. In his promise to his uncle he had given himself over to the mightier powers of the world. Now what must come must come.

"I thank you," said the old lord, and made a little stiff gesture with his hand. "I am happy to hear you say so. We should not let the difference in our ages, or of our views, separate us. In our family we have been wont to keep peace and faith with one another. You have made my heart lighter."

Something within his uncle's speech faintly recalled to Adam the misgivings of the afternoon. He rejected them; he would not let them trouble the new, sweet felicity which his resolution to stay had brought him.

"I shall go on now," said the old lord. "But there is no need for you to follow me. I will tell you tomorrow how the matter has ended." "No," said Adam, "I shall come back by sunset, to see the end of it myself."

All the same he did not come back. He kept the hour in his mind, and all through the evening the consciousness of the drama, and the profound concern and compassion with which, in his thoughts, he followed it, gave to his speech, glance and movements a grave and pathetic substance. But he felt that he was, in the rooms of the manor, and even by the harpsichord on which he accompanied his aunt to her air from *Alceste*, as much in the centre of things as if he had stood in the rye field itself, and as near to those human beings whose fate was now decided there. Anne-Marie and he were both in the hands of destiny, and destiny would, by different ways, bring each to the designated end.

Later on he remembered what he had thought that evening.

But the old lord stayed on. Late in the afternoon he even had an idea; he called down his valet to the pavilion and made him shift his clothes on him and dress him up in a brocaded suit that he had worn at Court. He let a lace-trimmed shirt be drawn over his head and stuck out his slim legs to have them put into thin silk stockings and buckled shoes. In this majestic attire he dined alone, of a frugal meal, but took a bottle of Rhenish wine with it, to keep up his strength. He sat on for a while, a little sunk in his seat; then, as the sun neared the earth, he straightened himself, and took the way down to the field.

The shadows were now lengthening, azure blue along all the eastern slopes. The lonely trees in the corn marked their site by narrow blue pools running out from their feet, and as the old man walked a thin, immensely elongated reflection stirred behind him on the path. Once he stood still; he thought he heard a lark singing over his head, a spring-like sound; his tired head held no clear perception of the season; he seemed to be walking, and standing, in a kind of eternity.

The people in the field were no longer silent, as they had been in the afternoon. Many of them talked loudly among themselves, and a little farther away a woman was weeping.

When the bailiff saw his master, he came up to him. He told him, in great agitation, that the widow would, in all likelihood, finish the mowing of the field within a quarter of an hour.

"Are the keeper and the wheelwright here?" the old lord asked him. "They have been here," said the bailiff, "and have gone away, five times. Each time they have said that they would not come back. But they have come back again, all the same, and they are here now." "And where is the boy?" the old lord asked again. "He is with her," said the bailiff. "I have given him leave to follow her. He has walked close to his mother all the afternoon, and you will see him now by her side, down there."

Anne-Marie was now working her way up towards them more evenly than before, but with extreme slowness, as if at any moment she might come to a standstill. This excessive tardiness, the old lord reflected, if it had been purposely performed, would have been an inimitable, dignified exhibition of skilled art; one might fancy the Emperor of China advancing in like manner on a divine procession or rite. He shaded his eyes with his hand, for the sun was now just beyond the horizon, and its last rays made light, wild, many-coloured specks dance before his sight. With such splendour did the sunset emblazon the earth and the air that the landscape was turned into a melting-pot of glorious metals. The meadows and the grasslands became pure gold; the barley field near by, with its long ears, was a live lake of shining silver.

There was only a small patch of straw standing in the rye field, when the woman, alarmed by the change in the light, turned her head a little to get a look at the sun. The while she did not stop her work, but grasped one handful of corn and cut it off, then another, and another. A great stir, and a sound like a manifold, deep sigh, ran through the crowd. The field was now mowed from one end to the other. Only the mower herself did not realize the fact; she stretched out her hand anew, and when she found nothing in it, she seemed puzzled or disappointed. Then she let her arms drop, and slowly sank to her knees.

Many of the women burst out weeping, and the swarm drew close round her, leaving only a small open space at the side where the old lord stood. Their sudden nearness frightened Anne-Marie; she made a slight, uneasy movement, as if terrified that they should put their hands on her.

The boy, who had kept by her all day, now fell on his knees beside her. Even he dared not touch her, but held one arm low behind her back and the other before her, level with her collar-bone, to catch hold of her if she should fall, and all the time he cried aloud. At that moment the sun went down.

The old lord stepped forward and solemnly took off his hat. The crowd became silent, waiting for him to speak. But for a minute or two he said nothing. Then he addressed her, very slowly.

"Your son is free, Anne-Marie," he said. He again waited a little, and added: "You have done a good day's work, which will long be remembered."

Anne-Marie raised her gaze only as high as his knees, and he understood that she had not heard what he said. He turned to the boy. "You tell your mother, Goske," he said, gently, "what I have told her."

The boy had been sobbing wildly, in raucous, broken moans. It took him some time to collect and control himself. But when at last he spoke, straight into his mother's face, his voice was low, a little impatient, as if he were conveying an everyday message to her. "I am free, Mother," he said. "You have done a good day's work that will long be remembered."

At the sound of his voice she lifted her face to him. A faint, bland shadow of surprise ran over it, but still she gave no sign of having heard what he said, so that the people round them began to wonder if the exhaustion had turned her deaf. But after a moment she slowly and waveringly raised her hand, fumbling in the air as she aimed at his face, and with her fingers touched his cheek. The cheek was wet with tears, so that at the contact her fingertips lightly stuck to it, and she seemed unable to overcome the infinitely slight resistance, or withdraw her hand. For a minute the two looked each other in the face. Then, softly and lingeringly, like a sheaf of corn that falls to the ground, she sank forward onto the boy's shoulder, and he closed his arms round her.

He held her thus, pressed against him, his own face buried in her hair and head-cloth, for such a long time that those nearest to them, frightened because her body looked so small in his embrace, drew closer, bent down and loosened his grip. The boy let them do so without a word or a movement. But the woman who held Anne-Marie, in her arms to lift her up, turned her face to the old lord. "She is dead," she said.

The people who had followed Anne-Marie all through the day kept standing and stirring in the field for many hours, as long as the evening light lasted, and longer. Long after some of them had made a stretcher from branches of the trees and had carried away the dead woman, others wandered on, up and down the stubble, imitating and measuring her course from one end of the rye field to the other, and binding up the last sheaves, where she had finished her mowing.

The old lord stayed with them for a long time, stepping along a little, and again standing still.

In the place where the woman had died the old lord later on had a stone set up, with a sickle engraved in it. The peasants on the land then named the rye field "Sorrow-Acre." By this name it was known a long time after the story of the woman and her son had itself been forgotten.

Leo Tolstoy

1828–1910

Count Leo Tolstoy was born into a family of landed gentry at Yasnaya Polyana, Tula, Russia, on August 28, 1828 (Old Style). Both parents died when he was a child. In 1844 he entered Kazan University, but showed more taste for society than for the academic. By 1850 he was living the life of a young man about town in Moscow. He enlisted in the artillery and did garrison duty among the Cossacks. In 1852 his first published work, *Childhood*, appeared in a magazine. Commissioned in 1854, he saw action against the Turks and served through the siege of Sevastopol.

He was afterward posted to St. Petersburg. He frequented society and made two visits to Western Europe. *The Cossacks*, begun in 1854, was not published until 1862. Meantime he produced *Two Hussars, Lucerne, Boyhood, Youth,* and other works. In 1857 he resigned from the army and five years later married Sophie Behrs. They spent a large part of each year at Yasnaya Polyana, where Tolstoy became an efficient manager of his estates and began work on his masterpiece, *War and Peace*.[1]

In 1869, after several years of work, the final installment was published. Four years later he embarked on *Anna Karenina*, his second great work. Distracted by other projects, he did not finish the book

[1] *Great Books of the Western World*, Vol. 51.

Notes from the artist: "Tolstoy in the peasant garb he adopted in his later years after his conversion and renunciation of his worldly belongings. . . . The quotation is from his aesthetic credo, What Is Art.*"*

Art is not a handicraft. it is the transmission of feeling the artist has experienced.

Толстой

until 1877. Before it was ended he had undergone a religious conversion, set off by his famous experience at Arzamas, the hallucination of sudden death. He wrote an account of these experiences later in *A Confession* and *Notes of a Madman*.

This change of heart was accompanied by a change in his way of life and in his view of literature. He stated this view in *What Is Art?* and it is reflected in *Resurrection,* perhaps the least effective of his novels. But it must also have been applied to such masterly later fiction as *The Death of Ivan Ilyitch* (see below), *Master and Man, Hadji Murad,* and *The Kreutzer Sonata.*

Tolstoy had nine children. With the exception of works written after 1880, he gave his wife power of attorney over all his property and lived like a peasant guest in his own household. He became a vegetarian, did manual labor, and devoted himself to social and ethical teaching. Like his friend Gandhi and Thoreau he preached the doctrine of nonviolence. He is regarded as one of the two or three greatest novelists in literature. His ethical views made him a world figure. He died in a railway station at Astapovo on November 7, (O. S. 20) 1910.

Ιn reading Tolstoy's later works, we need to distinguish between those that seem to be addressed to the same world audience as *War and Peace* and what he called his Popular Stories. The latter are no less serious, but they are much more plainly written. They make a simple religious point. They were meant to be read by the peasants and poor people in general. We may define the difference in another way by saying that the stories of the first kind were usually *about* people of the middle and upper classes, whereas the popular stories were *about* poor people and embodied their viewpoint. In Tolstoy's Russia, as he knew very well, these were all but separate cultures.

The Death of Ivan Ilyitch belongs in the first class. No word but *genius* will do for it. Perhaps nothing else in literature speaks so directly to the final point of human life: that every man must die, and that every man must face his own dying and somehow make peace with it. Certain men, soldiers and others in dangerous trades, may face it many times in their lives. But to Ivan Ilyitch, who has lived with serene equanimity on the level of the acceptable and conventional, it comes only once, for the first and last time.

It comes as pure horror. Beginning as an ordinary household accident, it is dismissed and returns, variously diagnosed by various physicians. It strikes down through layer after layer of Ivan Ilyitch's consciousness, in three ways: (1) as an increasing bodily pain and disintegration; (2) as a withdrawal from and slight disturbance of his bourgeois family and professional circle; (3) as a rising terror of death, which turns into something else.

This "something else" is what Tolstoy is chiefly concerned with. In the end, it absorbs every other element in the story and transforms it. We begin with the formal announcement of Ivan Ilyitch's death and the conventional reaction of his colleagues. When we have read the story, we will see that this is its final irony. In effect, nothing has happened. The waters of Ivan Ilyitch's world have closed over him without a ripple. But *we* know that it is not true. We have taken part in his dying. We have seen that, like Marcher in Henry James's *The Beast in the Jungle,* he discovers, too late, that he has never truly lived. But in the last two hours left to him, he falls through into "light." What is this light? The end of his terror? Understanding? Love? The knowledge of God? In the perfect rightness of his art, Tolstoy does not tell us.

Both *What Men Live By* and *The Three Hermits* belong among his Popular Stories. In his old age Tolstoy was asked which of his works he considered the best. He mentioned, not *War and Peace,* but *What Men Live By* and one other devotional story. We are troubled at first by the events in *What Men Live By.* How can this be a just God, this God who punishes his servant Mikhaïla for showing Christian compassion to a mother and her newborn children? We read it again, and though we may not agree, we understand that this is part of the lesson Tolstoy wishes us to learn. And how can we help but be enchanted by the simple men of God in *The Three Hermits?* These are true parables transfigured into art.

The Death
of Ivan Ilyitch

In the great building of the law courts, while the proceedings in the Mielvinsky suit were at a standstill, the members of the board and the prokuror met in Ivan Yegorovitch Shebek's private room, and the conversation turned on the famous Krasovsky suit. Feodor Vasilyevitch talked himself into a passion in pointing out the men's innocence; Ivan Yegorovitch maintained his side; but Piotr Ivanovitch, who had not entered into the discussion at first, took no part in it even now, and was glancing over the *Vyedomosti*, which had just been handed to him.

"Gentlemen!" said he, "Ivan Ilyitch is dead!"

"Is it possible?"

"Here! read for yourself," said he to Feodor Vasilyevitch, handing him the paper, which had still retained its odor of freshness.

Heavy black lines enclosed these printed words:

> Praskovia Feodorovna Golovina, with heartfelt sorrow, announces to relatives and friends the death of her beloved husband, Ivan Ilyitch Golovin, member of the Court of Appeal, who departed this life on the 16th February, 1882. The funeral will take place on Friday, at one o'clock in the afternoon.

Ivan Ilyitch had been the colleague of the gentlemen there assembled, and all liked him. He had been ill for several weeks, and it was said that his case was incurable. His place was kept vacant for him; but it had been decided that, in case of his death, Alekseyef might be assigned to his place, while either Vinnikof or Schtabel would take Alekseyef's place. And so, on hearing of Ivan Ilyitch's death, the first thought of each of the gentlemen gathered in that room was in regard to the changes and promotions which this death might bring about among the members of the council and their acquaintances.

"Now, surely, I shall get either Schtabel's or Vinnikof's place," was Feodor Vasilyevitch's thought. "It has been promised me for a long time; and this promotion will mean an increase in my salary of eight hundred rubles, besides allowances."

"I must propose right away to have my brother-in-law transferred from Kaluga," thought Piotr Ivanovitch. "My wife will be very glad. Then it will be impossible for her to say that I have never done anything for her relations."

"I have been thinking that he wouldn't get up again," said Piotr Ivanovitch aloud. "It is too bad."

"But what was really the matter with him?"

"The doctors could not determine. That is to say, they determined it, but each in his own way. When I saw him the last time, it seemed to me that he was getting better."

"But I haven't been to see him since the Christmas holidays. I kept meaning to go."

"Did he have any property?"

"His wife had a very little, I think. But a mere pittance."

"Well, we must go to see her. They live a frightful distance off."

"That is, from you. Everything is far from you!"

"Now, see here! He can't forgive me because I live on the other side of the river," said Piotr Ivanovitch to Shebek, with a smile.

And then they talked about the long distances in cities, till the recess was over.

Over and above the considerations caused by the death of this man, in regard to the mutations and possible changes in the court that might result from it, the very fact of the death of an intimate friend aroused as usual in all who heard about it a feeling of pleasure that "it was he, and not I, who was dead."

Each one said to himself, or felt: "Well, he is dead, and I am not."

The intimate acquaintances, the so-called friends, of Ivan Ilyitch could not help having these thoughts, and also felt that now it was incumbent on them to fulfill the very melancholy obligation of propriety, in going to the funeral and paying a visit of condolence to the widow.

Feodor Vasilyevitch and Piotr Ivanovitch had been more intimate with him than the others.

Piotr Ivanovitch had been his fellow in the law school, and had felt under obligations to Ivan Ilyitch.

Having, at dinnertime, informed his wife of Ivan Ilyitch's death, and his reflections as to the possibility of his brother-in-law's transfer into their circle, Piotr Ivanovitch, not stopping to rest, put on his dress coat, and drove off to Ivan Ilyitch's.

At the door of Ivan Ilyitch's residence stood a carriage and two *izvozchiks*. At the foot of the stairs, in the hallway by the hat rack, pushed back against the wall, was the brocaded coffin cover, with tassels and lace full of purified powdered camphor. Two ladies in black were taking off their shubkas.[1] One whom he knew was Ivan Ilyitch's sister; the other lady he did not know. Piotr Ivanovitch's colleague, Schwartz, was just coming downstairs; and, as he recognized the newcomer, he stopped on the upper step, and winked at him as much as to say: "Ivan Ilyitch was a bad manager; you and I understand a thing or two."

Schwartz's face, with its English side whiskers, and his spare figure under his dress coat, had, as always, an elegant solemnity; and this solemnity, which was forever contradicted by Schwartz's jovial nature, here had a peculiar piquancy, so Piotr Ivanovitch thought.

Piotr Ivanovitch gave precedence to the ladies, and slowly followed them upstairs. Schwartz did not make any move to descend, but waited at the landing. Piotr Ivanovitch understood his motive; without doubt, he wanted to make an appointment for playing cards that evening. The ladies mounted the stairs to the widow's room; and Schwartz, with lips gravely compressed and firm, and with mischievous eyes, indicated to Piotr Ivanovitch, by the motion of his brows, the room at the right, where the dead man was.

Piotr Ivanovitch entered, having that feeling of uncertainty, ever present under such circumstances, as to what would be the proper thing to do. But he knew that in such circumstances the sign of the cross never came amiss. As to whether he ought to make a salutation or not, he was not quite sure; and he therefore took a middle course. As he went into the room, he began to cross himself, and, at the same time, he made an almost imperceptible inclination. As far as he was permitted by the motion of his hands and head, he took in the appearance of the room. Two young men, apparently nephews—one, a scholar at the gymnasium—were just leaving the room, making the sign of the cross. An old woman was standing motionless; and a lady, with strangely arched eyebrows, was saying something to her in a whisper. A hearty-looking, energetic sacristan in a frock was reading something in a loud voice, with an expression which forbade all objection. The muzhik, Gerasim, who acted as butler, was sprinkling something on the floor, passing slowly in front of Piotr Ivano-

---

1. Fur garments.

vitch. As he saw this, Piotr Ivanovitch immediately became cognizant of a slight odor of decomposition.

Piotr Ivanovitch, at his last call on Ivan Ilyitch, had seen this muzhik in the library. He was performing the duties of nurse, and Ivan Ilyitch was extremely fond of him.

Piotr Ivanovitch kept crossing himself, and bowing impartially toward the corpse, the sacristan, and the icons that stood on a table in the corner. Then, when it seemed to him that he had already continued too long making signs of the cross with his hand, he stopped short, and began to gaze at the dead man.

The dead man lay in the drapery of the coffin, as dead men always lie, a perfectly lifeless weight, absolutely unconscious, with stiffened limbs, with head forever at rest on the pillow; and showing, as all corpses show, a brow like yellow wax, with spots on the sunken temples, and a nose so prominent as almost to press down on the upper lip.

He had greatly changed, and was far more emaciated than when Piotr Ivanovitch had last seen him; but, as in the case of all the dead, his face was more beautiful, especially more dignified, than it had been when he was alive. On his face was an expression signifying that what was necessary to do, that had been done, and had been done in due form. Besides this, there was in his expression a reproach or warning to the living. This warning seemed ill-judged to Piotr Ivanovitch, or at least was not applicable to him. There was something displeasing in it; and therefore Piotr Ivanovitch again crossed himself hastily, and, it seemed to him, too hastily for proper decorum, turned around and went to the door.

Schwartz was waiting for him in the next room, standing with legs wide apart, and with both hands behind his back twirling his "cylinder" hat. Piotr Ivanovitch was cheered by the first glance at Schwartz's jovial, tidy, elegant figure. Piotr Ivanovitch comprehended that Schwartz was superior to these things, and did not give way to these harassing impressions. His appearance alone said: The incident of Ivan Ilyitch's funeral cannot serve as a sufficient reason for breaking into the order of exercises of the session; that is to say, nothing shall hinder us this very evening from opening and shuffling a pack of cards while the servant is putting down four fresh candles; in general, there is no occasion to presuppose that this incident can prevent us from having a good time this evening, as well as any other.

He even said this in a whisper to Piotr Ivanovitch as he joined him, and proposed that they meet for a game at Feodor Vasilyevitch's. But evidently it was not Piotr Ivanovitch's fate to play cards that evening.

Praskovia Feodorovna, a short woman, and stout in spite of all her efforts to the contrary—for her figure grew constantly wider and wider from her shoulders down—dressed all in black, with lace on her head, and with the same extraordinarily arched eyebrows as the lady who had been standing by the coffin, came out from her rooms with other ladies; and as she preceded them through the door of the death chamber, she said: "Mass will take place immediatcly. Plcase come in."

Schwartz, making a slight, indefinite bow, stood still, evidently undecided whether to accept or to decline this invitation. Praskovia Feodorovna, as soon as she recognized Piotr Ivanovitch, sighed, came quite close to him, took him by the hand, and said: "I know that you were a true friend of Ivan Ilyitch's." And she fixed her eyes on him, awaiting his action to respond to her words.

Piotr Ivanovitch knew that, just as in the other case it had been incumbent upon him to make the sign of the cross, so here he must press her hand, sigh, and say, "Why, certainly." And so he did. And having done so, he realized that the desired result was obtained—that he was touched, and she was touched.

"Come," said the widow; "before it begins, I must have a talk with you. Give me your arm."

Piotr Ivanovitch offered her his arm; and they walked along to the inner rooms, passing by Schwartz, who winked compassionately at Piotr Ivanovitch.

His jovial glance said: "It's all up with your game of vint; but don't be concerned, we'll find another partner. We'll cut in when you have finished."

Piotr Ivanovitch sighed still more deeply and grievously, and Praskovia Feodorovna pressed his arm gratefully.

When they entered her drawing room, which had hangings of rose-colored cretonne, and was dimly lighted by a lamp, they sat down near a table—she on a divan, but Piotr Ivanovitch on a low ottoman, the springs of which were out of order, and yielded unevenly under his weight.

Praskovia Feodorovna wanted to suggest to him to take another chair; but to make such a suggestion seemed out of place in her situation, and she gave it up. As he sat down on the ottoman, Piotr Ivanovitch remembered how, when Ivan Ilyitch was decorating that drawing room, he had asked his opinion about this very same rose-colored cretonne, with its green leaves.

As the widow passed by the table in going to the divan—the whole room was crowded with ornaments and furniture—she caught the black lace of her black mantilla on the woodwork. Piotr Ivanovitch got up, in order to detach it; and the ottoman, freed from his weight, began to shake and jostle him. The widow herself was busy disengaging her lace; and Piotr Ivanovitch sat down again, flattening out the ottoman which had rebelled under him. But still the widow could not get free, and Piotr Ivanovitch again arose; and again the ottoman rebelled, and even creaked.

When all this was arranged, she took out a clean cambric handkerchief, and began to weep. The episode with the lace and the struggle with the ottoman had thrown a chill over Piotr Ivanovitch, and he sat with a frown. This awkward situation was interrupted by Sokolof, Ivan Ilyitch's butler, with the announcement that the lot in the graveyard which Praskovia Feodorovna had selected would cost two hundred rubles. She ceased to weep, and, with the air of a martyr, looked at Piotr Ivanovitch, saying in French that it was very trying for her. Piotr Ivanovitch made a silent gesture, signifying his undoubted belief that this was inevitable.

"Smoke, I beg of you!" she said with a voice expressive of magnanimity as well as melancholy. And she discussed with Sokolof the price of the lot.

As Piotr Ivanovitch began to smoke, he overheard how she very circumstantially inquired into the various prices of land, and finally determined on the one which it suited her to purchase. When she had settled upon the lot, she also gave her orders in regard to the singers. Sokolof withdrew.

"I attend to everything myself," she said to Piotr Ivanovitch, moving to one side the albums that lay on the table; and then, noticing that the ashes were about to fall on the table, she hastened to hand Piotr Ivanovitch an ash tray, and continued: "It would be hypocritical for me to declare that grief prevents me from attending to practical affairs. On the contrary, though it cannot console me, yet it may divert my mind from my troubles."

Again she took out her handkerchief, as if preparing to weep; and suddenly, apparently making an effort over herself, she shook herself, and began to speak calmly: "At all events, I have some business with you."

Piotr Ivanovitch bowed, not giving the springs of the ottoman a chance to rise up against him, since only the moment before they had been misbehaving under him.

"During the last days, his sufferings were terrible."

"He suffered very much?" asked Piotr Ivanovitch.

"Oh! terribly! For hours before he died he did not cease to shriek. For three days and nights he shrieked all the time. It was unendurable. I cannot understand how I stood it. You could hear him through three doors! Akh! how I suffered!"

"And was he in his senses?" asked Piotr Ivanovitch.

"Yes," she said in a whisper, "to the last moment. He bade us farewell a quarter of an hour before he died, and even asked us to send Volodya out."

The thought of the sufferings of a man whom he had known so intimately, first as a jolly child and schoolboy, and then in adult life as his colleague, suddenly filled Piotr Ivanovitch with terror in spite of the unpleasant sense of this woman's hypocrisy and his own. Once more he saw that forehead, that nose nipping on the lip, and he felt frightened for himself.

"Three days and nights of horrible sufferings and death! Perhaps this may happen to me also, immediately, at any moment," he said to himself. And for an instant he felt panic-stricken. But immediately, though he himself knew not how, there came to his aid the common idea that this had happened to Ivan Ilyitch, and not to him, and therefore such a thing had no business to happen to him, and could not be possible; that, in thinking so, he had fallen into a melancholy frame of mind, which was a foolish thing to do, as was evident by Schwartz's face.

In the course of these reflections, Piotr Ivanovitch became calm, and began with interest to ask for the details of Ivan Ilyitch's decease, as if death were some accident peculiar to Ivan Ilyitch alone, and absolutely remote from himself.

After speaking at greater or less length of the details of the truly terrible physical sufferings endured by Ivan Ilyitch—Piotr Ivanovitch listened to these details simply because Praskovia Feodorovna's nerves had been affected by her husband's sufferings—the widow evidently felt that it was time to come to the point.

"Oh! Piotr Ivanovitch! how painful! how horribly painful! how horribly painful!" and again the tears began to flow.

Piotr Ivanovitch sighed, and waited till she had blown her nose. When she had blown her nose, he said: "Believe me . . ."

And again the springs of her speech were unloosed, and she explained what was apparently her chief object in seeing him: this matter concerned the problem of how she should make her husband's death secure her funds from the treasury.

She pretended to ask Piotr Ivanovitch's advice about a pension; but he clearly saw that she had already mastered the minutest points, even those that he himself knew not, in the process of extracting from the treasury the greatest possible amount in case of death. But what she wanted to find out was whether it were not possible to become the recipient of still more money.

Piotr Ivanovitch endeavored to devise some means to this effect; but, having pondered a little, and out of politeness condemned our government for its niggardliness, he said that it seemed to him impossible to obtain more. Then she sighed, and evidently began to devise some means of getting rid of her visitor. He understood, put out his cigarette, arose, pressed her hand, and passed into the anteroom.

In the dining room, where stood the clock that Ivan Ilyitch had taken such delight in, when he purchased it at a bric-a-brac shop, Piotr Ivanovitch met the priest and a few more acquaintances who had come to the funeral; and he recognized Ivan Ilyitch's daughter, a pretty young lady, whom he knew. She was all in black. Her very slender figure seemed more slender than usual. She looked melancholy, determined, almost irritated. She bowed to Piotr Ivanovitch as if he were in some way to blame. Behind the daughter, with the same melancholy look, stood a rich young man, a magistrate of Piotr Ivanovitch's acquaintance, who, as he heard, was her betrothed. He bowed to them disconsolately, and was about to pass into the death chamber, when he saw coming up the stairs the slender form of Ivan Ilyitch's son—a gymnasium student, and a striking image of Ivan Ilyitch. It was the same little Ivan Ilyitch whom Piotr Ivanovitch remembered at the law school. His eyes were wet with tears, and had the faded appearance common to unhealthy boys of thirteen or fourteen. The boy, as soon as he saw Piotr Ivanovitch, scowled rudely and bashfully. Piotr Ivanovitch nodded at him, and entered the death chamber.

The mass had begun; there were candles, groans, incense, tears, and sobs. Piotr Ivanovitch stood looking gloomily down at his feet. He did not once glance at the corpse, and to the end did not yield to the softening influences; and he was one of the first to leave. There was no one in the anteroom. Gerasim, the butler, rushed from the dead man's late room, tossed about all the fur garments with his strong hands in order to find Piotr Ivanovitch's shuba, and handed it to him.

"Well, brother Gerasim," said Piotr Ivanovitch, so as to say something, "it's too bad, isn't it?"

"God's will. We shall all be there," said Gerasim, showing his close, white, peasant's teeth; and, like a man earnestly engaged in some great work, he opened the door with alacrity, called the coachman, helped

Piotr Ivanovitch into the carriage, and then hastened back up the front steps, as if he were eager to find something else to do.

It was particularly agreeable to Piotr Ivanovitch to breathe the fresh air, after the odor of the incense, of the dead body, and carbolic acid.

"Where shall I drive to?" asked the coachman.

"It's not too late. I'll go to Feodor Vasilyevitch's, after all."

And Piotr Ivanovitch drove off. And, in fact, he found them just finishing the first rubber, so that it was convenient for him to cut in.

The past history of Ivan Ilyitch's life was most simple and uneventful, and yet most terrible.

Ivan Ilyitch died at the age of forty-five, a member of the Court of Justice. He was the son of a functionary who had followed, in various ministries and departments at Petersburg, a career such as brings men into a position from which, on account of their long service and their rank, they are never turned adrift, even though it is plainly manifest that their actual usefulness is at an end; and consequently they obtain imaginary, fictitious places, and from six to ten thousand that are not fictitious, on which they live till a good old age.

Such had been Ilya Yefimovitch Golovin, privy councilor, a useless member of various useless commissions.

He had three sons; Ivan Ilyitch was the second. The eldest had followed the same career as his father's, but in a different ministry, and was already nearing that period of his service in which inertia carries a man into emoluments. The third son had been a failure. He had completely gone to pieces in several positions, and he was now connected with railways; and his father and his brothers and especially their wives not only disliked to meet him, but, except when it was absolutely necessary, even forgot that he existed.

A sister was married to Baron Gref, who, like his father-in-law, was a Petersburg chinovnik [official]. Ivan Ilyitch had been *le phénix de la famille*, as they used to say. He was neither so chilling and formal as the eldest brother, nor so unpromising as the youngest. He was the mean between them—an intelligent, lively, agreeable, and polished man. He had studied at the law school with his younger brother, who did not graduate but was expelled from the fifth class; Ivan Ilyitch, however, finished his course creditably. At the law school he showed the same characteristics by which he was afterward distinguished all his life: he was capable, good-natured even to gaiety, and sociable, but strictly fulfilling all that he considered to be his duty; duty, in his opinion, was all that is considered to be such by men in the highest station. He was not one to curry favor, either as a boy, or afterward in manhood; but from his earliest years he had been attracted by men in the highest station in society, just as a fly is by the light; he adopted their ways, their views of life, and entered into relations of friendship with them. All the passions of childhood and youth had passed away, not leaving serious traces. He had yielded to sensuality and vanity, and, toward the last of his life, to the higher forms of liberalism, but all within certain limits which his nature faithfully prescribed for him.

While at the law school, he had done some things which hitherto had seemed to him very shameful, and which while he was engaged in them aroused in him deep scorn for himself. But afterward, finding that these things were also done by men of high position, and were not considered by them disgraceful, he came to regard them, not indeed as worthy, but as something to put entirely out of his mind, and he was not in the least troubled by the recollection of them.

When Ivan Ilyitch had graduated from the law school with the tenth rank, and received from his father some money for his uniform, he ordered a suit of Scharmer, added to his trinkets the little medal with the legend *respice finem* [look to the end], bade the prince and principal farewell, ate a dinner with his classmates at Donon's, and, furnished with new and stylish trunk, linen, uniform, razors, and toilet articles, and a plaid, ordered or bought at the very best shops, he departed for the province, as chinovnik and private secretary to the governor—a place which his father procured for him.

In the province, Ivan Ilyitch at once got himself into the same sort of easy and agreeable position as his position in the law school had been. He attended to his duties, pressed forward in his career, and at the same time enjoyed life in a cheerful and circumspect manner. From time to time, delegated by his chief, he visited the districts, bore himself with dignity toward both his superiors and subordinates, and, without overweening conceit, fulfilled with punctuality and incorruptible integrity the duties imposed upon him, pre-eminently in the affair of the dissenters.[2]

Notwithstanding his youth, and his tendency to be gay and easygoing, he was, in matters of state, thoroughly discreet, and carried his official reserve even to sternness. But in society he was often merry and witty, and

---

2. The first body of *raskolniks,* or dissenters, called the "Old Believers," arose in the time of the Patriarch Nikon, who, in 1654, revised the Scriptures. A quarrel as to the number of fingers to be used in giving the blessing, and the manner of spelling Jesus, seems to have been the chief cause of the *raskol,* or schism.

always good-natured, polite, and *bon enfant,* as he was called by his chief and his chief's wife, at whose house he was intimate.

While he was in the province, he had maintained relations with one of those ladies who are ready to fling themselves into the arms of an elegant young lawyer. There was also a dressmaker; and there were occasional sprees with visiting flügel-adjutants, and visits to some out-of-the-way street after supper; he had also the favor of his chief and even of his chief's wife, but everything of this sort was attended with such a high tone of good breeding that it could not be qualified by hard names; it all squared with the rubric of the French expression, *Il faut que jeunesse se passe.*[3]

All was done with clean hands, with clean linen, with French words, and, above all, in company with the very highest society, and therefore with the approbation of those high in rank.

In this way Ivan Ilyitch served five years, and a change was instituted in the service. The new tribunals were established; new men were needed.

And Ivan Ilyitch was chosen as one of the new men.

He was offered the position of examining magistrate; and accepted it, notwithstanding the fact that this place was in another government, and that he would be obliged to give up the connections he had formed, and form new ones.

Ivan Ilyitch's friends saw him off. They were photographed in a group, they presented him a silver cigarette case, and he departed for his new post.

As an examining magistrate, Ivan Ilyitch was just as *comme il faut* [proper], just as circumspect, and careful to sunder the obligations of his office from his private life, and as successful in winning universal consideration, as when he was a chinovnik with special functions. The office of magistrate itself was vastly more interesting and attractive to Ivan Ilyitch than his former position had been.

To be sure, it used to be agreeable to him, in his former position, to pass with free and easy gait, in his Scharmer-made uniform, in front of trembling petitioners and petty officials waiting for an interview and envying him as he went without hesitation into his chief's private room, and sat down with him to drink a cup of tea and smoke a cigarette; but the men who had been directly dependent on his pleasure were few— merely police captains and dissenters, if he were sent out with special instructions. And he liked to meet these men, dependent on him, not only

---

3. "A man must sow his wild oats."

politely, but even on terms of comradeship; he liked to make them feel that he, who had the power to crush them, treated them simply, and like friends. Such men at that time were few.

But now, as examining magistrate, Ivan Ilyitch felt that all, all without exception, even men of importance, of distinction, all were in his hands, and that all he had to do was to write such and such words on a piece of paper with a heading, and this important, distinguished man would be brought to him in the capacity of accused or witness, and, unless he wished to ask him to sit down, he would have to stand in his presence, and submit to his questions. Ivan Ilyitch never took undue advantage of this power; on the contrary, he tried to temper the expression of it. But the consciousness of this power, and the possibility of tempering it, furnished for him the chief interest and attractiveness of his new office.

In the office itself, especially in investigations, Ivan Ilyitch was very quick to master the process of eliminating all circumstances extraneous to the case, and of disentangling the most complicated details in such a manner that the case would be presented on paper only in its essentials, and absolutely shorn of his own personal opinion, and, last and not least, that every necessary formality would be fulfilled. This was a new mode of doing things. And he was one of the first to be engaged in putting into operation the code of 1864.

When he took up his residence in the new city, as examining magistrate, Ivan Ilyitch made new acquaintances and ties; he put himself on a new footing, and adopted a somewhat different tone. He held himself rather aloof from the provincial authorities, and took up with a better circle among the judges and wealthy nobles living in the city; and he adopted a tone of easygoing criticism of the government, together with a moderate form of liberalism and "civilized citizenship." At the same time, though Ivan Ilyitch in no wise diminished the elegance of his toilet, yet he ceased to shave his chin, and allowed his beard to grow as it would.

Ivan Ilyitch's life in the new city also passed very agreeably. The society which *fronded* against the government was good and friendly; his salary was larger than before; and, while he had no less zest in life, he had the additional pleasure of playing whist, a game in which, as he enjoyed playing cards, he quickly learned to excel, so that he was always on the winning side.

After two years of service in the new city Ivan Ilyitch met the lady who became his wife. Praskovia Feodorovna Mikhel was the most fascinating, witty, brilliant young girl in the circle where Ivan Ilyitch moved. In the multitude of other recreations, and as a solace from the labors of his office,

Ivan Ilyitch established sportive easygoing relations with Praskovia Feo-dorovna.

At the time when Ivan Ilyitch was a chinovnik with special functions, he had been a passionate lover of dancing; but now that he was examining magistrate, he danced only as an occasional exception. He now danced with the idea that, "though I am an advocate of the new order of things, and belong to the fifth class, still, as far as the question of dancing goes, I can at least show that in this respect I am better than the rest."

Thus, it frequently happened that, toward the end of a party, he danced with Praskovia Feodorovna; and it was principally at the time of these dances, that he made the conquest of Praskovia Feodorovna. She fell in love with him. Ivan Ilyitch had no clearly decided intention of getting married; but when the girl fell in love with him, he asked himself this question: "In fact, why should I not get married?" said he to himself.

The young lady, Praskovia Feodorovna, came of a good family belonging to the nobility, far from ill-favored, had a small fortune. Ivan Ilyitch might have aspired to a more brilliant match, but this was an excellent one. Ivan Ilyitch had his salary; she, he hoped, would have as much more. She was of good family; she was sweet, pretty, and a thoroughly well-bred woman. To say that Ivan Ilyitch got married because he was in love with his betrothed, and found in her sympathy with his views of life, would be just as incorrect as to say that he got married because the men of his set approved of the match.

Ivan Ilyitch took a wife for two reasons: he gave himself a pleasure in taking such a wife; and, at the same time, the people of the highest rank considered such an act proper.

And so Ivan Ilyitch got married.

The wedding ceremony itself, and the first few days of their married life with its connubial caresses, their new furniture, their new plate, their new linen, everything, even the prospects of an increasing family, were all that could be desired. So that Ivan Ilyitch began to think that marriage not only was not going to disturb his easygoing, pleasant, gay, and always respectable life, so approved by society, and which Ivan Ilyitch considered a perfectly natural characteristic of life in general, but was also going to add to it. But from the first months of his wife's pregnancy, there appeared something new, unexpected, disagreeable, hard, and trying, which he could not have foreseen, and from which it was impossible to escape.

His wife, without any motive, as it seemed to Ivan Ilyitch, *de gaité de coeur,* as he said to himself, began to interfere with the pleasant and decent current of his life; without any cause she grew jealous of him, demanded attentions from him, found fault with everything, and caused him disagreeable and stormy scenes.

At first Ivan Ilyitch hoped to free himself from this unpleasant state of things by the same easygoing and respectable acceptation of life which had helped him in days gone by. He tried to ignore his wife's disposition, and continued to live as before in an easy and pleasant way. He invited his friends, he gave card parties, he attempted to make his visits to the club or to friends; but his wife began one time to abuse him with rough and energetic language, and continued persistently to scold him each time that he failed to fulfill her demands, having evidently made up her mind not to cease berating him until he was completely subjected to her authority—in other words, until he would stay at home, and be just as deeply in the dumps as she herself—a thing which Ivan Ilyitch dreaded above all.

He learned that married life, at least as far as his wife was concerned, did not always add to the pleasantness and decency of existence, but, on the contrary, disturbed it, and that, therefore, it was necessary to protect himself from such interference. And Ivan Ilyitch tried to devise means to this end. His official duties were the only thing that had an imposing effect upon Praskovia Feodorovna; and Ivan Ilyitch, by means of his office, and the duties arising from it, began to struggle with his wife for the defense of his independent life.

When the child was born, and in consequence of the various attempts and failures to have it properly nursed, and the illnesses, real and imaginary, of both mother and child, wherein Ivan Ilyitch's sympathy was demanded, but which were absolutely foreign to him, the necessity for him to secure a life outside of his family became still more imperative.

According as his wife grew more irritable and exacting, so Ivan Ilyitch transferred the center of his life's burdens more and more into his office. He began to love his office more and more, and became more ambitious than he had ever been.

Very soon, not longer than a year after his marriage, Ivan Ilyitch came to the conclusion that married life, while affording certain advantages, was in reality a very complicated and burdensome thing, in relation to which, if one would fulfill his duty, that is, live respectably and with the approbation of society, one must work out a certain system, just as in public office.

And such a system Ivan Ilyitch secured in his matrimonial life. He demanded of family life only such conveniences in the way of home dinners, a housekeeper, a bed, as it could furnish him, and, above all, that respectability in external forms which was in accordance with the opinions of society. As for the rest, he was anxious for pleasant amenities; and if he found them, he was very grateful. On the other hand, if he met with opposition and complaint, then he immediately took refuge in the far-off world of his official duties, which alone offered him delight.

Ivan Ilyitch was regarded as an excellent magistrate, and at the end of three years he was appointed deputy prokuror. His new functions, their importance, the power vested in him of arresting and imprisoning anyone, the publicity of his speeches, his success obtained in this field—all this still more attached him to the service.

Children came; his wife kept growing more irritable and ill-tempered; but the relations which Ivan Ilyitch maintained toward family life made him almost proof against her temper.

After seven years of service in one city, Ivan Ilyitch was promoted to the office of prokuror in another government. They moved; they had not much money, and the place where they went did not suit his wife. Although his salary was larger than before, yet living was more expensive; moreover, two of their children died; and thus family life became still more distasteful to Ivan Ilyitch.

Praskovia Feodorovna blamed her husband for all the misfortunes that came on them in their new place of abode. Most of the subjects of conversation between husband and wife, especially the education of their children, led to questions which were productive of quarrels, so that quarrels were always ready to break out. Only at rare intervals came those periods of affection which distinguish married life, but they were not of long duration. These were little islands in which they rested for a time; but then again they pushed out into the sea of secret animosity, which expressed itself by driving them farther and farther apart.

This alienation might have irritated Ivan Ilyitch, if he had not considered that it was inevitable; but he now began to look on this situation not merely as normal, but even as the goal of his activity in the family. This goal consisted in withdrawing as far as possible from these unpleasantnesses, or of giving them a character of innocence and respectability; and he attained this end by spending less and less time with his family; but when he was to do so, then he endeavored to guarantee his position by the presence of strangers.

But Ivan Ilyitch's chief resource was his office. In the world of his duties was concentrated all his interest in life. And this interest wholly absorbed him. The consciousness of his power of ruining any one whom he might wish to ruin; the importance of his position manifested outwardly when he came into court or met his subordinates; his success with superiors and subordinates; and, above all, his skill in the conduct of affairs—and he was perfectly conscious of it—all this delighted him, and, together with conversations with his colleagues, dinners and whist, filled all his life. Thus, for the most part, Ivan Ilyitch's life continued to flow in its even tenor as he considered that it ought to flow—pleasantly and respectably.

Thus he lived seven years longer. His eldest daughter was already sixteen years old; still another little child had died; and there remained a lad, the one who was in school, the object of their wrangling. Ivan Ilyitch wanted to send him to the law school; but Praskovia, out of spite toward him, selected the gymnasium. The daughter studied at home, and made good progress; the lad also was not at all backward in his studies.

Thus seventeen years of Ivan Ilyitch's life passed since the time of his marriage. He was already an old prokuror, having declined several transfers in the hope of a still more desirable place, when there occurred unexpectedly an unpleasant turn of affairs which was quite disturbing to his peaceful life.

Ivan Ilyitch had been hoping for the position of president in a university city; but Hoppe got in ahead of him, and obtained the place. Ivan Ilyitch became irritated, began to make recriminations, got into a quarrel with him and his next superior: signs of coolness were manifested toward him, and in the subsequent appointments he was passed over.

This was in 1880. This year was the most trying of Ivan Ilyitch's life. It happened, on the one hand, that his salary did not suffice for his expenses; on the other, that he was forgotten by all, and that what seemed to him a great, an atrocious, injustice toward himself was regarded by others as a perfectly natural thing. Even his father did not think it his duty to come to his aid. He felt that he was abandoned by all his friends, who considered that his position, worth thirty-five hundred rubles a year, was very normal and even fortunate. He alone knew that with the consciousness of the injustice which had been done him, and with his wife's everlasting rasping, and with the debts which began to accumulate, now that he lived beyond his means—he alone knew that his situation was far from normal.

The summer of that year, in order to lighten his expenses, he took leave of absence, and went with his wife to spend the summer at the country place belonging to Praskovia Feodorovna's brother.

In the country, relieved of his official duties, Ivan Ilyitch for the first time felt not only irksomeness, but insupportable anguish; and he made up his mind that it was impossible to live in such a way, and that he must take immediate and decisive steps, no matter what they were.

After a long, sleepless night, which he spent walking up and down the terrace, Ivan Ilyitch decided to go to Petersburg, to bestir himself and to get transferred into another ministry so as to punish *them* who had not known how to appreciate him.

On the next day, notwithstanding all the protests of his wife and brother-in-law, he started for Petersburg.

He wanted only one thing—to obtain a place worth five thousand a year. He would not stipulate for any special ministry, any special direction, any form of activity. All that he needed was a place—a place with a salary of five thousand, in the administration, in the banks, on the railways, in the institutions of the Empress Maria, even in the customs service; but the sole condition was the five thousand salary, the sole condition to be relieved from the ministry where they did not know how to appreciate him.

And lo! this trip of Ivan Ilyitch's met with astonishing, unexpected success. At Kursk an acquaintance of his, F. S. Ilyin, came into the first-class carriage, and informed him of a telegram just received by the governor of Kursk to the effect that a change was about to be made in the ministry: in Piotr Ivanovitch's place would be appointed Ivan Semyonovitch.

This probable change, over and above its significance for Russia, had a special significance for Ivan Ilyitch, from the fact that by bringing up a new official, Piotr Petrovitch, and probably his friend Zakhar Ivanovitch, it was in the highest degree favorable for Ivan Ilyitch. Zakhar Ivanovitch was a colleague and friend of Ivan Ilyitch.

In Moscow the tidings were confirmed. And when he reached Petersburg, Ivan Ilyitch sought out Zakhar Ivanovitch, and obtained the promise of a sure position in his old ministry—that of justice.

At the end of a week he telegraphed his wife: ZAKHAR, IN MILLER'S PLACE; IN THE FIRST REPORT SHALL BE APPOINTED.

Ivan Ilyitch, thanks to this change of administration, suddenly obtained in his old ministry such an appointment as put him two grades above his colleagues—five thousand salary, and thirty-five hundred for traveling expenses.

All his grievances against his former rivals and against the whole ministry were forgotten, and Ivan Ilyitch was entirely happy.

Ivan Ilyitch returned to the country, jocund, contented, as he had not been for a long time. Praskovia Feodorovna also brightened up, and peace was re-established between them. Ivan Ilyitch related how he was honored by everyone in Petersburg; how all those who had been his enemies were covered with shame and now fawned on him; how they envied him his position, and especially how dearly everyone in Petersburg loved him.

Praskovia Feodorovna listened to this, and made believe that she believed it, and did not contradict him in anything, but only made plans for the arrangement of their new life in the city where they were going. And Ivan Ilyitch had the joy of seeing that these plans were his plans, that they coincided, and that his life, interrupted though it had been, was now about to regain its own character of festive pleasure and decency.

Ivan Ilyitch went back for a short visit only. On the 22nd of September he was obliged to assume his duties; and, moreover, he needed time to get established in his new place, to transport all his possessions from the province, to buy new things, to give orders for still more—in a word, to install himself as it seemed proper to his mind, and pretty nearly as it seemed proper to Praskovia Feodorovna's ideas.

And now, when all was ordered so happily, and when he and his wife were in accord, and, above all, lived together but a small portion of the time, they became better friends than they had been since the first years of their married life.

Ivan Ilyitch at first thought of taking his family with him immediately; but the insistence of his sister- and brother-in-law, who suddenly manifested an extraordinary friendliness and brotherly love for Ivan Ilyitch and his family, induced him to depart alone.

Ivan Ilyitch took his departure; and his jocund frame of mind, arising from his success and his reconciliation with his wife, the one consequent upon the other, did not for a moment leave him.

He found admirable apartments, exactly coinciding with the dreams of husband and wife—spacious, lofty reception rooms in the old style; a convenient, grandiose library; rooms for his wife and daughter; study room for his son—all as if expressly designed for them. Ivan Ilyitch himself took charge of the arrangements. He selected the wallpapers; he bought the furniture, mostly antique, to which he attributed a specially *comme-il-faut* style; hangings and all took form, and took form and approached that ideal which he had established in his conception.

When his arrangements were half completed, they surpassed his expectations. He perceived what a *comme-il-faut*, exquisite, and far from commonplace character all would have when completed. When he lay down to sleep, he imagined his "hall" as it would be. As he looked about his drawing room, still unfinished, he already saw the fireplace, the screen, the little *étagère*, and those easy chairs scattered here and there, those plates and saucers on the walls, and the bronzes, just as they would be when all was in place.

He was delighted with the thought of how he should astonish Pasha and Lizanka, who also had such good taste in these things. "They would never look for this. Especially that he would have the thought of going and buying, at such a low price, these old things that gave the whole an extraordinary character of gentility."

In his letters he purposely represented everything worse than it really was—so as to surprise them. All this so occupied him, that even his new duties, much as he enjoyed them, were not so absorbing as he expected. Even while court was in session, he had his moments of abstraction; he was cogitating as to what sort of cornices he should have for his curtains —straight or matched. He was so interested in this that often he himself took hold, rearranged the furniture, and even rehung the curtains himself.

One time, when he was climbing on a pair of steps, so as to explain to a dull-minded upholsterer how he wished a drapery to be arranged, he slipped and fell; but, being a strong, dexterous man, he saved himself. He only hit his side on the edge of the frame. He received a bruise, but it quickly passed away. Ivan Ilyitch all this time felt perfectly happy and well. He wrote, "I feel as if I were fifteen years younger."

He expected to finish in September, but circumstances delayed it till the middle of October But it was all admirable; not only he himself said so, but all who saw it said the same.

In reality, it was exactly what is customary among those people who are not very rich, but who like to ape the rich, and therefore only resemble one another—silken fabrics, mahogany, flowers, carpets, and bronzes, dark and shining, all that which all people of a certain class affect, so as to be comparable to all people of a certain class. And in his case, there was a greater resemblance, so that it was impossible to single out anything for attention; but still. this to him was something extraordinary.

When he met his family at the railway station, he took them to their apartments. freshly put in order for them; and the lackey, in a white necktie, opened the door into the vestibule, ornamented with flowers; and then they went into the parlor, the library, and ohed and ahed with delight; and he was very happy; he showed them everything, drank in their praises, and shone with satisfaction. On that very evening at tea, when Praskovia Feodorovna asked him, among other things, how he fell, he laughed, and illustrated in pantomime how he went head over heels. and scared the upholsterer

"I'm not a gymnast for nothing. Another man would have been killed, but I just struck myself here a little; when you touch it, it hurts; but it's already wearing off—it's a mere bruise."

And they began to live in the new domicile, in which, as always, after one has become fairly established, it was discovered that there was just one room too few; and with their new means, which, as always, lacked a little of being sufficient; about five hundred rubles additional, and it would have been well.

All went extraordinarily well at first, while still their arrangements were not wholly regulated, and there was still much to do—buying this thing, giving orders for that, rearranging, mending. Although there were occasional disagreements between husband and wife, yet both were so satisfied, and they had so many occupations, that no serious quarrel resulted. Still, when there was nothing left to arrange, they became a trifle bored, and felt that something was lacking; but now they began to form new acquaintances, new habits, and their lives became full.

Ivan Ilyitch spent the morning at court, but returned home to dinner; and at first he was in excellent humor, although sometimes he was a little vexed by something or other in the household management.

Any kind of spot on the tablecloth, on the draperies, any break in the curtain cords, irritated him. He had taken so much pains in getting things in order that any kind of harm befalling was painful to him.

But, on the whole, Ivan Ilyitch's life ran on, as in his opinion life ought to run, smoothly, pleasantly, and decently.

He rose at nine o'clock, drank his coffee, read the paper, then donned his uniform, and went down to court. There he instantly got himself into the harness to which he had been so long accustomed—petitioners, inquiries at the chancery, the chancery itself, sessions public and administrative. In all this, it was necessary to devise means to exclude all those external concerns of life which forever tend to trespass on the accuracy of conducting official duties; it was necessary that he should tolerate no relations with people except on an official basis; and the cause for such relations must be official, and the relations themselves must be only official.

For example, a man comes, and wants to know something or other. Ivan Ilyitch, as a man apart from his office, cannot have any relations with this man; but if the relationship of this man to the magistrate is such that it can be expressed on letterhead paper, then, within the limits of these relations, Ivan Ilyitch would do all, absolutely all, in his power, and at the same time preserve the semblance of affable, philanthropical relations—in other words, of politeness. The point where his official life and his private life joined was very strictly drawn. Ivan Ilyitch had a high degree of skill in separating the official side from the other without confounding them; and his long practice and talent gave him such finesse that he sometimes, as a virtuoso, allowed himself, by way of a jest, to confound the humanitarian and his official relations.

This act in Ivan Ilyitch's case was played, not only smoothly, pleasantly, and decently, but also in a virtuoso manner. During the intervals, he smoked, drank tea, talked a little about politics, a little about affairs in general, a little about cards, and more than all about appointments; and when weary, but still conscious of his virtuosity, as of one who has well played his part, like one of the first violins of an orchestra, he went home.

At home the mother and daughter had been receiving or making calls; the son was at the gymnasium, preparing his lessons with tutors; and he learned accurately whatever was taught him in the gymnasium. All was excellent.

After dinner, unless he had guests, Ivan Ilyitch sometimes read some book which was much talked about; and during the evening he sat down to his work—that is, read papers, consulted the laws, compared depositions and applied the law to them.

This was neither tedious nor inspiriting. It was tedious when he had the chance to play vint; but if there was no vint, then it was far better than to sit alone or with his wife.

Very delightful to Ivan Ilyitch were the little dinners to which he invited ladies and gentlemen holding high positions in society; and such entertainments were like the entertainments of people of the same class, just as his drawing room was like all drawing rooms.

One evening they even had a party; they danced, and Ivan Ilyitch felt gay, and all was good; only a great quarrel arose between husband and wife about the patties and sweetmeats. Praskovia Feodorovna had her ideas about them; but Ivan Ilyitch insisted on buying them all of an expensive confectioner, and he got a great quantity of patties; and the quarrel was because there was an extra quantity, and the confectioner's bill amounted to forty-five rubles.

The quarrel was sharp and disagreeable, inasmuch as Praskovia Feodorovna called him, "Fool! Pighead!"

And he, putting his hands to his head in his vexation, muttered something about divorce.

But the party itself was gay. The very best society were present; and

Ivan Ilyitch danced with the Princess Trufonova, the sister of the well-known founder of the society called *Unesi tui mayo gore* [Take away my sorrow].

Ivan Ilyitch's official pleasures were the pleasures of self-love; his pleasures in society were pleasures of vanity; but his real pleasures were the pleasures of playing vint. He confessed that, after all, after any disagreeable event befalling his life, the pleasure which, like a candle, glowed brighter than all others was that of sitting down—four good players, and partners who did not shout—to a game of vint—and always four, for it is very bad form to have any one cut in, even though you say, "I like it very much"—and have a reasonable, serious game—when the cards run well—and then to eat a little supper, and drink a glass of wine. And Ivan Ilyitch used to go to sleep, especially after a game of vint, when he had won a little something—a large sum is disagreeable—and feel particularly happy in his mind.

Thus they lived. The circle of their friends consisted of the very best society; men of high position visited them, and young men came.

As far as their views upon the circle of their acquaintance were concerned, husband, wife, and daughter were perfectly unanimous. And tacitly they each in the same way pushed aside, and rid themselves of, certain friends and relatives—the undesirable kind, who came fawning around them in their drawing room decorated with Japanese plates on the wall. Very soon these undesirable friends ceased to flutter around them, and the Golovins had only the very best society.

Young men were attracted to Lizanka; and the examining magistrate, Petrishchef, the son of Dmitri Ivanovitch Petrishchef and the sole heir to his wealth, began to flutter around Liza so assiduously that Ivan Ilyitch already asked Praskovia Feodorovna whether it would not be a good plan to take them on a troika ride together, or arrange some private theatricals.

Thus they lived. And thus all went along in its even course, and all was very good.

All were well. It was impossible to see any symptom of ill-health in the fact that Ivan Ilyitch sometimes spoke of a strange taste in his mouth and an uneasiness in the left side of his abdomen.

But it happened that this unpleasant feeling kept increasing; it did not as yet become a pain, but he was all the time conscious of a dull weight in his side, and of an irritable temper. This irritability, constantly increasing and increasing, began to disturb the pleasant, easygoing, decent life that had been characteristic of the Golovin family. The husband and wife began to quarrel more and more frequently; and before long their easy, pleasant relations were broken up, and even the decency was maintained under difficulties.

Scenes once more became very frequent. Once more, but quite infrequently, the little islands appeared, on which husband and wife could meet without an explosion. And Praskovia Feodorovna now said, with some justification, that her husband had a very trying disposition. With her peculiar tendency to exaggeration, she declared that he had always had such a horrible disposition, that nothing but her good nature had enabled her to endure it for twenty years.

It was indeed true that now he was the one that began the quarrels. His querulousness began always before dinner, and often, indeed, just as they sat down to eat the soup. Sometimes he noticed that a dish was chipped; sometimes the food did not suit him; now his son rested his elbows on the table; now it was the way his daughter dressed her hair. And he blamed Praskovia Feodorovna for everything. At first Praskovia Feodorovna answered him back, and said disagreeable things to him; but twice, during dinnertime, he broke out into such a fury that she perceived this to be an unhealthy state, which proceeded from the assimilation of his food; and she held her peace; she did not reply, and merely hastened to finish dinner.

Praskovia Feodorovna regarded her meekness as a great merit. As she had made up her mind that her husband had a horrible disposition, and was making her life wretched, she began to pity herself. And the more she pitied herself, the more she detested her husband. She began to wish that he would die; but she could not wish it, because then they would not have his salary any more. And this actually exasperated her still more against him. She regarded herself as terribly unhappy, from the very fact that his death could not relieve her; and she grew bitter, but concealed it; and this concealed bitterness strengthened her hatred of him.

After one scene in which Ivan Ilyitch was particularly unjust, and which he afterward explained on the ground of his irritability being the result of not being well, she told him that, if he was ill, then he ought to take some medicine; and she begged him to go to a famous physician.

He went. Everything was as he expected: everything was done according to the usual way—the delay; and the pompous *doctorial* air of importance, so familiar to him, the same as he himself assumed in court; and the tapping and the auscultation; and the leading questions requiring answers predetermined, and apparently not heard; and the look of superlative wisdom which seemed to say, "You, now, just trust yourself to us, and we will do everything; we understand without fail how to manage; everything is done in the same way for any man."

Everything was just exactly as in court. The airs he put on in court for the benefit of those brought before him, the same were assumed by the famous doctor for his benefit.

The doctor said, "Such and such a thing shows that you have such and such a thing in you; but if this is not confirmed according to the investigations of such and such a man, then you must suppose such and such a thing. Now, if we suppose such and such a thing, then"—and so on.

For Ivan Ilyitch, only one question was momentous: Was his case dangerous, or not? But the doctor ignored this inconvenient question. From a doctor's point of view, this question was idle, and deserved no consideration; the only thing to do was to weigh probabilities—floating kidney, chronic catarrh, appendicitis.

It was not a question about Ivan Ilyitch's life, but there was doubt whether it was floating kidney, or appendicitis; and this doubt the doctor, in Ivan Ilyitch's presence, settled in the most brilliant manner in favor of the appendix, making a reserve in case an analysis of the urine should give new results, and then the case would have to be examined anew.

All this was exactly what Ivan Ilyitch himself had done a thousand times in the same brilliant manner for the benefit of the prisoner at the bar. Thus, even more brilliantly, the doctor made his résumé, and with an air of still more joyful triumph gazed down from over his spectacles on the prisoner at the bar. From the doctor's résumé, Ivan Ilyitch came to the conclusion that, as far as he was concerned, it was bad; but as far as the doctor, and perhaps the rest of the world, was concerned, it made no difference; but for him it was bad!

And this conclusion struck Ivan Ilyitch with a painful shock, causing in him a feeling of painful pity for himself, and of painful wrath against this physician who showed such indifference to such a vital question.

But he said nothing; then he got up, laid some money on the table, and, with a sigh, said: "Probably we sick men often ask you foolish questions," said he; "but, in general, is this trouble serious, or not?"

The doctor gave him a severe glance with one eye, through the spectacles, as if to say: "Prisoner at the bar, if you do not confine yourself to the limits of the questions already put to you, I shall be constrained to take measures for having you put out of the audience chamber."

"I have already told you what I considered necessary and suitable," said the doctor; "a further examination will complete the diagnosis"; and the doctor bowed him out.

Ivan Ilyitch went out slowly, lugubriously took his seat in his sledge, and drove home. All the way he kept repeating what the doctor had said, endeavoring to translate all those involved scientific phrases into simple language, and find in them an answer to the question, "Is it a serious, very serious, case for me, or is it a mere nothing?"

And it seemed to him that the sense of all the doctor's words indicated a very serious case. The aspect of everything in the streets was gloomy. The *izvozchiks* were gloomy; gloomy the houses, the pedestrians; the shops were gloomy. This pain, this obscure, dull pain, which did not leave him for a second, seemed to him, when taken in connection with the doctor's ambiguous remarks, to gather a new and more serious significance. Ivan Ilyitch, with a new sense of depression, now took heed of it.

He reached home, and began to tell his wife. His wife listened, but while he was in the midst of his account, his daughter came in with her hat on; she was ready to go out with her mother. She sat down with evident disrelish to listen to this wearisome tale, but she was not detained long; her mother did not hear him out.

"Well," said she, "I am very glad, for now you will be careful, and take your medicine properly. Give me the prescription, and I will send Gerasim to the apothecary's."

And she went to get dressed.

He could not get a long breath all the time that she was in the room, and he sighed heavily when she went out.

"Well," said he, "perhaps it's a mere nothing, after all."

He began to take his medicine, and to follow the doctor's prescriptions, which were somewhat modified after the urine had been analyzed. But just here it so happened exactly that in this analysis, and in what ought to have followed it, there was some confusion. It was impossible to trace it back to the doctor, but the result was that what the doctor said to him did not take place. Either he had forgotten or neglected or concealed something from him.

But Ivan Ilyitch nevertheless began faithfully to follow the doctor's prescriptions, and in this way at first he found consolation.

Ivan Ilyitch's principal occupation, after he went to consult the doctor, consisted in carefully carrying out the doctor's prescription in regard to hygiene, and taking his medicine, and watching the symptoms of his malady, all the functions of his organism. Ivan Ilyitch became chiefly interested in human disease and human health. When people spoke in his presence of those who were sick, of those who had died, of those who were recuperating, especially from diseases like his own, he would listen.

endeavoring to hide his agitation, would ask questions, and make comparisons with his own ailment.

The pain did not diminish, but Ivan Ilyitch compelled himself to feign that he was getting better. And he was able to deceive himself as long as there was nothing to irritate him. But the moment that he had any disagreeable scene with his wife, any failure at court, a bad hand at vint, then he instantly felt the full force of his malady; formerly he endured these reverses, hopefully saying to himself: "Now I shall straighten out this wretched business, shall conquer, shall attain success, win the next hand."

But now every little failure cut him down, and plunged him in despair. He said to himself: "Here I was just beginning to get a little better, and the medicine was already helping me, and here this cursed bad luck or this unpleasantness. . . ."

And he would break out against his bad luck, or against the people that brought him unpleasantness, and were killing him; and he realized how this fit of anger was killing him, but he could not control it.

It would seem that it must be clear to him that these fits of anger against circumstances and people made his malady worse, and that, therefore, he ought not to notice disagreeable trifles; but he reasoned in precisely the opposite way: he said that he needed quiet; he was on the watch for everything which disturbed this quiet, and at every least disturbance his irritation broke out.

His condition was rendered worse by the fact that he read medical works, and consulted doctors. The progress of his disease was so gradual that he was able to deceive himself by comparing one evening with the next; there was little difference. But when he consulted the doctors, then it seemed to him that it was growing worse, and very rapidly also. And notwithstanding that he constantly consulted doctors.

During this month he went to another celebrity; the second celebrity said pretty much the same as the first had said, but he asked questions in a different way. And the consultation with this celebrity redoubled Ivan Ilyitch's doubt and fear.

A friend of a friend of his—a very good doctor—gave an absolutely different definition of his malady; and, notwithstanding the fact that he predicted recovery, his questions and hypotheses still further confused Ivan Ilyitch, and increased his doubts.

A homeopathist defined his disease in a still different manner, and gave him some pellets; and Ivan Ilyitch, without being suspected by any one, took them for a week. But at the end of the week, not perceiving that any relief came of them, and losing faith, not only in this, but in his former methods of treatment, he fell into still greater melancholy.

One time a lady of his acquaintance was telling him about cures effected by means of icons. Ivan Ilyitch surprised himself by listening attentively, and believing in the reality of the fact. This circumstance frightened him.

"Is it possible that I have reached such a degree of mental weakness?" he asked himself. "Nonsense! All rubbish! One must not give way to mere fancies. Now I'm going to select one physician, and rigorously follow his advice. That's what I will do. That's the end of it. I will not bother my brain, and till summer I will strictly carry out his prescription; and then the result will be seen. Now for an end to these hesitations."

It was easy to say this, but impossible to carry it out. The pain in his side kept troubling him, kept growing if anything worse, became incessant; the taste in his mouth became always more and more peculiar; it seemed to him that his breath was disagreeable, and that he was all the time losing his appetite and strength.

It was impossible to deceive himself; something terrible, novel, and significant, more significant than anything which had ever happened before to Ivan Ilyitch, was taking place in him. And he alone was conscious of it; those who surrounded him did not comprehend it, or did not wish to comprehend it, and thought that everything in the world was going on as before.

This more than aught else pained Ivan Ilyitch. His family—especially his wife and daughter, who were in the very white heat of social pleasures— he saw, did not comprehend at all, were vexed with him because he was gloomy and exacting, as if he were to blame for it. Even though they tried to hide it, he saw that he was in their way, but that his wife had definitely made up her mind in regard to his trouble, and stuck to it, no matter what he might say or do.

This mental attitude was expressed in some such way as this: "You know," she would say to an acquaintance, "Ivan Ilyitch, like all easy-going men, can't carry out the doctor's prescriptions strictly. One day he will take his drops, and eat what is ordered for him, and go to bed in good season; then all of a sudden, if I don't look out, he will forget to take his medicine, will eat sturgeon—though it is forbidden—yes, and sit up at vint till one o'clock."

"Well, now, when?" asks Ivan Ilyitch, with asperity. "Just once at Piotr Ivanovitch's."

"And last evening with Shebek."

"All right—I could not sleep from pain."

"Yes, no matter what it comes from; only you will never get over it in this way, and will keep on tormenting us."

Praskovia Feodorovna's settled conviction in regard to his ailment—and she impressed it on every one, and on Ivan Ilyitch himself—was that he was to blame for it, and that his whole illness was a new affliction which he was causing his wife. Ivan Ilyitch felt that this was involuntary on her part, but it was not on that account any easier for him to bear it.

In court Ivan Ilyitch noticed, or thought he noticed, the same strange behavior toward him; now it seemed to him that he was regarded as a man who was soon to give up his place; again, his friends would suddenly begin to rally him about his low spirits, as if this horrible, strange, and unheard-of something that was breeding in him and ceaselessly sucking up his vitality, and irresistibly dragging him away, were a pleasant subject for raillery! Schwartz especially irritated him with his jocularity, his lively ways, and his *comme-il-faut-ness*, reminding Ivan Ilyitch of himself as he had been ten years before.

Friends came in to have a game of cards. They sat down, they dealt, new cards were shuffled, diamonds were thrown on diamonds—seven of them. His partner said, "No trumps," and held up two diamonds. What more could be desired? It ought to have been a gay proud moment,—a clean sweep.

And suddenly Ivan Ilyitch was conscious of that living pain, of that taste in his mouth, and it seemed to him barbarous that he should be able thus to rejoice in this hand. He looked at Mikhaïl Mikhaïlovitch, his partner, as he rapped the table with his big red hand, and courteously and condescendingly refrained from gathering up the tricks, but pushed them over to Ivan Ilyitch that he might have the pleasure of counting them, without inconveniencing himself, without putting his hand out.

"What! does he think that I am so weak that I can't put my hand out?" said Ivan Ilyitch to himself; then he forgot what were trumps; trumped his partner's trick, and lost the sweep by three points. And what was more terrible than all was that he saw how Mikhaïl Mikhaïlovitch suffers, and yet to him it was a matter of indifference. And it was terrible to think why it was a matter of indifference to him.

All could see that it was hard for him, and they said to him: "We can stop playing if you are tired. You rest awhile."

Rest? No, he was not tired at all; they would finish the rubber. All were gloomy and taciturn. Ivan Ilyitch felt that he was the cause of their gloominess, and he could not enliven it. They had supper, and then went home; and Ivan Ilyitch was left alone, with the consciousness that his life is poisoned for him, and that he is poisoning the lives of others, and that this poison is not growing weaker, but is always working its way deeper and deeper into his being.

And with this consciousness, sometimes also with physical pain, sometimes with terror, he would have to go to bed, and frequently not sleep from anguish the greater part of the night. And in the morning he would have to get up again and dress and go to court and speak, write, and, unless he went out to ride, stay at home for those twenty-four hours, each one of which was a torture. And he had to live thus on the edge of destruction—alone, without anyone to understand him and pity him.

Thus passed one month and two.

Before New Year's his brother-in-law came to their city, and stopped at their house. Praskovia Feodorovna had gone out shopping. Ivan Ilyitch was in court. When he came home, and went into his library, he found his brother-in-law there, a healthy, sanguine man, engaged in opening his trunk. He raised his head as he heard Ivan Ilyitch's steps, and looked at him a moment in silence. This look revealed all to Ivan Ilyitch. His brother-in-law opened his mouth to exclaim at him, and refrained. This motion confirmed everything.

"What? Have I changed?"

"Yes . . . there is a change."

And whenever afterward Ivan Ilyitch tried to bring the conversation round to the subject of his external appearance, his brother-in-law avoided it. Praskovia Feodorovna came in and his brother-in-law went to her room. Ivan Ilyitch locked the door, and began to look at himself in the glass, first front face, then his profile. He took his portrait painted with his wife, and compared it with what he saw in the mirror. The change was portentous. Then he bared his arm to the elbow, looked at it, pulled down his sleeve, sat down on the otomanka, and it became darker than night.

"It must not . . . it must not be!" said he to himself; jumped up, went to the table, unfolded a document, began to read it, but could not. He opened the door, went out into the hall. The drawing-room door was shut. He tiptoed up to it, and began to listen.

"No, you exaggerate," Praskovia Feodorovna was saying.

"How do I exaggerate? Isn't it plain to you? He's a dead man. Look at his eyes, no light in them. . . . But what's the matter with him?"

"No one knows. Nikolayef"—that was another doctor—"says one thing,

but I don't know about it. Leshchititsky"—that was the famous doctor—
"says the opposite."

Ivan Ilyitch turned away, went to his room, lay down, and began to
think: "Kidney—a floating kidney!"

He recalled all that the doctors had told him—how it was torn away, and
how it was loose. And by an effort of his imagination he endeavored to
catch this kidney, to stop it, to fasten it. "It is such a small thing to do,"
it seemed to him.

"No; I will make another visit to Piotr Ivanovitch."

This was the friend whose friend was a doctor.

He rang, ordered the horse to be harnessed, and got ready to go out.

"Where are you going, *Jean?*" asked his wife, with a peculiarly gloomy
and unusually gentle expression.

This unusually gentle expression angered him. He looked at her grimly.

"I have got to go to Piotr Ivanovitch's."

He went to the friend whose friend was a doctor. They went together
to this doctor's. He found him and had a long talk with him.

As he examined the anatomical and physiological details of what, according to the doctor, was taking place in him, he comprehended it perfectly.

There was one more trifle—the least bit of a trifle in the vermiform
appendix. All that could be put to rights. Strengthen the force of one
organ, weaken the activity of another—assimilation ensues, and all is set
to rights.

He was a little late to dinner. He ate heartily, he talked gaily, but for a
long time he was not able to make up his mind to go to work.

At last he went to his library, and immediately sat down to his labors.
He read his documents, and labored over them; but he did not get rid of
the consciousness that he had before him an important, private duty,
which he must carry out to a conclusion.

When he had finished with his documents, he remembered that this
private duty was the thought about the vermiform appendix. But he did
not give in to it; he went to the drawing room to tea. They had callers;
there was conversation, there was playing on the pianoforte, and singing;
the examining magistrate, the desirable match for their daughter, was
there. Ivan Ilyitch spent the evening, as Praskovia Feodorovna observed,
more cheerfully than usual; but he did not for a moment forget that he
had before him those important thoughts about the vermiform appendix.

At eleven o'clock he bade his friends good night, and retired to his own
room. Since his illness began, he had slept alone in a little room off the

library. He went to it, undressed, and took a romance of Zola's; but he did not read it; he thought. And in his imagination the longed-for cure of the vermiform appendix took place. Assimilation, secretion, were stimulated; regulated activity was established.

"Yes, it is just exactly so," said he to himself. "It is only necessary to help nature."

He remembered his medicine, got up, took it, lay on his back, waiting for the medicine to have its beneficent effect, and gradually ease his pain.

"Only take it regularly, and avoid unhealthy influences; even now I feel a little better, considerably better."

He began to punch his side; it was not painful to the touch.

"No, I don't feel it . . . already I feel considerably better."

He blew out the candle, and lay on his side. . . . "The vermiform appendix becomes regulated, is absorbed . . ."

And suddenly he began to feel the old, well-known, dull, lingering pain, stubborn, silent, serious; in his mouth the same well-known taste. His heart sank within him; his brain was in a whirl.

"My God! my God!" he cried, "again, again! and it will never cease!"

And suddenly the trouble presented itself to him absolutely in another guise.

"The vermiform appendix! the kidney!" he said to himself. "The trouble lies, not in the blind intestine, not in the kidney . . . but in life . . . and death! Yes, once there was life; but now it is passing away, passing away, and I cannot hold it back. Yes. Why deceive oneself? Is it not evident to every one, except myself, that I am going to die? and it is only a question of weeks, of days . . . maybe instantly. It was light, but now darkness. . . . Now I was here, but then I shall be there! Where?"

A chill ran over him, his breathing ceased. He heard only the thumping of his heart.

"I shall not be, but what will be? There will be nothing. Then, where shall I be when I am no more? Will that be death? No, I will not have it!"

He leaped up, wished to light the candle, fumbled about with trembling hands, knocked the candle and candlestick to the floor, and again fell back on the pillow.

"Wherefore? It is all the same," he said to himself, gazing into the darkness with wide-open eyes.

"Death! Yes, death! And *they* know nothing about it, and wish to know nothing about it; and they do not pity me. They are playing." He heard through the door the distant sound of voices and *ritornelles*. "To them it is all the same . . . and they also will die. Little fools! I first, and they after me. It will be their turn also. But they are enjoying themselves! Cattle!"

Anger choked him, and he felt an insupportably heavy burden of anguish.

"It cannot be that all men have been exposed to this horrible terror." He lifted himself once more.

"No, it is not so at all. I must calm myself; I must think it all over from the beginning."

And here he began to reflect: "Yes, the beginning of the trouble. I hit my side, and I was just the same as before, one day and the next, only a little ache, then more severe, then the doctor, then low spirits, anxiety, the doctor again. And I am all the time coming nearer and nearer to the abyss. Less strength. Nearer, nearer! And how wasted I am! I have no light in my eyes. And death . . . and I thinking about the intestine! I am thinking only how to cure my intestine; but this is death!—Is it really death?"

Again fear fell on him. He panted, bent over, tried to find the matches, hit his elbow against the table. It hindered him, and hurt him; he lost his patience, pushed angrily against it with more violence, and tipped it over. And in despair, all out of breath, he fell back, expecting death instantly.

At this time the visitors were going. Praskovia Feodorovna was showing them out. She heard the table fall, and came in.

"What is the matter?"

"Nothing . . . I unintentionally knocked it over."

She went out, and brought in a candle. He was lying, breathing heavily, and quickly, like a man who has just run a verst; his eyes were staring at her.

"What is it, *Jean?*"

"No-o-thing. I . . . knock-ed . . . over. . . . Why say anything? she will not understand," he thought.

She did not in the least understand. She picked up the table, lighted the candle for him, and hurried out. She had to say good night to her company.

When she came back, he was still lying on his back, looking up.

"What is the matter? Are you worse?"

"Yes."

She shook her head, and sat down.

"Do you know, *Jean,* I think we had better send for Leshchititsky? Don't you?"

That meant, send for the celebrated doctor, and not mind the expense. He smiled bitterly, and said: "No."

She sat a moment, then came to him, and kissed him on the forehead.

He abhorred her, with all the strength of his soul, at that moment when she kissed him; and he had to restrain himself from pushing her away.

"Good night! God give you pleasant sleep!"

"Yes."

Ivan Ilyitch saw that he was going to die, and he was in perpetual despair. In the depths of his soul, he knew that he was going to die; but he not only failed to get used to the thought, but also simply did not comprehend it, could not comprehend it.

This form of syllogism, which he had studied in Kiziveter's "Logic"— "Kaï is a man, men are mortal, therefore Kaï is mortal"—had seemed to him all his life true only in its application to Kaï, but never to himself. It was Kaï as man, as man in general, and in this respect it was perfectly correct; but he was not Kaï, and not man in general, and he had always been an entity absolutely, absolutely distinct from all others; he had been Vanya with mamma and papa, with Mitya and Volodya, with his playthings, the coachman, with the nurse; then with Katenka, with all the joys, sorrows, enthusiasms of childhood, boyhood, youth.

Was it Kaï who smelt the odor of the little striped leather ball that Vanya had loved so dearly? Was it Kaï who had kissed his mother's hand? and was it for Kaï that the silken folds of his mother's dress had rustled so pleasantly? Was it he who made a conspiracy for the tarts at the law school? Was it Kaï who had been so deeply in love? Was it Kaï who had such ability in conducting the sessions?

"And Kaï is certainly mortal, and it is proper that he should die; but for me, Vanya, Ivan Ilyitch, with all my feelings, my thoughts—for me, that is another thing, and it cannot be that I must take my turn and die. That would be too horrible."

This was the way that he felt about it: "If I were going to die, like Kaï, then, surely, I should have known it; some internal voice would have told me; but nothing of the sort happened in me, and I myself, and my friends, all of us, have perceived that it was absolutely different in our case from what it was with Kaï. But now how is it?" he said to himself. "It cannot be, it cannot be, but it is! How is this? How understand it?"

And he could not understand it; and he endeavored to put away this thought as false, unjust, unwholesome, and to supplant it with other thoughts true and wholesome. But this thought, not merely as a thought, but, as it were, a reality, kept recurring and taking form before him.

And he summoned in place of this thought other thoughts, one after the other, in the hope of finding succor in them. He strove to return to his former course of reasoning, which hid from him of old the thought of death. But, strangely enough, all that which formerly hid, concealed, destroyed the image of death, was now incapable of producing that effect.

Ivan Ilyitch came to spend the larger part of his time in these attempts to restore the former current of feeling which put death out of sight. Sometimes he said to himself: "I will take up my duties again; they certainly kept me alive."

And he went to court, driving away every sort of doubt. He joined his colleagues in conversation, and sat down, according to his old habit, pensively looking with dreamy eyes on the throng, and resting his two emaciated hands on the arms of his oak chair, leaning over, just as usual, toward his colleague, running through the brief, whispering his comments; and then, suddenly lifting his eyes, and sitting straight, he pronounced the well-known words, and began business.

But suddenly, right in the midst of it, the pain in his side, entirely disregarding the time of public business, began its simultaneous business. Ivan Ilyitch perceived it, tried to turn his thoughts from it; but it took its course, and DEATH came up and stood directly before him, and gazed at him: and he was stupefied; the fire died out in his eyes, and he began once more to ask himself: "Is there nothing true save IT?"

And his colleagues and subordinates saw with surprise and concern that he, this brilliant, keen judge, was confused, was making mistakes.

He shook himself, tried to collect his thoughts, and in a way conducted the session till it adjourned, and then returned home with the melancholy consciousness that he no longer had the ability, as of old, to separate between his judicial acts and what he wished to put out of his thoughts; that even in the midst of his judicial acts, he could not deliver himself from IT. And what was worse than all, was the fact that IT distracted his attention, not to make him do anything, but only to make him look at IT, straight in the eye—look at IT, and, though doing nothing, suffer beyond words.

And, while attempting to escape from this state of things, Ivan Ilyitch sought relief, sought other shelter; and other aids came along, and for a short time seemed to help him; but immediately they not so much failed, as grew transparent, as if IT became visible through all, and nothing could hide it.

It happened in this latter part of the time that he went into the drawing room which he had decorated—that very drawing room where he had met with the fall, for which he—as he had to think with bitterness and scorn—for the decoration of which he had sacrificed his life; because he knew that his malady began with that bruise: he went in, and saw that on the varnished table was a scratch, cut by something. He sought for the cause of it, and found it in the bronze decoration of an album, which was turned up at the edge. He took the precious album, lovingly filled by him, and broke out in a passion against the carelessness of his daughter and her friends, who destroyed things so, who dog-eared photographs. He put this carefully to rights, and bent back the ornament.

Then the idea occurred to him to transfer this *établissement,* albums and all, to the other corner, where the flowers were. He summoned a servant. Either his wife or his daughter came to his help; they did not agree with him; they argued against the change: he argued, he lost his temper; but everything was good, because he did not think about IT, IT did not appear.

But here, as he himself was beginning to shift the things, his wife said: "Hold on! the men will attend to that; you will strain yourself again."

And suddenly IT gleamed through the shelter; he saw IT. IT gleamed; he was already hoping that IT had disappeared, but involuntarily he watched for the pain in his side—there it was, all the time, always making its advance; and he could not forget it, and IT clearly gazed at him from among the flowers. What was the purpose of it all?

"And it is true that here I have lost my life on that curtain as in a charge! Is it possible? How horrible and how ridiculous! It cannot be! It cannot be! but it is."

He went back to his library, went to bed, and found himself again alone with IT. Face to face with IT. But to do anything with IT—impossible! Only to look at IT, and grow chill!

How it came about in the third month of Ivan Ilyitch's illness, it was impossible to say, because it came about step by step, imperceptibly; but it came about that his wife and daughter, and his son and the servants, and his acquaintances and the doctors, and chiefly he himself, knew that all the interest felt in him by others was concentrated in this one thing—how soon he would vacate his place, would free the living

from the constraint caused by his presence, and be himself freed from
his sufferings.

He slept less and less; they gave him opium, and began to try hypo-
dermic injections of morphine. But this did not relieve him. The dull distress which he experienced in his half-drowsy condition at first merely
afforded the relief of change; but soon it came back as severe as ever, or
even more intense than open pain.

They prepared for him special dishes, according to the direction of the
physicians; but these dishes became ever more and more tasteless, more
and more repugnant to him.

Special arrangements also had been made, so that he might perform the
wants of nature; and each time it became more trying for him. The torture
came from the uncleanliness, the indecency, of it, and the ill odor, from
the knowledge that he required the assistance of another.

But from this very same disagreeable circumstance Ivan Ilyitch drew a
consolation. His butler, the muzhik Gerasim, always came to set things to
rights.

Gerasim was a clean, ruddy young muzhik, who had grown stout in
waiting on the table in the city houses. He was always festive, always
serene. From the very first, the sight of this man, always so neatly attired
in his Russian costume, engaged in this repulsive task, made Ivan Ilyitch
ashamed.

One time, after he had got up and was feeling too weak to lift his
pantaloons, he threw himself into an easy chair and was contemplating
with horror his bare thighs with their strangely flabby muscles standing
out.

Gerasim came in with light, buoyant steps, in thick boots, diffusing an
agreeable odor of tar from his boots, and the freshness of the winter air.
He wore a clean hempen apron and a clean cotton shirt, with the cuffs
rolled up on his bare, strong young arms; and, not looking at Ivan Ilyitch,
evidently curbing the joy in life which shone in his face, so as not to
offend the sick man, he began to do his work.

"Gerasim," said Ivan Ilyitch, in a weak voice.

Gerasim started, evidently fearing that he had failed in some duty,
and turned toward the sick man his fresh, good, simple young face, on
which the beard was only just beginning to sprout.

"What can I do for you?"

"This, I am thinking, is disagreeable to you. Forgive me. I cannot
help it."

"Do not mention it." And Gerasim's eyes shone, and he showed his white young teeth. "Why should I not do you this service? It is for a sick man."

And with expert, strong hands, he fulfilled his wonted task and went out with light steps. After five minutes he returned, still walking with light steps. He had made everything clean and sweet.

Ivan Ilyitch was still sitting in his arm chair.

"Gerasim," he said, "be good enough to assist me. Come here."

Gerasim went to him.

"Lift me up. It is hard for me alone, and I sent Dmitri away."

Gerasim went to him. In just the same way as he walked, he lifted him with his strong arm, deftly, gently, and held him. With his other hand he adjusted his clothing, and then was about to let him sit down. But Ivan Ilyitch requested him to help him to the divan. Gerasim, without effort, and exercising no sensible pressure, supported him, almost carrying him, to the divan, and set him down.

"Thank you. How easily, how well, you do it all!"

Gerasim again smiled, and was about to go. But Ivan Ilyitch felt so good with him, that he wanted him to stay.

"Wait! Please bring me that chair . . . no; that one there. Put it under my feet. It is easier for me when my feet are raised."

Gerasim brought the chair, put it down noiselessly, arranged so that it sat even on the floor, and put Ivan Ilyitch's legs on the chair. It seemed to Ivan Ilyitch that he felt more comfortable while Gerasim was holding up his legs.

"It is better when my legs are up," said Ivan Ilyitch. "Bring me that cushion."

Gerasim did this. Again he lifted his legs, and arranged it all. Again Ivan Ilyitch felt better while Gerasim was holding his legs. When he put them down, he felt worse.

"Gerasim," said he, "are you busy just now?"

"Not at all," said Gerasim, having learned of city people how to speak with gentlefolk.

"What more have you to do?"

"What more have I to do? Everything has been done, except splitting wood against tomorrow."

"Then, hold my legs a little higher, can you?"

"Why not? Of course I can!"

Gerasim lifted his legs higher, and it seemed to Ivan Ilyitch that in this position he felt no pain at all.

"But how about the wood?"

"Don't be worried about that. We shall have time enough."

Ivan Ilyitch bade Gerasim to sit down and hold his legs, and he talked with him. And, strangely enough, it seemed to him that he felt better while Gerasim was holding his legs.

From that time forth Ivan Ilyitch would sometimes call Gerasim, and make him hold his legs on his shoulders, and he liked to talk with him. Gerasim did this easily, willingly, simply, and with a goodness of heart which touched Ivan Ilyitch. In all other people, good health, strength, and vigorous life affronted Ivan Ilyitch; but Gerasim's strength and vigorous life did not affront Ivan Ilyitch, but calmed him.

Ivan Ilyitch's chief torment was a lie—the lie somehow accepted by everyone, that he was only sick, but not dying, and that he needed only to be calm, and trust to the doctors, and then somehow he would come out all right. But *he* knew that, whatever was done, nothing would come of it, except still more excruciating anguish and death. And this lie tormented him; it tormented him that they were unwilling to acknowledge what all knew as well as he knew, but preferred to lie to him about his terrible situation, and made him also a party to this lie. This lie, this lie, it clung to him, even to the very evening of his death; this lie, tending to reduce the strange, solemn act of his death to the same level as visits, curtains, sturgeon for dinner—it was horribly painful for Ivan Ilyitch. And strange! many times, when they were playing this farce for his benefit, he was within a hairbreadth of shouting at them: "Stop your foolish lies! you know as well as I know that I am dying, and so at least stop lying."

But he never had the spirit to do this. The strange, terrible act of his dissolution, he saw, was reduced by all who surrounded him to the grade of an accidental unpleasantness, often unseemly—when he was treated as a man who should come into the drawing room and diffuse about him a bad odor—and contrary to those principles of "propriety" which he had served all his life. He saw that no one pitied him, because no one was willing even to appreciate his situation. Only Gerasim appreciated his situation, and pitied him. And, therefore, Ivan Ilyitch was contented only when Gerasim was with him.

He was contented when Gerasim for whole nights at a time held his legs, and did not care to go to sleep, saying: "Don't you trouble yourself, Ivan Ilyitch; I shall get sleep enough."

Or when suddenly, using *thou* instead of *you*, he would add: "If thou wert not sick . . . but since thou art, why not serve thee?"

Gerasim alone did not lie: in every way it was evident that he alone comprehended what the trouble was, and thought it unnecessary to hide it, and simply pitied his sick barin,[4] who was wasting away. He even said directly when Ivan Ilyitch wanted to send him off to bed: "We shall all die. Then, why should I not serve you?" he said, meaning by this that he was not troubled by his extra work, for precisely the reason that he was doing it for a dying man, and he hoped that, when his time came, some one would undertake the same service for him.

Besides this lie, or in consequence of it, Ivan Ilyitch felt the greatest torment from the fact that no one pitied him as he longed for them to pity him. At some moments after long agonies he yearned more than all— although he would have been the last to confess it—he yearned for some one to pity him as a sick child is pitied. He longed to be caressed, to be kissed, to be wept for, as a child is caressed and comforted. He knew that he was a magistrate of importance, that his beard was turning gray, and that hence it was impossible; but nevertheless he longed for it. And in his relations with Gerasim there was something that approached this. And, therefore, his relations with Gerasim comforted him.

Ivan Ilyitch would have liked to weep, would have liked to be caressed, and have tears shed for him; and here came his colleague, the member Shebek, and, instead of weeping and being caressed, Ivan Ilyitch puts on a serious, stern, melancholy expression of countenance, and with all his energy speaks his opinions concerning the significance of a judgment of cassation, and obstinately stands up for it.

This lie surrounding him, and existing in him, more than all else poisoned Ivan Ilyitch's last days.

It was morning.

It was morning merely because Gerasim had gone, and Piotr, the lackey, had come. He put out the candles, opened one curtain, and began noiselessly to put things to rights. Whether it were morning, whether it were evening, Friday or Sunday, all was a matter of indifference to him, all was one and the same thing. The agonizing, shooting pain, never for an instant appeased; the consciousness of a life hopelessly wasting away, but not yet departed; the same terrible, cursed death coming nearer and nearer, the one reality, and always the same lie—what matter, then, here, of days, weeks, and hours of the day?

"Will you not have me bring the tea?"

"He must follow form, and that requires masters to take tea in the morning," he thought; and he said merely: "No."

"Wouldn't you like to go over to the divan?"

---

4. The ordinary title of a landowner or noble.

"He has to put the room in order, and I hinder him; I am uncleanness, disorder!" he thought to himself, and said merely: "No: leave me!"

The lackey still bustled about a little. Ivan Ilyitch put out his hand. Piotr officiously hastened to him: "What do you wish?"

"My watch."

Piotr got the watch, which lay nearby, and gave it to him.

"Half-past eight. They aren't up yet?"

"No one at all. Vasili Ivanovitch"—that was his son—"has gone to school, and Praskovia Feodorovna gave orders to wake her up if you asked for her. Do you wish it?"

"No, it is not necessary.—Shall I not try the tea?" he asked himself. "Yes . . . tea . . . bring me some."

Piotr started to go out. Ivan Ilyitch felt terror-stricken at being left alone. "How can I keep him? Yes, my medicine. Piotr, give me my medicine.—Why not? perhaps the medicine may help me yet."

He took the spoon, sipped it.

"No, there is no help. All this is nonsense and delusion," he said, as he immediately felt the familiar, mawkish, hopeless taste.

"No, I cannot have any faith in it. But this pain, . . . why this pain? Would that it might cease for a minute!"

And he began to groan. Piotr came back.

"Nothing . . . go! Bring the tea."

Piotr went out. Ivan Ilyitch, left alone, began to groan, not so much from the pain, although it was horrible, as from mental anguish.

"Always the same thing, and the same thing; all these endless days and nights. Would it might come very soon! What very soon? Death, blackness? No, no! Anything rather than death!"

When Piotr came back with the tea on a tray, Ivan Ilyitch stared long at him in bewilderment, not comprehending who he was, what he was. Piotr was abashed at this gaze; and when Piotr showed his confusion, Ivan Ilyitch came to himself.

"Oh, yes," said he, "the tea; very well, set it down. Only help me to wash, and to put on a clean shirt."

And Ivan Ilyitch began to perform his toilet. With resting spells he washed his hands and face, cleaned his teeth, began to comb his hair, and looked into the mirror. It seemed frightful, perfectly frightful, to him, to see how his hair lay flat upon his pale brow.

While he was changing his shirt, he knew that it would be still more frightful if he gazed at his body; and so he did not look at himself. But now it was done. He put on his khalat, wrapped himself in his plaid, and sat down in his easy chair to take his tea. For a single moment he felt refreshed; but as soon as he began to drink the tea, again that same taste, that same pain. He compelled himself to drink it all, and lay down, stretching out his legs. He lay down, and let Piotr go.

Always the same thing. Now a drop of hope gleaming, then a sea of despair rising up, and always pain, always melancholy, and always the same monotony. It was terribly melancholy to the lonely man; he longed to call in someone, but he knew in advance that it is still worse when others are present.

"Even morphine again . . . to get a little sleep! . . . I will tell him, tell the doctor, to find something else. It is impossible, impossible so."

One hour, two hours, would pass in this way. But there! the bell in the corridor. Perhaps it is the doctor. Exactly: it is the doctor, fresh, hearty, portly, jovial, with an expression as if he said, "You may feel apprehension of something or other, but we will immediately straighten things out for you."

The doctor knows that this expression is not appropriate here; but he has already put it on once for all, and he cannot rid himself of it—like a man who has put on his dress coat in the morning, and gone to make calls.

The doctor rubs his hands with an air of hearty assurance.

"I am cold. A healthy frost. Let me get warm a little," says he, with just the expression that signifies that all he needs is to wait until he gets warmed a little, and, when he is warmed, then he will straighten things out.

"Well, now, how goes it?"

Ivan Ilyitch feels that the doctor wants to say, "How go your little affairs?" but that he feels that it is impossible to say so; and he says, "What sort of a night did you have?"

Ivan Ilyitch would look at the doctor with an expression which seemed to ask the question, "Are you never ashamed of lying?"

But the doctor has no desire to understand his question.

And Ivan Ilyitch *says:* "It was just horrible! The pain does not cease, does not disappear. If you could only give me something for it!"

"That is always the way with you sick folks! Well, now, it seems to me I am warm enough; even the most particular Praskovia Feodorovna would not find anything to take exception to in my temperature. Well, now, how are you really?"

And the doctor shakes hands with him.

And, laying aside his former jocularity, the doctor begins with serious mien to examine the sick man, his pulse and temperature, and he renews the tappings and the auscultation.

Ivan Ilyitch knew for a certainty, and beyond peradventure, that all this was nonsense and foolish deception; but when the doctor, on his knees, leaned over toward him, applying his ear, now higher up, now lower down, and with most sapient mien performed various gymnastic evolutions on him, Ivan Ilyitch succumbed to him, as once he succumbed to the discourses of the lawyers, even when he knew perfectly well that they were deceiving him, and why they were deceiving him.

The doctor, still on his knees on the divan, was still performing the auscultation, when at the door were heard the rustle of Praskovia Feodorovna's silk dress, and her words of blame to Piotr because he had not informed her of the doctor's visit.

She came in, kissed her husband, and immediately began to explain that she had been up a long time; and only through a misunderstanding she had not been there when the doctor came.

Ivan Ilyitch looked at her, observed her from head to foot, and felt a secret indignation at her fairness and her plumpness, and the cleanliness of her hands, her neck, her glossy hair, and the brilliancy of her eyes, brimming with life. He hated her with all the strength of his soul, and her touch made him suffer an actual paroxysm of hatred of her.

Her attitude toward him and his malady was the same as before. Just as the doctor had formulated his treatment of his patient and could not change it, so she had formulated her treatment of him, making him feel that he was not doing what he ought to do, and was himself to blame; and she liked to reproach him for this, and she could not change her attitude toward him.

"Now, just see! he does not heed, he does not take his medicine regularly; and, above all, he lies in a position that is surely bad for him—his feet up."

She related how he made Gerasim hold his legs.

The doctor listened with a disdainfully good-natured smile, as much as to say: "What is to be done about it, pray? These sick folks are always conceiving some such foolishness. But you must let it go."

When the examination was over, the doctor looked at his watch; and then Praskovia Feodorovna declared to Ivan Ilyitch that, whether he was willing or not, she was going that very day to call in the celebrated doctor to come and have an examination and consultation with Mikhaïl Danilovitch—that was the name of their ordinary doctor.

"Now, don't oppose it, please. I am doing this for my own self," she said ironically, giving him to understand that she did it all for him, and only on this account did not allow him the right to oppose her.

He said nothing, and frowned. He felt that this lie surrounding him was so complicated that it was now hard to escape from it.

She did all this for him, only in her own interest; and she said that she was doing it for him, while she was in reality doing it for herself, as some incredible thing, so that he was forced to take it in its opposite sense.

The celebrated doctor, in fact, came about half-past eleven. Once more they had auscultations; and learned discussions took place before him, or in the next room, about his kidney, about the blind intestine, and questions and answers in such a learned form that again the place of the real question of life and death, which now alone faced him, was driven away by the question of the kidney and the blind intestine, which were not acting as became them, and on which Mikhaïl Danilovitch and the celebrity were to fall instantly and compel to attend to their duties.

The famous doctor took leave with a serious but not hopeless expression. And in reply to the timid question which Ivan Ilyitch's eyes, shining with fear and hope, asked of him, whether there was a possibility of his getting well, it replied that it could not vouch for it, but there was a possibility.

The look of hope with which Ivan Ilyitch followed the doctor was so pathetic that Praskovia Feodorovna, seeing it, even wept, as she went out of the library door in order to give the celebrated doctor his honorarium.

The raising of his spirits, caused by the doctor's hopefulness, was but temporary. Again the same room, the same pictures, curtains, wallpaper, vials, and his aching, pain-broken body. And Ivan Ilyitch began to groan. They gave him a subcutaneous injection, and he fell asleep.

When he woke up it was beginning to grow dusky. They brought him his dinner. He forced himself to eat a little bouillon. And again the same monotony, and again the advancing night.

About seven o'clock, after dinner, Praskovia Feodorovna came into his room, dressed as for a party, with her exuberant bosom swelling in her stays, and with traces of powder on her face. She had already that morning told him that they were going to the theater. Sarah Bernhardt had come to town, and they had a box which he had insisted on their taking.

Now he had forgotten about that, and her toilet offended him. But he concealed his vexation when he recollected that he himself had insisted on their taking a box, and going, on the ground that it would be an instructive, aesthetic enjoyment for the children.

Praskovia Feodorovna, came in self-satisfied, but, as it were, feeling a little to blame. She sat down, asked after his health, as he saw, only for the sake of asking, and not so as to learn, knowing that there was nothing to learn, and began to say what was incumbent on her to say—that she would not have gone for anything, but that they had taken the box; and that Elen and her daughter and Petrishchef—the examining magistrate, her daughter's betrothed—were going, and it was impossible to let them go alone, but that it would have been more agreeable to her to stay at home with him. Only he should be sure to follow the doctor's prescriptions in her absence.

"Yes—and Feodor Petrovitch"—the betrothed—"wanted to come in. May he? And Liza!"

"Let them come."

The daughter came in, in evening dress, with her fair young body, her body that made his anguish more keen. But she paraded it before him, strong, healthy, evidently in love, and irritated against the disease, the suffering, and death which stood in the way of her happiness.

Feodor Petrovitch also entered, in his dress coat, with curly hair *á la Capoul*, with long, sinewy neck tightly incased in a white standing collar, with a huge white bosom, and his long, muscular legs in tight black trousers, with a white glove on one hand, and with an opera hat.

Immediately behind him, almost unnoticed, came the gymnasium scholar, in his new uniform, poor little fellow, with gloves on, and with that terrible blue circle under the eyes, the meaning of which Ivan Ilyitch understood.

He always felt a pity for his son. And terrible was his timid and compassionate glance. With the exception of Gerasim, Vasya alone, it seemed to Ivan Ilyitch, understood and pitied him.

All sat down; again they asked after his health. Silence ensued. Liza asked her mother if she had the opera glasses. A dispute arose between mother and daughter as to who had mislaid them. It was a disagreeable episode.

Feodor Petrovitch asked Ivan Ilyitch if he had seen Sarah Bernhardt. Ivan Ilyitch did not at first understand his question, but in a moment he said: "No . . . why, have you seen her yet?"

"Yes, in 'Adrienne Lecouvreur.'"

Praskovia Feodorovna said that she was especially good in that. The daughter disagreed with her. A conversation arose about the grace and realism of her acting—the same conversation which is always and forever one and the same thing.

In the midst of the conversation, Feodor Petrovitch glanced at Ivan

Ilyitch, and grew silent. The others glanced at him, and grew silent. Ivan Ilyitch was looking straight ahead with gleaming eyes, evidently indignant at them. Some one had to extricate them from their embarrassment, but there seemed to be no way out of it. No one spoke; and a panic seized them all, lest suddenly this ceremonial lie should somehow be shattered, and the absolute truth become manifest to all.

Liza was the first to speak. She broke the silence. She wished to hide what all felt, but she betrayed it.

"One thing is certain—*if we are going*, it is time," she said, glancing at her watch, her father's gift; and giving the young man a sign, scarcely perceptible, and yet understood by him, she smiled, and arose in her rustling dress.

All arose, said good-by, and went.

When they had gone, Ivan Ilyitch thought that he felt easier: the lying was at an end; it had gone with them; but the pain remained. Always this same pain, always this same terror, made it hard as hard could be. There was no easing of it. It grew ever worse, always worse.

Again minute after minute dragged by, hour after hour, forever the same monotony, and forever endless, and forever more terrible—the inevitable end.

"Yes, send me Gerasim," was his reply to Piotr's question.

Late at night his wife returned. She came in on her tiptoes, but he heard her; he opened his eyes, and quickly closed them again. She wanted to send Gerasim away, and sit with him herself. He opened his eyes, and said: "No, go away."

"You suffer very much."

"It makes no difference."

"Take some opium."

He consented, and drank it. She went.

Until three o'clock he was in a painful sleep. It seemed to him that they were forcing him cruelly into a narrow sack, black and deep; and they kept crowding him down, but could not force him in. And this performance, horrible for him, was accompanied with anguish. And he was afraid, and yet wished to get in, and struggled against it, and yet tried to help.

And here suddenly he broke through, and fell . . . and awoke.

There was Gerasim still sitting at his feet on the bed, dozing peacefully, patiently.

But he was lying there with his emaciated legs in stockings resting on his shoulders, the same candle with its shade, and the same never ending pain.

"Go away, Gerasim," he whispered.

"It's nothing; I will sit here a little while."

"No, go away."

He took down his legs, lay on his side on his arm, and began to pity himself. He waited only until Gerasim had gone into the next room, and then he no longer tried to control himself, but wept like a child. He wept over his helplessness, over his terrible loneliness, over the cruelty of men, over the cruelty of God, over the absence of God.

"Why hast Thou done this? Why didst Thou place me here? Why, why dost Thou torture me so horribly?"

He expected no reply; and he wept because there was none, and could be none. The pain seized him again; but he did not stir, did not call. He said to himself: "There, now, again, now strike! But why? What have I done to Thee? Why is it?"

Then he became silent; ceased not only to weep, ceased to breathe, and became all attention: as it were, he heard, not a voice speaking with sounds, but the voice of his soul, the tide of his thoughts, arising in him.

"What dost thou need?" was the first clear concept possible to be expressed in words which he heard.

" 'What dost thou need? What dost thou need?' " he said to himself. "What? Freedom from suffering. To live," he replied.

And again he gave his attention, with such effort that already he did not even notice his pain.

"To live? how live?" asked the voice of his soul.

"Yes, to live as I used to live—well, pleasantly."

"How didst thou live before when thou didst live well and pleasantly?" asked the voice.

And he began to call up in his imagination the best moments of his pleasant life. But, strangely enough, all these best moments of his pleasant life seemed to him absolutely different from what they had seemed then —all, except the earliest remembrances of his childhood. There, in childhood, was something really pleasant, which would give new zest to life if it were to return. But the person who had enjoyed that pleasant existence was no more; it was as if it were the remembrance of someone else.

As soon as the period began which had produced the present *he*, Ivan Ilyitch, all the pleasures which seemed such then, now in his eyes dwindled away, and changed into something of no account, and even disgusting.

And the farther he departed from infancy, and the nearer he came to the present, so much the more unimportant and dubious were the pleasures.

This began in the law school. There was still something even then which was truly good; then there was gaiety, there was friendship, there were hopes. But in the upper classes these good moments became rarer.

Then, in the time of his first service at the governor's, again appeared good moments; these were the recollections of love for a woman. Then all this became confused, and the happy time grew less. The nearer he came to the present, the worse it grew, and still worse and worse it grew.

"My marriage . . . so unexpected, and disillusionment and my wife's breath, and sensuality, hypocrisy! And this dead service, and these labors for money; and thus one year, and two, and ten, and twenty, and always the same thing. And the longer it went, the more dead it became.

"It is as if all the time I were going down the mountain, while thinking that I was climbing it. So it was. According to public opinion, I was climbing the mountain; and all the time my life was gliding away from under my feet. . . . And here it is already . . . die!

"What is this? Why? It cannot be! It cannot be that life has been so irrational, so disgusting. But even if it is so disgusting and irrational, still, why die, and die in such agony? There is no reason.

"Can it be that I did not live as I ought?" suddenly came into his head. "But how can that be, when I have done all that it was my duty to do?" he asked himself. And immediately he put away this sole explanation of the enigma of life and death as something absolutely impossible.

"What dost thou wish now?—To live? To live how? To live as thou livest in court when the usher proclaims, 'The court is coming! the court is coming'?

"The court is coming—the court," he repeated to himself. "Here it is, the court. Yes; but I am not guilty," he cried with indignation. "What for?"

And he ceased to weep; and, turning his face to the wall, he began to think about that one thing, and that alone. "Why, wherefore, all this horror?"

But, in spite of all his thoughts, he received no answer. And when the thought occurred to him, as it had often occurred to him, that all this came from the fact that he had not lived as he should, he instantly remembered all the correctness of his life, and he drove away this strange thought.

Thus two weeks longer passed. Ivan Ilyitch no longer got up from the divan. He did not wish to lie in bed, and he lay on the divan. And, lying almost all the time with his face to the wall, he still suffered in solitude the same inexplicable sufferings, and still thought in solitude the same inexplicable thought.

"What is this? Is it true that this is death?"

And an inward voice responded: "Yes, it is true."

"Why these torments?"

And the voice responded: "But it is so. There is no why."

Farther and beyond this, there was nothing.

From the very beginning of his malady, from the time when Ivan Ilyitch for the first time went to the doctor, his life was divided into two conflicting tendencies, alternately succeeding each other. Now it was despair, and the expectation of an incomprehensible and frightful death; now it was hope, and the observation of the functional activity of his body, so full of interest for him. Now before his eyes was the kidney, or the intestine, which, for the time being, failed to fulfill its duty. Then it was that incomprehensible, horrible death, from which it was impossible for anyone to escape.

These two mental states, from the very beginning of his illness, kept alternating with one another. But the farther the illness progressed, the more dubious and fantastical became his ideas about the kidney, and the more real his consciousness of approaching death.

He had but to call to mind what he had been three months before, and what he was now, to call to mind with what regularity he had been descending the mountain; and that was sufficient for all possibility of hope to be dispelled.

During the last period of this solitude through which he was passing, as he lay with his face turned to the back of the divan—a solitude amid a populous city, and amid his numerous circle of friends and family, a solitude deeper than which could not be found anywhere, either in the depths of the sea, or in the earth—during the last period of this terrible solitude, Ivan Ilyitch lived only by imagination in the past.

One after another, the pictures of his past life arose before him. They always began with the time nearest to the present, and went back to the very remotest—to his childhood, and there they rested.

If Ivan Ilyitch remembered the stewed prunes which they had given him to eat that very day, then he remembered the raw, puckery French prunes of his childhood, their peculiar taste, and the abundant flow of saliva caused by the stone. And in connection with these recollections of taste started a whole series of recollections of that time—his nurse, his brother, his toys.

"I must not think about these things; it is too painful," said Ivan Ilyitch to himself. And again he transported himself to the present—the button on the back of the divan, and the wrinkles of the morocco. "Morocco is costly, not durable. There was a quarrel about it. But there was some other morocco, and some other quarrel, when we tore father's portfolio and got punished, and mamma brought us some tarts."

And again his thoughts reverted to childhood; and again it was painful to Ivan Ilyitch, and he tried to avoid it, and think of something else.

And again, together with this current of recollections, there passed through his mind another current of recollections about the progress and rise of his disease. Here, also, according as he went back, there was more and more of life. There was more, also, of excellence in life, and more of life itself. And the two were confounded.

"Just as this agony goes from worse to worse, so also all my life has gone from worse to worse," he thought. "One shining point, there back in the distance, at the beginning of life; and then all growing blacker and blacker, swifter and swifter, in inverse proportion to the square of the distance from death," thought Ivan Ilyitch.

And the comparison of a stone falling with accelerating rapidity occurred to his mind. Life, a series of increasing tortures, always speeding swifter and swifter to the end—the most horrible torture.

"I am falling."

He shuddered, he tossed, he wished to resist it. But he already knew that it was impossible to resist; and again, with eyes weary of looking, but still not able to resist looking at what was before him, he stared at the back of the divan, and waited, waited for this frightful fall, shock, and destruction.

"It is impossible to resist," he said to himself. "But can I not know the wherefore of it? Even that is impossible. It might be explained by saying that I had not lived as I ought. But it is impossible to acknowledge that," he said to himself, recollecting all the legality, the uprightness, the propriety of his life.

"It is impossible to admit that," he said to himself, with a smile on his lips, as if someone were to see that smile of his, and be deceived by it.

"No explanation! torture, death . . . why?"

Thus passed two weeks. In these weeks, there occurred an event desired by Ivan Ilyitch and his wife. Petrishchef made a formal proposal. This took place in the evening. On the next day, Praskovia Feodorovna went to her husband, meditating in what way to explain to him Feodor

Petrovitch's proposition; but that very same night, a change for the worse had taken place in Ivan Ilyitch's condition. Praskovia Feodorovna found him on the same divan, but in a new position. He was lying on his back; he was groaning, and looking straight up with a fixed stare.

She began to speak about medicines. He turned his eyes on her. She did not finish saying what she had begun, so great was the hatred against her expressed in that look.

"For Christ's sake, let me die in peace!" said he.

She was about to go out; but just at this instant the daughter came in, and came near to wish him good morning. He looked at his daughter as he had looked at his wife, and, in reply to her questions about his health, told her dryly that he would quickly relieve them all of his presence. Neither mother nor daughter said anything more; but they sat for a few moments longer, and then went out.

"What are we to blame for?" said Liza to her mother. "As if we had made him so! I am sorry for papa, but why should he torment us?"

At the usual time the doctor came. Ivan Ilyitch answered "yes," "no," not taking his angry eyes from him; and at last he said: "Now see here, you know that you don't help any, so leave me!"

"We can appease your sufferings," said the doctor.

"You cannot even do that; leave me!"

The doctor went into the drawing room, and advised Praskovia Feodorovna that it was very serious, and that there was only one means —opium—of appeasing his sufferings, which must be terrible.

The doctor said that his physical sufferings were terrible, and this was true; but more terrible than his physical sufferings were his moral sufferings, and in this was his chief torment.

His moral sufferings consisted in the fact that that very night, as he looked at Gerasim's sleepy, good-natured face, with its high cheekbones, it had suddenly come into his head: "But how is it if in reality my whole life, my conscious life, has been wrong?"

It came into his head that what had shortly before presented itself to him as an absolute impossibility—that he had not lived his life as he ought—might be true. It came into his head that the scarcely recognizable desires to struggle against what men highest in position considered good —desires scarcely recognizable, which he had immediately banished— might be true, and all the rest might be wrong. And his service, and his course of life, and his family, and these interests of society and office—all this might be wrong.

He endeavored to defend all this before himself. And suddenly he realized all the weakness of what he was defending. And there was nothing to defend.

"But if this is so," he said to himself, "and I am departing from life with the consciousness that I have wasted all that was given me, and that it is impossible to rectify it, what then?"

He lay flat on his back, and began entirely anew to examine his whole life.

When in the morning he saw the lackey, then his wife, then his daughter, then the doctor, each one of their motions, each one of their words, confirmed for him the terrible truth which had been disclosed to him that night. He saw in them himself, all that for which he had lived; and he saw clearly that all this was wrong, all this was a terrible, monstrous lie, concealing both life and death.

This consciousness increased his physical sufferings, added tenfold to them. He groaned and tossed, and threw off the clothes. It seemed to him that they choked him, and loaded him down.

And that was why he detested them.

They gave him a great dose of opium; he became unconscious, but at dinnertime the same thing began again. He drove them from him, and threw himself from place to place.

His wife came to him, and said: "Jean, darling, do this for me (*for me!*). It cannot do any harm, and sometimes it helps. Why, it is a mere nothing. And often well people try it."

He opened his eyes wide.

"What? Take the sacrament? Why? It's not necessary. But, however . . ."

She burst into tears.

"Will you, my dear? I will get our priest. He is so sweet!"

"Excellent! very good," he continued.

When the priest came, and confessed him, he became calmer, felt, as it were, an alleviation of his doubts, and consequently of his suffering; and there came a moment of hope. He again began to think about the blind intestine and the possibility of curing it. He took the sacrament with tears in his eyes.

When they put him to bed after the sacrament, he felt comfortable for the moment, and once more hope of life appeared. He began to think of the operation which they had proposed.

"I want to live, to live," he said to himself.

His wife came to congratulate him. She said the customary words, and added: "You feel better, don't you?"

Without looking at her, he said: "Yes."

Her hope, her temperament, the expression of her face, the sound of her voice, all said to him one thing:

"Wrong! all that for which thou hast lived, and thou livest, is falsehood, deception, hiding from thee life and death."

And as soon as he expressed this thought, his exasperation returned, and, together with his exasperation, the physical, tormenting agony; and, with the agony, the consciousness of inevitable death close at hand. Something new took place: a screw seemed to turn in him, twinging pain to show through him, and his breathing was constricted.

The expression of his face, when he said "yes," was terrible. After he had said that "yes," he looked straight into her face, and then, with extraordinary quickness for one so weak, he threw himself on his face and cried: "Go away! go away! leave me!"

From that moment began that shriek that did not cease for three days, and was so terrible that, when it was heard two rooms away, it was impossible to hear it without terror. At the moment that he answered his wife, he felt that he was lost, and there was no return, that the end had come, absolutely the end, and the question was not settled, but remained a question.

"U! uu! u!" he cried in varying intonations. He began to shriek, "*N'ye khotchu*—I won't"; and thus he kept up the cry on the letter *u*.

Three whole days, during which for him there was no time, he struggled in that black sack into which an invisible, invincible power was thrusting him. He fought as one condemned to death fights in the hands of the hangman, knowing that he cannot save himself, and at every moment he felt that, notwithstanding all the violence of his struggle, he was nearer and nearer to that which terrified him. He felt that his suffering consisted, both in the fact that he was being thrust into that black hole, and still more that he could not make his way through into it. What hindered him from making his way through was the confession that his life had been good. This justification of his life caught him, and did not let him advance, and more than all else tormented him.

Suddenly some force knocked him in the breast, in the side, still more forcibly compressed his breath; he was hurled through the hole, and there at the bottom of the hole some light seemed to shine on him. It happened to him as it sometimes does on a railway carriage when you think that you are going forward, but are really going backward, and suddenly recognize the true direction.

"Yes, all was wrong," he said to himself; "but that is nothing. I might, I might have done right. What is right?" he asked himself, and suddenly stopped.

This was at the end of the third day, two hours before his death. At this very same time the little student noiselessly stole into his father's room, and approached his bed. The moribund was continually shrieking desperately, and tossing his arms. His hand struck upon the little student's head. The little student seized it, pressed it to his lips, and burst into tears.

It was at this very same time that Ivan Ilyitch fell through, saw the light, and it was revealed to him that his life had not been as it ought, but that still it was possible to repair it. He was just asking himself, "What is right?" and stopped to listen.

Then he felt that someone was kissing his hand. He opened his eyes, and looked at his son. He felt sorry for him. His wife came to him. He looked at her. With open mouth, and with her nose and cheeks wet with tears, with an expression of despair, she was looking at him. He felt sorry for her.

"Yes, I am a torment to them," he thought. "I am sorry for them, but they will be better off when I am dead."

He wanted to express this, but he had not the strength to say it.

"However, why should I say it? I must do it."

He pointed out his son to his wife by a glance, and said: "Take him away . . . I am sorry . . . and for thee."

He wanted to say also, "*Prosti*—Forgive," but he said, "*Propusti*—Let it pass"; and, not having the strength to correct himself, he waved his hand, knowing that he would comprehend who had the right.

And suddenly it became clear to him that what oppressed him, and was hidden from him, suddenly was lighted up for him all at once, and on two sides, on ten sides, on all sides.

He felt sorry for them; he felt that he must do something to make it less painful for them. To free them, and free himself, from these torments, "How good and how simple!" he thought.

"But the pain," he asked himself, "where is it?—Here, now, where art thou, pain?"

He began to listen.

"Yes, here it is! Well, then, do your worst, pain!"

"And death? where is it?"

He tried to find his former customary fear of death, and could not.

"Where is death? What is it?"

There was no fear, because there was no death.

In place of death was light!

"Here is something like!" he suddenly said aloud. "What joy!"

For him all this passed in a single instant, and the significance of this instant did not change.

For those who stood by his side, his death agony was prolonged two hours more. In his breast something bubbled up, his emaciated body shuddered. Then more and more rarely came the bubbling and the rattling.

"It is all over," said someone above him.

He heard these words, and repeated them in his soul.

"It is over! death!" he said to himself. "It does not exist more."

He drew in one more breath, stopped in the midst of it, stretched himself, and died.

The Three Hermits

But when ye pray, use not vain repetitions, as the heathen do:
for they think that they shall be heard for their much speaking.

Be ye not therefore like unto them: for your Father knoweth what
things ye have need of, before ye ask him.

Matthew, VI, 7–8.

A bishop set sail in a ship from the city of Archangel to Solovki.[1] In the same ship sailed some pilgrims to the saints.

The wind was propitious, the weather was clear, the sea was not rough. The pilgrims, some of whom were lying down, some lunching, some sitting in little groups, conversed together.

The bishop also came on deck and began to walk up and down on the bridge. As he approached the bow, he saw a knot of people crowded together. A little muzhik was pointing his hand at something in the sea, and talking; and the people were listening.

The bishop stood still, and looked where the little muzhik was pointing; nothing was to be seen, except the sea glittering in the sun.

The bishop came closer and began to listen. When the little muzhik saw the bishop, he took off his cap, and stopped speaking. The people also, when they saw the bishop, took off their hats, and paid their respects.

"Don't mind me, brothers," said the bishop. "I have also come to listen to what you are saying, my good friend."

"This fisherman was telling us about some hermits," said a merchant, who was bolder than the rest.

---

1. The Slovetsky Monastery, at the mouth of the Dvina River.

"What about the hermits?" asked the bishop, as he came to the gunwale, and sat down on a box. "Tell me too; I should like to hear. What were you pointing at?"

"Well, then, yonder's the little island just heaving in sight," said the little peasant; and he pointed toward the port side. "On that very islet, three hermits live, working out their salvation."

"Where is the little island?" asked the bishop.

"Here, look along my arm, if you please. You see that little cloud? Well, just below it to the left it shows like a streak."

The bishop looked and looked; the water gleamed in the sun, but from lack of practice he could not see anything.

"I don't see it," says he. "What sort of hermits are they who live on the little island?"

"God's people," replied the peasant. "For a long time I had heard tell of them, but I never chanced to see them until last summer."

And the fisherman again began to relate how he had been out fishing, and how he was driven to that island, and knew not where he was. In the morning he started to look around, and stumbled upon a little earthen hut; and he found in the hut one hermit, and then two others came in. They fed him, and dried him, and helped him repair his boat.

"What sort of men were they" asked the bishop.

"One was rather small, humpbacked, very, very old; he was dressed in well-worn stole; he must have been more than a hundred years old; the gray hairs in his beard were already turning green; but he always had a smile ready, and he was as serene as an angel of heaven. The second was taller, also old, in a torn caftan; his long beard was growing a little yellowish, but he was a strong man; he turned my boat over as if it had been a tub, and I didn't even have to help him: he was also a jolly man. But the third was tall, with a long beard reaching to his knee, and white as the moon; but he was gloomy; his eyes glared out from under beetling brows; and he was naked, all save a plaited belt."

"What did they say to you?" asked the bishop.

"They did everything mostly without speaking, and they talked very little among themselves; one had only to look, and the other understood. I began to ask the tall one if they had lived there long. He frowned, muttered something, grew almost angry: then the little old man instantly seized him by the hand, smiled, and the large man said nothing. But the old man said, 'Excuse us,' and smiled."

While the peasant was speaking, the ship had been sailing nearer and nearer to the islands.

"There, now you can see plainly," said the merchant. "Now, please look, your reverence," said he, pointing.

The bishop tried to look, and he barely managed to make out a black speck—the little island.

The bishop gazed and gazed; and he went from the bow to the stern, and he approached the helmsman.

"What is that little island," says he, "that you see over yonder?"

"As far as I know, it has no name; there are a good many of them here."

"Is it true as they say, that some monks are winning their salvation there?"

"They say so, your reverence, but I don't rightly know. Fishermen, they say, have seen them. Still, folks talk a good deal of nonsense."

"I should like to land on the little island, and see the hermits," said the bishop. "How can I manage it?"

"It is impossible to go there in the ship," said the helmsman. "You might do it in a boat, but you will have to ask the captain."

They summoned the captain.

"I should like to have a sight of those hermits," said the bishop. "Is it out of the question to take me there?"

The captain tried to dissuade him.

"It is possible, quite possible, but we should waste much time; and I take the liberty of assuring your reverence, they are not worth looking at. I have heard from people that those old men are perfectly stupid; they don't understand anything, and can't say anything, just like some sort of sea fish."

"I wish it," said the bishop. "I will pay for the trouble, if you will take me there."

There was nothing else to be done: the sailors arranged it; they shifted sail. The helmsman put the ship about and they sailed toward the island. A chair was set for the bishop on the bow. He sat down and looked. And all the people gathered on the bow, all looked at the little island. And those who had trustworthy eyes already began to see rocks on the island, and point out the hut. And one even saw the three hermits. The captain got out a spyglass, gazed through it, handed it to the bishop.

"He is quite right," said the captain; "there on the shore at the right, standing on a great rock, are three men."

The bishop also looked through the glass; he pointed it in the right direction and plainly saw the three men standing there—one tall, the second shorter, but the third very short. They were standing on the shore, hand in hand.

The captain came to the bishop: "Here, your reverence, the ship must come to anchor; if it suit you, you can be put ashore in a yawl, and we will anchor out here and wait for you."

Immediately they got the tackle ready, cast anchor, and furled the sails; the vessel brought up, began to roll. They lowered a boat, the rowers manned it, and the bishop started to climb down by the companionway. The bishop climbed down, took his seat on the thwart; the rowers lifted their oars; they sped away to the island. They sped away like a stone from a sling; they could see the three old men standing—the tall one naked, with his plaited belt; the shorter one in his torn caftan; and the little old humpbacked one, in his old stole—all three were standing there, hand in hand.

The sailors reached shore and caught hold with the boat hook. The bishop got out.

The hermits bowed before him; he blessed them; they bowed still lower. And the bishop began to speak to them: "I heard," says he, "that you hermits were here, working out your salvation, that you pray Christ our God for your fellow men; and I am here by God's grace, an unworthy servant of Christ, called to be a shepherd to His flock; and so I desired also, if I might, to give instruction to you, who are the servants of God."

The hermits made no reply; they smiled, they exchanged glances.

"Tell me how you are working out your salvation, and how you serve God," said the bishop.

The middle hermit sighed, and looked at the aged one, at the venerable one; the tall hermit frowned, and looked at the aged one, at the venerable one. And the venerable old hermit smiled, and said: "Servant of God, we have not the skill to serve God; we only serve ourselves, getting something to eat."

"How do you pray to God?" asked the bishop.

And the venerable hermit said: "We pray thus: 'You three, have mercy on us three.'"

And as soon as the venerable hermit said this, all three of the hermits raised their eyes to heaven, and all three said, "*Troe vas, troe nas, pomiluï nas!*"

The bishop smiled, and said: "You have heard this about the Holy Trinity, but you should not pray so. I have taken a fancy to you, men of God. I see that you desire to please God, but you know not how to serve Him. You should not pray so; but listen to me, I will teach you. I shall not teach you my own words, but shall teach you from God's scriptures how God commanded all people to pray to God."

And the bishop began to explain to the hermits how God revealed Himself to men. He taught them about God the Father, God the Son, and God the Holy Spirit, and said: "God the Son came upon earth to save men, and this is the way He taught all men to pray; listen, and repeat after me—"

And the bishop began to say: "*Our Father.*"

And one hermit repeated: "*Our Father.*"

And then the second repeated: "*Our Father.*"

And the third also repeated: "*Our Father.*"

"*Who art in heaven*"; and the hermits tried to repeat, "*Who art in heaven.*"

But the middle hermit mixed the words up, he could not repeat them so; and the tall, naked hermit could not repeat them—his mustache had grown so as to cover his mouth, he could not speak distinctly; and the venerable, toothless hermit could not stammer the words intelligibly.

The bishop said it a second time; the hermits repeated it again. And the bishop sat down on a little boulder, and the hermits stood about him; and they looked at his lips, and they repeated it after him until they knew it. And all that day till evening the bishop labored with them; and ten times, and twenty times, and a hundred times, he repeated each word, and the hermits learned it by rote. And when they got mixed up, he set them right, and made then begin all over again.

And the bishop did not leave the hermits until he had taught them the whole of the Lord's Prayer. They repeated it after him, and then by themselves.

First of all, the middle hermit learned it, and he repeated it from beginning to end; and the bishop bade him say it again and again, and still again to repeat it; and the others also learned the whole prayer.

It was already beginning to grow dark, and the moon was just coming up out of the sea, when the bishop arose to go back to the ship.

The bishop said farewell to the hermits; they all bowed very low before him. He raised them to their feet and kissed each of them, bade them pray as he had taught them; and he took his seat in the boat, and returned to the ship.

And while the bishop was rowed back to the ship, he heard all the time how the hermits were repeating the Lord's Prayer at the top of their voices.

They returned to the ship, and here the voices of the hermits could no longer be heard; but they could still see, in the light of the moon, the three old men standing in the very same place on the shore—one shorter than the rest in the middle, with the tall one on the right, and the other on the left hand.

The bishop returned to the ship, climbed up on deck; the anchor was hoisted; the sails were spread, and bellied with wind; the ship began to move, and they sailed away.

The bishop came to the stern, and took a seat there, and kept looking at the little island. At first the hermits were to be seen; then they were hidden from sight, and only the island was visible; and then the island went out of sight, and only the sea was left playing in the moonlight.

The pilgrims lay down to sleep, and all was quiet on deck. But the bishop cared not to sleep; he sat by himself in the stern, looked out over the sea in the direction where the island had faded from sight, and thought about the good hermits.

He thought of how they had rejoiced in what they had learned in the prayer; and he thanked God because He had led him to the help of the hermits, in teaching them the word of God.

Thus the bishop was sitting and thinking, looking at the sea in the direction where the little island lay hidden. And his eyes were filled with the moonlight, as it danced here and there on the waves. Suddenly he saw something shining and gleaming white in the track of the moon. Was it a bird, a gull, or a boat sail gleaming white? The bishop strained his sight.

"A sailboat," he said to himself, "is chasing us. Yes, it is catching up with us very rapidly. It was far, far off, but now it is close to us. But, after all, it is not much like a sailboat. Anyway, something is chasing us, and catching up with us."

And the bishop could not decide what it was—a boat, or not a boat; a bird, or not a bird; a fish, or not a fish. It was like a man, but very great; but a man could not be in the midst of the sea.

The bishop got up and went to the helmsman.

"Look!" says he, "what is that? what is that, brother? what is it?" said the bishop.

But by this time he himself saw. It was the hermits running over sea. Their gray beards gleamed white, and shone; and they drew near the ship as if it were stationary.

The helmsman looked. He was scared, dropped the tiller, and cried with a loud voice: "Lord! the hermits are running over the sea as if it were dry land!"

The people heard and sprang up; all rushed aft. All beheld the hermits running, hand in hand. The end ones swung their arms; they signaled the ship to come to. All three ran over the water as if it were dry land, and did not move their feet.

It was not possible to bring the ship to before the hermits overtook it, came on board, raised their heads, and said with one voice: "We have forgotten, servant of God, we have forgotten what thou didst teach us. While we were learning it, we remembered it; but when we ceased for an hour to repeat it, one word slipped away; we have forgotten it: the whole was lost. We remembered none of it; teach it to us again."

The bishop crossed himself, bowed low to the hermits, and said: "Acceptable to God is your prayer, yo hermits. It is not for me to teach you. Pray for us sinners."

And the bishop bowed before the feet of the hermits. And the hermits paused, turned about, and went back over the sea. And until the morning, there was something seen shining in the direction where the hermits had gone.

What Men Live By

We know that we have passed out of death into life, because we
love the brethren. He that loveth not abideth in death.

I John, III, 14.

But whoso hath the world's goods, and beholdeth his brother in
need, and shutteth up his compassion from him, how doth the love
of God abide in him?

My little children, let us not love in word, neither with the tongue,
but in deed and truth.   I John, III, 17–18.

Love is of God; and every one that loveth is begotten of God and
knoweth God.

He that loveth not knoweth not God; for God is love.

I John, IV, 7–8.

No man hath beheld God at any time: if we love one another,
God abideth in us.   I John, IV, 12.

God is love; and he that abideth in love abideth in God, and God
abideth in him.   I John, IV, 16.

If a man say, I love God, and hateth his brother, he is a liar; for
he that loveth not his brother whom he hath seen cannot love God
whom he hath not seen.   I John, IV, 20.

A cobbler and his wife and children had lodgings with a
peasant. He owned neither house nor land, and he supported himself and
his family by shoemaking.

Bread was dear and labor was poorly paid, and whatever he earned
went for food.

The cobbler and his wife had one shuba between them, and this had
come to tatters, and for two years the cobbler had been hoarding in order
to buy sheepskins for a new shuba.

When autumn came, the cobbler's hoard had grown; three paper rubles lay in his wife's box, and five rubles and twenty kopecks more were due the cobbler from his customers.

One morning the cobbler betook himself to the village to get his new shuba. He put on his wife's wadded nankeen jacket over his shirt, and outside of all a woolen caftan. He put the three-ruble note in his pocket, broke off a staff, and after breakfast he set forth.

He said to himself: "I will get my five rubles from the peasant, and that with these three will buy pelts for my shuba."

The cobbler reached the village and went to one peasant's; he was not at home, but his wife promised to send her husband with the money the next week, but she could not give him any money. He went to another, and this peasant swore that he had no money at all; but he paid him twenty kopecks for cobbling his boots.

The cobbler made up his mind to get the pelts on credit. But the fur dealer refused to sell on credit.

"Bring the money," said he; "then you can make your choice; but we know how hard it is to get what is one's due."

And so the cobbler did not do his errand, but he had the twenty kopecks for cobbling the boots, and he took from a peasant an old pair of felt boots to mend with leather.

At first the cobbler was vexed at heart; then he spent the twenty kopecks for vodka, and started to go home. In the morning he had felt cold, but after having drunk the brandy he was warm enough even without the shuba.

The cobbler was walking along the road, striking the frozen ground with the staff which he had in one hand, and swinging the felt boots in the other, and thus he talked to himself:

"I am warm even without a shuba," said he. "I drank a glass, and it dances through all my veins. And so I don't need a sheepskin coat. I walk along, and all my vexation is forgotten. What a fine fellow I am! What do I need? I can get along without the shuba. I don't need it at all. There's one thing: the wife will feel bad. Indeed, it is too bad; here I have been working for it, and now to have missed it! You just wait now! if you don't bring the money, I will take your hat, I vow I will! What a way of doing things! He pays me twenty kopecks at a time! Now what can you do with twenty kopecks? Get a drink; that's all! You say, 'I am poor!' But if you are poor, how is it with me? You have a house and cattle and everything; I have nothing but my own hands. You raise your own grain, but I have to buy mine, when I can, and it costs me three rubles a week for food alone. When I get home now, we shall be out of bread. Another ruble and a half of outgo! So you must give me what you owe me."

By this time the cobbler had reached the chapel at the crossroads, and he saw something white behind the chapel.

It was already twilight, and the cobbler strained his eyes, but he could not make out what the object was.

"There never was any such stone there," he said to himself. "A cow? But it does not look like a cow! The head is like a man's; but what is that white? And why should there be any man there?"

He went nearer. Now he could see plainly. What a strange thing! It was indeed a man, but was he alive or dead? sitting there stark naked, leaning against the chapel, and not moving.

The cobbler was frightened. He said to himself: "Some one has killed that man, stripped him, and flung him down there. If I go near, I may get into trouble."

And the cobbler hurried by.

In passing the chapel he could no longer see the man; but after he was fairly beyond it, he looked back, and saw that the man was no longer leaning against the chapel, but was moving, and apparently looking after him.

The cobbler was still more scared by this, and he said to himself: "Shall I go back to him or go on? If I go back to him, there might something unpleasant happen; who knows what sort of a man he is? He can't have gone there for any good purpose. If I went to him, he might spring on me and choke me, and I could not get away from him; and even if he did not choke me, why should I try to make his acquaintance? What could be done with him, naked as he is? I can't take him with me, and give him my own clothes! That would be absurd."

And the cobbler hastened his steps. He had already gone some distance beyond the chapel, when his conscience began to prick him.

He stopped short.

"What is this that you are doing, Semyon?" he asked himself. "A man is perishing of cold, and you are frightened, and hurry by! Are you so very rich? Are you afraid of losing your money? Aï, Sema! That is not right!"

Semyon turned and went back to the man.

Semyon went back to the man, looked at him, and saw that it was a young man in the prime of life; there were no bruises visible on him, but he was evidently freezing and afraid; he was sitting there, leaning back, and he did not look at Semyon; apparently he was so weak that he could not lift his eyes.

.Semyon went up close to him, and suddenly the man seemed to revive; he lifted his head and fastened his eyes on Semyon.

And by this glance the man won Semyon's heart.

He threw the felt boots down on the ground, took off his belt and laid it on the boots, and pulled off his caftan.

"There's nothing to be said," he exclaimed. "Put these on! There now!"

Semyon put his hand under the man's elbow, to help him, and tried to lift him. The man got up.

And Semyon saw that his body was graceful and clean, that his hands and feet were comely, and that his face was agreeable. Semyon threw the caftan over his shoulders. He could not get his arms into the sleeves. Semyon found the place for him, pulled the coat up, wrapped it around him, and fastened the belt.

He took off his tattered cap, and was going to give it to the stanger, but his head felt cold, and he said to himself: "The whole top of my head is bald, but he has long curly hair."

So he put his hat on again.

"I had better let him put on my boots."

He made him sit down and put the felt boots on him.

After the cobbler had thus dressed him, he says: "There now, brother, just stir about, and you will get warmed up. All these things are in other hands than ours. Can you walk?"

The man stood up, looked affectionately at Semyon, but was unable to speak a word.

"Why don't you say something? We can't spend the winter here. We must get to shelter. Now, then, lean on my stick, if you don't feel strong enough. Bestir yourself!"

And the man started to move. And he walked easily, and did not lag behind. As they walked along the road Semyon said: "Where are you from, if I may ask?"

"I do not belong hereabouts."

"No; I know all the people of this region. How did you happen to come here and get to that chapel?"

"I cannot tell you."

"Someone must have treated you outrageously."

"No one has treated me outrageously. God has punished me."

"God does all things, but you must have been on the road bound for somewhere. Where do you want to go?"

"It makes no difference to me."

Semyon was surprised. The man did not look like a malefactor, and his speech was gentle, but he seemed reticent about himself.

And Semyon said to himself: "Such things as this do not happen every day." And he said to the man, "Well, come to my house, though you will find it very narrow quarters."

As Semyon approached the yard, the stranger did not lag behind, but walked abreast of him. The wind had arisen, and searched under Semyon's shirt, and as the effect of the wine had now passed away, he began to be chilled to the bone. He walked along, and began to snuffle, and he muffled his wife's jacket closer around him, and he said to himself: "That's the way you get a shuba! You go after a shuba, and you come home without your caftan! yes, and you bring with you a naked man—besides, Matriona won't take kindly to it!"

And as soon as the thought of Matriona occurred to him, he began to feel downhearted.

But as soon as his eyes fell on the stranger, he remembered what a look he had given him behind the chapel, and his heart danced with joy.

Semyon's wife had finished her work early. She had chopped wood, brought water, fed the children, taken her own supper, and was now deliberating when it would be best to mix some bread, "today or to-morrow?"

A large crust was still left. She said to herself: "If Semyon gets something to eat in town, he won't care for much supper, and the bread will last till tomorrow."

Matriona contemplated the crust for some time, and said: "I am not going to mix any bread. There's just enough flour to make one more loaf. We shall get along till Friday."

Matriona put away the bread, and sat down at the table to sew a patch on her husband's shirt.

She sewed, and thought how her husband would be buying sheepskins for the shuba.

"I hope the fur dealer will not cheat him. For he is as simple as he can be. He, himself, would not cheat anybody, but a baby could lead him by the nose. Eight rubles is no small sum. You can get a fine shuba with it. Perhaps not one tanned, but still a good one. How we suffered last winter without any shuba! Could not go to the river nor anywhere! And whenever he went outdoors, he put on all the clothes, and I hadn't anything to wear. He is late in getting home. He ought to be here by this time. Can my sweetheart have got drunk?"

Just as these thoughts were passing through her mind the doorsteps creaked: someone was at the door. Matriona stuck in the needle, and went to the entry. There she saw two men had come in—Semyon, and with him a strange peasant, without a cap and in felt boots.

Matriona perceived immediately that her husband's breath smelled of liquor.

"Now," she said to herself, "he has gone and got drunk."

And when she saw that he had not his caftan on, and wore only her jacket, and had nothing in his hands, and said nothing, but only simpered, Matriona's heart failed within her.

"He has drunk up the money, he has been on a spree with this miserable beggar; and, worse than all, he has gone and brought him home!"

Matriona let them pass by her into the cottage; then she herself went in; she saw that the stranger was young, and that he had on their caftan. There was no shirt to be seen under the caftan; and he wore no cap.

As soon as he went in, he paused, and did not move and did not raise his eyes.

And Matriona thought: "He is not a good man; his conscience troubles him."

Matriona scowled, went to the oven, and watched to see what they would do.

Semyon took off his cap and sat down on the bench good-naturedly.

"Well," said he, "Matriona, can't you get us something to eat?"

Matriona muttered something under her breath.

She did not offer to move, but as she stood by the oven she looked from one to the other and kept shaking her head.

Semyon saw that his wife was out of sorts and would not do anything, but he pretended not to notice it, and took the stranger by the arm.

"Sit down, brother," says he; "we'll have some supper."

The stranger sat down on the bench.

"Well," says Semyon, "haven't you cooked anything?"

Matriona's anger blazed out.

"I cooked," said she, "but not for you. You are a fine man! I see you have been drinking! You went to get a shuba, and you have come home without your caftan. And, then, you have brought home this naked vagabond with you. I haven't any supper for such drunkards as you are!"

"That'll do, Matriona; what is the use of letting your tongue run on so? If you had only asked first: 'What kind of a man . . .'"

"You just tell me what you have done with the money!"

Semyon went to his caftan, took out the bill, and spread it out.

"Here's the money, but Trifonof did not pay me; he promised it tomorrow."

Matriona grew still more angry: "You didn't buy the new shuba, and you have given away your only caftan to this naked vagabond whom you have brought home!"

She snatched the money from the table, and went off to hide it away, saying: "I haven't any supper. I can't feed all your drunken beggars!"

"Hey there! Matriona, just hold your tongue! First you listen to what I have to say . . ."

"Much sense should I hear from a drunken fool! Good reason I had for not wanting to marry such a drunkard as you are. Mother gave me linen, and you have wasted it in drink; you went to get a shuba, and you spent it for drink."

Semyon was going to assure his wife that he had spent only twenty kopecks for drink; he was going to tell her where he had found the man; but Matriona would not give him a chance to speak a word; it was perfectly marvelous, but she managed to speak two words at once! Things that had taken place ten years before—she called them all up.

Matriona scolded and scolded; then she sprang at Semyon, and seized him by the sleeve.

"Give me back my jacket! It's the only one I have, and you took it from me and put it on yourself. Give it here, you miserable dog! bestir yourself, you villain!"

Semyon began to strip off the jacket. As he was pulling his arms out of the sleeves, his wife gave it a twitch and split the jacket up the seams. Matriona snatched the garment away, threw it over her head, and started for the door. She intended to go out, but she paused, and her heart was pulled in two directions—she wanted to vent her spite, and she wanted to find what kind of a man the stranger was.

Matriona paused, and said: "If he were a good man, then he would not have been naked; why, even now, he hasn't any shirt on; if he had been engaged in decent business, you would have told where you discovered such an elegant fellow!"

"Well, I was going to tell you. I was walking along, and there, behind the chapel, this man was sitting, stark naked, and half frozen to death. It is not summer, mind you, for a naked man! God brought me to him, else he would have perished. Now what could I do? Such things don't happen every day. I took and dressed him, and brought him home with me. Calm your anger. It's a sin, Matriona; we must all die."

Matriona was about to make a surly reply, but her eyes fell on the stranger, and she held her peace.

The stranger was sitting motionless on the edge of the bench, just as he had sat down. His hands were folded on his knees, his head was bent on his breast, his eyes were shut, and he kept frowning, as if something stifled him.

Matriona made no reply.

Semyon went on to say: "Matriona, can it be that God is not in you?"

Matriona heard his words, and glanced again at the stranger, and suddenly her anger vanished. She turned from the door, went to the corner where the oven was, and brought the supper.

She set a bowl on the table, poured out the kvass, and put on the last of the crust. She gave them the knife and the spoons.

"Have some victuals," she said.

Semyon touched the stranger.

"Draw up, young man," said he.

Semyon cut the bread and crumbled it into the bowl, and they began to eat their supper. And Matriona sat at the end of the table, leaned on her hand, and gazed at the stranger. And Matriona began to feel sorry for him, and she took a fancy to him.

And suddenly the stranger brightened up, ceased to frown, lifted his eyes to Matriona, and smiled.

After they had finished their supper, the woman cleared off the things, and began to question the stranger: "Where are you from?"

"I do not belong hereabouts."

"How did you happen to get into this road?"

"I cannot tell you."

"Who maltreated you?"

"God punished me."

"And you were lying there stripped?"

"Yes; there I was lying all naked, freezing to death, when Semyon saw me, had compassion on me, took off his caftan, put it on me, and bade me come home with him. And here you have fed me, given me something to eat and to drink, and have taken pity on me. May the Lord requite you!"

Matriona got up, took from the window Semyon's old shirt which she had been patching, and gave it to the stranger; then she found a pair of drawers and gave them also to him.

"There now," said she, "I see that you have no shirt. Put these things on, and then lie down wherever you please, in the loft or on the oven."

The stranger took off the caftan, put on the shirt, and went to bed in the loft. Matriona put out the light, took the caftan, and lay down beside her husband.

Matriona covered herself up with the skirt of the caftan, but she lay without sleeping; she could not get the thought of the stranger out of her mind.

When she remembered that he had eaten her last crust, and that there was no bread for the morrow, when she remembered that she had given him the shirt and the drawers, she felt disturbed; but then came the thought of how he had smiled at her, and her heart leaped within her.

Matriona lay a long time without falling asleep, and when she heard that Semyon was also awake, she pulled up the caftan, and said: "Semyon!"

"Ha?"

"You ate up the last of the bread, and I did not mix any more. I don't know how we shall get along tomorrow. Perhaps I might borrow some of neighbor Malanya."

"We shall get along; we shall have enough."

The wife lay without speaking. Then she said: "Well, he seems like a good man; but why doesn't he tell us about himself?"

"It must be because he can't."

"Siom!" [1]

"Ha?"

"We are always giving; why doesn't someone give to us?"

Semyon did not know what reply to make. He said: "You have talked enough!"

Then he turned over and went to sleep.

In the morning Semyon woke up.

His children were still asleep; his wife had gone to a neighbor's to get some bread. The stranger of the evening before, dressed in the old shirt and drawers, was sitting alone on the bench, looking up. And his face was brighter than it had been the evening before. And Semyon said:

"Well, my dear, the belly asks for bread, and the naked body for clothes. You must earn your own living. What do you know how to do?"

"There is nothing that I know how to do."

Semyon was amazed, and he said: "If one has only the mind to, men can learn anything."

"Men work, and I will work."

"What is your name?"

---

1. Diminutive of Semyon, or Simon.

"Mikhaïla."

"Well, Mikhaïla, if you aren't willing to tell about yourself, that is your affair; but you must earn your own living. If you will work as I shall show you, I will keep you."

"The Lord requite you! I am willing to learn; only show me what to do."

Semyon took a thread, drew it through his fingers, and showed him how to make a waxed end.

"It does not take much skill . . . look . . ."

Mikhaïla looked, and then he also twisted the thread between his fingers; he instantly imitated him, and finished the point.

Semyon showed him how to make the welt. This also Mikhaïla immediately understood. The shoemaker likewise showed him how to twist the bristle into the thread, and how to use the awl; and these things also Mikhaïla immediately learned to do.

Whatever part of the work Semyon showed him he imitated him in, and in two days he was able to work as if he had been all his life a cobbler. He worked without relaxation, he ate little, and when his work was done he would sit silent, looking up. He did not go on the street, he spoke no more than was absolutely necessary, he never jested, he never laughed.

The only time that he was seen to smile was on the first evening, when the woman got him his supper.

Day after day, week after week, rolled by for a whole year. Mikhaïla lived on in the same way, working for Semyon. And the fame of Semyon's apprentice went abroad; no one, it was said, could make such neat, strong boots as Semyon's apprentice, Mikhaïla. And from all around people came to Semyon to have boots made, and Semyon began to lay up money.

One winter's day, as Semyon and Mikhaïla were sitting at their work, a sleigh drawn by a troika drove up to the cottage, with a jingling of bells.

They looked out of the window; the sleigh stopped in front of the cottage; a footman jumped down from the box and opened the door. A barin in a fur coat got out of the sleigh, walked up to Semyon's cottage, and mounted the steps. Matriona hurried to throw the door wide open.

The barin bent his head and entered the cottage; when he drew himself up to his full height, his head almost touched the ceiling; he seemed to take up nearly all the room.

Semyon rose and bowed; he was surprised to see the barin. He had never before seen such a man.

Semyon himself was thin, the stranger was spare, and Matriona was like a dry chip; but this man seemed to be from a different world. His face was ruddy and full, his neck was like a bull's, it seemed as if he were made out of cast iron.

The barin got his breath, took off his shuba, sat down on the bench, and said: "Which is the master shoemaker?"

Semyon stepped out, saying: "I, your honor."

The barin shouted to his footman: "Hey, Fedka,[2] bring me the leather."

The young fellow ran out and brought back a parcel. The barin took the parcel and laid it on the table.

"Open it," said he.

The footman opened it.

The barin touched the leather with his finger, and said to Semyon: "Now listen, shoemaker. Do you see this leather?"

"I see it, your honor," says he.

"Well, do you appreciate what kind of leather it is?"

Semyon felt of the leather, and said: "That's good leather."

"Indeed it's good! Fool that you are! you never in your life saw such before! German leather. It cost twenty rubles."

Semyon was startled. He said: "Where, indeed, could we have seen anything like it?"

"Well, that's all right. Can you make from this leather a pair of boots that will fit me?"

"I can, your honor."

The barin shouted at him: " 'Can' is a good word. Now just realize whom you are making those boots for, and out of what kind of leather. You must make a pair of boots, so that when the year is gone they won't have got out of shape, or ripped. If you can, then take the job and cut the leather; but if you can't, then don't take it and don't cut the leather. I will tell you beforehand, if the boots rip or wear out of shape before the year is out, I will have you locked up; but if they don't rip or get out of shape before the end of the year, then I will give you ten rubles for your work."

Semyon was frightened, and was at a loss what to say.

He glanced at Mikhaïla. He nudged him with his elbow, and whispered: "Had I better take it?"

Mikhaïla nodded his head, meaning: "You had better take the job."

Semyon took Mikhaïla's advice; he agreed to make a pair of boots that would not rip or wear out of shape before the year was over.

---

2. Diminutive of Feodor, Theodore.

The barin shouted to his footman, ordered him to take the boot from his left foot; then he stretched out his leg: "Take the measure!"

Semyon cut off a piece of paper seventeen inches long, smoothed it out knelt down, wiped his hands nicely on his apron, so as not to soil the barin's stockings, and began to take the measure.

Semyon took the measure of the sole, he took the measure of the instep; then he started to measure the calf of the leg, but the paper was not long enough. The leg at the calf was as thick as a beam.

"Look out; don't make it too tight around the calf!"

Semyon was going to cut another piece of paper. The barin sat there, rubbing his toes together in his stockings, and looking at the inmates of the cottage; he caught sight of Mikhaïla.

"Who is that yonder?" he asked; "does he belong to you?"

"He is a master workman. He will make the boots."

"Look here," says the barin to Mikhaïla, "remember that they are to be made so as to last a whole year."

Semyon also looked at Mikhaïla; he saw that Mikhaïla was paying no attention, but was standing in the corner, as if he saw someone there behind the barin. Mikhaïla gazed and gazed, and suddenly smiled, and his whole face lighted up.

"What a fool you are, showing your teeth that way! You had better see to it that the boots are ready in time."

And Mikhaïla replied: "They will be ready as soon as they are needed."

"Very well."

The barin drew on his boot, wrapped his shuba round him, and went to the door. But he forgot to stoop, and so struck his head against the lintel.

The barin stormed and rubbed his head; then he got into his sleigh and drove off. After the barin was gone Semyon said: "Well, he's as solid as a rock! You could not kill him with a mallet. His head almost broke the doorpost, but it did not seem to hurt him much."

And Matriona said: "How can they help getting fat, living as they do? Even death does not carry off such a nail as he is."

And Semyon said to Mikhaïla: "Now, you see, we have taken this work, and we must do it as well as we can. The leather is expensive, and the barin gruff. We must not make any blunder. Now, your eye has become quicker, and your hand is more skillful, than mine; there's the measure. Cut out the leather, and I will be finishing up those vamps."

Mikhaïla did not fail to do as he was told; he took the barin's leather, stretched it out on the table, doubled it over, took the knife, and began to cut.

Matriona came and watched Mikhaïla as he cut, and she was amazed to see what he was doing. For she was used to cobbler's work, and she looked and saw that Mikhaïla was not cutting the leather for boots, but in rounded fashion.

Matriona wanted to speak, but she thought in her own mind: "Of course I can't be expected to understand how to make boots for gentlemen; Mikhaïla must understand it better than I do; I will not interfere."

After he had cut out the work, he took his waxed ends and began to sew, not as one does in making boots, with double threads, but with one thread, just as slippers are made.

Matriona wondered at this also, but still she did not like to interfere. And Mikhaïla kept on steadily with his work.

It came time for the nooning; Semyon got up, looked, and saw that Mikhaïla had been making slippers out of the barin's leather. Semyon groaned.

"How is this?" he asked himself. "Mikhaïla has lived with me a whole year, and never made a mistake, and now he has made such a blunder! The barin ordered thick-soled boots, and he has been making slippers without soles! He has ruined the leather. How can I make it right with the barin? We can't find such leather."

And he said to Mikhaïla: "What is this you have been doing? . . . My dear fellow, you have ruined me! You know the barin ordered boots, and what have you made?"

He was in the midst of his talk with Mikhaïla when a knock came at the rapper; someone was at the door. They looked out of the window, someone had come on horseback, and was fastening the horse. They opened the door. The same barin's footman came walking in.

"Good day."

"Good day to you; what is it?"

"My mistress sent me in regard to a pair of boots."

"What about the boots?"

"It is this. My barin does not need the boots; he has gone from this world."

"What is that you say?"

"He did not live to get home from your house; he died in the sleigh. When the sleigh reached home, we went to help him out, but there he had fallen over like a bag, and there he lay stone dead, and it took all our strength to lift him out of the sleigh. And his lady has sent me, saying: 'Tell the shoemaker of whom your barin just ordered boots from leather which he left with him—tell him that the boots are not needed, and that he is to make a pair of slippers for the corpse out of that leather just as quick as possible.' And I was to wait till they were made, and take them home with me. And so I have come."

Mikhaïla took the rest of the leather from the table and rolled it up; he also took the slippers, which were all done, slapped them together, wiped them with his apron, and gave them to the young man. The young man took them.

"Goodby, friends! Good luck to you!"

Still another year, and then two more passed by, and Mikhaïla had now been living five years with Semyon. He lived in just the same way as before. He never went anywhere, he kept his own counsels, and in all that time he smiled only twice—once when Matriona gave him something to eat, and the other time when he smiled on the barin.

Semyon was more than contented with his workman, and he no longer asked him where he came from; his only fear was lest Mikhaïla should leave him.

One time they were all at home. The mother was putting the iron kettles on the oven, and the children were playing on the benches and looking out of the window. Semyon was pegging away at one window, and Mikhaïla at the other was putting lifts on a heel.

One of the boys ran along the bench toward Mikhaïla, leaned over his shoulder, and looked out of the window.

"Uncle Mikhaïla, just look! a merchant's wife is coming to our house with some little girls. And one of the little girls is a cripple."

The words were scarcely out of the boy's mouth before Mikhaïla threw down his work, leaned over toward the window, and looked out-of-doors. And Semyon was surprised. Never before had Mikhaïla cared to look out, but now his face seemed soldered to the window; he was looking at something very intently.

Semyon also looked out of the window: he saw a woman coming straight through his yard; she was neatly dressed; she had two little girls by the hand; they wore shubkas, and kerchiefs over their heads. The little girls looked so much alike that it was hard to tell them apart, except that one of the little girls was lame in her foot; she limped as she walked.

The woman came into the entry, felt about in the dark, lifted the latch, and opened the door. She let the two little girls go before her into the cottage, and then she followed.

"How do you do, friends?"

"Welcome! What can we do for you?"

The woman sat down by the table; the two little girls clung to her knee; they were bashful.

"These little girls need to have some goatskin shoes made for the spring."

"Well, it can be done. We don't generally make such small ones; but it's perfectly easy, either with welts or lined with linen. This here is Mikhaïla; he's my master workman."

Semyon glanced at Mikhaïla, and saw that he had thrown down his work, and was sitting with his eyes fastened on the little girls.

And Semyon was amazed at Mikhaïla. To be sure the little girls were pretty; they had dark eyes, they were plump and rosy, and they wore handsome shubkas and kerchiefs; but still Semyon could not understand why he gazed so intently at them, as if they were friends of his.

Semyon was amazed, and he began to talk with the woman, and to make his bargain. After he had made his bargain, he began to take the measures. The woman lifted on her lap the little cripple, and said: "Take two measures from this one; make one little shoe from the twisted foot, and three from the well one. Their feet are alike; they are twins."

Semyon took his tape, and said in reference to the little cripple: "How did this happen to her? She is such a pretty little girl. Was she born so?"

"No; her mother crushed it."

Matriona joined the conversation; she was anxious to learn who the woman and children were, and so she said: "Then you aren't their mother?"

"No, I am not their mother; I am no relation to them, good wife, and they are no relation to me at all; I adopted them."

"If they are not your children, you take good care of them."

"Why shouldn't I take good care of them? I nursed them both at my own breast. I had a baby of my own, but God took him. I did not take such good care of him as I do of these."

"Whose children are they?"

The woman became confidential, and began to tell them about it.

"Six years ago," said she, "these little ones were left orphans in one week; the father was buried on Tuesday, and the mother died on Friday. Three days these little ones remained without their father, and then their mother followed him. At that time I was living with my husband in the country: we were neighbors; we lived in adjoining yards. Their father was a peasant, and worked in the forest at woodcutting. And they were felling a tree, and it caught him across the body. It hurt him all inside. As soon as they got him out, he gave his soul to God, and that same week his wife gave birth to twins—these are the little girls here. There they were, poor and alone, no one to take care of them, either grandmother or sister.

"She must have died soon after the children were born. For when I went in the morning to look after my neighbor, as soon as I entered the cottage, I found the poor thing dead and cold. And when she died she must have rolled over on this little girl. . . . That's the way she crushed it, and spoiled this foot.

"The people got together, they washed and laid out the body, they had a coffin made, and buried her. The people were always kind. But the two little ones were left alone. What was to be done with them? Now I was the only one of the women who had a baby. For eight weeks I had been nursing my first-born, a boy. So I took them for the time being. The peasants got together; they planned and planned what to do with them, and they said to me:

"'Marya, you just keep the little girls for a while, and give us a chance to decide.'

"So I nursed the well one for a while, but did not think it worthwhile to nurse the deformed one. I did not expect that she was going to live. And, then, I thought to myself, why should the little angel's soul pass away? and I felt sorry for it. I tried to nurse her, and so I had my own and these two besides; yes, I had three children at the breast. But I was young and strong, and I had good food! And God gave me so much milk in my breasts that I had enough and to spare. I used to nurse two at once and let the third one wait. When one had finished, I would take up the third. And so God let me nurse all three; but when my boy was in his third year, I lost him. And God never gave me any more children. But we began to be in comfortable circumstances. And now we are living with the trader at the mill. We get good wages and live well. But we have no children of our own. And how lonely it would be, if it were not for these two little girls! How could I help loving them? They are to me like the wax in the candle!"

And the woman pressed the little lame girl to her with one arm, and with the other hand she tried to wipe the tears from her cheeks.

And Matriona sighed, and said: "The old saw isn't far wrong, 'Men can live without father and mother, but without God one cannot live.'"

While they were thus talking together, suddenly a flash of lightning seemed to irradiate from that corner of the cottage where Mikhaïla was sitting. All looked at him; and, behold! Mikhaïla was sitting there with his hands folded in his lap, and looking up and smiling.

The woman went away with the children, and Mikhaïla arose from the bench and laid down his work; he took off his apron, made a low bow to the shoemaker and his wife, and said: "Farewell, friends; God has forgiven me. Do you also forgive me?"

And Semyon and Matriona perceived that it was from Mikhaïla that the light had flashed. And Semyon arose, bowed low before Mikhaïla, and said to him: "I see, Mikhaïla, that you are not a mere man, and I have no right to detain you nor to ask questions of you. But tell me one thing: when I had found you and brought you home, you were sad; but when my wife gave you something to eat, you smiled on her, and after that you became more cheerful. And then when the barin ordered the boots, why did you smile a second time, and after that become still more cheerful; and now when this woman brought these two little girls, why did you smile for the third time and become perfectly radiant? Tell me, Mikhaïla, why was it that such a light streamed from you, and why you smiled three times?"

And Mikhaïla said: "The light blazed from me because I had been punished, but now God has forgiven me. And I smiled the three times because it was required of me to learn three of God's truths, and I have now learned the three truths of God. One truth I learned when your wife had pity on me, and so I smiled; the second truth I learned when the rich man ordered the boots, and I smiled for the second time; and now that I have seen the little girls, I have learned the third and last truth, and I smiled for the third time."

And Semyon said: "Tell me, Mikhaïla, why God punished you, and what were the truths of God, that I, too, may know them."

And Mikhaïla said: "God punished me because I disobeyed Him. I was an angel in heaven, and I was disobedient to God. I was an angel in heaven, and the Lord sent me to bring back the soul of a certain woman. I flew down to earth and I saw the woman lying alone—she was sick—she had just borne twins, two little girls. The little ones were sprawling about near their mother, but their mother was unable to lift them to her breast. The mother saw me; she perceived that God had sent me after her soul; she burst into tears, and said:

" 'Angel of God, I have just buried my husband; a tree fell on him in the forest and killed him. I have no sister, nor aunt, nor mother to take care of my little ones; do not carry off my soul; let me bring up my children myself, and nurse them and put them on their feet. It is impossible for children to live without father or mother.'

"And I heeded what the mother said; I put one child to her breast, and laid the other in its mother's arms, and I returned to the Lord in heaven. I flew back to the Lord, and I said:

" 'I cannot take the mother's soul. The father has been killed by a tree, the mother has given birth to twins, and begs me not to take her soul; she says:

" ' "Let me bring up my little ones; let me nurse them and put them on their feet. It is impossible for children to live without father and mother." I did not take the mother's soul.'

"And the Lord said: 'Go and take the mother's soul, and thou shalt learn three lessons: Thou shalt learn *what is in men,* and *what is not given unto men,* and *what men live by.* When thou shalt have learned these three lessons, then return to heaven.'

"And I flew down to earth and took the mother's soul. The little ones fell from her bosom. The dead body rolled over on the bed, and fell on one of the little girls and crushed her foot. I rose above the village and was going to give the soul to God, when a wind seized me, my wings ceased to move and fell off, and the soul arose alone to God, and I fell back to earth."

And Semyon and Matriona now knew whom they had clothed and fed, and who it was that had been living with them, and they burst into tears of dismay and joy; and the angel said:

"I was there in the field naked and alone. Hitherto I had never known what human poverty was; I had known neither cold nor hunger, and now I was a man. I was famished, I was freezing, and I knew not what to do. And I saw across the field a chapel made for God's service. I went to God's chapel, thinking to get shelter in it. But the chapel was locked, and I could not enter. And I crouched down behind the chapel, so as to get shelter from the wind. Evening came; I was hungry and chill, and ached all over. Suddenly I hear a man walking along the road, with a pair of boots in his hand, and talking to himself. I now saw for the first time since I had become a man the face of a mortal man, and it filled me with dismay, and I tried to hide from him. And I heard this man asking himself how he should protect himself from cold during the winter, and how get food for his wife and children. And I thought: 'I am perishing with cold and hunger, and here is a man whose sole thought is to get a shuba for himself and his wife and to furnish bread for their sustenance. It is impossible for him to help me.'

"The man saw me and scowled; he seemed even more terrible than before; then he passed on. And I was in despair. Suddenly I heard the man coming back. I looked up, and did not recognize that it was the same man as before; then there was death in his face, but now it had suddenly become alive, and I saw that God was in his face. He came to me, put clothes on me, and took me home with him.

"When I reached his house, a woman came out to meet us, and she began to scold. The woman was even more terrible to me than the man; a dead soul seemed to proceed forth from her mouth, and I was suffocated by the stench of death. She wanted to drive me out into the cold, and I knew that she would die if she drove me out. And suddenly her husband reminded her of God. And instantly a change came over the woman. And when she had prepared something for me to eat, and looked kindly on me, I looked at her, and there was no longer anything like death about her; she was now alive, and in her also I recognized God.

"And I remembered God's first lesson: 'Thou shalt learn what is in men.'

"And I perceived that LOVE was in men. And I was glad because God had begun to fulfill His promise to me, and I smiled for the first time. But I was not yet ready to know the whole. I could not understand what was not given to men, and what men lived by.

"I began to live in your house, and after I had lived with you a year the man came to order the boots which should be strong enough to last him a year without ripping or wearing out of shape. And I looked at him, and suddenly perceived behind his back my comrade, the Angel of Death. No one besides myself saw this angel; but I knew him, and I knew that before the sun should go down he would take the rich man's soul. And I said to myself: 'This man is laying his plans to live another year, and he knows not that ere evening comes he will be dead.'

"And I realized suddenly the second saying of God: 'Thou shalt know what is not given unto men.'

"And now I knew what was in men. And now I knew also what was not given unto men. It is not given unto men to know what is needed for their bodies. And I smiled for the second time. I was glad because I saw my comrade, the angel, and because God had revealed unto me the second truth.

"But I could not yet understand all. I could not understand what men live by, and so I lived on, and waited until God should reveal to me the third truth also. And now in the sixth year the little twin girls have come with the woman, and I recognized the little ones, and I remembered how they had been left. And after I had recognized them, I thought: 'The mother besought me in behalf of her children, because she thought that it would be impossible for children to live without father and mother, but another woman, a stranger, has nursed them and brought them up.'

"And when the woman caressed the children that were not her own, and wept over them, then I saw in her THE LIVING GOD, and knew *what people live by*. And I knew that God had revealed to me the last truth, and had pardoned me, and I smiled for the third time."

And the angel's body became manifest, and he was clad with light so bright that the eyes could not endure to look on him, and he spoke in clearer accents, as if the voice proceeded not from him, but came from heaven.

And the angel said: "I have learned that every man lives, not through care of himself, but by love.

"It was not given to the mother to know what her children needed to keep them alive. It was not given the rich man to know what he himself needed, and it is not given to any man to know whether he will need boots for daily living, or slippers for his burial.

"When I became a man, I was kept alive, not by what thought I took for myself, but because a stranger and his wife had love in their hearts, and pitied and loved me. The orphans were kept alive, not because other people deliberated about what was to be done with them, but because a strange woman had love for them in her heart, and pitied them and loved them. And all men are kept alive, not by their own forethought, but because there is LOVE IN MEN.

"I knew before that God gave life to men, and desired them to live; but now I know something above and beyond that.

"I have learned that God does not wish men to live each for himself, and therefore He has not revealed to them what they each need for themselves, but He wishes them to live in union, and therefore He has revealed to them what is necessary for each and for all together.

"I have now learned that it is only in appearance that they are kept alive through care for themselves, but that in reality they are kept alive through love. *He who dwelleth in love dwelleth in God, and God in him, for God is love.*"

And the angel sang a hymn of praise to God, and the cottage shook with the sound of his voice.

And the ceiling parted, and a column of fire reached from earth to heaven. And Semyon and his wife and children fell prostrate on the ground. And pinions appeared on the angel's shoulders, and he soared away to heaven.

And when Semyon opened his eyes, the cottage was the same as it had ever been, and there was no one in it save himself and his family.

The three foregoing selections were translated by Nathan Haskell Dole.

GATEWAY TO THE GREAT BOOKS